READER'S DIGEST
SELECT EDITIONS

READER'S DIGEST
SELECT EDITIONS

The condensations in this volume
are published with the consent of the authors
and the publishers © 2006 Reader's Digest.

www.readersdigest.co.uk

The Reader's Digest Association Limited
11 Westferry Circus Canary Wharf London E14 4HE

For information as to ownership of
copyright in the material of this book,
and acknowledgments, see last page.

Printed in Germany
ISBN 0 276 44107 9

SELECTED AND CONDENSED
BY READER'S DIGEST

THE READER'S DIGEST ASSOCIATION LIMITED, LONDON

CONTENTS

Prepare to be dazzled by Michael Connelly's new legal thriller, which has a twist to it that will keep you turning pages long into the night. When defence lawyer Mickey Haller takes on the case of Louis Roulet, he gets his first high-paying client in years. Better still, from the evidence, it looks like an easy win. But Haller is forgetting that any trial can turn on a dime and, if you swim with the sharks, it's easy to wind up as prey.

From the author of *The Food of Love*, a Richard and Judy book of the year, comes a new novel as irresistibly luscious as its predecessor. Set in occupied Naples in 1944, it tells the story of young, naive army officer, James Gould, newly appointed as the local 'Wedding Officer'. When the lovely Livia Pertini comes to cook for Gould, he is spellbound—and before long must face a difficult choice between love and duty.

In London, an Auschwitz survivor is murdered in his hospital bed, while in Prague a painting mysteriously disappears from a synagogue. Then, in Maryland, a vicious gang breaks into a heavily guarded museum and steals an Enigma machine. Three apparently unrelated crimes around the globe. And yet maverick art expert Tom Kirk is convinced that there is a connection between them, however deeply buried in the past.

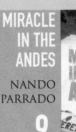

MIRACLE IN THE ANDES

NANDO PARRADO

9

Imagine surviving at high altitude for over two months without water, warm clothing, proper food or shelter. Imagine, in that weakened state, attempting to scale some of the world's highest peaks. Nando Parrado did all the above, and now tells his remarkable story in *Miracle in the Andes*.

The book, however, delivers more than just an extraordinary account of courage and determination. Parrado states that part of his purpose is to share, with as many people as possible, what his terrifying and potentially spirit-crushing experiences taught him. 'My hope is that you who are reading this book will not wait so long to realise what treasures you have,' he writes. 'In the Andes we lived heartbeat-to-heartbeat. Every second was a gift, glowing with purpose and meaning. I have tried to live that way ever since and it has filled my life with more blessings than I can count. I urge you to do the same. As we used to say in the mountains, "Breathe. Breathe again. With every breath, you are alive."

After all these years, this is still the best advice I can give you: Savour your existence. Live every moment. Do not waste a breath.'

Thoughts of his father (centre) kept Nando Parrado going during the toughest moments of his ordeal. On the right is his wife Veronique, whom he married in 1979.

MIRACLE IN THE ANDES
NANDO PARRADO

On October 13, 1972, an aeroplane
carrying a team of young rugby
players from Uruguay crashed
in the high Andes, killing many
of the people on board instantly.
For those still alive, an epic feat
of survival was about to begin.
Until recently, Nando Parrado
has remained too haunted by
his experiences to share them
with the world.
Now he tells his story . . .

Prologue

In the first hours there was nothing, no fear or sadness, no sense of the passage of time, not even the glimmer of a thought or a memory, just a black and perfect silence. Then light appeared, a thin grey smear of daylight, and I rose to it out of the darkness like a diver swimming to the surface. Consciousness seeped through my brain and I awoke, with great difficulty, into a twilight world halfway between dreaming and awareness. I heard voices and sensed motion all around me, but my thoughts were murky and my vision blurred. I could see only pools of light and shadow. As I stared in confusion, I saw that some of the shadows were moving, and finally I realised that one of them was hovering over me.

'*Nando, podés oírme?* Can you hear me? Are you OK?'

The shadow drew closer to me, and gathered itself into a human face. I saw a tangle of dark hair and a pair of deep brown eyes.

'Come on, Nando, wake up!'

Why am I so cold? Why does my head hurt so badly? I tried to speak these thoughts, but my lips could not form the words. I closed my eyes and let myself drift back into the shadows. But soon I heard other voices, and when I opened my eyes, more faces were floating above me.

'Is he awake? Can he hear you?'

'Say something, Nando!'

'Don't give up, Nando. We are here with you. Wake up!'

I tried again to speak, but all I could manage was a hoarse whisper. Then someone bent down close to me and spoke very slowly in my ear.

'*Nando, el avión se estrelló! Caimos en las montañas.*'

We crashed, he said. The plane crashed. We fell into the mountains.

'Do you understand me, Nando?'

I did not. I understood, from the quiet urgency with which these words were spoken, that this was news of great importance. But I could not fathom their meaning. Reality seemed distant and muffled, as if I were trapped in a dream. I hovered in this haze for hours, but at last my senses began to clear and I was able to survey my surroundings. Since my first bleary moments of awareness, I had been puzzled by a row of circular lights floating above me. Now I recognised them as the rounded windows of a plane. I was lying on the floor of the passenger cabin of a commercial aircraft, but nothing about this aircraft seemed right. The fuselage had rolled to the side, so that my back and head were resting against the lower wall of the plane's right side, while my legs stretched out into the upward-slanting aisle. Most of the plane's seats were missing. Wires and pipes dangled from the ceiling, and torn flaps of insulation hung from holes in the walls. The floor was strewn with scraps of plastic and metal. It was daylight. The air was very cold—a savage, bone-crushing cold that scalded my skin like acid. Lying on the draughty floor of the plane, there was no way to warm myself, and I felt the pain in every cell of my body.

But the cold was not my only concern. There was also a throbbing pain in my head, a pounding so ferocious it seemed that a wild animal had been trapped inside my skull and was clawing to get out. I reached up to touch the crown of my head. Clots of dried blood were matted in my hair, and three bloody wounds formed a jagged triangle above my right ear. I felt rough ridges of broken bone, and when I pressed down lightly I felt a spongy sense of give. My stomach heaved as I realised what this meant—I was pressing shattered pieces of my skull against the surface of my brain. My heart knocked against my chest. My breath came in shallow gasps. Just as I was about to panic, I saw those brown eyes above me, and at last I recognised the face of my friend Roberto Canessa.

'What happened?' I asked him. 'Where are we?'

Roberto bent to examine my wounds. 'You have been unconscious for three days,' he said, with no emotion in his voice. 'We had given up on you.'

These words made no sense. 'What happened to me?' I asked. 'Why is it so cold?'

'Do you understand me, Nando?' said Roberto. 'We crashed into the mountains. The aeroplane crashed. We are stranded here.'

I shook my head feebly in confusion, or denial, but I could not deny for long what was happening around me. I heard soft moans and sudden cries of pain, and I began to understand that these were the sounds of other people suffering. I saw the injured lying in makeshift beds and hammocks throughout the fuselage, and other figures bending down to help them.

'Do you understand, Nando?' Roberto asked again. 'Do you remember, we were in the plane . . . going to Chile . . .?'

I closed my eyes and nodded. I was out of the shadows now; my confusion could no longer shield me from the truth. I understood, and as Roberto gently washed the crusted blood from my face, I began to remember.

1: Before

It was Friday, October 13. We joked about that—flying over the Andes on such an unlucky day—but young men make those jokes so easily. Our flight had originated one day earlier in Montevideo, my hometown in Uruguay, its destination Santiago in Chile. It was a chartered flight on a Fairchild twin-engine turbo-prop carrying my rugby team, the Old Christians, to play an exhibition match against a top Chilean squad. There were forty-five people aboard, including five crew members. Most of the passengers were my teammates, but we were accompanied by supporters, friends and family members, including my mother, Eugenia, and my younger sister, Susy, who were sitting across the aisle one row in front of me. We were to fly nonstop to Santiago, a trip of about three and a half hours, but, after just a few hours of flying, reports of bad weather in the mountains ahead forced the pilot to put the plane down in the old Spanish colonial town of Mendoza, just east of the Andean foothills.

We landed at lunchtime with hopes that we would be back in the air in a few hours. But the weather reports were not encouraging, and it was soon clear that we would have to stay the night. None of us liked the idea of losing a day from our trip, but we decided to make the best of our time in Mendoza. I spent the afternoon with some friends, watching motor racing at a track outside town. My mother and Susy explored Mendoza's gift shops, buying presents for friends in Chile and souvenirs for the people at home. In the evening we went to a movie, while some of the others went dancing.

Most of us slept late the next morning, and when we woke we were anxious to leave, but there was still no word about our departure, so we all went our separate ways to see a little more of Mendoza.

Finally we received word to gather at the airport at 1 p.m. sharp, but we arrived only to discover that the pilot, Julio Ferradas and his copilot, Dante Lagurara, had not yet decided whether or not we would fly. We reacted with frustration and anger, but none of us understood the difficult decision confronting the pilots. After speaking with the pilot of a cargo plane that had just flown in from Santiago, Ferradas was confident the Fairchild could fly safely above the weather. But by the time the passengers were boarded and all the necessary arrangements were made with airport officials, it would be well past two o'clock. In the afternoon, warm air rises from the Argentine foothills and meets the frigid air above the snow line to create treacherous instability in the atmosphere above the mountains. Our pilots knew that this was the most dangerous time to fly across the Andes. And there was no way to predict where these swirling currents might strike.

On the other hand, we couldn't stay put in Mendoza. Our aircraft was leased from the Uruguayan air force, and the laws of Argentina forbade a foreign military aircraft to stay on Argentine soil longer than twenty-four hours. Ferradas and Lagurara had to make a quick decision: should they take off for Santiago and brave the afternoon skies, or fly the Fairchild back to Montevideo and put an end to our vacation?

As they pondered, our impatience grew. We were bold young men, fearless and full of ourselves, and it angered us that our vacation was slipping away because of what we regarded as the timidity of our pilots. When we saw them at the airport, we jeered and whistled. We teased them and questioned their competence. There is no way to know whether or not we influenced their decision—it did seem to unsettle them—but finally, after one last consultation with Lagurara, Ferradas announced that the flight would continue. We greeted this news with a rowdy cheer.

The Fairchild departed from Mendoza airport at eighteen minutes after two o'clock, local time. As we climbed, the plane banked steeply into a left turn and soon we were flying south, with the Argentine Andes rising to our right on the western horizon. I gazed through the windows at the mountains that thundered up from the dry plateau below us, so bleak and majestic, so astonishingly vast and huge. To the north, south and west, they sprawled as far as the eye could see, and even though they were many miles away, their height and mass made them seem impassable. No wonder the ancients thought of them as holy places, as the dwelling place of the gods.

The Andes form the second-highest mountain range on the planet; in terms of average elevation, only the Himalayas are higher. The section of the Andes that separates Mendoza from Santiago is one of the highest in the chain and home to some of the tallest mountains in the world. Somewhere out there, for example, was Aconcagua, one of the seven tallest peaks on the planet. At 22,831 feet tall, it stands just 6,200 feet shy of Everest.

With such towering summits rising along the way, there was no chance that the Fairchild could fly a direct east–west route to Santiago. Instead, the pilots had charted a course that would take us about one hundred miles south of Mendoza to Planchón Pass, a narrow corridor through the mountains with ridges low enough for the plane to clear. When we had cleared the mountains on the Chilean side, we would fly north. The flight should take about an hour and a half, and we would be in Santiago before dark.

On this first leg of the trip, the skies were calm, and in less than an hour we had reached the vicinity of Planchón Pass. I didn't know the name of the pass, of course, or any of the flight details, but I couldn't help noticing that, after flying for miles with the mountains in the western distance, we had banked to the west and were now flying into the heart of the cordillera. I was sitting in a window seat on the left side of the plane and, as I watched, the flat, featureless landscape changed, first into rugged foothills then into the awesome convolutions of true mountains. Shark-finned ridges rose like soaring black sails. Menacing peaks pushed up like gigantic spearheads or broken hatchet blades. Narrow glacial valleys gashed the steep slopes, forming rows of deep, winding, snow-packed corridors that folded one upon the other to create an endless maze of ice and rock.

As I looked down into all that rugged wildness, I noticed that wisps of fog were gathering. I felt a hand on my shoulder.

'Switch seats with me, Nando. I want to look at the mountains.'

It was my friend Panchito, who was sitting beside me. I nodded and rose from my seat. When I stood to change places someone yelled, 'Think fast, Nando!' and I turned just in time to catch a rugby ball someone had tossed from the rear of the cabin. I passed the ball forward, then sank into my seat. All around us there was laughing and talking as people moved from seat to seat, visiting friends up and down the aisle. Some were in the back of the plane playing cards with crew members, including the flight steward, but when the ball began bouncing around the cabin the steward tried to calm things down. 'Put the ball away,' he shouted. 'Settle down, and please take your seats!' But we were young rugby players and we did not want to settle down. Our team, the Old Christians, was one of the best in Uruguay, and we took our regular matches seriously. In Chile, however, we would be playing an exhibition match only, so this trip was really a holiday for us, and on the plane there was the feeling that the holiday had begun.

Many of us on the Old Christians had known each other for more than ten years, since our days as schoolboys playing under the guidance of the Irish Christian Brothers at the Stella Maris College, a private Catholic school for boys between the ages of nine and sixteen. For the Christian Brothers, the first goal of a Catholic education was to build character, not intellect, and their teaching methods stressed discipline, piety, selflessness and respect. To promote these values outside the classroom, the Brothers discouraged our natural South American passion for soccer—a game that, in their view, fostered selfishness and egotism—and steered us towards the rougher game of rugby. At first the game seemed strange, so brutal and painful to play, with so much pushing and shoving and so little of soccer's flair. But the Christian Brothers firmly believed that the qualities required to master the sport were the same that one needed to live a decent Catholic life—humility, tenacity, self-discipline and devotion to others—and they were determined that we would play the game well.

In long, tough practices on the fields behind the school, the Brothers drilled us in all the rugged intricacies of the game, the mucks and rauls, scrumdowns and lineouts. Rugby was more than a game of brute strength; it required sound strategy, quick thinking, agility and, most of all, an unshakeable trust. The Brothers explained that when one of our teammates fell or was knocked to the ground, he 'became grass'—he could be stomped on and trampled by the opposition as if he were part of the turf. 'You must become his protector,' they taught. 'You must sacrifice yourself to shield him. He must know he can count on you.'

To the Christian Brothers, rugby was sport raised to the level of a moral discipline. No other sport taught so forcefully the importance of striving, suffering and sacrifice in the pursuit of a common goal. They were so passionate on this point that we had no choice but to believe them, and as we grew to understand the game, we saw for ourselves that they were right.

For me, the essence of rugby lies in the brutal, controlled melee known as the scrum. My job in the second row, or lock, was to line up behind the crouching first row, my head wedged between their hips, my shoulders butting their thighs, my arms spread over their backsides. When the ball was put in, I would try with all my might to push the scrum forward. I remember moments of extreme exertion, straining until my legs were completely extended, with my body low, straight and parallel to the ground, pushing hopelessly against what seemed like a solid stone wall. Still you dug at the turf, refused to quit. Sometimes it seemed to last for ever, but if we held our positions and each man did his job, the resistance would soften and the immovable object would begin to budge. The remarkable thing is this: you cannot tell where your strength ends and that of the others begins. In a sense, you no longer exist as an individual; for a brief moment you become part of something larger and more powerful. Your effort and will vanish into the collective will of the team, and, if this is focused, the team surges forward and the scrum magically begins to move.

For eight years we played our hearts out for the Brothers, proudly wearing the bright green shamrock on our uniforms. The game became so much a part of us that, when we graduated from Stella Maris at the age of sixteen, many of us could not bear the thought that our playing days were over. Our salvation came in the form of the Old Christians Club, a private rugby team formed in 1965 by previous alumni to give Stella Maris players a chance to continue playing the game after school years ended.

By the late 1960s, rugby was gaining in popularity, and there were plenty of good teams for the Old Christians to challenge. In 1965 we joined the National Rugby League, and soon we had established ourselves as one of the country's top teams, winning the national championship in 1968 and 1970. Encouraged by our success, we began to schedule matches in Argentina, and we quickly discovered that we could hold our own with the best teams that country had to offer. In 1971 we travelled to Chile, where we fared well in matches against tough competition. The trip was such a success that it was decided we would return again this year, 1972.

I had been looking forward to the trip for months, and as I glanced around the passenger cabin I was happy to see so many of my friends. There was Coco Nicolich, our other lock forward and one of the biggest and strongest players on the team. Enrique Platero, serious and steady, was a prop, one of the burly guys who helped anchor the line in a scrum. Roy Harley was a tall, swift flanker, who used his speed to sidestep tacklers and leave them clutching air. Roberto Canessa was a wing, and one of the strongest and toughest players on the squad. Arturo Nogueira was our fly half, a great long passer and the best kicker on the team. You could tell by looking at Antonio Vizintín, with his broad back and thick neck, that he was one of the front line forwards who bore most of the weight in the scrum. Gustavo Zerbino—whose guts and determination I admired—was a versatile player who manned many positions. And Marcelo Pérez del Castillo, another flanker, was very fast and very brave, a great ball carrier and ferocious tackler. Marcelo was also our team captain, a leader we would trust with our lives. It had been his idea to return to Chile and he had worked hard to make it all possible: he had leased the plane, hired the pilots, arranged the games and created tremendous excitement about the trip.

There were others—Alexis Hounié, Gastón Costemalle, Daniel Shaw—all of them great players and all of them my friends. But my oldest friend was Guido Magri. He and I had met on my first day at Stella Maris—I was eight years old and Guido was one year older—and we had been inseparable ever since. When I was fifteen we both had mopeds that we had modified in silly ways—removing the mufflers, turn signals and fenders—and we would ride them to a famous ice cream parlour in our neighbourhood, where we would drool over the girls, hoping to impress them with our souped-up scooters. Guido was a dependable friend, with a good sense of humour and an easy laugh. He was also an outstanding scrum half, as quick and smart as a fox. By the time I was fifteen we had both earned a spot on the starting line-up of the Stella Maris First XV and, after graduation, both of us went on to join the Old Christians.

My other great friend was Panchito Abal. We had met only a few years earlier when Panchito joined the Old Christians, but had grown as close as brothers. Panchito was our winger, a position that requires a combination of power, intelligence, agility and lightning-quick reactions. If there is a glamourous position on a rugby team, winger is it, and Panchito was perfect for the role. Long-legged and broad-shouldered, with the speed of a cheetah, he played the game with such natural grace that even his most brilliant moves seemed effortless. But everything seemed that way for Panchito, especially his other great passion—chasing pretty girls. It didn't hurt, of course, that he had the blond good looks of a movie star, or that he was blessed with the kind of natural charisma most of us can only dream of.

Like Panchito, I had a great passion for rugby, but the game was never effortless for me. As a small child I had broken both my legs in a fall from a balcony, and the injuries had left me with a slightly knock-kneed stride that robbed me of the nimbleness required to play rugby's more glamorous positions. But I was tall and tough and fast, so they made me a second row forward. We forwards were good foot soldiers, always butting shoulders in rucks, mauls and scrums and jumping high to claw for the ball in lineouts. Forwards are usually the largest and strongest players on the team, but while I was one of our tallest players, I was thin for my height. When the large bodies started flying, it was only through hard work and determination that I was able to hold my own.

I was just as obsessed with pretty girls as Panchito was, but I knew I wasn't in his class. A little shy, long-limbed and gangly, with thick horn-rimmed glasses and average looks, I had to face the fact that most girls did not find me extraordinary. It wasn't that I was unpopular—I had my share of dates—but it would be a lie to say that girls were waiting in line for Nando. I had to work hard to catch their interest.

I could see much strength and depth in Panchito, in his loyalty as a friend, in the fiercely protective way he watched out for my sister Susy, in the quiet respect he showed my parents. More than anything, though, I saw in him a man who wanted nothing more than the joys of a happy family. He would become a good husband and a loving father. Our families would be like one; our children would grow up together. We never spoke of these things, of course, but I think he knew I understood these things about him, and I think that knowledge strengthened our friendship.

Still, we were young and responsibility could wait. Like Panchito, I lived for the moment and was in no hurry to grow up. Life for me was something that was happening today. I had no strong principles, no defining goals. In those days, if you had asked me the purpose of life, I might have laughed and answered, 'To have fun.' It did not occur to me that I could only afford the luxury of this carefree attitude because of the sacrifices of my father, who, from a very young age, had taken life seriously, planned carefully, and given me a life of privilege and security.

My father, Seler Parrado, was born at Estación Gonzales, a dusty outpost in Uruguay's rich agricultural interior, where vast cattle ranches, or *estancias*, produced the prized high-quality beef for which Uruguay is known. His own father was a peddler who travelled by horse and cart from one *estancia* to the next, selling saddles, bridles and other staples to ranch owners or the rugged gauchos who watched over their herds. It was a difficult life, full of hardship and uncertainty. By the time my father was eight, he had become his father's assistant, spending long hours in the peddler's cart as they made their rounds. His childhood was not carefree, but it showed him the value of hard work and taught him that nothing would be handed to him, that his life would be only what he made of it.

When he was eleven years old, his family moved to Montevideo, where his father opened a shop selling the same goods he had peddled to ranchers and farmers in the countryside. Seler became a motor mechanic—he had had a passion for cars and engines since he was a very young boy—but when he was in his mid-twenties my grandfather decided to retire, and my father assumed ownership of the shop. Grandfather had located the shop wisely, near Montevideo's main railway station, and when ranchers and gauchos came to town to buy supplies they would step off the trains and walk directly past his door. But by the time Seler took control of the business, things had changed. Buses had replaced trains as the most popular form of transportation, and the bus station was nowhere near the shop. To make things worse, the machine age had reached the Uruguayan countryside. Trucks and tractors were rapidly reducing the farmer's dependence on horses and mules, and that meant a dramatic drop in demand for the saddles and bridles my father was selling. Sales lagged. It seemed the business would fail.

Then Seler tried an experiment—he cleared the farm goods from half of his store's floor space and devoted that space to basic hardware—nuts and bolts, nails and screws, wire and hinges. Immediately his business began to thrive. Within months he had removed all the country goods and stocked the shelves with hardware. He was still living on the edge of poverty, and sleeping on the floor in a room above the shop but, as sales continued to rise, he knew that he had found his future.

In 1945 that future became richer when Seler married my mother, Eugenia. She was just as ambitious as he was, and from the start they were more than a married couple: they were a strong team who shared a bright vision of the future. Like my father, Eugenia had struggled through a difficult youth. In 1939, when she was sixteen years old, she had emigrated from the Ukraine with her parents and grandmother to escape the ravages of World War II. Her parents were beekeepers and they settled in the Uruguayan countryside and managed a modest living by raising bees and selling honey. It was a life of hard work and limited opportunity, so, when she was twenty, Eugenia moved to Montevideo, like my father, to seek a better future.

She had a clerical job at a large medical laboratory in the city when she married my father, and at first she helped out at the hardware store only in her spare time. In the early days of their marriage, they struggled. Money was so tight that they could not afford furniture, and they began their lives together in an empty apartment. But eventually their hard work paid off and the hardware store began to turn a profit. By the time my older sister, Graciela, was born in 1947, my mother was able to quit her job at the laboratory and work full-time with my father. I came along in 1949. Susy followed three years later. By then, Eugenia had become a major force in the family business, and her hard work and business savvy had helped to give us a very nice standard of living.

One day, when I was twelve, my mother announced that she had found the perfect house for us in Carrasco, one of Montevideo's finest residential districts. I'll never forget the look of happiness in her eyes as she described the modern, two-storey home near the beach. It had big windows, large bright rooms, broad lawns and a breezy verandah, she said. It also had a beautiful view of the ocean. I still remember the delight in her voice when she told us, 'We can watch the sunset over the water!' Her blue eyes were shining with tears. She had started out with so little and now she had found a place that would be home for a lifetime.

In Montevideo, a Carrasco address is a mark of prestige, and we found ourselves living among the upper crust of Uruguayan society: the nation's most prominent industrialists, professionals, artists and politicians. But my mother had her feet planted too firmly on the ground to be overly impressed with the neighbourhood. She was not about to abandon the values she was raised on, or forget who she was.

One of the first things she did at the house was to help her own mother, Lina, who had lived with us since we were small, dig up a broad patch of lush, green lawn behind the house to make way for a huge vegetable garden. (Lina also raised a small flock of ducks and chickens in the yard, and it must have startled the neighbours when they realised that this blue-eyed, white-haired old woman was running a small working farm in one of the city's most manicured neighbourhoods.) Under Lina's loving attention, the garden was soon producing bumper crops of beans, peas, greens, peppers, squash, corn and tomatoes. My mother spent hours in the kitchen with Lina, storing the surplus produce in mason jars, so that we could enjoy the fruits of the garden all year round. My mother hated waste and pretence, and never lost her faith in the value of hard work. But the centre her life was always her home and family. She was always there to send us off to school or welcome us home, never missing my soccer and rugby games, or my sisters' plays and recitals. She was a woman of great, quiet energy, full of encouragement and sage advice, with deep reserves of resourcefulness and good judgment that won the respect of everyone who knew her.

By the time I was in high school, my parents owned three large, thriving hardware stores. My father was also importing merchandise from all over the world and wholesaling it to smaller stores across South America. The poor country boy from Estación Gonzales had come a long way, and I think this gave him a great sense of satisfaction, but there was never a doubt in my mind that he had done it all for us, to protect us in the best way he could.

When I was small, he would take me to the hardware store, walk me along the shelves, and patiently share with me the secrets of all the shiny merchandise on which our family's prosperity was founded: This is a toggle bolt, Nando. You use this to fasten things to a hollow wall. This is a grommet—it reinforces a hole in a canvas tarp so you can thread a rope through it to tie it down. This is an anchor bolt. These are wing nuts. Here is where we keep the washers—split washers, lock washers, ring washers and flat washers in every size. There are common nails, roofing nails, ring-shank nails, masonry nails, double-headed nails . . .

I loved the gentle seriousness with which he shared his knowledge, and it made me feel close to him to know he thought I was big enough to be trusted with it. He was teaching me the things I would need to know to help him at the store, but even as a kid I sensed he was teaching me a deeper lesson: that life is orderly, life makes sense. See, Nando, for every job there is the right tool. Don't let your head get lost in the clouds. Pay attention to the details. You can't build a life on dreams and wishes. You build a life from the ground up, with hard work and clear thinking. There are rules and realities that will not change to suit your needs. It's your job to understand those rules. If you do, and if you work hard and work smart, you will be all right.

I wanted desperately to be like my father, but by the time I reached high school I had to face the fact that we were very different men. I did not have his clear vision, or his pragmatic tenacity. For my father, life was something you created out of hard work and sheer force of will. For me, life was something to be discovered, something that arrived in its own time. I was not lazy or self-indulgent, but I was something of a dreamer. I could not imagine myself selling hardware all my life. I wanted to travel. I wanted adventure and excitement and creativity. More than anything, I dreamed of becoming a racing car driver like my idol Jackie Stewart, the three-time world champion and maybe the greatest driver of all time.

But these dreams seemed unreachable, and so when it finally came time to choose a college, I decided to enrol in agricultural school, because that was where my friends were going. When my father heard the news, he smiled. 'Nando,' he said, 'your friends' families own farms and ranches. We have hardware stores.' It was not hard for him to talk me into changing my mind. In the end I did what made sense: I entered business school with no serious thought about where this decision might lead. I would graduate or I would not. I would run the hardware stores or maybe I wouldn't. My life would present itself to me when it was ready. In the meantime I spent the summer being Nando: I played rugby, I chased girls with Panchito, I raced my little Renault along the beach roads at Punte del Este, I went to parties and lay in the sun; I lived for the moment, happy to let others lead the way.

I COULDN'T HELP thinking of my father now, as we flew above the Andes. He had dropped us off at the airport in Montevideo. 'Have fun,' he had said. 'I will pick you up on Monday.' He had kissed my mother and my sister, given me a warm embrace, then turned to go back to the office. While we had fun in Chile he would do what he always did: take care of things, work hard, provide. He had planned well, so the Parrados would always be fortunate people. He believed in this so firmly, how could we ever doubt him?

'Fasten your seat belts, please,' the steward said. 'There is going to be some turbulence ahead.'

Panchito was still at the window, but we were flying through thick fog and there wasn't much to see. The Fairchild dipped sideways, then we felt four sharp bumps as the belly of the plane skipped hard over pockets of turbulence. I leaned forward and smiled reassuringly at Susy and my mother. My mother looked worried. She had put away the book she was reading and was holding my sister's hand. I wanted to tell them not to worry, but before I could, the bottom seemed to fall out of the fuselage, and my stomach pitched as the plane dropped for what must have been several hundred feet.

As the pilots fought to stabilise the Fairchild, I felt Panchito's elbow in my side. 'Look, Nando,' he said. 'Should we be so close to the mountains?'

I bent to look out of the small window. Through breaks in the cloud I could see a wall of rock and snow flashing past. The Fairchild was bobbing roughly, and the swaying tip of the wing was no more than twenty-five feet from the black slopes. For a second or so I stared in disbelief, then the plane's engines screamed as the pilots tried desperately to climb. The fuselage vibrated so violently I feared it would shake itself to pieces. My mother and sister turned to look at me over the seats. Our eyes met for an instant, then a powerful tremor rocked the plane. There was a howl of grinding metal. Suddenly I saw open sky above me. Icy air blasted my face and I noticed, with an odd calmness, that clouds were swirling in the aisle. There was no time to make sense of things. It all happened in a heartbeat.

I was torn from my seat with incredible force and hurled forward into darkness and silence.

2: Everything Precious

'Here, Nando, are you thirsty?'

It was my teammate Gustavo Zerbino crouching beside me, pressing a ball of snow to my lips. The snow was cold and it burned my throat as I swallowed, but my body was so parched I gobbled it in lumps and begged for more. Several hours had passed since I woke from the coma. My mind was clearer now, and I was full of questions.

I motioned Gustavo closer. 'Where is my mother? Where is Susy? Are they all right?'

Gustavo's face betrayed no emotion. 'Get some rest,' he said. 'You're still very weak.' He walked away, and for a while the others kept their distance. Again and again I pleaded with them to give me some news of my loved ones, but my voice was just a whisper and it was easy for them to pretend they didn't hear.

I lay shivering on the cold floor of the fuselage as the others bustled around me. How desperately I wanted to see my mother's warm smile, to be swept up in her arms and told that we would be OK. Eugenia was the emotional heart of our family, and I needed her so badly now that missing her felt like a physical pain, worse than the cold or the throbbing in my head.

When Gustavo came again with another ball of snow, I grabbed his sleeve. 'Where are they, Gustavo?' I insisted. 'Please.'

Gustavo looked into my eyes and must have seen that I was ready to have an answer. 'Nando, you must be strong,' he said. 'Your mother is dead.'

For a brief moment, grief and panic exploded in my heart so violently that I feared I would go mad, but then a thought formed in my head, in a voice so lucid and so detached from everything that I was feeling that it could have been someone whispering in my ear. The voice said: *Do not cry. Tears waste salt. You will need salt to survive.*

I was astounded at the calmness of this thought, and shocked at the cold-bloodedness of the voice that spoke it. Not cry for my mother?

The voice spoke again. *Do not cry.*

'There is more,' Gustavo told me. 'Panchito is dead. Guido, too. And many others.' I shook my head feebly in disbelief. How could this be happening? Sobs gathered in my throat, but before I could surrender to my grief and shock, the voice spoke again: *They are all gone. They are all a part of your past. Don't waste energy on things you can't control. Look forward. Think clearly. You will survive.*

Then I remembered my sister, and through no effort of my own, I did what the voice wanted; I let my grief for my mother and friends slip into the past, as my mind filled with fear for my sister's safety. I gathered my courage for the question I had to ask. 'Gustavo, where is Susy?'

'She's over there,' he said, pointing to the rear of the plane, 'but she is hurt very badly.' Suddenly, my own suffering faded and I was filled with an urgent desire to reach my sister. Struggling to my feet, I tried to walk, but the pain in my head made me swoon and I slumped back roughly to the floor. I rested for a moment, then rolled onto my stomach and dragged myself on my elbows towards my sister. The floor all around me was littered with cracked plastic cups, splayed magazines, playing cards and paperback books. Damaged seats were stacked in a tangled pile near the cockpit bulkhead, and I could see, on either side of the aisle, the broken metal brackets that had held them down. For a moment I imagined the terrible force it must have taken to tear the seats loose from such sturdy anchors.

I inched slowly towards Susy, but soon my strength gave out. I let my head slump to the floor to rest, then felt arms lifting me and carrying me forward. Someone helped me to the rear of the plane and there, lying on her back, was Susy. At first glance she did not seem to be badly injured. There were traces of blood on her brow, but someone had obviously washed her face. Her hair had been smoothed back. She was wearing the new antelope leather coat she had purchased just for this trip—and the soft fur collar moved against her cheek in the frigid breeze.

My friends helped me lie down beside her. I wrapped my arms round her and whispered, 'I am here, Susy. It's Nando.' She turned and looked at me, but her gaze was unfocused and I couldn't be sure she knew it was me. She rolled in my arms as if to move closer, but then groaned and pulled away. I let her find a less painful position, then wrapped my arms and legs round her to protect her from the cold. I lay that way for hours. Sometimes she would sob or moan. From time to time she would call out for our mother.

'Mamá, please,' she would cry. 'I'm so cold. Please, Mamá, let's go home.' These words pierced my heart like arrows. Susy was my mother's baby and the two of them had always shared a special tenderness. They were so similar in temperament, so gentle and patient, so at ease in each other's company that I don't remember them ever having a fight. They would spend hours together, cooking, taking walks or just talking. I believe my sister told my mother everything.

When Susy and I were small, we were each other's favourite playmates. As we grew older, I, too, became a trusted confidant. She shared her secrets with me, told me her hopes and worries. I remember that she was always concerned about her weight. She thought she was too heavy, but she was not. Susy had the strong, shapely build of a gymnast or a swimmer. She was young and had not yet had a serious boyfriend, and I knew she worried that boys would not find her attractive. But I saw the beauty of her deep, clear caramel eyes, fine skin and kind face. How could I convince her that she was a treasure? My little sister Susy had been precious to me from the moment she was born, and I knew it would always be my job to protect her.

Now, as I held her in my arms, I felt a pang of helplessness. I would have given my own life to end her suffering and send her home to my father.

My father! In all the chaos and confusion, I had not had time to consider what he must be going through. He would have heard the news three days ago, and for all that time he would have lived believing he had lost us all. I knew he would not allow himself the luxury of false hope. To survive a plane crash in the Andes? At this time of year? Impossible. I saw him tossing in his bed, staggered by his unimaginable loss. After all his work and planning, all his trust in the orderliness of the world and the certainty of our happiness, how could he bear the brutal truth: he could not protect us. My heart broke for him. I could not stand the idea that he thought I was dead. I felt a violent longing to be with him, to show him he had not lost us all.

But as the afternoon passed and it grew colder and darker, I sank into a mood of pure despair. It seemed that we had fallen through a crack in the sky into some frozen hell from which no return to the ordinary world was possible. I knew myths and legends in which heroes had fallen into an evil underworld, or an enchanted forests from which there was no escape. In their struggles to return to their homes, they had to battle dragons and demons, match wits with sorcerers, sail across treacherous seas. But even those heroes needed magical help: a flying carpet, a secret charm, a magic sword. We were a group of untested boys who had never set foot in the mountains. Few of us had ever seen snow. Where would we find our hero? What magic would carry us home?

I buried my face in Susy's hair to keep myself from sobbing. Then an old memory began to glow in my mind, a story my father had told me countless times. When he was a young man, he had been one of Uruguay's top rowers, and one summer he travelled to Argentina to compete in a race on a section of the Uruguay River known as the Delta del Tigre. Seler quickly pulled away from most of the field, but one Argentine racer stayed with him. They raced neck and neck, both of them straining with all their might to gain the slightest advantage, but as the finish line approached it was still a close call. My father's lungs were burning and his legs were seized with cramps. All he wanted was to end his suffering. There will be other races, he told himself, as he eased his grip on the oars. But then he glanced at his competitor and saw pure agony in that man's face. 'I realised he was suffering as much as I was,' my father told me. 'So I decided I would not quit after all. I decided I would suffer a little longer.' With new resolve, Seler dug the oars into the water and stroked with all the power he could muster. His heart pounded and his muscles felt as if they were being torn from the bone, but he forced himself on, and when the racers reached the finish line the prow of my father's scull got there first, by inches.

I was five years old the first time my father told me that story, and I never grew tired of hearing it. Many years later, when I'd see him at the hardware store, weary, stooped over his desk and squinting through his thick glasses at stacks of invoices and order forms, I still saw that heroic young man on the river, suffering, struggling, but refusing to give in.

As I huddled in the plane with Susy, I tried to find the same strength in myself, but all I felt was hopelessness and fear. I heard my father's voice: *Be strong, Nando, be smart. Make your own luck. Take care of the people you love.* The words inspired nothing in me but a black sense of loss.

Susy shifted in my arms. 'Don't worry,' I whispered to her, 'they will find us. They will bring us home.' Whether I believed those words or not, I can't say. My only thought was to comfort my sister. The sun was setting, and as the light dimmed, the frigid air took on an even sharper edge. The others, who had already lived through two long nights in the mountains, found their sleeping places and braced for the misery they knew lay ahead.

Soon the darkness in the plane was absolute, and the cold closed on us like the jaws of a vice. The ferocity of it stole my breath away. It seemed to have a malice in it, a predatory will, but there was no way to fight off its attack except to huddle closer to my sister. Time itself seemed to be frozen. I lay on the cold floor, tormented by the icy gusts blowing in through every gap and crack, shivering uncontrollably through the long night, suffering from one frozen heartbeat to the next. When I thought I couldn't stand it any longer, I would draw Susy closer, and the thought that I was comforting her kept me sane. I couldn't see her face; I could only hear her laboured breathing. I wrapped my arms round her as gently as I could, mindful of her injuries and fighting the urge to squeeze her with all my might. I pressed my cheek against hers so I could feel her warm breath on my face, and held her that way all night, embracing her as if I were embracing all the love and peace and joy I had ever known and would ever know, as if by holding on tight I could keep everything precious from slipping away.

3: A Promise

I slept very little that first night out of the coma, and it seemed that dawn would never come. But at last a thin light slowly brightened the windows of the fuselage, and the others began to stir. My heart sank when I first saw them—their hair, eyebrows and lips glistened with thick silver frost, and they moved stiffly and slowly, like old men. As I rose, I realised that my clothes had frozen stiff on my body, and frost had clumped on my brows and lashes. I forced myself to stand. The pain inside my skull still throbbed, but the bleeding had stopped, so I staggered outside to take my first look at the strange white world into which we had fallen.

The morning sun lit the snow-covered slopes with a hard white glare, and I had to squint as I surveyed the crash site. The Fairchild's battered fuselage had come to rest nose downwards on a glacier that flowed down the eastern slope of a massive mountain, then streamed off into a broad valley that wound through the cordillera and disappeared into a maze of snow-capped ridges on the eastern horizon. East was the only direction in which we could see for any great distance. To the north, south and west, the view was blocked by towering mountains. We knew we were high in the Andes, but the slopes above us rose up even higher, so that I had to tilt my head back to see their summits. At the very top, the black peaks broke through the snow cover like huge, broken molars. The ridges formed a ragged semicircle that ringed the crash site like the walls of a monstrous amphitheatre, with the wreckage of the Fairchild lying centre stage.

I was so baffled by the dreamlike strangeness of the place that at first I struggled to convince myself it was real. The mountains were so profoundly removed from anything in my previous experience that I simply could not find my bearings. I had lived all my life in Montevideo, a city of 1.5 million people—a manufactured thing, built to suit human beings. But the Andes had been thrust up from the earth's crust millions of years before human beings ever walked the planet. Nothing in this place welcomed human life, or even acknowledged its existence. The cold tormented us, the thin air starved our lungs and the unfiltered sun blinded us and blistered our lips and skin. In all the endless miles of frozen slopes that entrapped us, there was not a bird, not an insect, not a single blade of grass. Our chances of survival would have been better if we'd been stranded in the open ocean, or lost in the Sahara. We were absurdly out of place, like a seahorse in the desert, or a flower on the moon. A dreadful thought began to form in my mind: life is an anomaly here, and the mountains will tolerate that anomaly for only so long. We were playing a game against an unknown and unforgiving opponent. The stakes were terrible—and we didn't even know the ground rules. I knew that in order to save my life I would have to understand those rules, but the cold white world around me was offering up no clues.

I might have felt more grounded in my new reality if I had remembered more of the crash. Because I'd blacked out, I had no recollection of anything until I came to my senses three days later. But most of the other survivors had been conscious for every second, and as they recounted the details of the crash and the desperate days that followed, I realised it was a miracle that any of us were alive.

I remembered the flight through Planchón Pass, and that at one point we hit an air pocket that forced the plane to drop several hundred feet below the clouds. That was probably the moment when the pilots first saw the black ridge rising dead ahead. They gunned the Fairchild's engines and managed to raise the plane's nose a few degrees, preventing a head-on collision, but their actions were too late to lift the plane completely over the mountain. The Fairchild's belly slammed into the ridge at roughly the point where the wings met the body, and the damage was catastrophic. First the wings broke away. The right wing spiralled down into the pass, and the left wing slammed back against the plane, where its propeller sliced through the Fairchild's hull. A split second later the fuselage fractured along a line directly above my head, and the tail section fell away. Everyone sitting behind me was lost, including the plane's navigator, the flight steward, and the three boys playing cards. One of those boys was Guido.

I remember being hurled forward and slamming into something, probably the bulkhead between the passenger cabin and the cockpit, then I lost

consciousness, and for me the crash was over. The others still faced a terrifying ride as the fuselage, stripped of its wings, engines and tail, sailed forward like an unguided missile. Then we were blessed with the first of many
miracles: the plane did not wobble or spiral. Instead, whatever aerodynamic
principles govern such things kept the remains of the Fairchild flying level
long enough to clear yet another black ridge. The plane lost momentum,
and, as the nose dipped and it began to fall, a second miracle saved us. The
Fairchild's angle of descent matched, almost exactly, the slope of the mountain. If this angle had been just a few degrees steeper or shallower, the fuselage would have cartwheeled and been slammed to pieces. Instead, it landed
on its belly and began to rocket down the snow-covered mountainside like a
toboggan. Passengers screamed and prayed out loud as it raced down the
slope at two hundred miles per hour, finding a fortunate path between boulders and rocky outcrops before slamming into a huge snow berm and
coming to a violent stop. The Fairchild's nose was crumpled like a paper
cup. Seats were ripped loose and hurled forward against the cockpit bulkhead. Several passengers were crushed instantly as the rows of seats closed
on them like the folds of an accordion, then tumbled into a mangled heap
that filled the front of the fuselage almost to the ceiling.

Coche Inciarte, one of the team's supporters, told me how he had
grasped the back of the seat in front of him as the plane streaked down the
mountain. After the impact, he said, the fuselage rolled slightly to the left,
then settled heavily in the snow. For moments there was nothing but silence,
but soon it was broken by soft moans, and then sharper cries of pain. Coche
found himself lying in the tangle of seats, uninjured and amazed to be alive.

Gustavo Zerbino explained that in the first impact, when the plane hit the
mountain ridge, he saw the seat across the aisle rip loose from the floor and
disappear into the sky. As the fuselage skidded down the slope, he stood
and grabbed the luggage rack above his head. He closed his eyes and
prayed, certain he was about to die. Miraculously, he was still standing
when the plane smashed into the snow bank and heaved to a sudden stop.

When he opened his eyes, he instinctively took a step back, and immediately sank to his hips in snow. Looking up, he saw the ragged line of the
fracture where the tail section had broken away from the fuselage, and
realised that everything and everyone behind him had disappeared. The
floor of the fuselage was at the level of his chest now, and as he pulled himself back up into the plane, he was forced to climb over the motionless body
of a middle-aged woman. Her face was bruised and covered with blood, but

he recognised her as my mother. Gustavo, a first-year medical student, bent down and took her pulse, but she was already gone.

He moved forward towards the pile of seats, prised one from the pile and found Roberto Canessa underneath. Canessa, also a medical student, was not injured, and within moments he and Gustavo began pulling more seats from the pile and tending the injured passengers they freed.

At the same time, Marcelo Pérez was pulling himself from the wreckage. Marcelo had hurt his side in the crash, and his face was bruised, but these injuries were minor, and as our longtime captain he immediately took control. His first action was to organise the uninjured boys and set them to work freeing those who were trapped in their seats.

As the passengers were pulled, one by one, from the impossible tangle, Roberto and Gustavo assessed their condition and did their best to tend to their injuries. Both of Arturo Nogueira's legs had been broken in several places. Alvaro Mangino had a broken leg, and so did Pancho Delgado. A six-inch steel tube had impaled Enrique Platero's stomach like the point of a spear, and Gustavo had to yank it from his friend's gut. The injury to Rafael Echavarren's right leg was even more gruesome. His calf muscle had been ripped off the bone and twisted forward so that it hung across his shin. When Gustavo found him, Echavarren's leg bone was completely exposed. Swallowing his revulsion, Gustavo grabbed the loose muscle, pressed it back in place, then bandaged the bloody leg with strips of someone's shirt. He bandaged Platero's stomach, too, and then the quiet, stoic Platero immediately went to work freeing others who were trapped.

The 'doctors' were amazed to see that most of the survivors had suffered only minor injuries. Gustavo and Roberto cleaned and bandaged their wounds, then sent those with injuries to arms and legs out onto the glacier, where they dulled their pain by cooling their limbs in the snow. Uninjured survivors became workers, and soon they had freed all the trapped passengers except one, a middle-aged woman named Señora Mariani, who had bought her ticket directly from the air force, as an inexpensive way of flying to Chile for her daughter's wedding. Her seat had collapsed forward in the crash, pinning her legs beneath it. No amount of effort could free her. She was screaming in agony, but there was nothing anyone could do.

And there was nothing to be done for our team doctor, Francisco Nicola, and his wife, Esther, who had been flung from their seats and were lying dead, side by side, at the front of the passenger cabin. Susy was lying beside my mother's body, conscious but incoherent, with blood streaming over her face. Roberto wiped the blood from her eyes, saw that it was coming from a superficial scalp wound, but suspected, correctly, that she had suffered much more serious internal injuries. A few feet away he found Panchito, bleeding from the head and rambling in semiconsciousness. Roberto cleaned the blood from his eyes, comforted him, then moved on.

In the front of the plane he found me lying senseless, my face covered in blood and bruises, my head swollen to the size of a basketball. He checked my pulse and found that my heart was still beating. But my injuries seemed so grave that he gave me no chance of surviving, and he and Gustavo moved on, saving their efforts for those they believed they could help.

There were moans coming from the cockpit, but the cockpit door was still barricaded by the wall of toppled seats, so Gustavo and Roberto had to step outside the fuselage and struggle through deep snow to the front of the plane, where they were able to climb up through the luggage compartment into the cockpit. They found Ferradas and Lagurara still strapped into their seats. The impact had crushed the Fairchild's nose and forced the instrument panel into their chests. Ferradas was dead. Lagurara was conscious, but gravely injured and in terrible pain. Gustavo and Roberto tried to prise the instrumental panel off the copilot's chest, but it wouldn't budge. 'We passed Curicó,' Lagurara muttered, as they tried to help him, 'we passed Curicó.' They removed the cushion of his seat back, relieving some of the pressure on his chest, but there was not much more they could do. They fed him snow to ease his thirst, then asked if they could use the Fairchild's radio. Lagurara told them how to set the dial for transmission, but when they tried to send a message they found the radio was dead. Lagurara begged for more snow and the doctors fed it to him then turned to leave. Lagurara pleaded with the boys to bring him the revolver he kept in his flight bag, but they ignored him and headed back to the passenger cabin.

Back in the fuselage, Marcelo was making some grim calculations. We had crashed at three thirty in the afternoon. He guessed it would be four o'clock before officials could confirm that the plane was missing. By the time they could organise a helicopter rescue, it would be five thirty or six. The helicopters would not reach us until seven thirty at the earliest, and, since no pilot in his right mind would fly in the Andes at night, Marcelo knew no rescue would be launched until the following day. We would have to spend the night there. The temperature, already well below freezing when we crashed, was dropping fast. Marcelo knew we were not prepared to weather a subzero night in the Andes. We were dressed only in light summer clothing. We had no warm coats, no blankets, nothing to protect us from the savage cold. Unless we found a way to turn the fuselage into a decent shelter, none of us would last until morning.

Marcelo gathered a crew of healthy survivors and gave them the task of removing the dead and injured from the fuselage. Then he directed them to clear as much clutter from the floor space as they could. The work was gruelling and excruciatingly slow. By the time darkness fell, they had cleared just a small space near the gaping hole at the rear of the fuselage.

At six o'clock, Marcelo directed them to move the injured back into the fuselage, then the healthy survivors filed in and prepared for the long night ahead. Once everyone was settled, Marcelo began to build a makeshift wall to seal off the huge opening where the tail section had broken away. With Roy Harley's help, he stacked suitcases, loose seats and fragments of the aircraft in the opening, then packed the gaps with snow. It was far from airtight, but he hoped it would shield us from the worst of the subzero cold.

Forty-five passengers and crew members had been on board the Fairchild. Five were now dead at the crash site and eight were unaccounted for, which left thirty-two people alive, most of them packed into a cramped space no more than eight by ten feet square. It was intensely uncomfortable, and despite Marcelo's wall the cold was unbearable. The survivors huddled together, and some of them begged those near them to punch their arms and legs to keep the blood flowing in their veins.

At some point, Roberto realised that the cloth seat covers could be unzipped and removed and used as blankets. They were made of thin nylon and offered little protection against the cold, but he knew the survivors had to do everything they could to conserve body heat.

They had laid me beside Susy and Panchito at the base of Marcelo's wall, the coldest part of the cabin, where the floor had been torn away in the crash and cold air streamed up from below. They placed us here because they had given up hope that we would live very long and were saving the warmer places for those who had a chance to survive. Susy and Panchito, who were still conscious, must have suffered terribly that first night, but I was still in a coma and was spared that agony. In fact, the freezing air may have saved my life by reducing the swelling that would have destroyed my brain.

As the last light faded, it was as if the mountain darkness was seeping into the survivors' souls. All the work they had done in the aftermath of the crash had kept them from dwelling on their fears and had helped them keep warm. But now there was nothing to protect them from the cold or, worse, from despair. Survivors who had performed stoically in the daylight now wept and screamed in pain. At some point, Diego Storm, another medical student, saw something in my face that made him think I might live, so he dragged me away from Marcelo's wall to a warmer place in the fuselage.

Some managed to sleep that night, but most simply endured, second by second, as sounds of suffering and delusion filled the darkness. In a thin voice, Panchito pleaded pathetically for help; Susy prayed and called for our mother; Señora Mariani screamed and wailed in her agony. In the cockpit, the raving copilot begged for his gun, and insisted, over and over, 'We passed Curicó, we passed Curicó . . .'

At last morning came. Marcelo was the first on his feet. The others were reluctant to rise, but he roused them, and as they moved around in the daylight filtering into the cabin their spirits began to rise. Surely the rescue party would find them today, and the worst of their ordeal would be over.

Gustavo and Roberto moved through the fuselage, checking on the injured. Panchito was lying still and stiff. He had died during the night. In the cockpit, they found Lagurara's lifeless body. Señora Mariani was motionless, but when Roberto tried to move her she screamed in agony, and he left her alone. When he checked on her again, she was dead.

They found Susy conscious, but still delusional. Roberto rubbed her feet, which were black with frostbite, then he wiped the blood from her eyes. She was lucid enough to thank him for his kindness.

While the doctors had been making their rounds, Marcelo and Roy Harley had knocked down part of the wall they'd built the night before, and the survivors now began their second day on the mountain. All day long they searched the skies for signs of rescue. Late afternoon, they heard a plane pass over, but it was overcast and they knew they hadn't been seen.

In the fast-fading twilight, they gathered again in the fuselage to face another long night. Marcelo built a better, more windproof wall, but still their suffering was grim.

In the afternoon of the third day, I finally woke from my coma. As I slowly gathered my wits, I saw that my friends' faces were drawn and pale from tension and lack of sleep. The energy-sapping effects of the thin air made their movements slow and uncertain, and many of them shuffled about the crash site as if they had grown decades older in the last thirty-six hours.

There were twenty-nine survivors now, most of us young men between the ages of eighteen and twenty-five. The oldest was thirty-eight-year-old Javier Methol, but he suffered so badly from altitude sickness that he could barely stand. The only crew member to survive was Carlos Roque, the plane's mechanic, but the shock of the crash had rattled him so badly that all we could get from him was senseless raving. He couldn't even tell us where emergency supplies like flares and blankets might be kept. There was no one to help us, no one with any knowledge of mountains or aeroplanes or the techniques of survival, but we did not panic. Leaders emerged, and we responded in the way we'd been taught by the Christian Brothers—as a team.

Much of the credit for our survival in those critical early days must go to Marcelo Pérez, whose decisive leadership saved many lives. From the very first moments of the ordeal, he responded to the staggering challenges before us with the same combination of courage, decisiveness and foresight with which he had led us to so many victories on the rugby field. He instantly understood that the margin for error here was slim, and that the mountain would make us pay dearly for stupid mistakes. The rescue operation he quickly organised saved many lives, and without the sheltering wall he built that first night we all would have frozen to death.

He slept at night in the coldest part of the fuselage, and asked the other uninjured boys to do the same. He forced us to keep busy, when many among us simply wanted to huddle together and wait to be saved. More than anything, he buoyed our spirits by assuring us that our suffering would be over soon. He was certain that rescue was on its way, and was forceful in convincing others that this was true. Yet some instinct for survival told him to err on the side of caution. He gathered everything edible that could be found in suitcases or scattered around the cabin. There wasn't much—a few chocolate bars and other candies, some nuts and crackers, some dried fruit, several small jars of jam, three bottles of wine, some whisky and a few bottles of liqueur. On the second day, he began to ration the food. Each meal was nothing more than a square of chocolate or a dab of jam, washed down with a sip of wine from the cap of an aerosol can. It was not enough to satisfy anyone's hunger, but as a ritual it gave us strength.

In those early days we all clung to hope of rescue with an almost religious zeal. Even as days passed and no rescue arrived, Marcelo would not let us doubt that we all would be saved. Whether he truly believed this, I cannot say. I didn't realise at the time how deeply he blamed himself for taking us all on this doomed journey.

On the afternoon of the fourth day, a small plane flew over and several of the survivors who saw it were certain that it had dipped its wings. This was taken as a signal that we had been sighted, and jubilation spread through the group. We waited, as the long shadows of late afternoon stretched down the mountains, but by nightfall no rescuers had arrived. Marcelo insisted that the pilots of the plane would send help, but others admitted their doubts.

'Why is it taking so long for them to find us?' someone asked.

Perhaps helicopters cannot fly in the thin mountain air, Marcelo would say, so the rescue party might be coming on foot, and that will take time.

'But why haven't they flown over to drop supplies?'

Impossible, Marcelo would say. Anything dropped from a plane would simply sink into the snow and be lost. The pilots would know this.

Most of the boys accepted the logic of Marcelo's explanations. They also trusted heavily in the goodness of God. 'God saved us from dying in the crash,' they'd say. 'Why would He do that just to leave us here to die?'

I listened to these discussions as I spent the long hours caring for Susy. I wanted so badly to trust in God as they did. But God had already taken my mother and Panchito and so many others. Why would He save us and not them? I could not chase away the gnawing sense that we were on our own. I felt a terrible helplessness and sense of urgency. I knew that Susy was dying, and that the only hope was to get her to a hospital soon. Each moment lost was an agony for me and, though I never stopped praying for rescuers or the intercession of God, it alarmed me that the others were placing so much trust in the hope that we would be saved.

Soon I realised that others thought like me. The 'realists', as I thought of us, included Gustavo and Roberto, Fito Strauch, a former member of the Old Christians who had come on the trip at the invitation of his cousin Eduardo, and Carlitos Páez, whose father was a famous painter and friend of Picasso. For days our group had been discussing a plan to climb the mountain above us and see what lay beyond. We had reason to believe that escape was possible, for we knew the words our copilot had moaned as he lay dying: *We passed Curicó, we passed Curicó* . . . Someone had found sets of flight charts in the cockpit, and Arturo Nogueira, whose shattered legs confined him to the fuselage, had spent hours studying them, searching for the town of Curicó. Finally he found it, situated inside the Chilean border, well beyond the western slopes of the Andes. None of us was an expert, but it seemed clear that if we had, in fact, travelled as far west as Curicó, then we had flown across the entire breadth of the cordillera. That meant the crash site must be somewhere in the western foothills of the Andes. We were encouraged in this belief by the reading on the Fairchild's altimeter, which showed our altitude to be 7,000 feet. If we were deep in the

Andes, our altitude would be much higher than that. Surely we were in the foothills, and the tall ridges to our west were the last high peaks of the Andes range. We grew certain that beyond those western summits were the green fields of Chile. We would find a village there, or at least a shepherd's hut. Someone would be there to help us. It gave us a small sense of control. We knew one fact at least: To the west is Chile. This phrase quickly became a rallying call for us, and we used it to bolster our hopes.

ON THE MORNING of October 17, our fifth day on the mountain, Carlitos, Roberto, Fito and a twenty-four-year-old survivor named Numa Turcatti decided the time had come to climb.

Numa was not an Old Christian—he had come on the trip as a guest of his friends, Pancho Delgado and Gastón Costemalle—but he was as fit as any of us, and had come through the crash with hardly a scratch. I did not know him well, but in the few difficult days we had spent together he had impressed me with his calmness and quiet strength. Numa never panicked or lost his temper. He never fell into self-pity or despair. There was something noble and selfless in him, and everybody saw it. He seemed to care about the welfare of the rest of us as much as he cared about himself, and we all drew strength from his example. I knew that if we ever escaped these mountains, Numa would have something to do with it, and I wasn't surprised that he had volunteered to go on the climb.

Shortly after the crash, when we were struggling to walk in the deep, soft snow surrounding the fuselage, Fito had realised that if we tied the cushions of the Fairchild's seats to our feet with seat belts or lengths of wire cable they would serve as makeshift snowshoes. Now, the four climbers had Fito's snowshoes strapped to their boots as they set off across the deep drifts towards the mountain, hoping to reach the summit. Along the way they would search for the Fairchild's missing tail section, which we all hoped would be filled with food and warm clothing. We even wondered if there could be other survivors living inside it. And Carlos Roque, the Fairchild's flight mechanic, who had slowly regained his senses, had remembered that the batteries that powered the Fairchild's radio were stored in a compartment in the tail. If we found them, it was possible we could fix the radio and broadcast a call for help.

The weather was clear as they set off. I wished them well, then busied myself with caring for my sister.

Afternoon shadows had fallen over the Fairchild by the time the climbers returned. I heard commotion in the fuselage as they arrived, and I looked up to see them stumble inside and sag to the floor. They were physically wasted and gasping for air. The others quickly surrounded them, badgering them with questions, eager for promising news.

I went to Numa and asked him how it was.

He shook his head and scowled. 'It was damned hard, Nando,' he said as he tried to catch his breath. 'It is much steeper than it looks from here.'

'There is not enough air,' Roberto said. 'You can't breathe. You can only move very slowly.'

Numa nodded. 'The snow is too deep; every step is agony. And there are crevasses under the snow. Fito almost fell into one.'

'Did you see anything to the west?' I asked.

'We barely made it halfway up the slope,' Numa said. 'We couldn't see anything. The mountains block the view.'

I turned to Roberto. 'What do you think?' I asked him. 'If we try again, can we climb it?'

'I don't know, man,' he whispered, 'I don't know . . .'

'We can't climb that mountain,' muttered Numa. 'We must find another route—if there is one.'

That night, gloom hung in the air. The four who had climbed were the strongest and healthiest among us, and the mountain had defeated them. I told myself that they were soft, afraid—they had quit too easily. I was certain that if we chose the right route and the right time, and refused to give in to the cold and exhaustion, we could reach the summit. I clung to this belief with the same blind faith that kept the others praying for rescue. It seemed grue-somely simple: *To the west is Chile. To the west is Chile.* I let those words echo in my mind like a mantra. I knew that someday I would have to climb.

IN THE FIRST few days of our ordeal, I rarely left my sister's side. I spent all my time with her, rubbing her frozen feet, giving her sips of water I had melted, feeding her little squares of chocolate that Marcelo would set aside. Mostly, I tried to comfort her and keep her warm. I was never sure if she was aware of my presence. She was always semiconscious. Her brow was constantly knit with worry and confusion, and there was always a forlorn sadness in her eyes. Many times she would call for our mother.

Late in the afternoon of the eighth day, I was lying with my arms round her when suddenly I felt her change. The worried look faded from her face. The tenseness eased from her body. Her breathing grew shallow and I felt her life slipping from my arms. Then her breathing stopped and she was still.

'Susy?' I cried. 'Oh God, Susy, please, no!'

I scrambled to my knees, rolled her onto her back and began to give her mouth-to-mouth resuscitation. I was not even sure how to do this, but I was desperate to save her. 'Come on, Susy, please,' I cried. 'Don't leave me!' I worked over her until I fell, exhausted, to the floor. Roberto took my place, with no success. Then Carlitos tried, but it was no good. The others gathered round me in silence.

'I'm sorry, Nando, she is gone,' Roberto said. 'Stay with her tonight. We will bury her in the morning.' I nodded and gathered my sister in my arms. Now at last I could embrace her with all my might, without the fear of hurting her. I tried to memorise this feeling, the feel of her body, the smell of her hair. As I thought of all I was losing, the grief surged inside me, and my body was shaken by sobs. But just as my sadness was about to overwhelm me, I heard, once again, that cool voice whisper in my ear: *Tears waste salt.*

I lay awake with her all night, my chest heaving with sobs, but I did not allow myself the luxury of tears.

IN THE MORNING we dragged Susy from the fuselage out into the snow. I watched as they pulled her to where the other dead were buried. The frozen corpses were clearly visible, their faces obscured by only a few inches of ice and snow. I dug a shallow grave for Susy next to my mother, laid her on her side and brushed back her hair. Then I covered her slowly with handfuls of crystallised snow, leaving her face uncovered until the very end. She seemed peaceful, as if she were sleeping under a thick fleece blanket. I took one last look at her, then gently tossed handfuls of snow across her cheeks until her face had vanished beneath the sparkling crystals.

After we finished, the others walked back inside the fuselage. I turned and looked up the slope of the glacier, to the ridges of mountains blocking our path to the west. I could still see the wide path the Fairchild had cut into the snow as it skied down the slope after clipping the ridge. I followed this with my eyes up to the very spot where we had fallen from the sky, and suddenly I was struck by a sickening sense of emptiness. I had spent all my time and energy until now caring for my sister. Comforting her had given me purpose. It had filled my hours and distracted me from my pain and fear. Now I was so terribly alone, with nothing to distance me from my awful circumstances. More than a week had passed, and still rescuers had not found us. I felt the brute power of the mountains around me, and as I understood, with a stinging new clarity, how far we were from home, I sank into despair.

I would never return to my father. In my mind I saw him again, in his suffering, and felt such a violent longing to be with him that it almost drove me to my knees. I gagged on the impotent rage that rose in my throat, and felt so beaten and trapped that for a moment I thought I would lose my mind. Then I saw my father on that river in Argentina, on the verge of surrender, and I remembered his words of defiance: *I decided I would not quit. I would suffer a little longer.*

An eerie calmness settled over me. I stared at the great mountains to the west, and imagined a path leading over them and back to my home. I felt my love for my father tugging at me like a lifeline, drawing me towards those slopes and I made a silent vow to my father: I will struggle. I will come home. I promise you, I will not die here!

4: Breathe Once More

In the hours after we buried Susy, I sat alone in the dark fuselage, slumped against the Fairchild's tilting wall with my shattered skull cradled in my hands. Powerful emotions stormed my heart—disbelief, outrage, sorrow, fear—then, finally, a weary feeling of acceptance washed over me. I was too depressed and confused to see it at the time, but my mind was racing through the stages of grief at breakneck speed. In my old life, my ordinary life in Montevideo, the loss of my little sister would have brought my existence to a standstill, but nothing was ordinary any more, and something primal in me understood that in this unforgiving place I could not afford the luxury of grieving.

As the long night passed, the intensity of my emotions began to fade and my feelings for my sister dissolved, the way a dream dissolves as you wake. By morning all I felt was a dull emptiness. The mountains were forcing me to change. Basic instincts were taking hold, suppressing complex emotions and narrowing the focus of my mind until my entire existence revolved around the two new principles of my life: the chilling apprehension that I was going to die, and the searing need to be with my father.

My love for my father was now the only thing that kept me sane, and time after time I would calm myself by reaffirming the promise I had made to return to him. Thinking of him always triggered in me a burst of love so radiant and urgent that it took my breath away. I couldn't stand the thought that he should suffer one second longer. In my desperation, I raged silently at the great peaks that blocked the path to him, trapping me in this evil place. That frustration gnawed at me until, like a man buried alive, I began to panic. Every moment was filled with a visceral fear, as if the earth beneath my feet were a ticking bomb that might explode at any second. This terrifying sense of vulnerability became the backdrop to every thought and conversation. And it produced in me a manic urge to flee. I tried to calm myself and think clearly, but there were moments when instinct threatened to overcome reason, and it would take me all my strength to keep from bolting off blindly into the cordillera.

At first, the only way I could quiet these fears was to picture in my mind the moment when rescuers would arrive. This was the hope we all clung to, and Marcelo fed it with assurances. But as the days passed and the absence of the rescuers became harder to explain, Marcelo, a devout Catholic, had to rely more and more upon the beliefs that had shaped his life. 'God loves us,' he would say. 'He would not ask us to endure such suffering only to turn his back on us and allow us to die meaningless deaths.' Our duty, Marcelo insisted—to God, to our families and to each other—was to accept our fears and suffering, and to be alive when the rescuers finally found us.

Marcelo's words had a powerful effect on most of the others. I wanted to believe them, but I could not silence the doubts growing in my mind. The fact that rescue hadn't come forced me to two grim conclusions: either the authorities had a mistaken idea of where we had fallen and were searching some other stretch of the cordillera, or they had no idea at all where we were in the sprawling mountains, and no way to narrow their search. If they didn't know even roughly where we are, they would never find us.

At first I kept these thoughts to myself, telling myself I didn't want to dash the hopes of the others. But perhaps I didn't want to speak my feelings out loud because I feared that would make them real. Despite all my doubts, I could not allow myself to shut the door on the possibility of a miracle. My heart continued to hope just as naturally as it continued to beat. So I prayed every night with the others, beseeching God to speed the rescuers on their way. I listened for the fluttering drone of helicopters. I nodded in agreement when Marcelo urged us to keep faith. Still, in every quiet moment a barrage of frightful questions would erupt in my brain: What if we have to climb out of here on our own? Do I have the strength to survive a trek through this wilderness? What would happen if I fell? And always: What lies to the west, beyond those black ridges?

Deep down, I always knew we'd have to save ourselves. Eventually I began to express this belief to the others, and the more I spoke of it, the more the thought of climbing obsessed me. I began to rehearse my escape so vividly and so often that my daydreams became as real as a movie playing in my head. I'd see myself climbing the white slopes towards those bleak summits; I'd visualise every fragile fingerhold, testing each rock before I grasped it, studying each careful placement of my feet. I'd be lashed by freezing winds, gasping in the thin air, struggling through hip-deep snow. In my daydream, each step of the ascent is an agony, but I do not stop. Finally I reach the summit and look to the west. Spread out before me is a broad valley sloping down towards the horizon, a neat patchwork of brown and green fields blanketing the valley floor. I stumble down the west-ward side of the mountain and hike for hours over rocky terrain until I reach a road. Then I walk west on a smooth asphalt surface. Soon I hear the rumble of an approaching truck. I flag down the startled driver. I have to make him understand: *Vengo de un avión que cayo en las montañas . . .*

I come from a plane that fell in the mountains . . .

He lets me climb into the cab, and we travel west through the green farm-lands to the nearest town, where I find a phone. I dial my father's number, and in moments I hear his astonished sobs as he recognises my voice. A day or two later we are together. He says nothing, just my name, and I feel him collapse against me when I take him into my arms.

This dream soon became my touchstone, my lifeline, and I nurtured it and refined it until it sparkled in my mind like a jewel, and the promise I made to my father took on the power of a sacred calling. It focused my mind, turned my fears to motivation, and gave me a sense of direction that lifted me out of the black well of helplessness in which I'd languished since the crash. I still prayed with Marcelo and the others, but when my fears grew so violent I thought they would drive me insane, I would close my eyes, renew my promise to my father, and, in my mind, I would climb.

AFTER SUSY'S DEATH, twenty-seven survivors remained. Considering the fact that we had experienced three severe impacts at very high speed, it was a miracle so few of us had been badly injured. Roberto, Gustavo and many of the others had suffered only light injuries. Those with more serious injuries, like Pancho Delgado and Alvaro Mangino, who had both broken a leg in the crash, were now on the mend, and able to hobble around the crash site. Antonio Vizintín, who had almost bled to death from a lacerated arm, was rapidly recovering his strength.

The damage to my head was one of the worst injuries suffered in the accident, but the shattered fragments of my skull were beginning to knit themselves together, which left only two of us with truly serious wounds: Arturo Nogueira, who suffered multiple fractures to both of his legs, and Rafael Echavarren, whose calf muscle had been ripped loose from the bone. Both boys were in severe and constant pain. We did what we could for them. Roberto fashioned simple hammocks, made from aluminium poles and sturdy nylon straps we'd salvaged from the luggage hold. Suspended in these, Rafael and Arturo were spared the agony of sleeping with the rest of us on the fuselage floor. In the swinging beds they no longer shared the warmth of our huddled bodies, and they suffered more intensely from the cold. But for them it was a smaller misery than the pain.

Rafael was not an Old Christian, but he had friends on the team who had invited him on the trip. I didn't know him before the flight, but I'd noticed him on the plane. He was laughing heartily with his friends, and he struck me as a friendly and open-hearted guy. I liked him immediately, and only liked him better as I saw how he bore his suffering. Roberto kept a close eye on Rafael's wounds and treated them as best he could, but our medical supplies were pathetic and the skin of Rafael's leg was already turning black. Gustavo and Roberto suspected gangrene, but Rafael never allowed himself to sink into self-pity, and kept his courage and humour, even as his leg rotted before his eyes. 'I am Rafael Echavarren!' he would shout every morning, 'and I will not die here!' There was no surrender in Rafael.

Arturo, on the other hand, was a teammate and a quieter, more serious boy. I hadn't been especially close to him before the crash, but the courage with which he bore his suffering drew me to him. Like Rafael, Arturo should have been in an intensive care ward, but he was here in the Andes, with no antibiotics or pain relief, and only a couple of first-year medical students and a gang of inexperienced boys to care for him. Pedro Algorta, another of the team's supporters, was especially close to Arturo, and he spent many hours with his friend, bringing him food and water, and trying to distract him from his pain. The rest of us also took turns sitting with Arturo and I always looked forward to our conversations.

At first we talked mostly about rugby. Arturo was the strongest and most accurate kicker on the team and I would remind him of great kicks he had made at crucial moments in our matches, and ask him how he'd managed to boot the ball with such precision. Sometimes he would forget himself and try to demonstrate a technique with one of his shattered legs, which would cause him to wince in pain.

As I got to know Arturo, our conversations went deeper than sport. I was especially intrigued by his thoughts about religion. Like most of the other survivors, I had been raised as a traditional Catholic, and though I was no one's idea of a devout practitioner, I never doubted the fundamental teachings of the Church. Talking with Arturo, however, forced me to examine principles and values I had never questioned.

'How can you be so sure that of all the sacred books in the world, the one you were taught to believe in is the only authentic word of God?' he would ask. 'How do you know that your idea of God is the only one that's true? We are a Catholic country because the Spanish came and conquered the Indians here, then they replaced the God of the Indians with Jesus Christ. If the Moors had conquered South America, we would all be praying to Muhammad instead of Jesus.'

Arturo's ideas disturbed me, but his thinking was compelling. And it fascinated me that despite all his religious scepticism, he was a very spiritual person who sensed my anger at God and urged me not to turn away from Him because of our suffering. 'You are angry at the God you were taught to believe in as a child,' Arturo said. 'The God who is supposed to watch over you and protect you, who answers your prayers and forgives your sins. This God is just a story. Religions try to capture God, but God is beyond religion. The true God lies beyond our comprehension. We can't understand His will; He can't be explained in a book. He didn't abandon us and He will not save us. He has nothing to do with our being here. He simply is. I don't pray to God for forgiveness or favours, I only pray to be closer to Him, and when I pray I fill my heart with love. When I pray this way I know that God is love, and when I feel that love I remember that we don't need angels or a heaven, because we are a part of God already.'

I shook my head. 'I have so many doubts,' I said.

'Trust your doubts,' said Arturo. 'If you have the balls to question all that you've been taught about Him, then you may find God for real. He is close, Nando. I feel Him all around us. Open your eyes and you will see Him, too.'

I looked at Arturo, lying in his hammock, his eyes shining with faith and encouragement, and I felt a strong surge of affection for him. How did such a young man come to know himself so well? Talking with Arturo forced me to face the fact that I had never taken my own life seriously. I had taken so much for granted, spending my energy on girls and cars and parties, coasting through my days. There was always tomorrow . . .

I laughed sadly to myself, thinking, If there is a God, and if He wants my attention, He certainly has it now.

The mountains showed me that there were many forms of bravery, and even the quietest boys displayed great courage simply by living from day to day. All of them contributed to the sense of community and common purpose that gave us some protection from the brutal reality surrounding us. Coche Inciarte, for example, gave us his quick, irreverent wit and warm smile. Carlitos was a source of constant optimism and humour. And Pedro Algorta was an unconventional thinker, highly opinionated and very smart. I felt especially protective of Alvaro Mangino, an amiable, soft-spoken supporter, and one of the youngest guys on the plane; and if not for Diego Storm, who had pulled me in from the cold while I lay in a coma, I would have frozen to death. Daniel Fernández, another cousin of Fito's, was a steady, level-headed presence who helped ward off panic. Pancho Delgado, a sharp-witted, articulate law student and supporter, helped keep our hopes alive with his eloquent assurances that rescue was on the way. And then there was Bobby François, whose forthright, unapologetic, almost cheerful refusal to fight for his life charmed us all. Bobby seemed unable to care for himself in the simplest ways, so we all looked out for him, doing our best to keep him from freezing at night, checking his feet for frostbite, making sure he rolled out of bed in the morning. All these boys were a part of our family in the mountains, contributing, in whatever way they could, to our common struggle.

I was especially impressed with the strength and courage of Liliana Methol, the thirty-five-year-old wife of Javier Methol. Liliana and Javier were extremely close and affectionate with each other. They were both avid fans of the team, but for them this trip was also to be a short romantic getaway, a chance to enjoy a rare weekend together, away from the four young children they had left with grandparents at home. Immediately after the crash, Javier had been stricken by a severe case of altitude sickness, which left him in a constant state of nausea and profound fatigue. His thinking was slow and muddled, and he could do little more than stumble about the crash site in a semi-stupor. Liliana spent much of her time caring for him, but she also found time to serve as a nurse, and was a great help to Roberto and Gustavo as they cared for the injured.

After Susy died, Liliana was the only woman survivor, and at first we treated her with deference, insisting that she sleep with the seriously injured in the Fairchild's luggage compartment, the warmest section of the plane. She did so for only a few nights, then she told us she would no longer accept such special treatment. From that point on, she slept in the main section of the fuselage with the rest of us, where she would gather the youngest boys around her, doing her best to comfort them and keep them warm. She worried constantly about the children she had left at home, but still had the courage and love to mother these frightened boys who were so far from their families. She became a second mother for all of us, and was everything you would want a mother to be: strong, loving, patient and brave.

Somehow we all remained comrades in our suffering. We had lost too many friends already. Every life was precious to us. We would do what we could to help all our friends survive. 'Breathe once more,' we would tell the weaker ones, when the cold, or their fears or despair, pushed them to the edge of surrender. 'Live for one more breath. As long as you breathe, you are fighting to survive.' In fact, all of us were living one breath at a time, struggling to find the will to endure from one heartbeat to the next. We suffered in many ways, but the source of our greatest suffering was the cold.

It was early spring in the Andes, very wintry still, and often blizzards raged around the clock, keeping us trapped inside the plane. But on clear days the sun beat down and we spent as much time as possible outside the fuselage, soaking up the warming rays. We had even dragged some of the Fairchild's seats outside and arranged them on the snow like lawn chairs so we could bask in the sun. But all too soon it would dip behind the ridges, and in what seemed like seconds the blue sky would fade to deep violet, stars would appear and shadows would stream down the mountain towards us like a tide. The temperature would plummet, and we would retreat to the fuselage to prepare for the misery of another night.

High-altitude cold invades every cell of your body, pressing down on you with a force that seems strong enough to crack bone. The draughty fuselage shielded us from the winds that would have killed us, but the air was still viciously cold. We had cigarette lighters to light a fire, but there was very little combustible material on the mountain. We burned all the paper money we had—almost $7,500 went up in smoke—and found enough scrap wood to fuel two or three small fires, but these burned out quickly, and the brief luxury of warmth only made the cold seem worse afterwards. Our best defence was to huddle together on the seat cushions we'd scattered over the aircraft's floor and draw our flimsy blankets round us, hoping to gather enough warmth from each other's bodies to survive another night. I would lie in the dark for hours, my teeth chattering violently, my body shivering so hard that the muscles of my neck and shoulders were constantly in spasm. I always slept with a blanket over my head to trap the warmth of my exhaled breath. Sometimes, I would lie with my head close to that of the boy next to me, to steal a little breath, a little warmth, from him. Some nights we talked, but it was difficult with chattering teeth and trembling jaws. Sometimes there was nothing you could do but count the seconds until morning.

The cold was our greatest agony, but the greatest threat we faced was thirst. At high altitude, because of the low levels of oxygen in the atmosphere, the human body dehydrates five times faster than it does at sea level. To draw sufficient oxygen from the lean mountain air, the lungs breathe very rapidly, but each time you exhale, precious moisture is lost. A human being can survive at sea level for a week or longer without water. In the Andes the margin of safety is much slimmer.

There certainly was no lack of water in the mountains—we were surrounded by millions of tons of frozen H_2O. Our problem was making the snow drinkable. We had no efficient way to melt it. At first we simply scooped handfuls of it into our mouths, but after only a few days our lips were so cracked and raw that it became an unbearable agony. We found that if we packed the snow into a ball and warmed it in our hands, we could suck drops of water from the snowball as it melted. We also melted snow by sloshing it around inside empty wine bottles, and we slurped from every small puddle we could find—for example, the snow on the top of the fuselage would melt in the sun, sending a trickle of water down the aircraft's windshield, where it would collect in a small aluminium channel. But there was never enough to satisfy our cravings or fight off dehydration. We were weakening, growing lethargic as toxins accumulated in our blood.

Finally, thanks to Fito's inventiveness, we found an efficient way to produce water. One sunny morning, he noticed that the sun was melting the thin crust of ice that formed every night on the snow. An idea came to him. He rummaged through a pile of wreckage and found, beneath the torn upholstery of a battered seat, a small sheet of thin aluminium. He turned up the corners to form a shallow basin, and pinched one corner to form a spout. Then he filled the basin with snow and set it in the bright sunshine. In no time the snow was melting and water was trickling steadily from the spout. Fito collected it in a bottle, and when the others saw how well his contraption worked, they gathered more aluminium sheets—there was one in every seat—and fashioned them in the same way. Marcelo was so impressed that he formed a crew of boys to tend Fito's contraptions, making sure we had a constant supply of water. Although we could not produce as much as we really needed, Fito's ingenuity gave us enough to keep us alive. Through cleverness and cooperation we were holding our own. But soon we faced a problem that teamwork alone could not resolve: we began to starve.

One morning near the end of our first week in the mountains, I found myself looking down at a single chocolate-covered peanut in my palm. Our supplies were exhausted and this was the last morsel of food I would be given. I was determined to make it last. On that first day, I slowly sucked the chocolate off the peanut, then I slipped it into the pocket of my slacks. The next day I carefully separated the peanut halves, slipping one half back into my pocket and placing the other half in my mouth. I sucked gently on it for hours, allowing myself only a tiny nibble now and then. I did the same on the third day, finally nibbling the peanut down to nothing.

At high altitude, the body's caloric needs are astronomical. A climber scaling any of the mountains around the crash site would have required as much as 15,000 calories a day just to maintain his body weight. Since the crash, even before our rations ran out, we'd never consumed more than a few hundred calories a day. For days, our intake had been down to zero. I saw the faces of my friends growing thin and drawn. Their movements were sluggish and there was a dullness in their eyes. Our hunger grew so voracious that we became obsessed by the search for food. What drove us was nothing like ordinary appetite. When the brain senses the onset of starvation—when it realises that the body has begun to break down its own tissue to use as fuel—it sets off a powerful adrenaline surge of alarm. This primal instinct—which was really fear more than hunger—compelled us to scour the fuselage again and again in search of crumbs and morsels. We tried to eat strips of leather torn from luggage, though we knew that the chemicals they'd been treated with would do us more harm than good. We ripped open seat cushions hoping to find straw, but found only upholstery foam. I would spend hours compulsively racking my brain for any possible source of food. Maybe there is a plant growing somewhere, or some insects under a rock. Maybe the pilots had snacks in the cockpit. Did we check the pockets of the dead before they were buried?

Again and again I came to the same conclusion: there was nothing here but aluminium, plastic, ice and rock. Sometimes I would shout out loud in my frustration: 'There is nothing in this fucking place to eat!'

But of course there was food—there was meat, plenty of it, and all in easy reach. It was as near as the bodies of the dead lying outside the fuselage under a thin layer of frost. It puzzles me that despite my compulsive drive to find anything edible, I ignored for so long the obvious presence of the only edible objects within a hundred miles. There are some lines, I suppose, that the mind is very slow to cross, but when my mind did finally cross that line, it did so with an impulse so primitive it shocked me.

It was late afternoon and we were lying in the fuselage, preparing for night. My gaze fell on the leg wound of a boy lying near me. The centre of the wound was moist and raw, and I could not stop looking at it. As I smelt the faint blood-scent in the air, I felt my appetite rising. Then I looked up and met the gaze of other boys who had also been staring at the wound. In shame we read each other's thoughts and quickly glanced away, but for me something had happened that I couldn't deny: I had looked at human flesh and instinctively recognised it as food. Once that door had been opened, it couldn't be closed, and from that moment on I knew those frozen bodies represented our only chance for survival.

Finally I couldn't stay silent any longer, and one night in the darkness, I decided to confide in Carlitos Páez, who was lying beside me. 'Carlitos,' I whispered, 'are you awake?'

'Yes,' he muttered. 'Who can sleep in this freezer?'

'Are you hungry?'

'What do you think?' he snapped. 'I haven't eaten in days.'

'We're going to starve,' I said. 'The rescuers won't find us in time.'

'You don't know that,' Carlitos answered.

'I know it and you know it,' I replied, 'but I will not die here.'

'Are you still thinking about climbing out of here?' he asked. 'Nando, you are too weak.'

'I am weak because I haven't eaten.'

'But what can you do?' he said. 'There is no food.'

'There is food,' I answered. 'You know what I mean.'

Carlitos shifted in the darkness, but he said nothing.

'There is plenty of food,' I whispered, 'but you must think of it only as meat. Our friends don't need their bodies any more.'

Carlitos sat silently for a moment before speaking. 'God help us,' he said softly. 'I have been thinking the very same thing . . .'

In the following days, Carlitos shared our conversation with some of the others. A few admitted to having had the same thoughts. For a few days we all discussed the subject, then we decided to call a meeting and bring the issue out into the open. We gathered inside the fuselage. It was late afternoon and the light was dim.

Roberto began to speak. 'We are starving,' he said. 'Our bodies are consuming themselves. Unless we eat some protein soon, we will die, and the only protein here is in the bodies of our friends.'

There was a heavy silence. Finally, someone spoke up. 'What are you saying?' he cried. 'That we eat the dead?'

'We don't know how long we will be trapped here,' Roberto continued. 'If we do not eat, we will die. It's that simple. If you want to see your families again, this is what you must do.'

The faces of the others showed astonishment as Roberto's words sank in.

Then Liliana spoke softly. 'I cannot do that. I could never do that.'

'You won't do it for yourself,' said Gustavo, 'but you must do it for your children. You must survive and go home to them.'

'But what will this do to our souls?' someone wondered. 'Could God forgive such a thing?'

'If you don't eat, you are choosing to die,' Roberto answered. 'Would God forgive that? I believe God wants us to do whatever we can to survive.'

'We must believe it is only meat now,' I told them. 'The souls are gone. If rescue is coming, we must buy time, or we will be dead when they find us.'

'And if we must escape on our own,' said Fito, 'we will need strength or we will die on the slopes.'

'Fito is right,' I said, 'and if the bodies of our friends can help us to survive, then they haven't died for nothing.'

The discussion continued all afternoon. Many refused to consider eating human flesh, but no one tried to talk the rest of us out of the idea. We realised we had reached a consensus. Now the grisly logistics had to be faced.

'How will this be done?' asked Pancho Delgado. 'Who is brave enough to cut the flesh from a friend?'

The fuselage was dark now. I could see only dimly lit silhouettes, but after a long silence Roberto spoke. 'I will do it,' he said.

Gustavo rose to his feet and said quietly, 'I will help.'

'But who will we cut first?' asked Fito. 'How do we choose?'

We all glanced at Roberto.

'Gustavo and I will take care of that,' he replied.

Fito got up. 'I'll go with you,' he said.

For a moment no one moved, then we all reached forward, joined hands,

MIRACLE IN THE ANDES | 49

and pledged that if any of us died here, the rest would have permission to use our bodies for food.

Roberto rose and rummaged in the fuselage until he found some shards of glass, then he led his assistants out to the graves. When they came back, they had small pieces of flesh in their hands. Gustavo offered me a piece and I took it. It was greyish white, as hard as wood and very cold. I reminded myself that this was no longer part of a human being; still, I found myself slow to lift the meat to my lips. I avoided meeting anyone's gaze, but out of the corner of my eye I saw the others around me. Some were sitting, like me, with the meat in their hands, summoning the strength to eat. Others were working their jaws grimly.

Finally, I found my courage and slipped the flesh into my mouth. It had no taste. I chewed, once or twice, then forced myself to swallow.

I understood the magnitude of the taboo we had just broken, but I felt no guilt or shame, just resentment that fate had forced us to choose between this horror and certain death. To the ordinary mind, these actions may seem incomprehensibly repulsive, but the instinct to survive runs very deep and when death is so near a human being gets used to anything.

Eating the flesh did not satisfy my hunger, but it calmed my mind. I knew that my body would use the protein to strengthen itself. That night, for the first time, I felt a flickering of hope. Our courage had gained us a small measure of control over our circumstances and bought us precious time. There were no illusions now. We all knew our fight for survival would be uglier and more harrowing than we had imagined, but, as a group, we had made a declaration to the mountain that we would not surrender.

5 : Abandoned

Early the next morning, our eleventh day on the mountain, I stood outside, leaning against the Fairchild's hull, warming myself in the first rays of the sun. It was a clear morning. Marcelo and Coco Nicolich were with me, and so was Roy Harley. Roy was the closest thing we had to an electronics expert. Just after the crash, he had found a battered transistor radio in the wreckage and, with a little tinkering, had coaxed it back to life. In the rocky cordillera, reception was very poor, but Roy fashioned an antenna from electrical wire he had stripped from the plane, and with a little effort we were able to tune into stations from Chile. Each morning, Marcelo would manipulate the antenna while Roy worked the dial. So far they had managed only to pick up soccer scores, weather reports and political propaganda.

This morning, like all the others, the signal faded in and out and, even with reception at its best, the radio's small speaker crackled with static. Roy did not want to waste the batteries, so, after fiddling with the dial for several minutes, he was about to turn the radio off when we heard an announcer reading the news. I will never forget the tinny sound of his voice and the dispassionate tone in which he spoke. After ten days of fruitless searching, he said, the Chilean authorities have called off all efforts to find the lost Uruguayan charter flight that disappeared over the Andes on October 13. Search efforts are simply too dangerous, and after so much time there is no chance that anyone has survived.

After a moment of stunned silence, Roy began to sob.

'What?' cried Marcelo. 'What did he say?'

'*Suspendieron la búsqueda!*' Roy shouted. 'They have cancelled the search! They are abandoning us!'

When Roy's words sank in, Marcelo dropped to his knees and let out an anguished howl that echoed through the cordillera. Reeling from shock, I watched my friends' reactions in silence. All the fears I'd been struggling to contain were now bursting like flood water over a crumbling dam. Driven more powerfully than ever by the animal urge to sprint off blindly into the cordillera, I manically scanned the horizon as if I might suddenly spot an escape route I hadn't seen before. Then, slowly, I turned west and faced the tall ridges that blocked me from my home. With new clarity, I saw what foolishness it was to have thought that an untested boy like me could conquer such merciless slopes! Reality bared its teeth at me, and I saw that all my dreams of climbing were nothing more than a fantasy. I knew what I had to do: I would run to a crevasse and leap into the green depths. I'd let the rocks smash all the life and fear and suffering from my body. But even as I pictured myself falling into silence and peace, my eye was on the western ridges, guessing at distances and trying to imagine the steepness of the slopes, and the cool voice of reason was whispering in my ear: *That grey line of rock might give some good footing . . .*

It was a kind of madness, really, clinging to hopes of escape even though I knew escape was impossible. But that inner voice gave me no choice.

With grim resolve, I accepted the simple truth that I would never stop fighting. Challenging the mountains was the only future this place would allow me. I was certain the effort would kill me, but frantic to start the climb.

A frightened voice drew my attention.

'Nando, please, tell me this is not true!' Coco Nicolich stammered.

'It is true,' I hissed. 'We are dead.'

'They are killing us! They are leaving us here to die!'

'I have to leave this place,' I cried. 'I can't stay here another minute!'

Coco nodded towards the fuselage. 'The others have heard us,' he said. I turned and saw several of our friends emerging from the plane.

'What's the news?' someone called out. 'Have they spotted us?'

'We have to tell them,' Coco whispered.

We both glanced at Marcelo, who sat slumped in the snow. 'I can't tell them,' he mumbled. 'I can't bear it.'

The others were closer now.

'What's going on?' someone asked. 'What did you hear?'

I tried to speak, but my words caught in my throat. Then Coco stepped forward and spoke firmly, despite his fear. 'Let's go inside,' he said, 'and I'll explain.' We all followed him into the fuselage and gathered round. 'Listen, guys,' he said, 'we have heard some news. They have stopped looking for us.'

The others were stunned. Some of them cursed, some began weeping, but most simply stared at Coco in disbelief.

'But don't worry,' he continued, 'this is good news. We have to stay calm. Now we know what we have to do. There's no reason to wait any longer. We can start making plans to get out on our own.'

'I have made my plans,' I snapped. 'I am leaving this place now! I will not die here!'

'Calm down, Nando,' said Gustavo.

'No, I will not calm down! Give me some meat to carry. Someone lend me another jacket. Who will come with me? I will go by myself if I have to. I will not stay here another second!'

Gustavo took my arm. 'You're talking nonsense,' he said. 'If you go now, you will die. You have no winter gear, you have no experience at climbing, you are weak. It would be suicide to leave now.'

'Gustavo is right,' said Numa. 'You are not strong enough yet. Your head is still cracked like an egg.'

'We have to go!' I shouted. 'They have given us a death sentence! Are you just going to wait here to die?' I was already rummaging through the fuselage blindly, searching for anything—gloves, blankets, socks—that I thought would help me on the trek, when Marcelo spoke to me softly.

'Whatever you do, Nando, 'you must think of the good of the others. Be smart. Don't waste yourself. We are still a team, and we need you.' His voice was steady, but there was a sadness in it, a resignation. Something inside him had shattered when he heard the search had been cancelled, and in seconds he had lost the strength and confidence that had made him such a trusted leader. Leaning against the cabin wall, Marcelo seemed smaller, greyer, and I knew he was slipping into despair. But my respect for him was deep, and I could not deny the wisdom of his words so, reluctantly, I nodded and found a place to sit beside the others on the fuselage floor.

'Nando is right,' said Gustavo. 'We will die if we stay here, and so sooner or later we will have to climb. But we must do it in the smartest way. We must know what we're up against. I say two or three of us climb today. Maybe we can get a look at what lies beyond these mountains.'

'It's a good idea,' said Fito. 'On the way, we can look for the tail section. There might be food and warm clothing inside, and batteries for the radio.'

'Good,' said Gustavo. 'I will go. If we leave soon, we can be back before the sun goes down. Who is coming with me?'

'I am,' said Numa, who had already survived the first attempt to climb the western slopes.

'Me too,' said Daniel Maspons.

Gustavo nodded. 'Let's find the warmest clothes we can, and get started. There is no time to lose.'

It took Gustavo less than an hour to organise the climb. Each climber would carry a pair of seat-cushion snowshoes and a pair of the sunglasses Fito's cousin Eduardo had made by cutting lenses from tinted plastic sun visors in the cockpit and linking them with copper wire. Otherwise they were poorly protected. They wore only sweaters over light cotton shirts, thin summer trousers and lightweight moccasins on their feet. None of them wore gloves, and they had no blankets, but it was a clear day, winds were light and the bright sun warmed the air enough to make it bearable. If the climbers returned before sundown, the cold should not be a danger.

'Pray for us,' Gustavo said, as they set off.

We watched the three of them stride across the glacier towards the high summits to the west, following the path the Fairchild had ploughed through the snow. They made their way slowly up the slope and into the distance, growing smaller and smaller until they were just three tiny specks.

All morning we watched them climb, until they disappeared from view. Then we kept vigil, scouring the slopes for signs of their return. As the light faded there was still no sign of them. Darkness fell and the bitter cold forced us back inside. That night, as stiff winds battered the Fairchild's hull, forcing jets of snow through every crevice, our thoughts were with our friends. We prayed earnestly for their safe return, but it was hard to be hopeful. All of us knew what death looked like now, and it was easy for me to imagine my friends lying stiff in the snow, the waxy, blue-tinged pallor of the skin, the crust of frost clinging to the eyebrows and lips . . .

'Maybe they have found shelter,' someone said.

'There is no shelter on that mountain,' Roberto replied.

'But you climbed, and you survived,' someone pointed out.

'We climbed in daylight and still we suffered,' Roberto answered. 'It must be forty degrees colder up there at night.'

'They are strong,' someone offered.

Others nodded and, out of respect, held their tongues.

Then Marcelo broke the silence. 'It's my fault,' he said softly. 'I have killed you all.'

'Don't think that way, Marcelo,' said Fito. 'We all share the same fate here. No one blames you.'

'I chartered the plane!' Marcelo snapped. 'I hired the pilots! I scheduled the matches and persuaded you all to come.'

'You did not persuade my mother and my sister,' I said. 'I did that, and now they're dead. But it's not our fault that a plane falls from the sky.'

'Each of us made his own choice,' someone said.

'You are a good captain, Marcelo. Don't lose heart.'

But Marcelo *was* losing heart, very rapidly, and it troubled me to see him in such misery. He had always been a hero to me. He had a commanding, enthusiastic presence on the rugby field, but it was more than that that had won my respect. Marcelo was more principled, more mature than the rest of us. He was a devout Catholic who tried his best to live a virtuous life. He was not self-righteous; in fact, he was one of the humblest guys on the team. But he knew what he believed, and often he would coax us to be better men. 'There is more to life than chasing girls,' he would tell Panchito and me with a wry smile. 'You two need to grow up a little, and get serious about your lives.'

Marcelo had thought carefully about important issues and knew where he stood. For him, the world was an orderly place, watched over by a wise and loving God who had promised to protect us. It was our job to follow His commandments, and to love others as Jesus had taught us. This wisdom had formed the foundation of his life, and was the source of his confidence and the charisma that made him such a strong leader. It is easy to follow a man who has no doubts. We had always trusted in Marcelo completely. How could he allow himself to falter now, when we needed him most?

Perhaps, I thought, he was not as strong as he'd seemed. Then I understood: Marcelo had been broken not because his mind was weak, but because it was too strong. His faith in a rescue was absolute and unyielding; when we heard that the search had been cancelled, it must have felt to him as if the earth beneath his feet was crumbling. God had turned His back. All the things that had made Marcelo such a great leader—his confidence, his decisiveness, his certainty—now prevented him from adjusting to the blow.

Watching as he quietly sobbed in the shadows, I suddenly understood that, in this awful place, too much certainty could kill us. I vowed to myself that I would never get trapped by my own expectations or pretend to know what might happen next. The rules here were too savage and strange. I would teach myself to live in constant uncertainty, moment by moment. I would live as if I had nothing to lose. That way, my fears would not block me from following my instincts, and no risk would be too great.

AT LAST morning came. We gathered outside the plane and began to scan the mountains for signs of our friends. The skies were clear, the sun had already warmed the air, and the winds had weakened into a light breeze. Visibility was quite good, but we could spot no movement on the slopes.

Then, late in the morning, someone shouted. 'Something is moving! There, above that ridge!'

'I see it, too!' said someone else.

I stared at the mountain and finally saw what the others were seeing: three black dots on the snow.

'Those are rocks,' someone muttered. 'Your mind is playing tricks.'

'Just watch. They are moving.'

A little lower on the slope was a dark outcrop of rock. Using this as a reference point, I kept my gaze on the dots. After a minute or two it was clear that they had moved closer to the outcrop. It was true! 'They are alive!'

Our spirits soared and we slapped each other in our happiness.

'*Vamos, Gustavo!*'

'Come on, Numa! Come on, Daniel! You can make it!'

It took the three of them two hours to work their way down the slope, and all that time we shouted encouragement. But the celebration ended abruptly when they got close enough for us to see their condition. They were almost too weak to lift their feet from the snow, leaning on each other for support, and Gustavo was squinting and groping as if he'd gone blind. The worst thing was their faces. They seemed to have aged twenty years overnight, and in their eyes I saw an unsettling combination of dread and resignation.

We rushed to meet them, helped them into the fuselage and gave them cushions to lie on. Roberto examined them. He saw that their feet were nearly frozen. And tears were streaming from Gustavo's bleary eyes.

'It was the glare,' said Gustavo. 'The sun was so strong . . .'

'Didn't you use your sunglasses?' Roberto asked.

'They broke,' said Gustavo. 'It feels like sand in my eyes. I think I'm blind.'

Roberto put some drops in Gustavo's eyes—something he'd found in a suitcase that he thought might soothe the irritation—and wrapped a T-shirt round Gustavo's head to shade his eyes from the light. Then he told the rest of us to take turns rubbing the climbers' frozen feet. Someone brought them large portions of meat, and the climbers ate ravenously. After they had rested, they began to talk about the climb.

'The mountain is so steep,' said Gustavo. 'In places it is like climbing a wall. You have to clutch the snow in front of you to pull yourself up.'

'And the air is thin,' said Maspons. 'You gasp, your heart pounds. You take five steps and it feels like you have run a mile.'

'Why didn't you come back before night?' I asked them.

'We climbed all day and were only halfway up the slope,' said Gustavo. 'We didn't want to come back and tell you we had failed. We wanted to come back with good news. So we decided to find shelter for the night, then climb again in the morning.'

They had found a level place near a rocky outcrop, made a wall out of large stones they found lying about, and huddled behind it, hoping it would shield them from the wind. They hadn't thought it was possible to suffer much more from the cold, but they discovered that they had been wrong.

'The cold up on those slopes is indescribable,' said Gustavo. 'It rips the life from you. It's as painful as fire.'

As the hours crawled by, they grew certain that their decision had cost them their lives, but somehow they lasted until dawn. Amazed to be alive, they had let the sunshine thaw their frozen bodies, then resumed the climb.

'Did you find the tail?' Fito asked.

'We found only pieces of wreckage and some luggage,' Gustavo answered.

And some bodies.' He explained how they had found the remains of people who had fallen from the plane, many of them still strapped to their seats. 'We took these things,' he said, pulling out watches, wallets, religious medallions and other personal effects. 'The bodies were very high up the slope, but we were still far from the summit. We didn't have the strength to keep climbing, and we didn't want to get trapped for another night.'

Later that night, when things were quiet, I went to Gustavo. 'What did you see up there?' I asked. 'Did you see beyond the peaks?'

He shook his head wearily. 'The peaks are too high. You can't see far.'

'But you must have seen something.'

He shrugged. 'I saw between two peaks, into the distance . . .'

'What did you see?'

'I don't know, Nando, something yellowish, brownish, I couldn't really tell. But one thing you should know: when we were high on the mountain I looked down at the crash site. The Fairchild is a tiny speck in the snow. You can't tell it from a rock or a shadow. There is no hope that a pilot could see it from a plane—there never was any chance we would be rescued.'

THE FAILURE of Gustavo's mission disheartened us, and our spirits were battered further by the realisation that Marcelo, in his despair, had quietly abdicated his role as our leader. There seemed to be no one to take his place. Gustavo had been devastated by the mountain, and could not regain his strength. Roberto was still a strong presence, and we had come to rely on his cleverness and keen imagination, but he was a headstrong young man, far too irritable and belligerent to inspire the kind of trust we'd had in Marcelo. Rapidly, in the absence of a single strong leader, a looser, less formal style of leadership emerged. Alliances formed, based on friendships, similar temperaments and common interests. The strongest of these was made up of Fito and his cousins Eduardo Strauch and Daniel Fernández. Fito was the youngest and most prominent of the three. He was a quiet, shy boy, but he soon proved himself to be bright and level-headed, and I knew he intended to fight with all his strength to help us all survive. The three were extremely close, and presented a unifying force. 'The cousins', as we called them, gave us a strong, stable centre that prevented the group from disintegrating into factions. They also were able to convince most of the survivors that each one of us now had to do everything they could to survive. Yielding to that advice, those who had held out against eating— Numa, Liliana, Coche and others—told themselves that drawing life from the bodies of their dead friends was like drawing spiritual strength from the body of Christ when they took Communion. Relieved that they were nourishing themselves, I didn't dispute their rationale, but for me eating the flesh of the dead was a hard, pragmatic choice I had made to survive.

All of us were eating enough now to keep starvation at bay. Out of respect for me, the others had promised not to touch the bodies of my mother and sister, but even so there were enough bodies to last us for weeks if we rationed the meat carefully.

Still, my hunger was never satisfied, and I was wasting away like the others. Time was running out, and my greatest fear was that we would soon grow so weak that escape would become impossible. The near disaster of Gustavo's expedition had given me a new understanding of how difficult the climb would be. In moments of weakness I would tell myself: It's impossible, we are trapped here. We are finished. All our suffering has been in vain.

But each time I gave in to defeat and self-pity, the face of my father would drift up from memory, reminding me of his suffering, and of the promise I had made to return to him. And the voice in my mind would tell me, *When you climb, make sure every fingerhold is a good one. Test every step. Probe the snow for hidden crevasses . . .*

I would think of my father and let my heart fill with love for him, and this love would be stronger than my suffering or my fear. I knew that someday I would have to climb, even though I'd be climbing to my doom. What did it matter? Why not die one step closer to home? But as inevitable as death seemed, I still felt a flicker of hope that I might somehow stumble through the wilderness and make it to safety. And though the thought of leaving the fuselage terrified me, I couldn't wait to leave. I knew that I would not be brave enough to face the mountains alone. I needed a companion, someone who would make me stronger and better, and so I began to study the others, weighing their strengths, their temperaments, trying to imagine which of these ragged, starving, frightened boys I would want by my side.

Twenty-four hours earlier the answer would have been Marcelo and Gustavo. But now Marcelo was in despair, and Gustavo had been battered and blinded by the mountain. So I turned my eye to the other healthy survivors. Fito Strauch had proved his bravery in the first attempt to climb the mountain, and earned our respect for his calmness and clear thinking. He was definitely high on my list. So was Numa Turcatti. Although he had been a stranger to most of us before the crash, he had quickly won the friendship and admiration of the survivors, making his presence felt through quiet heroics. No one inspired more hope, or showed more compassion for those who suffered. I believe Numa was the best loved man on the mountain.

Daniel Maspons, who had climbed bravely with Gustavo, was another candidate. So was Coco Nicolich, whose selflessness and composure had impressed me. Antonio Vizintín, Roy Harley and Carlitos Páez were all healthy and strong. And then there was Roberto, the brightest, most difficult, most complicated character on the mountain.

Roberto had always been hard to handle. The son of a renowned cardiologist in Montevideo, he was brilliant, egotistical and interested in following no one's rules but his own. He was constantly in trouble at school, and his mother was always being called into the headmaster's office to endure another conference about Roberto's transgressions. Hoping to find a constructive outlet for his unruliness, the Christian Brothers encouraged him to play rugby. He played left wing, the same position as Panchito played on the right, but where Panchito would gracefully dodge and weave his way towards the try line, Roberto battered a direct path through the opposition. He was not one of our bigger players, but his legs were impressively developed and, along with his famous muscle-headedness, they earned him the nickname *Músculo*—'Muscles'. Powered by those sturdy limbs and natural belligerence, Roberto was more than a match for much larger opponents.

Roberto's strong-mindedness made him a challenging friend, and he could be arrogant and brutally inconsiderate. He routinely ignored decisions made by the group and turned on anyone who challenged him. More than once, his abrasiveness almost led to a fight. But I respected him. He was the most intelligent and ingenious of us all, and without his quick-witted medical care in the wake of the crash, many of the boys who were now recovering might well be dead. It was Roberto who realised that the Fairchild's seat covers could be removed and used as blankets, and most of the tools we used, and our crude selection of medical supplies, had been improvised by him from articles he'd scavenged from the wreckage.

I knew Roberto's resourcefulness would be a great advantage. I also trusted his realistic view of how desperate things were. But more than anything, I wanted him with me simply because he was the most determined person I had ever known. He would not be the easiest travelling companion, but I knew that his willfulness would be the perfect complement to the wild impulses that drove me. Roberto was the one I needed by my side.

When the time seemed right and we were alone together, I asked him to come with me.

'You're crazy, Nando,' he snapped. 'Look at these fucking mountains. Do you have any idea how high they are?'

I gazed at the highest peak. 'Maybe two or three times the Pan de Azúcar,' I said, referring to the tallest 'mountain' in Uruguay.

Roberto snorted. 'Don't be an idiot! There's no snow on the Pan de Azúcar! It is only fifteen hundred feet high! This mountain is ten times higher, at least!'

'What choice do we have?' I answered. 'We have to try. For me, the decision is made. I am going to climb, Roberto, but I need you to come with me.'

Roberto shook his head ruefully. 'You saw what happened to Gustavo,' he said. 'And they only made it halfway up the slope.'

'We can't stay here. You know that. We need to leave as soon as possible.'

'No way!' shouted Roberto. 'It would have to be planned. We must do it the smartest way. We need to think through every detail. How would we climb? Which slope? Which direction?'

'I think of these things constantly,' I said. 'We will need food, water, warm clothing . . .'

'Timing is important,' he said. 'We have to wait for the weather to improve.'

'But we can't wait so long that we are too weak to make the climb.'

Roberto was silent for a moment. 'It will kill us, you know.'

'It probably will,' I replied, 'but if we stay here we are dead already. I cannot do this alone, Roberto. Please, come with me.'

Roberto studied me with his penetrating gaze, as if he'd never seen me before. Then he nodded towards the fuselage. 'Let's go inside,' he said. 'The wind is picking up.'

6 : Tomb

By the last week in October, we had chosen the group that would leave the crash site and try to reach help. There was no question in anyone's mind that I was going—they would have had to tie me to a rock to keep me from leaving. Roberto had agreed to go; Fito and Numa would complete the team. The other survivors began to refer to us as 'the expeditionaries'. It was decided that we would receive larger rations of food to build our strength. We would also be given the warmest clothing and the best places to sleep, and would be excused from routine chores so that we could conserve energy for the trek.

The spirits of the group began to rise, and things seemed more stable. After two weeks on the mountain, we found reasons to hope. Perhaps we had seen the last of the horrors. Perhaps all twenty-seven of us were destined to survive. Many of us were comforted by these thoughts as we filed into the fuselage on the evening of 29 October and prepared ourselves for sleep.

It was a windy night, but soon I closed my eyes and drifted off into a half-slumber. I dozed for a while, then I woke, frightened and disoriented, as a heavy force thumped against my chest. Something was terribly wrong. An icy wetness pressed against my face and a crushing weight was forcing the air from my chest. After a few seconds of confusion I realised what had happened—an avalanche had rolled down the mountain and filled the fuselage with snow. There was a moment of silence, then I heard a slow, wet creak as the loose snow settled under its own weight and packed around me like rock. I tried to move, but it felt as if my body were encased in concrete. I couldn't even wiggle a finger. I managed a few shallow breaths but soon snow packed into my mouth and nostrils and I began to suffocate.

My thoughts grew calm. 'This is my death,' I told myself. 'Now I will see what lies on the other side.' I didn't try to shout or struggle. I simply waited, and, as I accepted my helplessness, a sense of peace overtook me. I waited patiently for my life to end. It was over. No more struggle.

Then a hand clawed the snow from my face and I was yanked back into the world of the living. Someone had dug a narrow shaft down through several feet of snow to reach me. I spat the snow from my mouth and gulped cold air into my lungs.

I heard Carlitos's voice above me. 'Who is it?' he shouted.

'Me,' I sputtered. 'It's Nando.'

Then he left me. I heard chaos above me, voices shouting and sobbing.

'Dig for the faces!' someone shouted. 'Give them air!'

'Coco! Where is Coco?'

'Help me here!'

'Has anyone seen Marcelo?'

'How many do we have? Someone count!'

The chaos lasted just a few minutes, then everything fell silent.

A few moments later they dug me out, and I was able to lift myself up from the snow. The dark fuselage was lit eerily by the flames of the cigarette lighter Pancho Delgado was holding. I saw some of my friends lying motionless. Others were rising from the snow like zombies from the grave. Javier was kneeling beside me, with Liliana in his arms. I knew from the way her head hung limply that she was dead. I shook my head in disbelief as he began to sob. 'No,' I said flatly. 'No.' As if I could argue with what had just happened. As if I could refuse to allow it to be real.

I glanced at the others. Some were weeping, some were comforting Javier, others were simply gazing into the shadows with dazed looks on their faces. For a moment no one spoke, but when the shock eased, the others told me what they'd seen.

It had begun with a distant roar on the mountain. Roy Harley had heard the noise and jumped to his feet. Seconds later the avalanche swept through the makeshift wall at the rear of the fuselage, burying him to the hips. In horror, Roy saw that everyone sleeping on the floor had been buried in snow. He began to dig, and quickly uncovered Carlitos, Fito and Roberto. They also started digging, searching frantically for buried friends, but they were not fast enough to save us all. Our losses were heavy. Marcelo was dead. So were Enrique Platero, Coco Nicolich and Daniel Maspons. Carlos Roque, the plane's mechanic, and Juan Carlos Menéndez had died beneath the falling wall. Diego Storm and Liliana were also gone.

The deaths of our friends staggered us. We had allowed ourselves to believe that we had passed the point of danger, but now we saw that we would never be safe in this place. The mountain could kill us in so many ways. Daniel and Liliana had been only inches away from me; their fate had been decided by a simple stroke of bad luck. I thought of my mother and Susy choosing their seats on the plane; I thought of Panchito switching seats with me just moments before the crash. The arbitrariness of it all outraged and frightened me, because if death was so senseless and random, no amount of planning or determination could protect me from it.

Sometime later that night, as if to mock me for my fears, the mountain sent a second avalanche roaring down the slopes. We heard it coming and braced for the worst, but the snow simply rolled over us this time. The Fairchild had already been buried by snow.

As SOON AS we had the stomach for it, we stacked the dead at the rear of the plane where the snow was deepest, which left only a small clearing near the cockpit for the living to sleep. We packed into that space—nineteen of us now, jammed into an area that might have comfortably accommodated four—with no choice but to squeeze together, our knees, feet and elbows in a tangle. All of us had been covered with snow, which quickly melted, and soon our clothing was soaked through. To make matters worse, all our possessions now lay buried beneath several feet of snow. We had no makeshift blankets to warm us, no shoes to protect our feet from the cold, and no cushions to insulate us from the snow. There was so little clearance above our heads that we were forced to rest with our shoulders slumped forward and our chins pressed to our chests. As I struggled to find a comfortable position, I felt panic rising in my throat and I had to fight the urge to scream. I wondered how much snow lay above us. Two feet? Twenty feet? Were we buried alive? Had the Fairchild become our coffin? The snow insulating us from the noise of the wind outside also altered sounds inside the plane, creating a thick, muffled silence, and giving our voices a subtle echo, as if we were speaking at the bottom of a well. Now I know, I thought, how it feels to be trapped in a submarine on the ocean floor.

The following hours were some of the darkest of the entire ordeal. Javier wept miserably for Liliana, and almost all the other survivors mourned the loss of at least one especially close friend.

Soon some of the survivors began to cough and wheeze, and I realised that the air was growing stale, because the snow had sealed us in so tightly. If we didn't find an air supply soon, we would suffocate. I spotted the tip of an aluminium cargo pole jutting up from the snow. Without thinking, I pulled it out, grasped it like a lance, and, resting on my knees, began to drive its pointed tip into the ceiling. I stabbed with it again and again until somehow I managed to punch through the Fairchild's roof. Feeling the resistance of the snow, I pushed the pole upwards until it finally broke free.

We were not hopelessly buried. The Fairchild was covered by no more than a few feet of snow. Fresh air flowed in through the hole I'd made, and we all breathed easier as we settled back and tried to sleep.

When dawn finally arrived, the windows of the fuselage brightened slightly as light filtered down through the snow. We wasted no time trying to dig our way out of our aluminium tomb. Because of the way the plane was tilted on the glacier, the windows on the right side of the cockpit faced skyward and, with our usual exit at the rear of the aircraft blocked by snow, we knew that these would be our best route of escape. We began to dig our way towards the cockpit, using shards of metal and broken pieces of plastic as shovels. There was room for only one man to work at a time, so we took turns to do fifteen-minute shifts, one man chipping away at the rock-hard snow, the rest of us shoveling the loosened snow to the rear of the plane.

It took hours, but finally Gustavo dug his way to the pilot's seat, and was able to reach the window. He pushed against it, hoping to force it out of its frame, but the snow was too heavy and he couldn't muster the strength. Roy Harley tried and, with a furious shove, pushed the window free. Climbing through the opening, he dug up through a few feet of snow until he broke the surface and was able to look around. A storm was pounding the mountain with high winds and pelting snow that stung his face. Squinting into the wind, he saw that the avalanche had buried the fuselage completely.

'There's a blizzard,' he said, when he climbed back down. 'And the snow all round the plane is too deep to walk on. I think we would sink into it and be lost. We are trapped inside until the storm ends, and that won't be soon.'

We had no choice but to hunker down in our wretched prison. To brighten our mood, we discussed our escape plan—and, as the discussion progressed, a new idea emerged. Two failed efforts to climb to the mountains above us had convinced many in the group that escape to the west was impossible. They turned their attention eastwards, to the broad valley that sloped away from the crash sight. If we were as close to Chile as we believed, their theory went, then all meltwater in this region must drain through the Chilean foothills and into the Pacific Ocean. If we could find the path of that flow down through the cordillera, we would find our route of escape.

I did not have much faith in this plan. It seemed insane to ignore the one fact we knew to be true—to the west is Chile—and follow a path that would almost certainly take us deeper into the heart of the Andes. But as the others decided to place their faith in this new plan, I did not argue.

'I am tired of waiting,' I told them. 'How do we know the weather will ever get better in this damned place?'

Pedro Algorta remembered a conversation he'd had with a taxi driver in Santiago. 'He said that summertime in the Andes comes like clockwork on November fifteenth.'

'That's only a little more than two weeks, Nando,' said Fito. 'You can wait that long.'

'I will wait,' I answered. 'But only until November fifteenth. If no one else is ready to go by then, I will go alone.'

THE DAYS WE SPENT beneath the avalanche were the grimmest. We were trapped inside so Fito's water-making machines were useless to us, and the only way to ease our thirst was to gnaw chunks of the filthy snow on which we were crawling and sleeping. With no access to the bodies outside, we had no food and we rapidly began to weaken. The bodies of the avalanche victims lay within easy reach, but we were slow to face the prospect of cutting them. Until now, when meat had been cut, no one but those doing the cutting had had to see it or know whose body the flesh had been taken from. Also, the bodies outside had frozen so solidly it was easier to think of them as lifeless objects. There was no way to objectify the bodies inside the fuselage. Just a day earlier they had been warm and animated. How could we cut flesh from them? Silently, we all agreed that we would rather starve.

But by October 31, our third day under the avalanche, we knew we couldn't hold out any longer. Someone found a piece of glass, swept the snow from one of the bodies, and began to cut. When a piece of flesh was handed to me, I was revolted. Before, the meat had been dried in the sun before we ate it, which weakened its taste and gave it a more palatable texture, but the chunk of flesh Fito gave me was soft and greasy. I gagged hard when I placed it in my mouth and had to use all my will-power to force myself to swallow. Fito had to urge many of the others to eat—he even forced some into the mouth of his cousin Eduardo. But some, including Numa and Coche, could not be persuaded. I was especially troubled by Numa's obstinacy. He was an expeditionary, a great source of strength for me, and I did not like the idea of challenging the mountains without him.

'Numa,' I said to him, 'you have to eat. We need you with us when we hike out of here. You must stay strong.'

Numa grimaced and shook his head. 'I could barely swallow the meat before,' he said. 'I could never stand it like this.'

'If you want to see your family again,' I told him, 'you must eat.'

'I'm sorry, Nando,' he said, turning away from me. 'I simply can't.'

I knew there was more to Numa's refusal than simple disgust. On some level, he had had enough, and his refusal to eat was his rebellion against the inescapable nightmare our lives had become. Who could survive the horrors that we had been forced to endure? What had we done to deserve such misery? What kind of God could be so cruel? These questions plagued me, but I understood that they were dangerous. They led to nothing but an impotent rage that quickly soured into apathy, and in this place, apathy meant death. I fought off the questions by conjuring thoughts of my family. I pictured my sister Graciela with her new baby boy. I wanted so badly to be an uncle to him. I still had the red baby shoes my mother had bought for him in Mendoza, and I imagined myself slipping them on his little feet, kissing his head, whispering to him, *'Soy tu tío, Nando.'* I thought of my grandmother Lina, who had my mother's bright blue eyes and loving smile. What would I give to feel her arms around me? I even thought of my dog, Jimmy, a playful boxer, who went with me everywhere. It broke my heart to think of him waiting by the front door for me to come home.

As I shivered in the clammy snow, forced to chew the raw flesh that had been hacked from my friends before my eyes, it was hard to believe in anything before the crash, hard to connect to the happy life I'd had before. For the first time, my promise to my father began to ring hollow. Death was drawing closer. There was something sordid and rank in our suffering now.

October 31, our third day under the avalanche, was Carlitos's nineteenth birthday. Lying beside him in the fuselage that night, I promised him we would celebrate when we were home. 'My birthday is December the 9th,' I told him. 'We'll all go to my parents' place in Punta del Este and celebrate the birthdays we missed.'

'Speaking of birthdays,' he said, 'tomorrow is my father's birthday, and my sister's birthday, too. I have been thinking about them, and now I am certain I will see them again. God has saved me from the crash and from the avalanche. He must want me to survive and return to my family.'

'I don't know what to think about God any more,' I said.

'But can't you feel how near He is to us?' he said. 'I feel His presence so strongly here. Look how peaceful the mountains are, how beautiful. God is in this place, and when I feel His presence I know we will be all right.'

I admired Carlito for the courage of his optimism.

'You are strong, Nando,' he said. 'You will make it. You will find help.'

I said nothing. Carlitos began to pray.

'Happy birthday, Carlitos,' I whispered, then I tried to sleep.

7: East

The blizzard finally ended on the morning of November 1. The skies were clear and the sun was strong, so a few of the guys climbed out onto the roof of the fuselage to melt snow for drinking water. The rest of us began the slow process of removing the tons of snow that packed the Fairchild's interior. It took eight days to clear it. As an expeditionary, I was officially excused from the gruelling labour, but I insisted on working anyway. Now that the date of our escape had been chosen, I had to keep busy, fearing that idle moments might weaken my resolve.

Meanwhile my fellow expeditionaries, Numa, Fito and Roberto, prepared for the trek. They made a sledge by tying a nylon strap to one half of a hard-shell plastic suitcase and loaded it with gear they thought we could use: nylon seat covers to use as blankets, Fito's seat-cushion snowshoes, a bottle in which we would melt water, and other supplies. Roberto had fashioned knapsacks for us by tying off the legs of trousers and threading nylon straps through them in such a way that we could sling them over our backs. We packed the knapsacks with more gear, leaving room for the meat that had been cut for us and was cooling in the snow. We all watched the weather closely, waiting for signs that spring was on its way.

In the first week of November, we decided to add Antonio Vizintín, or 'Tintin' as we called him, to the ranks of the expeditionaries. With his broad shoulders and legs like tree trunks, he played rugby with the strength of a bull, and he had a bull's temperament. Tintin could be just as hot-tempered and overbearing as Roberto, and I worried that facing the mountains with these two might be a recipe for disaster, but Tintin was not as complicated as Roberto; he lacked Roberto's raging ego and the need to tell others what to do. And, despite my concerns, I was happy at the thought that, with five expeditionaries rather than four, we would improve the odds of one of us getting through alive. But as soon as we added this new member to our team, we lost another, as Fito was stricken by a severe case of haemorrhoids. There was no way he could cross the mountains in such pain, so it was agreed that we would travel with four, and Fito would stay behind.

As the day of our departure grew nearer, even though the spirits of the group were rising, all of us were growing weaker by the hour, and a few seemed to be sinking at an alarming rate. Coche Inciarte was one of the weakest. A longtime fan of the Old Christians, he was famous for wheedling his way into the warmest sleeping positions, but always with great charm, and it was impossible not to like him. Coche had an amiable spirit and an irresistible smile. His jovial nature brightened the mood even in the darkest moments. By diffusing tension and making us smile, he helped, in his way, to keep us all alive.

Coche was one of those who was still so repulsed by the idea of eating human flesh that he had never been able to force down enough to keep himself strong. He had grown shockingly thin, and his immune system had been so severely compromised that his body could no longer fight off infection.

As a result, minor wounds on his legs had gone septic, and now large, fierce boils bulged from his reed-thin legs.

'What do you think?' he asked me, as he drew his trouser leg to his knee and swivelled a calf flirtatiously from side to side. 'Pretty skinny, huh? Would you go for a girl with legs as skinny as these?' He had to be in great pain, but still Coche found a way to make me laugh.

Roy Harley seemed even worse. Roy also found it hard to eat human flesh, and so his tall, broad-shouldered frame had been rapidly stripped of fat and muscle. Now he walked with a hunched stride, as if his bones were flimsy sticks held together by skin. Roy's mental state was also deteriorating. He had always been a rugged and courageous rugby player, but the mountain had depleted all his emotional reserves, and now he seemed to live on the brink of hysterics, jumping at noises, weeping at the slightest provocation, always with his face drawn tight in a grimace of apprehension.

Many of the others were weakening, especially Moncho Sabella, Arturo Nogueira and Rafael Echavarren. Rafael had lost none of his fighting spirit. He remained defiant, and still began every day with a loud proclamation of his intention to survive. But Arturo had grown quieter and more introspective, and when I sat with him I sensed he was nearing the end of his fight.

'How are you feeling, Arturo?'

'I'm so cold, Nando,' he said. 'There's not much pain. I can't feel my legs any more. It's hard to breathe.' His voice was growing soft and thin, but his eyes brightened as he motioned me closer. 'I know I am getting closer to God,' he said. 'Sometimes I feel His presence so close to me. I can feel His love, Nando. There's so much love, I want to cry.'

'Try to hold on, Arturo.'

'I don't think it will be long for me,' he said. 'I feel myself being pulled to Him. Soon I will know God, and I will have answers to all your questions.'

'Can I get you some water, Arturo?'

'Nando, I want you to remember, even in this place, our lives have meaning. Our suffering is not for nothing. Even if we are trapped here for ever, we can love our families, and God, and each other as long as we live. Even in this place, our lives are worth living.'

His face was lit with a serene intensity when he said this. I kept my silence, for fear that my voice would crack if I tried to speak.

'You will tell my family that I love them, won't you? That's all that matters to me now.'

'You will tell them yourself,' I said.

Arturo smiled at the lie. 'I am ready, Nando. I made my confession to God. My soul is clean. I will die with no sins.'

'What's this?' I laughed. 'I thought you didn't believe in the kind of God who forgives your sins.'

Arturo looked at me and managed a thin, self-deprecating grin. 'At a time like this,' he said, 'it seems wise to cover all the angles.'

All through the first week of November, Arturo grew weaker and more distant. His best friend, Pedro Algorta, stayed close to him through it all, bringing him water, keeping him warm, and praying with him.

One night, Arturo started to cry softly. When Pedro asked why, he replied, with a faraway gaze in his eyes, 'Because I am so close to God.' The following day he developed a high fever and for forty-eight hours he was delirious, slipping in and out of consciousness. On his last night, we helped him down off the hammock so he could sleep beside Pedro and, sometime before morning, Arturo Nogueira, one of the bravest men I've ever known, quietly died in the arms of his best friend.

On the morning of November 15, Numa, Roberto, Tintin and I stood outside the fuselage, looking down the valley that sloped off to the east, ready to begin our escape. Though he was trying to hide it, I could see Numa was in pain. Since the avalanche, he had forced himself to eat, despite his revulsion, but, like Coche, he could not stomach more than a few scraps at a time. A few nights earlier, someone had accidentally stepped on his calf as he lay on the floor. An ugly bruise quickly appeared, and when Roberto saw how badly the leg had swollen, he advised Numa to drop out of the expedition. Numa assured Roberto that the bruise was nothing to be concerned about, and he firmly refused to let us leave without him.

'How are you feeling?' I asked him, after we had gathered our things and said goodbye to the others. 'Are you sure you can make it on that leg?'

Numa shrugged. 'It's nothing,' he said. 'I'll be fine.'

As we set off down the slope, the weather was overcast and the air was chilly but the winds were light. Despite all my misgivings about the eastern trip, it felt good to be leaving the crash site at last. We made good progress at first, but after an hour or so the skies darkened, temperatures dropped and, in the blink of an eye, snow began to squall in violent spirals all around us.

Knowing that every second counted, we fought our way back up the slope and stumbled into the fuselage, frightened and half frozen, just as the storm matured into a full-blown blizzard. Roberto and I exchanged a sober glance. We understood, without speaking, that if the storm had hit just an hour or two later, trapping us on the open slopes, we would be dying.

The blizzard, one of the worst we'd had in all our weeks in the Andes, kept us penned in the fuselage for two long days. While we waited, Roberto grew more concerned with Numa's leg. There were two large sores now, each almost as large as a billiard ball. As Roberto lanced and drained the sores, he realised Numa was in no shape to hike through the mountains.

'Your legs are getting bad,' said Roberto. 'You'll have to stay behind.'

For the first time on the mountain, Numa's temper flared. 'My leg is fine,' he shouted. 'I am not staying behind!'

Roberto glared at Numa and, with his characteristic bluntness, said, 'You are too weak. You will only slow us down. We can't afford to take you.'

Numa turned to me. 'Nando, please, I can make it. Don't make me stay.'

I shook my head. 'I'm sorry, Numa,' I said, 'I agree with Roberto. Your leg is bad. You should stay here.' As others gave the same advice, Numa fumed and drew into himself. I knew how badly he wanted to be with us, how hard it would be for him to watch us leave. I knew I would not be able to stand such a disappointment, and hoped it would not crush Numa's spirit.

FINALLY, on the morning of November 17, we woke to find a clear, calm day. Without much fanfare, Roberto, Tintin and I gathered our things and set off once more, this time in bright sunshine and a light breeze.

My strides quickly fell into a rhythm and, as the miles passed, the only sound was the crunching of my rugby boots in the snow. Roberto, who was dragging the sledge, had pulled ahead of us, and after about an hour and a half I heard him shout. He was standing on a tall snowdrift, and when we joined him there we saw what he was pointing at—the remains of the Fairchild's tail section lying a few hundred yards ahead.

We reached it in minutes. Suitcases were scattered everywhere and we tore through them to get at the treasures inside: socks, sweaters, warm trousers. Happily we tore off our tattered, filthy rags and dressed in clean clothes.

Inside the tail we found more luggage filled with clothing. We also found some rum, a box of chocolates, some cigarettes and a small camera loaded with film. The plane's small galley area was in the tail, and there we found three small meat pastries that we immediately devoured, and a mouldy sandwich wrapped in plastic, which we saved for later.

We were so excited by all this unexpected booty that we almost forgot about the radio batteries that Carlos Roque had told us about. After a short search, we found them in a recessed space in the exterior hull. They looked larger than I expected. We also found some empty Coca-Cola crates in the luggage hold, which we took outside and used as fuel for a fire. Roberto roasted some of the meat we'd brought with us and we ate with great appetite. We scraped the mould off the sandwich we'd found, and ate that, too. As night fell, we spread clothes from the suitcases on the floor of the luggage hold and laid down to rest.

Working with wires he'd stripped from the walls of the tail section, Roberto had connected the aeroplane's batteries to a light fixture bolted to the ceiling and, for the first time, we had light after sunset. We read some magazines and comic books salvaged from the luggage, and I took some pictures of Roberto and Tintin with the camera we had found. I thought that, if we didn't make it out alive, someone might find the camera and develop the film, and they would know that we had lived, at least for a while. For some reason this was important to me.

It was luxuriously warm and spacious in the luggage hold—what a pleasure to stretch my legs and to roll into any position I chose—and soon we grew drowsy. Roberto extinguished the light, we closed our eyes, and all of us enjoyed the best night of sleep we'd had since the plane fell into the mountains. In the morning we were tempted to stay for a while in these cosy quarters, but we reminded ourselves of the others and their hopes for our expedition, and soon we were once again trekking east.

It snowed that morning, but by late morning the skies cleared and the sun was hot on our shoulders as we hiked. After so many weeks of freezing temperatures, the sudden heat exhausted us quickly, and at noon we were forced to rest in the shade of a rocky outcrop. We ate some of our meat and melted some snow for water, but still none of us had the energy to continue, so we decided to camp at the rock for the night.

The sun grew stronger as the afternoon passed, but at sunset temperatures plummeted. We dug into the snow and wrapped up in our blankets, but it was no protection against the hard chill. The cold bore down on us so aggressively that I feared my blood had frozen solid in my veins. We discovered that by making a sandwich of our bodies—one of us lying between the others—we could keep the guy in the middle of the sandwich warm. We lay this way for hours, taking turns at the middle position, and though we didn't sleep at all, we survived until daylight. When morning came, we climbed out of our poor shelter and warmed ourselves in the first rays of the sun, stunned to be alive.

'We won't last another night like that,' said Roberto. He was gazing to the east, at the mountains that seemed to have grown larger and more distant as we trekked. 'And I don't think this valley ever turns west. We are only walking deeper into the cordillera.'

'You may be right,' I said. 'But the others are counting on us. Maybe we should go a little further.'

'It's hopeless!' he snapped. 'Are we any good to them if we're dead?'

'Then what should we do?'

'Let's get the batteries from the tail and take them to the Fairchild,' he said. 'We can drag them on the sledge. If we can make the radio work, we can save ourselves without risking our lives.'

I had no more faith in the radio than I had had in the prospects of trekking east, but I told myself we had to explore every hope, no matter how slim. So we gathered our things and returned to the tail section.

It took only moments to remove the batteries from the plane and set them side by side on our Samsonite sledge. But when Roberto tried to drag the sledge forward, it dug deep into the snow and wouldn't budge.

'Damn, these are too heavy,' he said. 'There is no way we can drag them up to the plane.'

'We can't carry them,' I said.

Roberto shook his head. 'No,' he said, 'but we can get the radio from the Fairchild and bring it here. We'll bring Roy with us. Maybe he can figure out how to connect it to the batteries.'

I didn't like the sound of this. I was certain the radio was damaged beyond repair, and I feared that Roberto's attempts to fix it would only distract him from what we now knew was our only chance to survive: climb the mountains to the west.

'I'm worried we will waste too much time,' I said.

'Do you have to argue about everything?' he cried. 'This radio could save our lives.'

'OK,' I said, 'I will help you. But if it doesn't work, then we climb. Do we have a deal?'

Roberto nodded, and after allowing ourselves a few more luxurious nights in the tail's luggage hold, we set off back to the fuselage. The walk down from the crash site had been easy, but just minutes into our uphill trek we were pushed to the limits of our stamina. In places we faced inclines as sharp as forty-five degrees, and the snow was often as deep as my hips. I was gasping for air, my muscles were burning, and I found myself forced to rest after every few steps. It had taken us less than two hours to descend; it would take us twice as long to make the same trip in reverse.

We reached the crash site midafternoon, and the survivors at the fuselage gave us a sombre greeting. It had been six days since we left them, and they had hoped we'd be close to civilisation by now. Our return had dashed those hopes, but that was not the only reason for their low spirits; while we were gone, Rafael Echavarren had died.

He had become such a symbol of courage and defiance that to see him struck down after all his brave resistance was one more reason to believe that the mountain would sooner or later claim us all. Since the avalanche, some had clung to the belief that God had seen nineteen of us through that disaster because we were the ones he'd chosen to survive. Rafael's passing made it harder to believe that God was paying any attention at all.

That night, Roberto explained the reason for our return. 'The route to the east is no good. It only leads deeper into the mountains. But we found the tail section, and most of the luggage. We brought warm clothes for everyone. And lots of cigarettes. And the good news is we found the batteries.'

The others listened as Roberto explained his plan to fix the Fairchild's radio. It was worth a try, they agreed, but with little enthusiasm and a weary look in their eyes. I felt their hopes were flickering, and I couldn't blame them. We had suffered so much, and the signs were so bad. It seemed that every door we tried to walk through was slammed in our faces.

The next morning, Roberto and I started working to remove the Fairchild's radio. The cockpit was packed with dials and complex instrumentation and, in our ignorance, it took guesswork to decide what was part of the radio and what was not. Finally we figured out that the radio was made up of two components, one anchored in the cockpit's control panel and the other tucked into a cavity in the wall of the luggage compartment. The one in the control panel came out easily; the other was anchored more firmly and much more difficult to get at. Working clumsily with the bits of metal and plastic we used as tools, we struggled to loosen the bolts and clips holding the transmitter in place. It was two frustrating days before we could remove it from the wall. When we finally pulled it free and set it beside the component from the cockpit, I saw the futility of our efforts. Bristling from the back of each component was a tangle of tiny electrical wires.

'*Carajo!*' I cried. 'Look at this mess! It's impossible!'

Roberto ignored me, and carefully counted the wires on each component. 'There are sixty-seven wires coming out of the back of this piece,' he said, 'and sixty-seven coming out of the transmitter.'

'But which wire connects to which?' I said.

'Do you see these markings?' he replied. 'Each wire has a different mark. The marks will tell us which wires match.'

'I don't know, Roberto,' I said. 'All this time we are spending, and we don't even know if the radio still works.'

Roberto's eyes flashed with anger. 'This radio can save our lives! We owe it to ourselves to try this before we go off blundering into the mountains and throw our lives away.'

'OK! OK!' I said, to calm him. 'But let's ask Roy to take a look.'

I called Roy over and showed him the radio.

He frowned and shook his head. 'I don't think this can be fixed,' he said.

'We are going to fix it,' Roberto replied. 'You are going to fix it.'

'I can't!' Roy cried, his voice growing shrill in protest. 'It's much too complicated. I don't know the first thing about a radio like this!'

'Get hold of yourself, Roy,' said Roberto. 'We're going to take this radio to the tail. You are coming with us. We are going to make this radio work and we are going to use it to call for help.'

Roy's eyes went wide with terror. 'I can't go there!' he shrieked, 'I'm too weak! Look at me! I can barely walk. I won't make it to the tail and back!'

'You'll make it because you have to,' Roberto replied.

Roy's face crumpled and he began to sob. The thought of leaving the fuselage terrified him, and in the days that followed he pleaded with anyone who would listen that he should be excused from the mission. Fito and the cousins were firm with him, insisting that he go for the good of the others. They even forced him to train by walking back and forth outside the fuselage. Roy reluctantly obeyed, but would often weep as he paced in the snow.

Roy was no coward. I knew that from the way he played rugby and from how he lived his life. In the early days of our ordeal, he had been at Marcelo's side as they organised the plane in the immediate aftermath of the crash, and had helped with the difficult work of building the wall that kept us all from freezing. And if not for Roy's quick action in the wake of the avalanche, we all would have suffocated beneath the snow. But he was young, his suffering had shattered his nerves and the ordeal had ravaged his body. He was one of the weakest among us, and I should have felt as much compassion for him as I felt for the others, but I found myself infuriated by his frequent displays of distress.

When he begged me, in desperation, not to make him go with us to the tail, I didn't even look him in the eyes.

'We are leaving soon,' I snapped. 'You'd better be ready.'

Roberto spent several days studying the radio, and as I waited for him to finish I grew more and more concerned about Numa. Since we dropped him from the expeditionary team, he had withdrawn into a brooding silence, furious at the way his body had betrayed him. As he refused to eat anything at all, he lost weight rapidly, and the two large boils on his leg were clearly infected. But what worried me most was the look of resignation in his eyes.

One night I sat beside him and tried to raise his spirits. 'Are you going to eat something for me, Numa?' I asked. 'We are going to the tail soon. It would be nice to see you eat before I leave.'

He shook his head feebly. 'I can't. It is too painful for me.'

'It's painful for all of us,' I said, 'but you must do it. You must remember it is only meat now.'

'I only ate before to strengthen myself for the trip,' he said. 'What reason do I have to force myself now?'

'Don't give up,' I told him. 'Hold on. We are going to get out of here.'

Numa shook his head. 'I am so weak, Nando. I can't even stand any more. I don't think I'm going to last much longer.'

'Don't talk that way, Numa. You will not die.'

Numa sighed. 'It's OK, Nando,' he said. 'I have examined my life, and I know that if I die tomorrow, I have still had wonderful years.'

I laughed. 'That's exactly what Panchito used to say,' I said. 'And he lived his life according to those words. He lived so many lifetimes, had so many adventures, and made love to so many beautiful girls.'

'Maybe that's why God took him,' said Numa. 'So that there would be a few girls for the rest of us.'

'There will be plenty of girls for you, Numa,' I said. 'But first you must eat, and live. I want you to live.'

Numa smiled and nodded. 'I will try,' he said. But later, when they brought him some meat, I saw him wave it away.

We left the next morning at eight o'clock, and made fast progress down the slope. As we approached the tail, I spotted a red leather bag lying in the snow, and immediately recognised it as my mother's cosmetics case. Inside I found some lipstick that I could use to protect my lips from the sun, some candy and a little sewing kit. I stashed these items in our knapsacks.

Less than two hours after leaving the Fairchild, we were at the tail again.

We rested that first day. The next morning, Roy and Roberto started working on the radio, trying to make the proper connections to the battery, but just when it seemed they were making progress, the wires would flash and sizzle and we'd hear a loud electrical pop. Roberto would swear and badger Roy to be more careful, and they'd start over.

Daytime temperatures were milder now, and the snow around the tail was melting fast. Suitcases that had been buried only days ago were now lying in plain view. Tintin and I rummaged through them, and in one we found two bottles of rum. We opened a bottle and took a few swigs.

'We'll save the other,' I said. 'We can use it when we climb.'

Tintin nodded. We both knew the radio would never work, but Roy and Roberto were still working furiously. They tinkered with it all afternoon and into the next morning. I was getting anxious to finish this experiment and get back to the fuselage, where we could prepare for the climb.

'How much longer do you think, Roberto?' I asked.

He glanced at me with irritation in his eyes. 'It will take as long as it takes,' he grumbled.

'We're low on food,' I said. 'Tintin and I should go back and get more.'

'That's a good idea,' he said. 'We'll keep working.'

Tintin and I gathered our things, and in minutes we were climbing up the valley towards the Fairchild.

We trudged for hours, and finally reached the plane late in the afternoon. Once again we received a sullen welcome, and I couldn't help noticing that the others seemed to have grown weaker and even more listless.

'We came for more meat,' I said. 'The radio's taking longer than expected.'

Fito frowned. 'We're running low,' he said. 'We've been looking everywhere for the bodies that were lost in the avalanche, but the snow is so deep and we are so tired. We even climbed up the slopes several times to fetch the bodies that Gustavo and the others found when they climbed.'

'Don't worry,' I said, 'Tintin and I will dig.'

'How is it going with the radio?'

'Not well,' I said. 'I don't think it is going to work.'

'We're running out of time,' said Fito. 'The food won't last much longer.'

'We need to go west,' I said. 'It's our only chance. We have to go very soon.'

'Does Roberto think the same?'

'I don't know what he is thinking,' I said. 'You know Roberto. He will do what he wants to do.'

'If he refuses,' said Fito, 'I will go with you.'

I smiled at Fito. 'That's brave of you,' I said, 'but you can barely walk fifteen feet. No, we must persuade Roberto to go west.'

Tintin and I stayed at the fuselage for two days, digging through the snow in search of fresh bodies. When we found what we were looking for, Fito and his cousins cut the meat for us, and, after resting a while, we hiked down the glacier once more.

We reached the tail section midmorning and found Roy and Roberto hard at work on the radio. They thought they had the connections right, but when they powered up the radio they heard nothing but static. Roy thought the radio's antenna, which had been damaged in the crash, might be defective, so he made a new one from copper wire stripped from the electrical circuits in the tail. When the new antenna was attached, the radio worked no better. Roy disconnected the long copper wires and attached them to the small transistor radio he'd brought along. The long antenna gave the transistor a strong signal. Roy tuned into a station with some music that we liked, and went back to work. Moments later the music was interrupted by a bulletin, and we heard the surprising news that the Uruguayan air force was sending a specially equipped Douglas C-47 to search for us.

Roy whooped in joy. Roberto turned to me, smiling broadly. 'Did you hear that, Nando? They're looking for us!'

'Don't get your hopes up,' I said. 'Remember what Gustavo said—from the slopes the Fairchild is just another speck on the glacier. And they don't know where we are. Even if they do find us, it could take months.'

'We need to make a sign for them,' Roberto said, ignoring my sceptical glare. In minutes he had us gathering suitcases and arranging them on the snow in the shape of a large cross.

When we'd finished, I asked Roberto about the radio.

'I don't think we can fix it,' he said. 'We should go back to the plane.'

'And get ready to go west,' I said, 'as we agreed.'

Roberto nodded absently and went to gather his things. As I rounded up my own gear, Tintin came to me with a small rectangular piece of cloth insulation he had taken from the tail. 'This stuff is wrapped round all the pipes in there,' he said. 'There must be some way we can use it.'

I felt the material. It was light and strong, fluffy on one side, with a tough, smooth fabric cover. 'Maybe we can use it to line our clothes,' I said. 'It seems like it would keep us warm.'

Tintin nodded, and we went into the tail. In moments we had stripped all the insulation from the pipes and stuffed it into our knapsacks. As we worked, we heard a racket outside, and when we looked we saw Roy angrily stomping the radio to pieces.

'He should save his energy,' I told Tintin. 'This climb's going to be tough.'

We set off up the slope midmorning, Roberto and Tintin in the lead, Roy straggling behind me. As before, fighting up the slope through the knee-deep snow was exhausting, and we stopped often to rest. I knew Roy was suffering, so I slowed my pace to keep him from slipping too far behind.

About an hour into our trek, I glanced at the sky and was startled to see that the clouds had turned an ominous dark grey. They hung so low I felt I could touch them. Then, as I watched, they rushed at us like the crest of a killer wave. Before I could react, we were swept up in one of the blitzkrieg blizzards that those who know the Andes call a 'white wind'. In a matter of seconds, everything was chaos. The temperature plummeted and snow swirled in thick whirlpools around me, stinging my face and robbing me of my bearings. I saw no sign of the others and, for a moment I panicked.

Then I heard Roberto's voice, faint and distant in the huge roar of the storm. 'Nando! Can you hear me?'

'Roberto! I am here!'

I looked behind me. Roy had vanished.

'Roy? Where are you?'

There was no response. About thirty feet behind me, I saw a blurred grey heap in the snow, and I realised Roy had fallen.

'Roy!' I bellowed. 'Come on!'

He didn't move, so I stumbled down the slope to the spot where he lay, curled up, his knees drawn in to his chest, his arms wrapped round his body.

'This storm will kill us if we don't keep moving!' I shouted.

'I can't,' Roy whimpered. 'I can't go another step.'

'Get up!' I shouted. 'We'll die here!'

Roy looked up at me. 'No, please,' he sobbed, 'I can't. Just leave me.'

As I stood over Roy, the winds gusted so ferociously I thought they would lift me off my feet. We were trapped in a total whiteout now and I had completely lost my sense of direction. My only hope of making it back to the fuselage was to follow the tracks Roberto and Tintin were leaving, but the snow was rapidly burying their footprints. I knew they would not wait for us—they were fighting for their lives, too—and I knew that each second I stayed with Roy brought us both closer to disaster. I looked down at him. His shoulders were quaking as he wept, and he was already half covered in snow.

I have to leave him or I will die, I thought. Can I do it? Do I have it in me to leave him here? I did not answer these questions in words, but with action. I turned away from Roy and followed the tracks of the others up the slope.

I thought of Roy watching my shadow disappear into the storm. How long would it take for him to lose consciousness? How long would he suffer? I was perhaps fifteen yards away now, and I couldn't erase the picture of him from my mind: slumped on the snow, helpless, defeated. I felt a wild surge of contempt for his weakness and lack of courage—or at least that was what it felt like then. In retrospect, things look quite different. Roy was no weakling. He had suffered more than most of us and had found the strength to endure, but his body had been ravaged so badly that all his resources, physical and mental, had been overwhelmed. It bothers me now that I did not show him more patience in the mountains, and I have realised, after years of reflection, that the reason I treated him as I did was that I saw too much of myself in him. The grating whine in Roy's trembling voice was unbearable to me because it was such a vivid expression of the terror I felt in my own heart. The twisted grimace he wore on his face maddened me only because it mirrored my own despair. Thinking of Roy lying still on the slope, slowly disappearing beneath the snow, I was forced to wonder how close my own moment of surrender might be. Where was the place where my own will would fail? Where, and when would I give up the struggle and lie down, defeated like Roy, in the soft comfort of the snow?

This was the true source of my anger: Roy was showing me my future, and in that moment I hated him for it.

Of course, there was no time for such introspection on that storm-swept mountain. I was acting on instinct alone, and as I pictured Roy sobbing in the snow, all the scorn I had felt towards him in the last few weeks exploded into fury. I swore like a madman into the gusting winds. I was out of my mind with anger, and before I knew it I was crashing down the slope to where Roy had fallen. When I reached him, I kicked him savagely in the rib cage. I fell on him, slamming my knees into his side. As he rolled and screamed in the snow, I attacked him with my fists. 'You son of a whore!' I shouted. 'Get on your feet. Stand up or I'll kill you, you bastard!'

I felt my soul emptying itself of all the venom that my time on the mountain had given me. I called Roy every foul name I could think of, and insulted his mother in ways I do not like to remember. Roy wept and screamed, but finally he rose to his feet. I shoved him forward, so hard that he almost fell again. And I kept shoving him roughly, forcing him to stumble up the slope a few feet at a time.

We battled through the blizzard, Roy suffering terribly from the exertion, my own strength rapidly fading. As I struggled to breathe the thin air, the swirling winds would snatch my breath away, then force it down my throat again, making me choke. Each step through the deep snow required a monumental act of will. I kept Roy in front of me, where I could keep shoving him forward, and we climbed foot by foot.

After a few hundred yards, Roy slumped forward, and I knew he had spent the last of his strength. This time I didn't try to rouse him. Instead I reached round him and lifted him from the snow. Even through all the layers of his clothing, I could feel how thin and weak he had become, and my heart softened. 'Think of your mother, Roy,' I told him, my lips pressed to his ear so he could hear me in the storm. 'If you want to see her again, you must suffer for her now.' His jaw was slack and his eyes were rolling up under their eyelids. He was on the verge of passing out, but still he managed a feeble nod: he would fight. His bravery was remarkable, and now, when I think of Roy, I always think of him in this moment—as a hero.

He leaned against me, and together we climbed. He struggled with all he had, but soon we reached a point where the slope swept sharply upwards. Roy looked at me calmly, in resignation, knowing the climb was beyond his strength. I squinted into the stinging snow, trying to gauge the steepness of the rise, then I tightened my grip round Roy's waist and, with what little strength I still had, lifted him off the ground, so that I bore his weight on my shoulder. Taking one slow, laboured step at a time, I carried him up the rise.

I climbed by intuition now towards the crash site, tormented by the thought that I might have drifted off course and was walking into the wild. But finally, as the light faded, I saw the faint silhouette of the plane through the heavy snow, and felt a boost of energy. At last we reached the fuselage. The others took Roy from my shoulders as we stumbled inside. Roberto and Tintin had collapsed on the floor, and I fell heavily beside them. I couldn't stop shivering, and my muscles burned and quivered with the most profound exhaustion I'd ever felt. I burrowed into the heap of bodies, drawing warmth from them, then fell asleep quickly and slept soundly for hours.

In the morning, I rested. The days I'd spent away from the Fairchild had given me perspective, and now I saw with fresh eyes the gruesomeness that had become a normal part of our daily lives. There were piles of bones scattered outside the fuselage, and strips of fat were spread on the roof to dry in the sun. The bodies of my mother, my sister and Liliana, all in easy reach, had not been touched, and it moved me to think that, even at the brink of starvation, a promise still meant something to my friends. The mountains had forced us to face intolerable horrors, and changed us in ways that would take years to understand. But despite all the suffering, the principles of friendship, loyalty and honour still mattered. The Andes had done much to crush us, but we were still fighting together, as a team. We hadn't let the mountains steal our souls.

IN THE FIRST WEEK of December, we began to prepare in earnest for the westward climb. As Tintin, Roberto and I gathered the clothing and equipment we would need, an odd mixture of excitement and gloom hung over us. We knew now that we would face two great challenges. The first would be the severe demands of high-altitude climbing, the second would be the dangers of exposure, especially after sundown. At this time of year we could expect daytime temperatures well above freezing, but the nights were still cold enough to kill us, and we needed a way to survive them.

The small rectangular patches of insulation we'd taken from the tail section gave us our solution. Stuffed between layers of clothing, they were very effective in shielding us from the cold. As we brainstormed about the trip, we realised we could sew the patches together to create a warm quilt. And by folding the quilt in half and stitching the seams together, we could create an insulated sleeping-bag large enough for all three of us to sleep in.

Carlitos took on the challenge. His mother had taught him to sew when he was a boy, and, with the sewing kit I'd found in my mother's cosmetics case, he began to work. It was meticulous labour, and he had to make sure all his stitching was strong enough to withstand hard use. To speed the progress, he taught others to sew, but many of us were too thick-fingered for the job.

By the middle of the first week in December, the sleeping-bag was finished. Our gear was all gathered, the meat for the trip was packed into socks, and everyone knew the time had come for our departure—everyone but Roberto, who found one maddening reason after another to delay. First he complained that the sleeping-bag wasn't strong enough, and insisted it be reinforced. Then he said he couldn't leave while Coche and Roy and the others needed his medical attention so badly. Finally, he declared that he hadn't rested sufficiently for the climb and would need more days to gather his strength. Fito and the cousins tried to pressure him into action, but he angrily rejected their authority and made it clear that he would not leave one moment before he was ready.

'This can't continue,' I told him. 'You know it's time to go.'

'We will go soon,' he said, 'but we must wait for the weather to improve.'

'I'm tired of waiting,' I said softly.

'I told you,' he snapped, 'we'll leave when the weather is better!'

I was trying to stay calm, but Roberto's aggressive tone set me off. 'Look around!' I shouted. 'We are running out of food! Our friends are dying. Coche has started to rave at night. Roy is even worse, skin and bone. Javier is fading, and the younger guys—Moncho, Alvaro, Bobby—are all so weak. And look at us! You and I are wasting away by the hour. We have to climb before we're too weak to stand!'

'Listen to me, Nando,' Roberto shot back. 'Remember the bad storm we had two days ago? If it had caught us on the slopes, it would have killed us.'

'And an avalanche would kill us,' I said, 'or we could fall into a crevasse. We can't eliminate these risks, Roberto, and we can't wait any longer!' I turned to walk away, then added, 'I am leaving the morning of December the 12th. If you aren't ready, I'll go without you.'

DECEMBER 9 was my twenty-third birthday. That night in the fuselage, the guys gave me one of the cigars we'd found in the luggage at the tail.

'It's not Punta del Este, as we planned,' joked Carlitos, 'but that is a Havana cigar.'

'The quality is lost on me,' I said, choking as I inhaled. 'All I know is that the smoke is warm.'

'We missed our birthdays,' said Carlitos, 'but I know we will be with our families for Christmas. You will make it, Nando. I am certain of it.'

I didn't answer, and I was glad the shadows of the fuselage hid the doubt in my eyes. 'Get some sleep,' I told Carlitos, then I blew a cloud of expensive Cuban smoke in his face.

On December 10, Gustavo and I spoke of our concerns about Numa.

'He asked me to check a sore on his backside,' Gustavo said, 'and I got a look under his clothes. There is no flesh at all on his bones. He can't last more than a couple of days.'

I left Gustavo and knelt at Numa's side. 'How are you feeling, Numa?'

He smiled weakly. 'I don't think it will be much longer for me.'

'Try to hold on,' I said. 'We'll be climbing soon. We're going west, at last.'

'"To the west is Chile",' he said, with a weary smile. 'You will make it, you are strong.'

'You must be strong, Numa, for your family. You will see them again.'

Numa just smiled. 'It's funny,' he said. 'I think most men die regretting errors they have made in their lives, but I have no regrets. I have tried to live a good life. I hope God will take that into account.'

'Don't talk like that, Numa.'

'But I'm at peace,' he said. 'I'm ready for whatever lies ahead.'

On the morning of December 11, Numa slipped into a coma. He died that afternoon. Numa was one of the best of us, a young man whose compassion and generosity never wavered, no matter how much he suffered.

As I looked at my friends, I wondered if their families would know them now, with their faces drawn, their brows and sunken cheeks ridged with bone, and most of them barely strong enough to stand without wobbling. Life was fading from them the way the colour fades from a fallen leaf. So much death, so many lives cut short. I felt a heavy weariness overtake me.

It was time to bring the story to a close. I found Roberto outside, slumped against the fuselage. 'Everything is ready,' I told him. 'Tintin and I are set to go. Tomorrow morning we leave. Are you coming?'

Roberto glanced at the mountains. I saw in his eyes that he was as shaken by Numa's death as the rest of us. 'Yes,' he said. 'I'll be ready. It's time to go.'

On the evening of December 11, our sixtieth evening in the Andes, I sat outside on one of the seats we'd dragged from the plane, and stared west at the mountains that blocked me from my home. As night fell, the largest of them, the one I'd have to climb, grew darker and more forbidding. It was hard to convince myself that the moment I had longed for had finally arrived. My mind was a blizzard of questions. What is it like to freeze to death? How does one die of exhaustion? Do you simply drop in your tracks? It would be horrible to starve to death, but I would rather starve than fall. Please, God, don't let me fall sliding down some steep slope for hundreds of feet, clutching at the snow, knowing I am heading for rocks a thousand feet below. Please, protect me from that kind of death.

I began to tremble, knowing I didn't have the courage to face what lay ahead. I cannot do this. I don't want to die. I resolved that I would tell the others I had changed my mind. Perhaps Roberto was right, and the rescuers would find us after all . . .

But I knew better, really. We were almost out of food. How long would it be before we ran out completely and began the horrific wait for someone to die? And what would it be like for the last one left alive? I looked again at the mountain, and knew that nothing it could do to me would be worse than what waited for me here. 'Tell me your secrets,' I whispered. 'Show me how to climb.' I gazed at the soaring ridges, trying, with an amateur's eye, to trace the best path to the summit. But the slopes disappeared into darkness and I went inside, lay down with my friends one last time, and tried to sleep.

8: The Opposite of Death

When the first light of morning glowed weakly through the Fairchild's windows, I had been lying awake for hours. None of the others spoke to me as I rose and readied myself to go. I had dressed for the mountain the night before. Next to my skin were a cotton polo shirt and a pair of women's woollen slacks I'd found in someone's luggage—Liliana's, probably. After two months in the mountains I had no trouble slipping them over my bony hips. I had three pairs of jeans over the slacks, and three sweaters over the polo. I wore four pairs of socks, and now I covered the socks with plastic bags to keep them dry. I stuffed my feet into my battered rugby boots and carefully tied the laces, then I pulled a woollen cap over my head and topped it with the hood and shoulders I'd cut from Susy's antelope coat. Everything I did that morning had the feel of ceremony, of consequence. My thoughts were razor sharp, but I felt as though I were watching myself from a distance. The others stood by quietly, not sure what to say. After so many weeks of intense camaraderie and common struggle, there was suddenly a distance between us. I had already begun to leave them.

I grabbed the aluminium pole I would use as a walking stick, and took my backpack down from the luggage compartment above me. It was packed with my meat rations and some odds and ends I thought might be useful—bands of cloth I could wrap round my hands to keep them warm, a lipstick to protect my blistered lips.

Roberto had finished dressing. We exchanged a silent nod, then I slipped Panchito's watch onto my wrist and followed Roberto outside. There was a sharp chill in the air, but the temperature was well above freezing. It was a perfect day for climbing; the wind was light and the sky was brilliant blue.

Fito and the cousins brought us some meat for breakfast and we ate quickly. There was little talk. When it was time to leave, Carlitos stepped forward and we embraced. He was smiling happily, and his voice was full of encouragement. 'You will make it!' he said. 'God will protect you!'

It broke my heart to think that this hopeless trek we were about to begin was his only chance of survival. I wanted to scream, What the fuck am I doing, Carlitos? I am so afraid! But I knew that if I allowed those feelings to rise in me, what was left of my courage would crumble. So, instead, I handed him one of the tiny red shoes my mother had purchased in Mendoza for my nephew. 'Keep this,' I told him. 'I'll keep the other one. When I come back for you, we'll have a pair again.'

The others said goodbye with embraces and glances of quiet encouragement. It was hard for me to look them in the eyes. After all, I was the one who had insisted most forcefully that it was possible to reach Chile on foot. I know the others saw my behaviour as confident and optimistic. But it was nothing of the sort. It was driven by panic. It was the same terror that drives a man to jump from the top of a burning building. I had always wondered how a person thinks in such a moment. What is the logic that tells you the time has come to step into thin air? This morning I had my answer. I turned away from Carlitos before he saw the anguish in my eyes. My gaze fell on the soft mound of snow marking the place where my mother and sister lay buried.

'Nando, are you ready?'

Roberto and Tintin were waiting. The mountain was behind them, its white slopes blazing in the early sunlight. I reminded myself that those brutal peaks were all that blocked my path to my father, and that the time had finally come to begin the long walk home.

I glanced at the graves again, then turned back to Carlitos. 'If you run out of food,' I said, 'I want you to use my mother and Susy.'

Carlitos was speechless for a moment, then he nodded. 'Only as a last resort,' he said softly.

'Nando,' said Roberto, 'it's time to go.'

'I'm ready,' I said. We waved one last time and then began to climb.

WE FOLLOWED the gentle incline of the glacier up to the mountain's lower slopes, thinking we were aware of the danger ahead. But we knew nothing about the techniques of mountaineering, and what we didn't know was enough to kill us.

We didn't know, for example, that the Fairchild's altimeter was wrong: the crash site wasn't at 7,000 feet, as we thought, but close to 12,000. Nor did we know that the mountain we were about to challenge was one of the highest in the Andes, soaring to a height of nearly 17,000 feet, with slopes so difficult they would test expert climbers. Experienced mountaineers, in fact, would not have gone anywhere near this mountain without an arsenal of specialised gear, including steel pitons, ice screws and safety lines. They would carry ice axes, weatherproof tents and sturdy thermal boots fitted with crampons. They would be in peak physical condition, and they would climb at a time of their own choosing, and carefully plot the safest route to the top. The three of us were climbing in street clothes, with only the crude tools we could fashion out of materials salvaged from the plane. Our bodies were ravaged from months of exhaustion, starvation and exposure, and none of us had seen real mountains before. Prior to the crash, Roberto and Tintin had never even seen snow. If we had known anything about climbing, we'd have seen we were doomed. Luckily, we knew nothing, and our ignorance provided our only chance.

Our first task was to choose a route up the slopes. Experienced climbers would have quickly spotted a ridge winding down from the summit to meet the glacier at a point less than a mile south of the crash site. If we had hiked to that ridge and climbed its long, narrow spine, we would have found better footing, and a safer and swifter path to the top. We never even noticed the ridge. For days I had marked with my eye the spot where the sun set behind the ridges, and, thinking the best path was the shortest, we used that point to chart a beeline due west. It was an amateurish mistake that would force us to weave our way up the mountain's steepest and most dangerous slopes.

Our beginning, though, was promising. The snow on the mountain's lower flank was firm and fairly level, and the cleats of my rugby boots bit well into the frozen crust. Driven by an intense adrenaline surge, I moved quickly and in no time had pulled fifty yards ahead of the others. But soon I was forced to slow my pace. The slope seemed to grow steeper with every step, and the effort of climbing left me gasping in the thin air, and I had to rest, with my hands on my knees, after every few yards of progress.

The sun was strong enough to warm us as we climbed, but it warmed the snow as well, and the firm surface beneath my feet began to weaken. Now, with every step, my foot would break through the thinning crust and I would sink up to my knees in the soft, deep drifts. I would have to lift my knee almost to my chest to clear my boot from the snow. In the thin air I needed to rest, exhausted, after every step. When I looked behind me I saw the others struggling too. I glanced at the sun above us, and realised that we had waited too long that morning to start the climb. Logic told us it would be wiser to climb in daylight, so we'd waited for the sun to rise. Experts, on the other hand, know that the best time for climbing is in the predawn hours, before the sun turns the slopes to mush. I wondered what other blunders lay ahead, and how many of them we'd be able to survive.

Eventually we were forced to wade uphill through heavy drifts that were as deep as my hips. 'Let's try the snowshoes!' I shouted. The others nodded, and in moments we had slipped Fito's makeshift snowshoes off our backs and strapped them to our feet. They worked well at first, allowing us to climb without sinking into the snow. But the size and bulk of the cushions forced us to bow our legs as we walked, and swing our feet in unnaturally wide circles to keep the cushions from colliding. To make things worse, the fabric and stuffing quickly became soaked. I felt as if I were climbing the mountain with manhole covers bolted to my shoes. My spirits were sinking. We were already on the verge of exhaustion, and the real climbing hadn't even begun.

The incline of the mountain grew sharper, and soon we reached slopes that were too steep and windblown to hold much snow. With relief, we removed the snowshoes, strapped them to our backs and kept climbing. By midmorning we had worked our way to a dizzying altitude. The world around us was now more blue air and sunlight than rock and snow, and the yawning openness of the vast slopes made my head spin. The slope was as steep as a roofer's ladder, and we had only the fading strength of our arms, legs, fingertips and freezing toes to keep us from sailing off into the blue void behind us. I was terrified, of course, but awed by the wild beauty all around me—the flawless sky, the frosted mountains, the glowing landscape of deep virgin snow. It was all so vast, so perfect, so silent and still.

I looked down to the crash site. From this altitude it was just a smudge on the pristine snow, and I saw how out of place it seemed. Everything about us being here was wrong—the violence and racket of our arrival, our lurid suffering, the noise and mess of our struggle to survive. Life did not fit here. It was a violation of the perfect serenity that had reigned for millions of years. We had upset an ancient balance, and that balance would have to be restored. It was all around me, in the silence, in the cold. Something in the mountain wanted that serenity back again, wanted us to be still.

By late morning we had climbed some 2,000 feet and were probably 14,000 feet or more above sea level. A vicious headache had tightened like an iron ring round my skull and my fingers felt thick and clumsy, my limbs heavy with fatigue. The slightest effort left me sucking for air as if I'd just run a mile, but no matter how forcefully I inhaled, I couldn't fill my lungs. I felt as if I were drawing breath through a piece of felt.

Altitude sickness, which generally strikes above 8,000 feet, can cause a range of debilitating symptoms, including headache, intense fatigue and dizziness. Above 12,000 feet, the condition can lead to cerebral and pulmonary oedemas, both of which can cause brain damage and rapid death. Experts recommend that climbers ascend no more than 1,000 feet per day, a rate that gives the body a chance to acclimatise. We had climbed twice that far in a single morning and were making matters worse by continuing when our bodies desperately needed to rest. Our only source of fluids was the snow we gulped in handfuls or melted in the glass bottle we had in one of the packs. It did little good. We climbed with a constant, searing thirst and became more severely dehydrated with every breath.

AFTER FIVE or six hours of hard climbing, the summit seemed no closer. My spirits sagged as I gauged the vast distance to the top, and saw with brutal clarity that we had taken on an inhuman task.

Overwhelmed with fear and a sense of futility, I felt the urge to sink to my knees and stay there. Then I heard the calm voice in my head, the voice that had steadied me in so many moments of crisis: *You are drowning in distances. Cut the mountain down to size.* I knew what I had to do. Ahead of me on the slope was a large rock. I decided I would forget about the summit and make that rock my goal. I trudged for it, without resting, and when I finally got there I picked another landmark and started all over again.

I climbed that way for hours, focusing my attention completely on some target—a rock, a shadow, a ruffle in the snow—until the distance to that target became all that mattered in the world. The only sounds were my own heavy breathing and the rhythmic crunch of my shoes in the snow. My steps became automatic, and I slipped into a trance. Step-push, step-push. Time melted away, distances dwindled, the snow seemed to glide beneath my feet. I kept up that pace until I had pulled far ahead of Roberto and Tintin, who had to shout to make me stop. I waited for them at an outcrop that offered a level place to rest. When they caught up, we ate some meat and melted some snow to drink. None of us had much to say.

'Do you think we can make the summit by nightfall?' asked Roberto.

I shrugged. 'We should look for a place to camp.'

I peered down at the crash site, and wondered how things looked from our friends' perspective. Could they tell how desperately we were struggling? But it was only a passing thought. I was no longer in the same world as the boys down below. The feelings of compassion or responsibility I had felt for the other survivors were now crowded out by my own terror and furious struggle to survive. I knew it was the same for Tintin and Roberto, and while I was certain we would fight side by side as long as possible, the mountain was teaching me a hard lesson: death was an opponent each of us would face alone.

As WE WORKED our way up the mountain, the snow cover gave way to an even more difficult landscape. Now rocks were jutting from the snow, some of them huge and impossible to climb. Massive outcrops above us blocked my view of the slope ahead, and I was forced to choose my path by instinct. Often I chose wrong, and found myself trapped under an impassable ledge or at the base of a vertical rock wall, and I would have to inch my way diagonally across the slope to find a new path.

At one point in the early afternoon, I found my way blocked by an extremely steep, snow-covered incline. I could see a level rock shelf at the upper edge. Unless we could climb the incline diagonally, we'd have to backtrack. That could cost us hours, and with sunset growing closer by the minute, I knew it was not an option. I looked back at Tintin and Roberto. They were watching to see what I would do. I studied the incline. The slope was sheer and smooth, there was nothing to grip with my hands, but the snow looked stable enough to support me. I'd have to dig my feet into it and keep my weight tilted forward. It would all be a matter of balance.

I began to climb, carving the snow with the edges of my shoes and pressing my chest against the slope to keep from toppling backwards. With great caution I inched my way to the rock ledge and scrambled up onto level ground. I waved to Tintin and Roberto.

'Follow my steps,' I shouted. 'Be careful, it is very steep.'

I turned away from them and began to climb the slopes above me. Moments later I glanced back to see that Roberto had made it across the incline. Now it was Tintin's turn. I had ascended thirty yards or so when a terrified shout echoed up the mountain. 'I'm stuck! I can't make it!'

I turned to see Tintin frozen in the middle of the incline.

'Come on, Tintin!' I shouted. 'You can do it!'

He shook his head. 'I can't move.'

'It's the backpack!' said Roberto. 'It's too heavy.'

Roberto was right. The weight of Tintin's backpack was pulling him off the face of the mountain. He was struggling to shift his balance forward, but there was nothing to offer him a handhold, and the look on his face told me he could not hold out for long. There was a dizzying drop behind him.

'Tintin, hold on!' I shouted.

Roberto was at the lip of the rock shelf, stretching his arm down to Tintin. His reach was short by inches. 'Take off your backpack!' he shouted. 'Give it to me!' Tintin removed the backpack carefully, struggling to keep his balance as he worked the straps off his arms, and handed it up to

Roberto. Without the weight, Tintin was able to find his balance and climb safely up the incline. When he reached the ledge, he slumped to the snow.

'I can't go any further,' he said. 'I'm too tired. I can't lift my legs.'

I knew we had to climb until we found a safe, level place to spend the night, so I kept going, leaving the others no choice but to follow. It was late afternoon, the sun had drifted behind the western ridges and shadows were stretching down the slopes. The temperature began to fall. A clot of panic rose in my throat.

As I scaled a tall rock outcropping to get a better view, I wedged my right foot in a crevice in the rock, then, with my left hand, reached up to grab a boulder jutting from the snow. It seemed solid, but when I pulled myself up, a rock the size of a cannon ball broke free and plummeted past me.

'Watch out below!' I shouted. I looked down to see Roberto beneath me. His eyes widened as the rock missed his head by inches. After a moment of stunned silence, he glared at me. 'You son of a bitch! Are you trying to kill me? Watch what you are doing!' Then he fell silent and leaned forward, and his shoulders started to heave. I realised he was crying. Hearing his sobs, I felt a pang of hopelessness so sharp I could taste it on my tongue.

I was overtaken by a sudden, inarticulate rage. 'Fuck this!' I muttered. 'I have had enough! I have had enough!' I just wanted it to be over. I wanted to rest, to sink into the snow, to lie still and quiet. I can't remember any other thoughts, so I don't know what led me to keep going, but once Roberto had gathered himself, we started climbing again in the fading light.

Finally I found a shallow depression in the snow beneath a large boulder. The sun had warmed the boulder all day, and the heat radiating from the rock had melted out this compact hollow. It was cramped, and its floor tilted sharply down the slope, but it would shelter us from the cold and wind. We laid the seat cushions on the floor then spread the sleeping-bag over them. Our lives depended upon this fragile thing, sewn together crudely with strands of copper wire, so we handled it with great care. To keep from tearing the seams, we removed our shoes before sliding in.

'Did you pee?' asked Roberto, as I eased myself into the bag. 'We can't be getting in and out of this bag all night.'

It reassured me that Roberto was becoming his grumbling self again.

'I peed,' I answered. 'Did you pee? I don't want you peeing in this bag.'

Roberto huffed at me. 'If anyone pees in the bag it will be you. And be careful with those big feet.'

When the three of us were all inside, we tried to get comfortable, but the ground was very hard, and the floor of the hollow was so steep we were almost standing up, with our backs pressed to the mountain and our feet braced against the lower rim of the hollow. We were exhausted, and quiet for a long time. The sky was as black as ink now, and studded with a billion stars, each of them blazing like a point of fire. At this altitude I felt I could reach out and touch them. In another time and place I would have been awe-struck by their beauty. But here, it seemed a brutal show of force. The world was showing me how weak and insignificant I was. And how temporary.

I listened to my own breathing, reminding myself that as long as I drew breath I was still alive. I promised myself I would live from moment to moment, from breath to breath, until I had used up all the life I had.

THE TEMPERATURE dropped so low that night that the water bottle we carried shattered from the cold. Huddled together in the sleeping-bag, we kept ourselves from freezing, but still suffered terribly. In the morning we placed our frozen shoes in the sun and rested in the bag until they thawed. Then, after eating and packing, we began to climb. It was another perfect day.

We were climbing above 15,000 feet now, and with every hundred yards or so the incline of the mountain tilted closer to the vertical, making the open slopes unclimbable. So we began to work our way up the winding couloirs— the plunging ravines that gashed the mountainside. Experienced climbers know couloirs can be killing zones—they are efficient chutes for all the rocks that tumble down the mountain—but the packed snow inside them gave us good footing, and the rock walls gave us something firm to grip.

Perhaps it was the altitude, fatigue or a trick of my oxygen-starved brain, but as we climbed I felt that the void behind me was no longer a passive danger. Now it had presence and intention, very bad intention, and I knew that if I didn't resist it with all my strength it would lure me off the mountain and toss me down the slope. One slip, one moment of inattention, one bit of bad judgment was all it would take. The only thing that could keep me from the void was the level of my own performance. My focus narrowed until there was no room in my thoughts for anything but a close and careful study of the rock I was reaching for, or the ledge on which I was about to brace my foot.

In the intensity of my concentration, I forgot my fear and fatigue and, for a while, I felt as if everything I had ever been had disappeared, and that I was now nothing more than the pure will to climb. It was a moment of animal exhilaration, of pure flow. I had never felt so focused, so fiercely alive and for those astonishing moments, my suffering was over.

The fear and exhaustion, however, soon returned and climbing once again became an ordeal. How we continued, I cannot say. I was shivering uncontrollably from cold and fatigue, and my body was on the verge of collapse. Then, in the distance above me, I saw the outline of a ridge in sharp relief against the clear blue sky, and no more mountain above it.

The summit! 'We made it!' I shouted, and with renewed energy, clawed my way upwards. But as I pulled myself over the edge of the ridge, it gave way to a shelf several yards wide, and above the shelf the mountain rose again. It was only another trick of the mountain, a false summit.

And it wasn't the last. We spent the afternoon struggling towards one false summit after another until, well before sunset, we found a sheltered spot and decided to make camp.

Roberto was sullen that night as we lay in the sleeping-bag. 'We will die if we keep climbing,' he said. 'The mountain is too high.'

'What can we do but climb?' I asked.

'Go back,' he said.

For a moment I was speechless. 'Go back and wait to die?'

He shook his head. 'Do you see across there, that dark line on the mountain? I think it's a road.' Roberto pointed across a wide valley to a ridge miles away. 'I think we should go back and follow it. It must lead somewhere.'

This was the last thing I wanted to hear. 'That mountain must be twenty-five miles away,' I said. 'If we hike there and climb to that black line, and find that it is just a layer of shale, we won't have the strength to return.'

'It's a road, Nando, I'm sure of it!'

'Perhaps it's a road, perhaps it's not,' I replied. 'The only thing we know for sure is that to the west is Chile.'

He scowled. 'You've been saying that for months, but we'll break our necks before we get there.'

Roberto and I argued for hours, but as we settled down to sleep I knew the matter had not been resolved.

I woke the next morning to yet another clear sky.

'We've been lucky with the weather,' said Roberto. He was still inside the sleeping-bag.

'What have you decided?' I asked him. 'Are you going back?'

'I'm not sure,' he said. 'I need to think.'

'I'm going to climb,' I said, 'maybe we'll reach the summit soon.'

Roberto nodded. 'You two leave your packs here. I'll wait until you return.'

The thought of going on without Roberto terrified me, but I had no intention of turning back now. I waited for Tintin to get ready, then we turned to the slope and began to climb. After hours of slow progress, we found ourselves trapped at the base of a cliff towering hundreds of feet above us. Its face was almost dead vertical and covered with hard-packed snow.

'How can we climb this?' asked Tintin.

I studied the wall. My mind was sluggish, but soon I remembered the aluminium walking stick strapped to my back. 'We need a stairway,' I said. I drew the stick off my back, and with its sharp tip I began to carve crude steps into the snow. Using the steps like the rungs of a ladder, we climbed with dull persistence, one step at a time. Dig, climb, dig, climb. Tintin followed me. He was frightened, I know, but he never complained.

The hours passed slowly. Sometime in the late morning I spotted blue sky above a ridge line and worked my way towards it. After so many false summits, I had learned to keep my hopes in check, but this time, as I climbed over the ridge's edge, the slope fell away and I found myself standing on a gloomy hump of rock and wind-scoured snow, with no more mountain above me. I had reached the top.

I don't remember if I felt any joy or sense of achievement in that moment. If I did, it vanished as soon as I glanced around. The summit gave me an unobstructed 360-degree view of creation. I could see the horizon circling the world like the rim of a colossal bowl, and in every direction, off in the blue distance, the bowl was crowded with legions of snow-covered mountains, each as steep and forbidding as the one I had just climbed. I understood immediately that the Fairchild's copilot had been badly mistaken. We had not passed Curicó. We were nowhere near the western limits of the Andes. Our plane had fallen somewhere in the middle of the vast cordillera.

I don't know how long I stood there, staring, motionless. But suddenly I felt a burning pressure in my lungs, and realised I had forgotten to breathe. I sucked air. My legs went rubbery and I fell to the ground. I cursed God and raged at the mountains. For all my striving, my hopes, my promises to myself and my father, it would end like this. Our loved ones would never know how hard we had struggled to return to them.

In that moment, all my expectations of life evaporated into the thin Andean air. I had always thought that life was the natural thing, and that death was simply the end of living. Now, I saw with a terrible clarity that death was the constant, and life was only a short, fragile dream, a game death let me play as it waited to take me.

In my despair, I felt a sharp and sudden longing for my mother and my sister, and the warm, strong embrace of my father. Love for him swelled in my heart, and the memory of him filled me with joy. It staggered me: the mountains, for all their power, were not stronger than my attachment to my father; they could not crush my ability to love. I felt a momentary clarity of mind and discovered a simple, astounding secret: death has an opposite, but the opposite is not mere living. It is not courage or faith or human will. The opposite is love. How had I missed that? How does anyone miss that? Love is our only weapon. Only love can turn mere life into a miracle, and draw precious meaning from suffering and fear. For a brief, magical moment, all my fears lifted, and I knew that I would not let death control me. I would walk through the godforsaken country that separated me from my home with hope in my heart. I would walk until I had walked all the life out of me, and when I fell I would die that much closer to my father.

I heard Tintin's voice calling to me from the slope below. 'Do you see any green, Nando?' he cried. 'Do you see any green?'

'Everything will be fine,' I called down to him. 'Tell Roberto to come up and see for himself.' While I waited for Roberto to climb, I pulled a plastic bag and the lipstick from my backpack. Using the lipstick as a crayon, I wrote the words 'Mt. Seler' on the bag and stuffed it under a rock. This mountain was my enemy, I thought, and now I will give it to my father. Whatever happens, at least I have this as my revenge.

It took three hours for Roberto to climb the steps. He looked around for a few moments, shaking his head. 'Well, we are finished,' he said flatly.

'There must be a way through the mountains,' I said. 'Do you see there, in the distance, two smaller peaks with no snow on them? Maybe the mountains end there. I think we should head that way.'

Roberto shook his head. 'It must be fifty miles,' he said. 'In our condition, how can we make such a trek?'

'Look down,' I said. 'Do you see the valley at the base of this mountain?'

He nodded. The valley wound through the mountains for miles, in the direction of the two smaller peaks. As it neared the small mountains, it split into two forks. We lost sight of them as they wound behind larger mountains, but I was confident the valley would take us where we needed to go.

'Chile is there,' I said. 'It's just farther than we thought.'

Roberto frowned. 'It's too far,' he said. 'We'll never make it. We don't have enough food.'

'We could send Tintin back,' I said. 'With his food and what's left of ours, we could easily last twenty days.'

Roberto looked off to the east again. I knew he was thinking about the road. My heart sank at the thought of trekking through the wilderness alone.

We were back at camp by late that afternoon. As we ate together, Roberto spoke to Tintin. 'Tomorrow morning we're going to send you back,' he said. 'The trip will be longer than we thought, and we're going to need your food. Anyway, two can move faster than three.' Tintin nodded in acceptance.

In the morning Roberto told me he had decided to stay with me. We embraced Tintin and sent him down the mountain.

'Remember,' I said as he left us, 'we will always be heading west. If rescuers come, send them to find us!'

We rested all that day in preparation for the trek that lay ahead. In the late afternoon we ate some meat and crawled into the sleeping-bag. As the sun slipped behind the ridge above us, the Andes blazed with the most spectacular sunset I had ever seen. The mountains turned to gleaming gold, and the sky above them was lit with swirls of scarlet and lavender. It occurred to me that Roberto and I were probably the first human beings to have such a vantage point on this majestic display, and I felt a momentary sense of privilege. But I knew that the Andes had staged this spectacle for millions of years, long before humans walked the earth, and would continue to do so after all of us were gone. My life or death would not make a bit of difference.

'Roberto,' I said, 'can you imagine how beautiful this would be if we were not dead men?'

I felt his hand wrap round mine. He was the only person who understood the magnitude of what we had done and of what we still had to do. I knew that he was as frightened as I was, but we drew strength from our closeness. We were bonded now like brothers. We made each other better men.

9: 'I See a Man ...'

In the morning, we climbed to the summit and eased ourselves over its western lip. I realised immediately that descending the mountain would be even more terrifying than the ascent. Climbing a mountain is a struggle, an attack. Descending is more like surrender. You are no longer fighting gravity, but trying to strike a bargain with it, and as you lower yourself carefully from one treacherous foothold to another, you know that, given the slightest chance, it will pull you off the mountain and into the blue void.

At the very top of the mountain, the wind had scoured the slopes down to bare rock, so we lowered ourselves inch by inch, grasping the edges of boulders and jamming our boots into spaces between small rocks. Sometimes we crab-walked down, with our backs to the mountain; other times we descended with our backs to the sky. We thought only about surviving the next step, and at times our haphazard path would lead us to an impassable wall, or to the lip of an outcrop with a heart-stopping view to the base of the mountain, thousands of feet below. We managed to work our way over or round these obstacles. Sometimes we had no choice but to hop from rock to rock, with nothing but a few thousand feet of thin air below us.

In three hours we covered no more than fifty yards, but finally the rocks gave way to open slopes under heavy snow cover. Slogging through the hip-deep snow was less frightening, but it was exhausting, and we were constantly fooled by the rolling, softly sculpted landscape. Again and again, a dead end forced us to retrace our steps and find another route.

When we had made our way a few hundred yards down the mountain, the footing changed dramatically. Because this portion of the west face was exposed each day to afternoon sun, much of the snow had melted off, and more of the rocky surface was exposed. The dry ground gave us easier passage but in places it was covered by a deep layer of loose stones and shale. This made for an unstable footing, and more than once I lost my grip and had to clutch desperately at rocks to keep myself from sliding down the mountain. When we could, we slid down on our backsides or lowered ourselves down huge, rubble-strewn couloirs.

By late afternoon we had made it about two-thirds of the way down the mountain. At the crash site, the shadows of the mountains to the west cut the days short. But here, on the western side, daylight lasted into the evening.

'Let's keep going until the sun sets,' I said.

Roberto shook his head. 'I need to rest.'

I saw that he was exhausted. I was, too, but the anxiety and desperation that drove me was stronger than my fatigue. 'Another hour,' I said.

'We need to stop,' Roberto snapped. 'We must be smart about this, or we will burn ourselves out.' His eyes were bleary with weariness, but there was determination in them, too, and I knew there was no use arguing.

We spread the sleeping-bag on a flat, dry rock, climbed in and rested for the night. Because of the lower altitude, and perhaps because of the solar energy stored in the rock we slept on, the night was not uncomfortably cold.

The next morning was December 15, the fourth day of our journey. I roused Roberto as the sun rose and we set off. When we reached the bottom of the mountain, sometime near noon, we found ourselves standing at the entrance to the valley that we hoped would be our pathway to civilisation. Glacial ice streamed along its floor, winding through the mountains that rose on either side. From a distance, the glacier looked as smooth as glass, but up close we saw that the surface had fractured into millions of small, icy boulders and jagged plates. It was difficult ground. Our ankles wobbled, and our feet slipped and got jammed into narrow spaces. We both knew that in this wilderness a broken ankle would be a death sentence.

I kept up my lunatic pace and was always drawing further and further ahead of Roberto. 'Slow down, Nando!' he would shout. 'You are going to kill us!' I would badger him to move faster and resented having to wait for him to catch up. Still, I knew he was right. Roberto was nearing the end of his strength. My own was fading, too. Agonising cramps seized my legs, and my breathing was rapid and shallow. I knew we were walking ourselves to death, but I couldn't make myself stop. The weaker I grew, the more frantically I wanted to keep moving. My body was just a vehicle now. I would burn myself to ashes if that was what it took to get home.

TEMPERATURES were mild enough that we could walk after sunset, and sometimes I was able to persuade Roberto to trek late into the night. Even in our battered state, we were awed by the wild beauty of the Andes after dark. The skies were the deepest indigo, and clustered with blazing stars. Moonlight softened the rugged peaks and gave the snowfields an eerie glow. Once, I saw dozens of shadowy figures ahead, like hooded monks gathered to pray. When we reached them, we found that they were tall pillars of snow—penitentes, as geologists call them—carved at the bases of snowy slopes by swirling wind. It was like weaving our way through a forest of frozen trees. Sometimes I watched my shadow gliding beside me on the snow, and took it as proof that I was real. But often I felt like a ghost, a spirit trapped between the worlds of the living and the dead, guided by nothing more than will and memory, and an indestructible longing for home.

On the morning of December 18, the seventh day of our trek, the punishing snow cover began to give way to scattered patches of grey ice and fields of sharp, loose rubble. I was weakening rapidly. Each step now required supreme effort, and total concentration of will. There was no room in my mind for anything but the next careful placement of my foot. My weariness, my pain, the plight of our friends, the hopelessness of our efforts—all that was forgotten. I'd even forget Roberto until I'd hear him calling and turn to see that once again he had fallen far behind. It was a kind of self-hypnosis, probably, brought on by the mesmerising effects of my rhythmic breathing. In this trancelike state, distances vanished and hours flowed.

At one point I noticed that the sole of my right rugby boot was tearing loose from the upper. My reaction was oddly detached. My mind showed me a picture of myself hobbling shoeless on ridges of rock and ice until my bare foot was too bloody to continue. Then I saw myself crawling, until my hands and knees were shredded. Finally, I fell to my belly and dragged myself with my elbows until my strength was gone. In my altered state of mind, I found these images reassuring. If the shoe fell apart, I had a plan. There would still be space between my death and me.

There were times when the beauty of the mountains yanked me out of my dull self-absorption. It would happen suddenly: I would apprehend their age, and realise that they stood here, silent and oblivious, as civilisations rose and fell. It struck me, too, that even the mountains were not eternal. If the earth lasts long enough, all these peaks will someday crumble to dust. So what is the significance of a single human life? Why do we struggle? Why do we endure suffering? What keeps us battling so desperately to live when we could simply sink into the shadows and know peace?

I had no answer to these questions, but when they troubled me too much, I would remind myself of my promise to my father. I would decide, as he did on that river in Argentina, to suffer a little longer. I would take one more step and tell myself that each one I took was a step stolen back from death.

THAT AFTERNOON, I heard a sound in the distance ahead—a muffled wash of white noise that grew louder as I approached it—and I soon recognised it as the roar of rushing water. I quickened my pace, terrified that the sound was from some impassable torrent that would cut us off and seal our fate. I made my way down a gentle slope then slid down a small, icy cliff. A gigantic mountain loomed in front of me. The valley we had been following led directly to its base, where it split into two smaller valleys that wound round either side of the mountain.

This is the Y we saw from the summit, I thought. We are on our way home, if we only have the strength to make it.

I turned to my left, and walked round the short, curving ice cliff towards the mysterious roar. I found myself standing at the base of an ice wall some fifteen feet high. A thick jet of water, fed by tons of melting snow, was spouting from the wall, through a crevice about five feet from the ground. The water splashed at my feet, then flowed swiftly across the ice and gravel and down into the valley ahead. I could see a point, just a few hundred yards in the distance, where it rapidly broadened into a forceful stream.

'This is the birth of a river,' I said to Roberto, when he'd reached me. 'It will lead us out of here.'

We followed the river, certain that it would lead us to some civilised place. Snow, rocks and grimy chunks of ice passed beneath my feet as I lumbered along, then the snow line ended abruptly, and at last we found ourselves trekking on dry ground. But our walk was no easier, because the flood plain on either side of the stream was littered with huge boulders, many taller than us, and we had to weave through them, or scale them, or hop from the top of one to another. It took us hours to cross the boulder fields, but eventually we reached a more manageable terrain of loose rocks and rubble.

The river beside us grew broader and stronger with every mile, until its roar drowned out all other sounds. As the miles crept by, the only fact of my existence was the small patch of ground that would provide a base for my next footfall. We walked until sunset that day, and when we rested, Roberto showed me a rock he'd picked up along the way.

'I'm keeping this as a souvenir for Laura,' he said. Laura Surraco was Roberto's fiancée.

'She must be worried about you,' I said.

'She is a wonderful girl. I miss her very much.'

'I envy you, Roberto,' I said. 'I have never had a serious girlfriend. I've never been in love.'

'Really?' He laughed. 'All those girls you chased with Panchito? None of them ever stole your heart?'

'I guess I never gave any of them the chance,' I said. 'I've been thinking, somewhere out there is the girl I would marry. She's walking around, living her life. Maybe sometimes she wonders about the man she might marry, where he is, what he's doing right now. Would she ever guess he is trying to cross the Andes to get to her? If we don't make it, I'll never meet her. She'll never know me, never guess I ever existed.'

'Don't worry,' said Roberto, 'we'll make it home and you will find someone. You'll make someone happy.'

I smiled at Roberto's kindness, but found no comfort in his words. I knew that somewhere, the woman I would have married was living her life, moving towards the point in time when we might have met and my future would have begun. Now I knew that when she reached that point, I would not be there. She would never know me. Our children would never be born. We would never make a home, or grow old together. The mountains had stolen these things from me; that was reality and I had begun to accept it.

DECEMBER 19 was the eighth perfect day in a row. We hiked for several hours, then late in the morning we spotted trees far ahead in the valley, and Roberto thought he saw something more.

'There,' he said, squinting at the horizon. 'I think I see cows.'

My nearsightedness prevented me from seeing anything so far away, and I worried that Roberto might be hallucinating. 'It could be deer,' I said. 'Let's keep going.'

A few hours later, Roberto bent over and picked something up. He showed it to me, and I saw it was a rusted soup can. 'People have been here,' he said.

I refused to let my hopes rise. 'That could have been here for years,' I said. 'Or maybe it fell from a plane.'

Roberto scowled and tossed the can away. 'You stupid bastard,' he said, 'aeroplane windows don't open.'

Later we found a horseshoe, then some piles of dung that Roberto insisted had come from a cow. 'Do you want to explain how cow shit might have fallen from a plane?' he asked.

'Keep walking,' I said. 'When we find a farmer, then I'll get excited.'

As we trekked further, we found more signs of human habitation: more cow droppings, horse dung, and tree stumps that showed the marks of an axe. Finally, as we rounded a bend of the valley, we saw, a few hundred yards away, the small herd of cows Roberto had spotted that morning.

'I told you,' Roberto said. 'There must be a farmhouse very close.'

'But it's hard to believe anyone lives in a place like this.'

'The proof is in front of your eyes,' said Roberto. 'We are saved. Tomorrow we will find the farmer who owns these cows.'

When we camped that evening, Roberto's spirits were high, but I knew he could not stand many more hours in the mountains.

ON THE NINTH day of our trek, we started out early and found a path beside the river, the first good footing we had had on our journey.

Roberto grew tired quickly, and I had to wait more often than usual for him to rest. Still, we made good progress and in late morning reached a point where a boulder as large as a two-storey house had tumbled into the stream. It blocked our path completely.

'We have to climb this,' I said.

Roberto studied the rock, and saw a narrow ledge winding round it above the rushing waters of the river.

'I'll go that way,' he said.

'It's too dangerous,' I said. 'One slip and you're in the river. We have to go over the top.'

'I'm too weak to climb,' he said. 'I'll take my chances on the ledge.' He eased his way onto the ledge and round the rock until I lost sight of him, then I started climbing. When I came down the far side of the rock, there was no sign of Roberto, even though the route he'd chosen was much shorter than mine. I waited with concern. When he finally appeared, he was doubled over, clutching his stomach, and his eyes were narrowed in pain.

'What's wrong?' I asked.

'My gut is exploding,' he grumbled. 'It's diarrhoea. Very bad. It hit while I was on the ledge.'

'Can you walk?' I asked. 'The path seems clear now.'

Roberto shook his head and sank to the ground in misery. 'I can't,' he muttered. 'It hurts too much.'

I was afraid that his sickness would drain the last of his energy, and I didn't want to leave him here. 'Come on,' I said, 'just a little further—'

'No, please,' he begged, 'let me rest.'

I looked to the horizon. A broad plateau rose in the distance. If we could scramble to the top of it, we would have a good vantage point. 'I'll carry your pack,' I said. 'Let's make it to the top of that plateau, then we'll rest.'

Before Roberto could answer, I took his pack and set off on the path, giving him no choice but to follow. He fell behind quickly, but I kept my eye on him. He was in great discomfort. 'Don't give up, Muscles,' I whispered to myself, and I knew that he wouldn't.

We reached the base of the plateau by late afternoon, and helped each other up a steep path to the top, where we found ourselves looking down across a meadow of thick grass. There were trees and wild flowers and, to our left, the low stone walls of some mountain farmer's corral. We were high above the gorge of the river now, and the land fell away steeply to the banks of the stream, which was about thirty-five yards wide at this point and flowing with torrential force. Roberto could barely walk any more, so I helped him to a small cluster of trees where we decided to camp.

'You rest,' I said. 'I'm going to explore a little. Maybe there's a farm-house somewhere near.'

Roberto nodded. He was very weak, and as he settled heavily on the soft turf, I knew he wouldn't be going any further. I didn't want to think about what would happen if I had to leave him.

The afternoon was fading as I followed the winding path of the river gorge to see what lay ahead. I saw some cows grazing and this raised my hopes, but after walking a few hundred yards, I saw exactly what I feared: another broad, swift river was flowing in from the left to join the river we had followed. We were cut off by the confluence of these two big streams. It didn't seem possible that we could cross either one. Barring a miracle, we had come to the end of our trail.

When I returned to Roberto, I told him about the river, and about the ani-mals I'd seen. We were both very hungry. What little meat we had was going bad in the warm temperatures and for a while we considered trying to kill one of the cows, but Roberto pointed out that it was doubtful that we had the strength between us to catch and subdue such a large animal, and we aban-doned the idea. Darkness was beginning to fall now, and a chill was rising.

'I'm going to find some firewood,' I said, but when I had walked only a few yards across the meadow, I heard Roberto shout. 'Nando, I see a man!'

'What? What did you say?'

'There! Look! A man on a horse!' Roberto was pointing at the slope on the far side of the river gorge.

I squinted into the evening shadows. 'I can't see anything.'

'Go! Run!' Roberto shouted. 'Go down to the river!'

Blindly, I stumbled down the slope towards the stream with Roberto cor-recting my course as I ran—'Go right, no, I said right! No, too far! Go left!'

I zigzagged down the slope, but I saw no sign of a man on horseback. I turned to see Roberto staggering down the slope behind me.

'I swear I saw something,' he said.

'It's dark over there,' I replied. 'Maybe it was the shadow of a rock.'

I took Roberto's arm and helped him back up the hill to the campsite. Then we heard, above the roar of the river, the unmistakable sound of a human voice. We whirled round, and this time I saw him, too—a rider on horseback. He was shouting to us, but the noise of the river drowned out most of what he said. Then he turned his horse and disappeared into the shadows.

'Did you hear him?' shouted Roberto. 'What did he say?'

'I only heard one word,' I answered. 'I heard him say *mañana*.'

'We are saved,' he said.

I helped Roberto back up the slope to the campsite, then I built a fire and we lay down to sleep. For the first time since the crash, I felt real hope. I would live. I would see my father again, I was sure of it. Then my concern shifted to the ones we'd left behind. Obsessed with my own survival, I had barely thought of them since leaving the crash site nine days ago.

'I'm worried about the guys,' I told Roberto. 'Roy and Coche were so weak. I hope there's still time.'

'Don't worry,' he said. 'When the man comes back tomorrow, we'll make him understand there's not a second to lose.'

Roberto and I awoke the next day before dawn, and glanced across the river. Three men were sitting in the glow of a fire. I ran down the slope and climbed down to the river bank. On the other side, one of the men, dressed in the work clothes of a hill-country peasant, did the same. I tried to shout, but the roar of the river drowned my words. I pointed to the sky, then made gestures with my hand to indicate an aeroplane falling. The peasant just stared. I began running up and down with my arms spread out like wings. The man turned away from me and shouted something to his friends. For a moment I panicked, thinking they would dismiss me as a lunatic and leave. Instead he took some paper from his pocket, scribbled on it, then tied the paper round a rock with some string. He slipped a pencil under the string and threw it across to me. When I unfolded the paper, I saw this message:

There is a man coming later that I told him to go. Tell me what you want.

I took the pencil and began to write on the back of the note. I knew I had to choose the words precisely, to make him understand the urgency of our situation. My hands were shaking, as the pencil touched the paper:

Vengo de un avión que cayó en las montañas . . . I come from a plane that fell into the mountains. I am Uruguayan. We have been walking for ten days. I have a friend up there who is injured. In the plane there are still fourteen injured people. We have to get out of here quickly and we don't know how. We don't have any food. We are weak. When are you going to come and fetch us? Please. We can't even walk. Where are we?

I wrapped the note round the rock just as the peasant had done, drew back my arm, summoned all my strength and hurled the rock. It bounced at the water's edge and rolled onto the bank. When the peasant read the message, he nodded and raised his palms in a gesture that said, Wait here. I understand. Before leaving, he threw some bread to me. I took it to Roberto and we devoured it, then we waited for help to arrive.

Around 9 a.m., another man came, riding a mule, this time on our side of the river. He introduced himself as Armando Serda. He took some cheese from his pocket and gave it to us, then asked us to wait while he tended his sheep in the high pastures. A few hours later he returned. When he saw that Roberto could not walk, he helped him onto the mule, then he led us to a gentle stretch of the river where the stream could be forded. After thirty minutes or so on wooded mountain trails, we came to a clearing. I saw two crude wooden huts near the banks of the river.

'Where are we?' I asked him.

'Los Maitenes,' said Armando, referring to a mountainous region in the Chilean province of Colchagua. 'We use these huts when we tend the flocks in the high pastures.'

'We have friends still in the mountains,' I said. 'They are dying and we need to get help to them as soon as possible.'

'Sergio has gone for help,' Armando answered. Sergio Catalan was the man on horseback who'd first spotted us, he explained. 'The nearest police outpost is at Puente Negro. About ten hours away on horseback.'

A second peasant came out of the larger hut, and Armando introduced him as Enrique Gonzales. He led us to a campfire, where we sat on some stumps. Enrique brought us cheese and milk while Armando started cooking, and in moments he served us plates of beans, macaroni and bread. We ate everything, and he laughed as he refilled our plates again and again. After eating our fill, we were led to the second hut, where two beds were waiting. There were no mattresses, just soft fleeces spread over the springs, but Roberto and I thanked Armando profusely, and were soon both sound asleep.

When we awoke, it was early evening. Armando and Enrique had another meal waiting for us—more cheese and milk, a stew of meat and beans, plus sweet caramel *dulce de leche* spread on bread, and hot coffee.

After eating, we all relaxed together round the fire, and the two peasants listened in fascination as Roberto and I told the story of our ordeal, but we were interrupted by the sight of two Chilean policemen running up the trail followed by ten more on horseback. Riding with them was Sergio Catalan.

When he dismounted, Roberto and I rushed forward and embraced him.

'There is no need to thank me,' he said quietly, and as we hugged him he only whispered, 'Thank God, Thank God.'

When the captain of the mounted police introduced himself, I explained that fourteen more survivors were waiting at the crash site. He asked for their names, but I refused to give them. 'Some of them were near death,' I explained. 'I'm afraid some may have died. If you release their names, it will give their parents false hope, then they will lose their sons a second time.'

The captain understood. 'Where is the plane?' he asked. I looked at Roberto. It was clear the captain did not understand how difficult this rescue would be, but when we had described our ten-day odyssey, and the approximate location of the crash site, he said, 'I'll send some men back to Puente Negro, and have them radio for a helicopter from Santiago.'

'How long will that take?' I asked.

'They could be here tomorrow, if the weather is clear.'

We had no choice but to wait. We talked for a while with Enrique and Armando and some of the police, then I went to bed, and spent a restless night in the hut. The next morning, when I went outside, I was distressed to see that a heavy fog had descended upon Los Maitenes.

'Do you think they can land in this?' I asked Roberto.

'Maybe it will burn off soon,' he replied.

Enrique and Armando had breakfast waiting for us at the fire. Sergio and some of the policemen joined us and, as we were eating, we heard the noise of an approaching crowd. Within seconds we were shocked to see a horde of reporters approaching the hut.

'Are those the survivors?' they shouted. 'Roberto? Fernando?' Cameras snapped, microphones were jabbed in our faces and reporters scribbled on notepads and shouted questions. 'How long did you trek?' 'Who else is alive?' 'How did you survive the cold?' 'What did you eat?'

I looked at Roberto in amazement. 'How did they find us,' I muttered, 'and how did they get here before the helicopters?'

The arrival of the journalists startled us, and we were rattled a little by the intensity of their questioning, but we tried our best to answer them, keeping the more sensitive facts to ourselves. The captain of the mounted police allowed the interviews to continue for a while, then he took us aside.

'The fog is still heavy,' he told us. 'I don't think the helicopters will come today. I'm going to send you down to Puente Negro to wait for the rescue team to arrive. It might be easier for them to land there.'

We nodded, and in moments Roberto and I were on horseback, following two of the mounted policemen down the trail, with the press in hot pursuit. Suddenly the entire noisy entourage came to a stop and gazed up at the overcast sky. There was commotion above us, the thunder of powerful engines and a roar of wind. The fog was still so thick that we couldn't see the helicopters land, but we followed the noise to a spot about 400 yards away, where three huge helicopters of the Chilean air force had just set down.

As we dismounted, medics and crew members leapt out of the helicopters and came forward to examine us. Roberto needed their attention badly, but I refused to be examined. Instead, I sought out two of the helicopter pilots, Carlos García and Jorge Massa, and tried to impress upon them the importance of leaving right away.

Commander García shook his head. 'There's no way we can fly in this fog,' he said. 'We have to wait for it to lift. In the meantime, what can you tell me about the location of the plane?'

Once again I described our trek through the Andes. García gave me a sceptical frown, then retrieved a flight chart from the helicopter and spread it on the grass. 'Do you think you can show me on the map?' he asked. He jabbed his finger at the chart and said, 'We are here.'

I stared at the map and once I got my bearings, it was easy to trace in reverse the route Roberto and I had followed. 'Here,' I said, tapping the map where the valley ended at the foot of the peak I had christened Mount Seler. 'They are on the far side of this mountain.'

Massa and García exchanged dubious glances.

'That's Argentina,' García said. 'The High Andes. That's more than seventy miles from here.'

Massa frowned. 'He's confused,' he said. 'They couldn't have crossed the Andes on foot! Impossible!'

'Are you sure you understand this map?' García asked me.

'I am sure of it,' I said. 'We came down this mountain, along this valley to where it splits, then we followed this fork and it brought us here! The plane lies beyond this mountain, on a glacier above a wide valley that goes east.'

García nodded and folded the map. I was still not sure he believed me.

'When will you go for them?' I asked.

'As soon as the fog lifts,' he said, then he and Massa walked off with their heads together, and I knew they were discussing my account of the trek.

Three hours later the fog had thinned a little and the pilots thought it was safe to fly. As the crews prepared for takeoff, García approached me. 'We're going now,' he said. 'But the location you showed us is in a very high and remote section of the Andes. Flying there will be very difficult, and with no landmarks we will never find your friends. Do you think you can come with us, and guide us to the plane?'

I don't remember how I answered him, or if I answered him at all, but in seconds I felt arms all over me as I was lifted into the helicopter and strapped into a jump seat in the cargo area. Someone slipped headphones over my ears, positioning the small attached microphone close to my mouth. Three members of the Andean Rescue Corps climbed in beside me. Commander García took the controls. As he revved the engines, I looked out of the window and saw Roberto, the only one who could understand how frightened I was to be flying back into the Andes. He didn't wave; we just exchanged glances. Then the helicopter lurched into the air and swooped off into the mountains.

My earphones crackled with technical chatter as the pilot and mechanic set our course, then García said to me, 'OK, Nando, show us the way.'

I guided them into the valley and we followed it across the Chilean border and into the Argentine Andes, with a second helicopter, piloted by Commander Massa, on our tail. The air was turbulent, and the helicopter danced and bobbed, but in less than twenty minutes we were hovering at the eastern end of the valley, where the massive bulk of Mount Seler towered above us.

García gazed up to the mountain's snow-capped peak and down the black slopes plunging to the floor of the valley, several thousand feet below. 'Mother of God,' he said, 'you didn't come down this?'

'Yes,' I said. 'This is the way.'

'Are you sure?' he said. 'Are you certain?'

'I'm certain,' I said. 'They're on the other side.'

García looked at his copilot.

'With so many people, we're heavy,' the copilot said. 'I don't know if we have the power to clear that mountain.'

García asked again. 'Nando, are you absolutely certain this is the way?'

I barked into the microphone, 'I am!'

García nodded. 'Hold on.' I felt the helicopter surge forward as the pilots gunned the engines. We raced at the face of the mountain, gathering speed, and then, slowly, the helicopter began to climb, battered by the swirling air rushing up from the slopes. García fought for control as it lurched wildly. The engines screamed, the windshield rattled in its frame, and my seat shook so violently it blurred my vision. It seemed that every bolt and rivet was being pushed beyond its limits, and I was certain the aircraft would soon shake itself to bits. I felt panic rising in my throat like vomit.

García and the copilot were barking commands so rapidly I couldn't tell who was speaking.

'The air is too thin! There's not enough lift.'

'Come on, push it!'

'One hundred percent, one hundred ten . . .'

'Keep it level! Keep it level!'

I glanced at the rescue team, hoping for a sign from them that any of this was normal, but their faces were drawn and pale. Finally García managed to force the helicopter above the mountain's summit, but the strong air currents streaming over the ridge threw us back violently, and García had no choice but to let the helicopter fall away in a long, swooping circle to keep it from being dashed against the slopes. As we fell, I began to scream, and I kept screaming as we swung round and made one more assault on the summit, only to be pushed back in the same terrifying fashion.

'We can't make it over this mountain,' García announced. 'We'll have to find a way round it. This is a life-threatening mission now, and I won't go forward unless everyone on board volunteers. I'll leave it to all of you. Shall we continue or go back?'

I exchanged glances with the others on board, then we turned to the captain and nodded.

'OK,' he said, 'but hold on, it will be rough going.'

My stomach pitched again as we banked to the right and flew over some lower peaks just south of Mount Seler. We were veering off the path Roberto and I had followed now, and I quickly lost my bearings.

'Which way?' García demanded.

'I'm not sure . . . I'm all turned around . . .'

I searched frantically for a point of reference. Everywhere I looked I saw an endless ocean of white snow and black rock . . . Then something in the jagged profile of one of the ridges caught my eye.

'Wait!' I shouted. 'I know that mountain! I know where we are! Go down!'

As we dropped lower I realised that García had found his way round the mountains that bordered the crash site to the south. We were above the valley we had trekked through on our attempts to escape to the east, and climbing west towards the eastern face of Mount Seler.

'They must be up there,' I said, pointing east. 'Keep going! They're on the glacier!'

'The wind is bad!' said the copilot. 'I don't know if we can land here.'

I stared at the slopes, and suddenly I spotted it, a faint dot in the snow. 'I see the plane!' I shouted. 'There, on the left.'

García scanned the slopes. 'Where . . . I can't see anything. Wait, OK, I see it. Shut up now, everyone shut up!'

In moments we were circling high above the crash site, and my heart pounded as García battled strong turbulence above the glacier. But my fears faded as I saw a line of tiny figures coming out of the fuselage. Even from that altitude I could make out some of them—I recognised Gustavo from his pilot's cap, Daniel, Pedro, Fito, Javier . . . There were others, running, waving. I tried to count them, but the lurching of the helicopter made it impossible. I could see no sign of Roy or Coche.

I heard García's voice in the headphones, speaking to the rescue team. 'The slope is too steep for a landing,' he said. 'I'm going to hover as low as I can. You'll have to jump out.' Then he switched his attention to the dicey business of bringing the helicopter down in the swirling winds. He turned it so that one side faced up the slope, then eased it down until one of its skis just touched the snow. 'Go!' he shouted.

The rescuers threw open the sliding door, tossed out their gear, then jumped down beneath the whirling blades. I looked out and saw Daniel running towards us. He ducked under the blades and tried to dive inside, but he misjudged his leap and slammed his chest against one of the helicopter's skis.

'Don't kill yourself now!' I cried. Then I reached down and pulled him inside. Alvaro Mangino climbed in after him.

'That's all we can take,' shouted García. 'We'll get the rest tomorrow. Now close the door!' I obeyed the captain's orders, and in seconds we were hovering above the crash site as the second helicopter dropped down and more rescuers leapt out onto the mountain. I saw Carlitos, Pedro and Eduardo climb into the waiting aircraft. Then I saw the emaciated figure of Coche Inciarte limping towards the helicopter.

'Coche is alive!' I said to Daniel. 'How is Roy?'

'Alive,' said Daniel, 'but barely.'

The flight back to Los Maitenes was just as harrowing as the earlier trip, but in less than twenty minutes we had landed safely in the meadow near the peasants' hut. As soon as the doors were opened, Daniel and Alvaro were whisked away by the medics. In moments the second helicopter set down about thirty yards away, and I was there as the doors slid open. Coche fell out happily into my arms, then Eduardo and Carlitos. Amazed to see flowers and greenery again, some of them fell to their knees in the grass. Others embraced and rolled about on the ground in each other's arms.

Carlitos wrapped his arms round me and wrestled me to the ground. 'You bastard!' he cried. 'You made it!' Then he reached into his pocket and drew out the little red shoe I had given him when I left the fuselage. He was beaming at me, his eyes lit with joy, his face only inches from mine.

'I'm happy to see you, Carlitos,' I said, 'but please, you aren't going to kiss me, are you?'

When the celebration ended, they brought us hot soup, cheese and chocolates. While the medics examined the six new arrivals, Commander García explained to me that it would be too dangerous to fly into the mountains at night. Further rescue would have to wait another day. But he assured me that the medics and the rescue workers who had stayed on the mountain would make sure all the boys were safe.

After we were all fed, we were loaded into the helicopters and flown to a military base near the town of San Fernando. Teams of doctors and nurses were there to help us into waiting ambulances. The ambulances left in a convoy, escorted by police on motorcycles, and in about ten minutes we had reached San Juan de Dios hospital in San Fernando. Hospital personnel met us in the parking lot with gurneys. Some of the guys needed this help, but I told the nurses I would walk. After hiking across the Andes, I was not about to let them carry me the last few yards.

They led me to a small, clean room and began peeling layers of filthy clothing from my body. They threw the dirty rags that had been my second skin into a corner. It felt good to shed them and put them in my past.

I was taken into the bathroom and given a warm shower. I felt hands washing my hair and a soft cloth scrubbing the dirt from my skin. When they'd dried me with soft towels, I caught sight of myself in the bathroom's full-length mirror. My jaw dropped. Before the crash, I had been an athlete, but now there was no trace of muscle anywhere on my frame. My arms and legs had withered so that my knees and elbows bulged like thick knots in a rope. The nurses dressed me in a hospital gown, then led me to a narrow bed and began to examine me, but I asked them to leave me alone for a while.

When they'd all gone, I quietly rejoiced in the comfort, cleanliness and peace of the little room. I lay back on the soft mattress, felt the smoothness of the crisp cotton sheets. Slowly I let it sink in: I was safe; I was going to go home. I drew a long breath and then, slowly, I exhaled. In my seventy-two days in the Andes, there had not been a single breath taken without fear. Now, at last, I enjoyed the luxury of ordinary breathing. With each long, unhurried breath I whispered to myself in amazement: I am alive.

Suddenly my thoughts were disturbed by shouting outside my door, and what sounded like a scuffle in the hallway. 'Calm down!' barked a firm male voice. 'No one is allowed in here.'

A woman's voice answered. 'My brother is in there!' she shouted. 'I have to see him! Please!'

I stepped into the hallway just in time to see my sister Graciela pushing past a group of hospital orderlies. I called her name, and she began to sob when she saw me. In seconds she was in my arms, and my heart swelled with love as I held her. With her was her husband, Juan, his eyes bright with tears, and for a moment the three of us embraced without a word. Then I looked up. At the end of the hallway, standing motionless in the thin fluorescent light, was the slim, bowed figure of my father. I walked to him and embraced him, then I hoisted him in my arms until his feet left the ground. 'You see, Papá,' I whispered as I set him down again, 'I am still strong enough to lift you.' He pressed himself against me, touching me, convincing himself that I was real. I held him for a long time, feeling his body tremble gently as he wept. For a while neither of us spoke. Then, with his head still pressed to my chest, he whispered, 'Mami? Susy?'

I answered him with a gentle silence, and he sagged a little in my arms as he understood. A few moments later my sister came and led us back to my room. They gathered round my bed, and I told them the story of my life in the mountains—the crash, the cold, the fear, the long journey I had made with Roberto. I explained how my mother had died, and how I had comforted Susy. I spared my father the details of her suffering, thinking it was enough to tell him she was never alone and that she had died in my arms. Graciela wept softly as I spoke. She could not take her eyes off me. My father sat listening, nodding, with a heartbreaking smile on his face. When I finished, there was a silence until my father found the strength to speak.

'How did you survive, Nando?' he asked. 'So many weeks without food . . .'

I told him that we had eaten the flesh of those who didn't survive.

The expression on his face didn't change. 'You did what you had to do,' he said, his voice cracking with emotion. 'I am happy to have you home.'

There was so much I wanted to tell him, that I had thought of him every moment, that his love had been the guiding light that led me to safety. But there would be time for that later. Right now I wanted to treasure every moment of our reunion, bittersweet as it was. There were no words to explain how I felt, so I simply sat in silence.

After a while we heard sounds of celebration in the hallway as the families of the other survivors found their sons. My sister rose and closed the door, and, in the privacy of my room, I shared with what was left of my family the simple miracle of being together again.

10: After

The following day, December 23, the eight survivors who had been left on the mountain were flown to Santiago, where they were examined at a hospital known as the Posta Centrale. The doctors decided to hold Javier and Roy for observation, but the rest were released and moved to the Sheraton San Cristóbal Hotel, where many of them were joined by their families. The eight of us at San Juan de Dios hospital were moved to Santiago that same afternoon. Alvaro and Coche, the weakest in our group, were admitted to the Posta Centrale, while the rest of us were taken to the Sheraton to be reunited with our friends.

The papers called our return 'The Christmas Miracle', and many people were regarding us as almost mystical figures: young boys who had been saved by the direct intercession of God. News of our survival was making headlines around the globe, and public interest was intense. The Sheraton's lobby and the street outside the hotel were jammed, around the clock, with reporters and news crews. We could not go to a café for a snack without microphones being poked at us and flashbulbs firing in our faces.

On Christmas Eve, a party was arranged for us in the ballroom. There was an air of joy and gratitude, as many of the survivors and their families gave thanks to God for saving us from death. 'I told you we would be home for Christmas,' Carlitos said to me. 'I told you God would not abandon us.' I was happy for him, and the others, but as I watched them sharing their joy with their loved ones I realised that, except for Javier, every one of my fellow survivors was returning to a life that was just as it had been before. Their families were intact. They would be embraced again by their parents, brothers and sisters, girlfriends. The party only underscored for me how much I had lost. I would never spend another Christmas with my mother, or with Susy. It was clear to me that my father had been shattered by the ordeal, and I wondered if he would ever again be the man I had known. I felt very alone, understanding that what was a triumph for the others was the beginning of an uncertain future for me.

After three days in Santiago, my father moved us to a house in the Chilean beach resort of Viña del Mar. We spent three quiet days there, lying in the sun. On the beach I felt like an oddity, and with my long beard and my bones showing through my skin it was easy to recognise me as a survivor. I couldn't walk far without being accosted by strangers, so I stayed close to the house and spent many hours with my father.

He told me that at three thirty in the afternoon of October 13, the very hour the plane had fallen from the sky, he was on his way to make a deposit at a bank near his office in Montevideo when something stopped him in his tracks. 'The door of the bank was only a few steps away,' he said, 'but I couldn't make myself go any further. It was so strange. My stomach tightened. I just wanted to go home.'

In his whole life, my father had missed work only a handful of times, but that day he forgot about the office and drove to our house in Carrasco. He turned on the television, where special bulletins were reporting that a Uruguayan charter plane had been lost in the Andes. Not knowing about our unscheduled overnight stay in Mendoza, he calmed himself with the thought that we would have reached Santiago the previous afternoon. Still, a sense of dread haunted him as he watched the news.

Then, about an hour after he had got home, there was a knock on the door. 'It was Colonel Jaume,' my father explained, mentioning a friend who was an officer in the Uruguayan air force. 'He said, "I have a car waiting. I want you to come with me. I'm afraid I have bad news."' The colonel took my father to his house, where he confirmed the worst—the lost plane was, in fact, our flight. The next day my father was on a plane to Santiago, bound for a meeting with Chilean officials who would explain what they knew of the crash. His route took him above the Andes, and as he gazed down into the mountains below, he was chilled by the thought that his wife and children had fallen into such a merciless place. 'In that moment,' he told me, 'I lost all hope. I knew I would never see any of you again.'

In the following weeks he couldn't sleep or eat. He found no comfort in prayer or in company. Many parents of other crash victims found ways to keep their hopes alive. Some of the mothers met regularly to pray for us. A group of the fathers, led by Carlitos's father, even mounted their own search efforts, hiring planes and helicopters to fly over the Andes where the authorities thought the Fairchild might have fallen. My father contributed money to these search efforts, though he was certain they were a waste of time. 'When a plane falls into the Andes, it is lost for ever,' he said. 'I knew we would be lucky if the mountains gave up even a small fragment of the wreckage.'

My father's emotional condition declined rapidly. He grew withdrawn and would sit alone, in silence, for hours, or wander the streets aimlessly, with my dog, Jimmy, as his only companion. 'Your mother was my strength,' he told me. 'Without her I was lost.' One day he walked all through the afternoon and into the night. He found himself on the broad lawn of the Plaza Matriz, Montevideo's historic central square. In front of him rose the dark, ornate towers of the Catedral Metropolitana, built in 1740. My father was not a religious man, but something drew him into the church. He knelt and tried to pray. Slumping in the pew, he looked at his watch, and saw that he had been walking for more than ten hours. Fearing that he was losing his mind, he left the church and, in the darkness, made his way home.

'I told myself, "I have to change everything",' he said. Then, as if he could shed his pain by severing his physical connections to the past, my father began to dismantle his life. He sold his prized Mercedes and my mother's Rover. He put the flat in Punta del Este on the market, and pre-pared to sell our house in Carrasco. He even tried to sell the businesses he had laboured a lifetime to build, but Graciela and Juan talked him out of his recklessness before too much damage had been done. 'I didn't know what I was doing,' he told me. 'Sometimes I was absolutely *loco*. Nothing mattered to me in those days. Nothing made sense after the plane went down.'

'Papa,' I said to him one day in Viña del Mar, 'I am sorry I could not save Mami and Susy.'

He smiled sadly and took my arm. 'When I was certain all of you were dead, I knew I would never recover from the loss. It was as if my house had burned to the ground and I had lost everything I owned. And now, to have you back, it's as if I have stumbled on something precious in the ashes. I feel I am reborn. From now on, I will try not to feel sorry for what was taken from me, but be happy for what was given back.' He advised me to do the same. 'The sun will come up tomorrow, and the day after that, and the day after that. Don't let this be the most important thing that ever happens to you. Look forward. You will have a future. You will live a life.'

WE LEFT Viña del Mar on December 30 in a plane bound for Montevideo. I was terrified to fly across the Andes again, but with the help of sedatives I made myself board the plane. When we arrived at our house in Carrasco, a crowd of friends and neighbours had gathered in the street to meet me. I shook hands and embraced them, then climbed the long set of steps to the front door, where my grandmother Lina was waiting. I fell into her arms, and she hugged me with such force that I knew in her mind she was embracing Susy and my mother, too.

We all stepped inside. Ahead of me, lying on the tiled floor of the hall-way, was my dog, Jimmy. He had been fast asleep, and now, hearing us enter, he opened his eyes wearily without lifting his big square head from his paws. His ears perked, then he sat up and cocked his head as if in disbe-lief. For a long moment he studied me then, with a happy yelp, he launched himself towards me so fast that his paws scrabbled on the slippery tiles. I hugged him as he leapt into my arms, and let him lick my face with his warm, wet tongue. For me, it was a fine welcome home.

THOSE FIRST WEEKS at home were a kind of limbo. So much had changed, and I couldn't seem to find my way back into my life. I passed much of my time alone, playing with Jimmy or riding my motorcycle—my father had sold it in my absence, but the friend who had bought it returned it the moment he heard of our rescue. Sometimes I walked the streets, but I was recognised everywhere I went, and after a while it was easier to stay at home. Our ordeal was being celebrated as a glorious adventure. People compared our accomplishments with the heroic achievements of the Uruguayan soccer team that had won the World Cup in 1950. Some even went so far as to tell me that they envied me for my experience in the Andes. I didn't know how to explain to them that there was no glory in those mountains. It was all ugliness and fear and desperation.

I was shaken by the sensationalism with which many in the press covered our story. News reports focused on the matter of our diet, in reckless and exploitative ways. Some newspapers ran lurid headlines above grisly front-page photos taken after our rescue by members of the Andean Rescue Corps, showing piles of bones and human body parts scattered on the snow.

However, shortly after our rescue, officials of the Catholic Church announced that, according to church doctrine, we had committed no sin by eating the flesh of the dead. They declared that, as Roberto had argued on the mountain, the sin would have been to allow ourselves to die. More satis-fying for me was the fact that many of the parents of the boys who had died publicly expressed their support for us, telling the world that they under-stood and accepted what we had done to survive. I will always be grateful for their courage and generosity.

As summer approached, I decided I would escape Montevideo, and all the memories there, to spend some time alone at my father's flat in Punta del Este. Our family had summered there for years, ever since Susy and I were small. Everything was different now, of course. Wherever I went I was surrounded by gawkers, well-wishers and autograph-seekers. At first I hid out in the flat but, as time passed, I must admit, part of me began to enjoy the attention—especially when I realised that so many attractive young women seemed determined to get to know me. I had always envied Panchito's effortless ability to attract the prettiest girls on the beach, and now these same girls were drawn to me. Was it simply because of my new celebrity? I didn't care. For weeks on end I partied with one beautiful woman after another, sometimes with two or three in a single day, and always I kept my eye peeled for someone new. I became one of Punta del Este's most visible playboys, with pictures of me at one fancy party or another often appearing in the society pages.

This notoriety did not escape the attention of my fellow survivors, who were not happy with my behaviour. For them the ordeal had been a trans-forming experience that had led them to commit themselves to living lives of morality and high principle. I thought they were taking themselves a bit too seriously. After all, considering what we'd been through, didn't the world owe us a little fun? I told myself I was making up for lost time. But perhaps I was fooling myself. I think now that at the centre of my soul there was an emptiness, and I was trying to fill it with night after night of carous-ing, denying the pain I still held inside me.

I was at a nightclub one evening when reality ambushed me. I had spent so many nights at the same club with Panchito, and now, out of habit, I found myself waiting for him to walk through the door. I had thought of him so many times since our rescue, but that night I felt his absence viscer-ally, as a pain in my gut, and I understood with brutal certainty that he was gone. The realisation of that loss brought all my other losses to the surface and, for the first time since the Fairchild fell in the mountains, I began to cry. I bowed my head and sobbed so hard I could not control myself. My date kindly helped me home, and for hours I sat on the balcony of my flat watching the ocean, alone with my thoughts.

As I brooded on all the things that had been taken from me, my grief soon gave way to outrage. Why had this happened? Why was I made to suffer so much loss when so many others were allowed to live their lives happily? For hours I sat cursing God, and torturing myself with possibili-ties: if only the pilots had seen that ridge sooner; if only Panchito had taken a different seat; if only I hadn't invited my mother and sister to come along. I thought of boys who had dropped out of the trip at the last moment. Why hadn't I been spared, like them?

As I sank deeper into these bitter thoughts, my anger grew so strong that I thought I would never forgive life for the way it had cheated me of a happy future. But then, sometime before dawn, as weariness softened my rage, I remembered the advice my father had given me at Viña del Mar: *You will have a future. You will live a life.*

As I pondered his words, I saw the error I was making. I had been thinking of the disaster as an interruption of my true destiny, a deviation from the happy story of the life I had been promised. But my ordeal in the Andes *was* my life, and the future that lay ahead was the only future available to me. To hide from this fact would only keep me from living any genuine life at all.

Before the crash, I took so much for granted, but the mountains showed me that life, any life, is a miracle. Miraculously, I had been granted a second chance to live, and it was my duty to do so as richly and as hopefully as I could. I vowed to try. I would savour every moment and try, every day, to become more human and more alive. So I opened myself up to life, and, to my great fortune, my new life began to happen.

In January of 1973, some friends invited me to go with them to see the Argentine Formula One Grand Prix in Buenos Aires. At the time I was not eager to travel, but this was a chance to see the greatest drivers in the world, so I agreed to go. We hadn't been at the track long before the press caught wind of my presence, and soon I found myself surrounded by photographers. I let them snap their pictures, then we moved on. A few moments later I was surprised by an announcement on the track's PA system. 'Will Nando Parrado please report to the Tyrell F1 pit area . . .'

'It's probably some newspaper wanting an interview,' I told my friends. 'But let's go. It's a chance to see the cars up close.'

When we arrived, the Tyrell pits were buzzing with activity. Some twenty mechanics in blue coveralls were busily attending to two beautiful Grand Prix racing cars. When I introduced myself, one of the mechanics led me past the cars to a patch of asphalt at the rear, where a long motor home was parked. The mechanic opened the door for me and motioned me in, then went back to the pits. I climbed inside the trailer. To my left, a slender, dark-haired man was sitting on a sofa, tugging grey fireproof racing coveralls over his legs. When he looked up, I gasped and took a step back.

'You're Jackie Stewart!' I blurted.

'Yes, I am,' he said, in the smooth Scottish accent I had heard on television a hundred times. 'Are you Nando Parrado?'

I nodded dumbly.

'I heard you were here,' he said, 'and I asked them to find you.' Then he told me that he had wanted to meet me since he'd heard the story of the Andes disaster. He was very impressed with what I'd done, and he hoped I wouldn't mind talking with him about it.

'Yes,' I stammered, 'I'd be happy to . . .'

He smiled and looked me over. 'Do you like racing?' he asked.

I drew a deep breath. 'I love it,' I said. 'I've loved racing since I was a kid. You're my favourite driver. I've read your books. I know all your races . . .' I wanted him to understand that I was no mere fawning fan, that I had studied his techniques and respected his mastery of the sport—how he balanced aggressiveness, grace, risk and control. I wanted him to see that I understood that good driving was more poetry than machismo.

Jackie smiled kindly as he finished dressing. 'I have to qualify now,' he said, 'but stick around and we'll talk when I come back.' In less than an hour, he returned. He showed me his car—he even let me sit behind the wheel—then he invited me to stay for his team's pre-race meeting. I listened in awe as he discussed with his engineers and mechanics the last-minute adjustments they'd make to the car's engine and suspension.

After the meeting, Jackie and I talked for hours. He asked about the Andes, and after a while it was not so mind-boggling to be with him. As we got to know each other, I realised, in amazement, that my boyhood idol and I were becoming friends.

A few months later, I accepted Jackie's invitation to visit him at his home in Switzerland, where I grew close to his family and our friendship deepened. We spent hours talking about cars and racing, and I confessed to him that I had dreamed of driving racing cars since I was a child.

Jackie took my interest seriously, and in 1974, at his recommendation, I enrolled in the Jim Russell driving school at Snetterton in Great Britain. At the time, this was the world's premier racing school, and its graduates—Emerson Fitipaldi among them—were racing at top tracks around the globe. At the school I trained in sleek Formula Fords, and proved to myself that I had what it takes to be an elite racer.

When classes ended, I went home to South America and spent the next two years racing motorcycles and stock cars in Uruguay, Argentina and Chile. I enjoyed my share of victories, but I always dreamed of driving on the great tracks of Europe, and it didn't take long for that dream to come true. In 1973, at the Buenos Aires Grand Prix—the same race at which I'd met Jackie Stewart—I'd been introduced to Bernie Ecclestone, the British racing impresario and one of the founding fathers of modern Formula One racing. Like Jackie, he recognised my passion for racing, and this became the basis of a strong friendship. In early 1977 I learned from Bernie that Alfa-Romeo's prestigious Autodelta racing team was looking for drivers. He offered to arrange an introduction for me, and a few weeks later I travelled to the Alpha-Romeo offices in Italy with three other South American drivers. Our meetings with Autodelta went well, and that May the three of us began driving as teammates in the European Touring Car Championship. We did well, finishing second at Silverstone and at Zandvoort in the Netherlands, and taking our first win at Pergusa, a very fast track in southern Italy. Little by little, I was realising the dream I had as a boy of finding poetry in the power and precision of a fine machine.

It was an incredible year, filled with excitement, challenges, interesting people and glamorous travel. I was living a dream come true, and had no reason to think it would end. But one day, at the Zolder track in Belgium, as our team prepared the cars, I wandered into a VIP hospitality area and noticed a tall blonde in a red blazer and white slacks. She was standing with her back to me, but something about her stopped me in my tracks.

She turned around and smiled. 'Nando?' she said.

'Veronique?' I stammered. 'What are you doing here?'

She was Veronique van Wassenhove, a Uruguayan by birth, whose parents had emigrated from Belgium. She was a striking girl, tall and willowy with long hair and wide-set green eyes. I had met her in Montevideo, three years earlier, when she was dating Gustavo Zerbino's younger brother, Rafael. She was only sixteen at the time, but she had an easy grace about her and a maturity that told me she had her feet planted firmly on the ground. I liked her right away. She was dating my friend, so I never thought of it as anything more than a casual acquaintance, but in the next few years I would often see Veronique at the beach, or at parties, and we would always say hello.

Now, here she was in Belgium, a few years older, no longer with Rafael, and looking even lovelier than I remembered. She told me that she had taken a temporary job in public relations here at the track and was planning on going to London to study English, but my thoughts were too scattered to register much of what she said. I couldn't stop looking at her. I had wondered, since I was a boy, what it would be like when I first met the woman I would marry. How would I know her? Now I knew. There was a firm, quiet voice of certainty whispering in my mind: Veronique. Of course . . .

I saw my future in her eyes. And I think she saw her future in mine. We spoke for a while, then she invited me to lunch on Monday at her family's apartment on the Avenue Louis in Brussels. Veronique's mother was an impressively aristocratic woman who greeted me warmly but must have been wary of a twenty-seven-year-old race car driver calling on her nineteen-year-old daughter. I tried to be on my best behaviour, but already I was madly in love, and it required all my effort to take my eyes off Veronique and to remind myself there was anyone else in the room.

After that we took a day trip to Bruges, the romantic medieval city of canals and cathedrals. With each step we walked, I felt the connection between us growing stronger. When the afternoon faded and it was time to take her home, I begged her to visit me in Milan.

She laughed. 'You're crazy! My mother would kill me if I even asked.'

'Come to Spain, then,' I persisted. 'I am racing next week at Jarama.'

'Nando, I can't. But we will see each other soon.'

I went back to my apartment in Milan, missing her terribly, but the next day she surprised me with a call saying she was on her way. There was nothing impulsive about her decision. She had thought things through and had made a choice. She was choosing her future now. Was I ready to do the same?

I met her at the train station. She stepped off the train with only a backpack and a small duffle bag, looking very beautiful, and I fell in love with her all over again. Veronique came with me to Jarama, then we travelled to Morocco and vacationed there for a couple of weeks. I realised I was facing a great decision. I had proved to myself that I had the makings of a top-flight driver, but to make that dream come true would require an ever-increasing commitment to the sport. Driving would have to be the centre of my life, and that was not the sort of life, I knew, that would interest a woman like Veronique. Could I give up all my racing dreams just as they were about to come true? I knew that if we settled down together, it would be in Uruguay. Did I have the strength to trade the glamorous life I was living for long days toiling at my father's hardware stores, balancing books, filling orders, tracking shipments? In the end, there really was no question. The lessons I'd learned on the mountain prevented me from doing anything but choosing correctly: I would make a future with the woman I loved.

By the spring of 1978, Veronique and I had returned to Montevideo. In 1979 we were married. We moved into a small house in Carrasco and began to build a life together. Veronique found work as a model, and I discovered that I liked working at the hardware stores. Graciela and Juan had been working there for years, and together, with the guidance of my father, we built our business into the largest chain of hardware stores in the country.

As years passed, other opportunities presented themselves. In 1984 I was asked to produce and anchor a show about motor sports for TV Nacional in Uruguay. I had never been in front of a camera before, but it was a chance to be part of the racing world again, so I jumped at the opportunity. In TV, I found a new passion that grew into a second career. Today, Veronique and I produce and host five programmes, including shows on travel, nature, fashion and current events, and we are involved in writing, editing and directing these shows. The broadcasting work satisfies my appetite for creativity, and our success in that field has led to other businesses, including a cable TV company. We have worked hard and we have been blessed many times over with success. But the greatest blessings of our lives, by far, have been the births of our two daughters.

Veronica was born in 1981. Until then, I had thought I could never love anything as much as I loved my wife, but when I gazed into my baby's face, I was struck senseless by my love for her. Just moments after her birth, she had become yet another treasure in my life, and I knew I would die for her without hesitation. I savoured every moment of fatherhood. Sometimes I would hold her, amazed by the sweetness and perfection of her little body, and remind myself that if I hadn't found my way out of the Andes this beautiful little person would not exist. I felt a staggering sense of gratitude for the rich joys of my life. I realised that every gruelling step I had taken through that godforsaken wilderness was a step towards the tiny, precious miracle I held in my arms.

Two and a half years later, my daughter Cecilia was born prematurely. She weighed only two and three-quarter pounds, and spent the first two months of her life in intensive care. There were many nights when the doctors told us to prepare for the worst, that we should go home and pray, and each of those nights was another Andes for me. But Veronique spent hours at the hospital every day, caressing our baby, speaking to her softly, coaxing her back to life, and slowly Cecilia grew stronger. Now both my daughters are beautiful young women in their early twenties, full of life and spirit, and ready to face the world on their own.

My father is entering his eighty-eighth year, still sound in mind and body. It is impossible to describe the closeness between us. In the many years since the disaster, he has become my closest and most intimate friend. We are bonded by our suffering and our losses, but also by a great sense of mutual respect and, of course, a deep love. I don't know if my father has ever understood how important he was to me when I was lost.

For all his efforts to keep us safe and happy, he had not been able to protect us, and somewhere in his heart was the notion that he had somehow let us down. I wanted to write this book to tell him he was wrong. He did not fail me. He saved my life. He saved me by telling me stories when I was a boy, and those stories helped me find my strength in the mountains. He saved me by working so hard, by never giving in, and by teaching me, through his example, that anything is possible if you are willing to suffer.

Mostly, he saved me with his love. He was never an openly affectionate man, but I never doubted his love when I was a boy. It was a quiet love, solid, deep and enduring. When I was in the mountains, stranded in the shadows of death, it was like a safety line. As long as I held on to it, I was not lost, I was connected to my home and to my future, and in the end it was that strong cord of love that led me out of danger.

EVEN NOW, people are curious about the psychological effects of my ordeal, and I am often asked how I have dealt with the trauma. Do I suffer nightmares? Flashbacks? Have I struggled with survivor guilt? These people are always surprised and sometimes, I suspect, dubious, when I tell them that I have experienced none of those things. I feel no guilt or resentment. I look forward to tomorrow, and expect the future to be good. I am at peace, not in spite of what I suffered but because of it. The Andes gave me the simple insight that has liberated me and illuminated my life: death is real, and very near.

In the mountains, there was never a minute when I did not feel death at my side, but in the moment that I stood on the summit, and saw nothing but towering peaks as far as the eye could see, all my doubts were swept away and the certainty of my own death became viscerally real. It was so clear and so potent that for a moment it burned away everything temporary and false. For a split second it seemed that beneath the fragile illusions of life, death was all there is. But then I saw that there was something else, just as enduring and profound. There was love. And for one incredible moment, as I felt this love swell—love for my father, for the simple wonder of being alive—death lost its power. In that moment, I stopped running from death. Instead, I made every step a step towards love, and that saved me.

Life has blessed me with material success. I believe life should be enjoyed, but my experiences have taught me that without the love of family and friends, all the trappings of worldly success would ring hollow. If I had not suffered as I did, and had not been forced to stare death in the face, I would not treasure the simple, precious pleasures of my life as richly as I do. There are so many perfect moments, and I don't want to miss a single one—my daughters' smiles, my wife's embrace, a slobbering welcome from my new puppy, the company of an old friend, the feel of sand beneath my feet and the sun on my face. These moments bring time to a stop. I savour them and let each one become a miniature eternity, and by living them so fully I defy the shadow of death that hovers over all of us.

IN THE YEARS since the disaster, I often think of my friend Arturo Nogueira, and the conversations we had in the mountains about God. Many of my fellow survivors say they felt the personal presence of God in the mountains. He mercifully allowed us to survive, they believe, in answer to our prayers, and they are certain it was His hand that led us home. I deeply respect their faith, but, to be honest, as hard as I prayed for a miracle in the Andes, I never felt the personal presence of God. At least, I did not feel God as most people see Him. I did feel something larger than myself, something in the mountains and the glowing sky that, in rare moments, reassured me and made me feel that the world was orderly and good.

Now I am convinced that if there is something divine in the universe, the only way I will find it is through the love I feel for my family and my friends, and through the simple wonder of being alive. I don't need any other wisdom or philosophy than this: my duty is to fill my time on earth with as much life as possible, and to understand that we only become human when we love. I have suffered great losses and have been blessed with great consolations, but whatever is given to me or taken away, this is the simple wisdom that will always light my life. For me, it is enough.

TWO YEARS AFTER the miracle in the Andes, my father and I returned to the crash site in the High Andes near Sosneado Mountain. A route had been discovered, passable only in summer, leading from the Argentine foothills to the glacier where the Fairchild lay. It's a gruelling, three-day trip that consists of an eight-hour drive in off-road vehicles across rugged terrain, then two and a half days on horseback.

We reached the base of the glacier at midday, then made our final climb to the site on foot. The grave itself, built just after our rescue, sits on a rocky promontory jutting above the snow. Beneath the rocks lie Susy and my mother, along with the remains of the others who died here, all safely out of reach of the grinding glacier a few hundred feet away. A simple pile of stones and a small steel cross rise above the grave. My father brought flowers and a stainless-steel box containing the teddy bear that Susy had slept with every night of her life. He placed these on the grave, and we stood there quietly in the silence of the mountains. I remembered that silence so well, a constant and absolute absence of sound. On calm days you heard nothing but your own breathing, your own thoughts.

My father's face was pale, and tears wet his cheeks as we shared this sad reunion, but I felt no pain or grief. I felt tranquillity. There was no more fear or suffering or struggle in that place. The dead were at peace.

My father turned to me with a sad smile. He looked at the glacier, at the black peaks above us, at the wide, savage Andean sky and the remains of the fuselage. Then he smiled tenderly, took me by the arm and whispered, 'Nando, now I understand . . .'

As we descended the mountain, the grandeur of the Andes thundered all around us—so silent, so massive, so perfect—and neither of us could imagine a more majestic shrine.

Epilogue

After we were rescued from the mountains, the newspapers called our survival 'The Miracle of the Andes'. For me, the true miracle is that by living so long in the shadow of death, we learned in the most vivid and transforming way exactly what it means to be alive. This is the knowledge that bonds the survivors together, and, while life has led some of us far away from our home town of Montevideo, we will never allow these bonds to be broken.

Even today, more than three decades after the disaster, I think of these men as my brothers. But no one has been a better brother to me than Roberto Canessa, my partner in that long trek through the Andes. More than thirty years later, I am proud to say that I am still best friends with Roberto, who has only grown more resourceful, more confident and, yes, more hard-headed with the passage of time. These qualities, which made him such a difficult character, have helped to make him one of the most respected paediatric cardiologists in Uruguay and earned him a reputation as a man ferociously determined to help his young patients. Roberto has also enjoyed a rich and peaceful personal life. Three years after our return from the Andes, he married Laura Surraco, the girl he had missed so badly in the mountains, and this was a lucky thing for him, because she may be the only woman who could stand up to his stubbornness and harness his boundless energy. They now have two sons and a daughter.

Gustavo Zerbino is another especially good friend, with whom I have grown very close over the years. He is a man of strong principles and straight talk, and when he speaks he makes his words count. In the Andes, he was always brave, smart and steady, and if he hadn't burned himself out on that nearly fatal attempt to climb the mountain, he most certainly would have been one of our most trusted expeditionaries. Today, Gustavo runs a large chemical company, is active in many community organisations, and is the vice-president of the Old Christians Rugby Club. He is divorced with four fine sons from his first marriage, and because he lives only blocks away I see him and his family often.

Carlitos Páez, another of my favourite friends, remains as irreverent, affectionate and loveable as he was in the mountains. I love him for his creativity and his outrageous humour and for the warmth he has always shown my daughters, who have been drawn to his magnetic personality since they were babies. Carlitos has faced more than his share of challenges. His first marriage ended after only two years, and he has been single ever since. About fifteen years ago he fell so deeply into alcohol and drug addiction that we all knew something had to be done. One afternoon, Gustavo and I showed up at Carlitos's house. We told him we were taking him to a rehab hospital, where he would stay until he had recovered completely. He was shocked and at first refused to budge, but we told him the decision was no longer his. All the arrangements had been made, and we let him see, in our faces, that there was no use in resisting. Happily, Carlitos recovered completely. He has been sober ever since, and now volunteers his time to counsel people who are battling substance abuse and addiction.

Alvaro Mangino, one of the younger boys in the disaster, has grown into a man of great common sense and inner calm who has now been married for many years to his wife, Margarita, and has raised four children. For many years he lived in Brazil, but he has recently returned to Montevideo, where he works for a heating and air-conditioning company and serves on the board of the Old Christians. He is a loyal and steady friend, and I am happy to have him back close to home.

Alvaro is particularly close to another of my good friends, Coche Inciarte, who may be the calmest, gentlest and most thoughtful of all the survivors. He speaks with great natural eloquence and sharp wit, but while he often jokes, he has a deep emotional understanding of what we suffered, and he never hides the closeness he feels for the rest of us. Coche married his childhood sweetheart Soledad. Their reunion was a miracle for both of them, and Coche has never let himself forget what a wonder it is to have her and the three children they have raised. For many years, Coche was a dairy farmer, one of the largest producers in Uruguay. He recently sold his holdings and retired to enjoy his family and to devote time to his great passion—painting. One of his pictures hangs in my office, and I think of him every time I see it.

As one of the triumvirate of leaders known as 'the cousins', Eduardo Strauch was an important figure in the mountains. Today he is still cool and collected, a man of few words, but always worth listening to. Eduardo and his wife, Laura, have five children. He is an accomplished architect in Montevideo and has built many fine homes and buildings, including my first house.

Eduardo's cousin Daniel Fernández still possesses the humour and charisma he used to ease the intense fears we faced. He is a great storyteller and has the ability to capture the imagination of his audience when he speaks. Sparks always fly when Daniel and Roberto discuss Uruguayan politics. Their arguments inevitably end in a stalemate, but no matter how hot these discussions grow they are always laced with humour, and the rest of us enjoy the show. Daniel runs a successful computer and technology firm based in Montevideo. He and his wife, Amalia, have three wonderful kids.

I have always admired Pedro Algorta, for his intelligence and wit. I have not seen him as much as I would like, because he lives in Argentina, where he works as the manager of a large brewery and beverage manufacturer. But recently he bought a ranch in Uruguay, and I hope this will allow me to see him more often. He and his wife, Noel, have two daughters and a son.

Antonio Vizintín, who bravely climbed the mountain with Roberto and me, has faced many difficulties in his life. His first marriage ended in divorce, and his second wife died tragically. He is now married for a third time, and we all pray that he has a happier future ahead. Tintin, as we still call him, has two children, a daughter and a son, from his second marriage. He has been successful as an importer of chemicals for the plastics industry. He still lives in Carrasco, but he is a bit of a loner, and in recent years we have seen less of him than we'd like. Still, he will always be one of us.

Roy Harley is one of the survivors I think about very often. For more than thirty years I have been troubled by the way Roy was portrayed in previous accounts of the disaster and puzzled by the way I treated him in the mountains. I have realised in writing this book that it was my own fear that fuelled the anger and frustration I felt towards Roy. We were young men then, and things seemed much simpler. In *Miracle in the Andes*, I have tried to set the record straight: in my eyes, Roy Harley was no coward. The fact that he wore his emotions close to the surface does not mean he was weaker or more frightened than the rest of us. He was and always will be a reliable friend and an important part of our circle. Over the years he has proved himself as a man of integrity and strength, and he is one of the guys I know I can count on. Today Roy is a successful engineer working for a large paint manufacturer. He lives in Montevideo with his wife, Cecilia, two lovely daughters and a son who is now playing for the Old Christians.

Fito Strauch was one of the most important guys on the mountain, and none of us has forgotten the many ways in which he contributed to our survival. Fito firmly believes that it was God's personal intervention that saved us, and that we should live our lives as His messengers. Sometimes I feel that Fito is unhappy with me for the way I have minimised God's role in our rescue, and that I have not been faithful to the spiritual lessons of the ordeal. I tell him I am not sure how to spread God's message, because I am not sure what that message could be. I don't want my life to be defined by what happened to me thirty years ago; I feel I am writing the script of my own life every day. For me, this is not a denial of the spiritual lessons we learned, but the very fulfilment of them. Fito and I will probably never see eye to eye on this issue, but this does not diminish the respect and friendship I feel for him, and when we meet we embrace like brothers. Fito owns a cattle ranch and he and his wife Paula have four children.

Sergio Catalán, the Chilean peasant who first spotted Roberto and me in the mountains, is not, technically, one of the survivors. But he is definitely part of our family, and we have kept in touch with him over the years, visiting him at his village in Chile, or flying him in to see us in Montevideo. He remains the same humble and gentle man who rode on horseback for ten hours to lead rescuers to us at Los Maitenes. He lives a simple life, spending weeks at a time in the mountain pastures tending his cattle and sheep. He and his wife have raised nine children, and it impresses me that even on the modest means of a mountain herdsman he has managed to send most of them to college. All of them are now established in good marriages and jobs.

FOR MANY YEARS, it was enough to know that these friends and my family understood what I had gone through. I had little interest in sharing my personal story with anyone outside our circle, and though I sometimes gave interviews or participated in documentaries, I was always wary of sharing too much of myself. All the public needed to know, I believed, was covered, masterfully, in Piers Paul Read's book, *Alive*. True, it concentrated almost entirely on the factual events of our ordeal; no reader could have more than just the slightest understanding of my inner struggle and the surging emotions that drove me to survive. But I did not care to reveal those things. I kept the most intimate, most painful memories to myself.

As the years passed I was approached on more than one occasion by publishers asking me to retell the story from my own personal perspective. I always refused. Those people wanted to celebrate the disaster as an inspirational story of triumph and perseverance. But they were missing the point. I was no hero. I was always frightened, weak and confused. Our story may have inspired millions around the world, but for me the months in the mountains were days of heartbreak, horror and loss. The disaster was not something to be celebrated. It was something to be outlived. I had no desire to rummage through dark memories with the unflinching honesty it would take to write a book.

Why, then, after thirty-odd years, did I agree to write the account you now hold in your hands? The answer begins in 1991, with a call from a man named Juan Cintrón who was organising a conference for young business owners in Mexico City. Having decided that my story would make a great motivational speech, he tracked me down by phone and asked me to deliver the keynote address. I politely refused. But Juan would not take no for an answer. He called me again and again, begging me to reconsider. Finally he flew to Montevideo to plead with me face to face. Impressed by his persistence, I succumbed and agreed to give the talk.

As I worked on the speech, as I tried to draw from so much misery and grief the kind of inspirational titbits that might help an audience of ambitious young entrepreneurs improve their bottom lines, I deeply regretted my decision to deliver the address. But there was no backing out.

Finally, the day arrived and I found myself on stage in Mexico City, with the notes on the podium in front of me. The polite applause had ended and it was time for me to begin, but, no matter how I tried, the words would not come. My heart was pounding and my hands were trembling. I stared at my notes. They made no sense. People shifted in their seats. The awkward silence grew so loud it sounded like thunder, and just as panic was about to overwhelm me, I heard myself speak.

'I should not be here,' I said. 'I should be dead on a glacier in the Andes.'

As if a floodgate had opened, I poured out my story, holding nothing back. I spoke from my heart. I walked them through all the important moments of the ordeal so that they experienced it all just as I had: the wild grief I felt when Susy died, the terror when we heard that the search had been cancelled. I took them with us inside the fuselage on the night of the avalanche and on the grim days that followed. I led them up the mountain and showed them the devastating view from the summit, then I took them with Roberto and me on the trek that we were certain would lead us to our deaths. I didn't say a word about creativity or teamwork or problem solving. I didn't mention the word success. Instead, I shared with them the lesson of my ordeal: it wasn't cleverness or courage or competence or savvy that had saved us, it was nothing more than our love for each other, for our families, for the lives we wanted so desperately to live. Each of us realised, with a clarity that is hard to describe, that the only crucial thing in life is the chance to love and be loved. The sixteen of us who were lucky enough to return will never forget this. No one should forget this.

When I finished, the hall was filled with silence for several seconds. Then applause swelled and the audience rose to their feet. Afterwards, strangers with tears in their eyes came forward to embrace me. Some took me aside to tell me about hardships and struggles they had faced. I felt a powerful connection with those people. They were not simply understanding my story; they were making it their own. This filled me with a great sense of peace and purpose, and while I didn't completely understand these emotions at the time, I knew I wanted to feel that way again.

After the success of the Mexico City speech, I was asked to give talks around the world, but my daughters were still small and my business obligations were heavy, so I was able to accept only a few of the invitations. As years passed, and I found the time, I began to speak more frequently. Today, I address audiences across the globe, although my responsibilities at home still force me to be selective. And each time I speak I simply do what I did the first time: I tell my story and share the plain wisdom I have learned.

I have realised that my story is the story of everyone who hears it. I'd always thought of it as something unique, something so extreme and outrageous that only those who had been there could genuinely understand it. But in its emotional essence it is the most familiar story in the world. We all, at times, face hopelessness and despair. We all experience grief, abandonment and crushing loss. And all of us, sooner or later, will face the inevitable nearness of death. We all have our own personal Andes.

It satisfies me deeply that so many can find strength and comfort in the things I have to say. In return, they have helped heal my wounded memories. My mother, my sister and the others did not die in vain, because our suffering really does add up to some kind of wisdom that can touch hearts across the planet. I now have a passion to share my story with as many people as possible, and out of that passion came the desire to write this book.

I began writing it, in my heart, several years ago, and finally the time felt right to put my thoughts on paper. It has been a remarkable experience—painful, humbling, surprising and very rewarding. I have tried to be as truthful as possible, and now I offer it as a gift: to my father, so that he can see how my love for him was the real power that saved me; to my fellow survivors, so that they will know the love and respect I will always feel for them; to my wife and my daughters, so that they can stand beside me in the mountains and see that, even though they were still just a part of my distant future, every step I took was a step closer to them; and finally, to those with whom I am bonded by suffering and the joys and disappointments of life—that is, everyone who reads this.

I am no wise man. Every day shows me how little I know about life, and how wrong I can be. But there are things I know to be true. I know I will die, and I know that the only sane response to such a horror is to love. My hope is that you who are reading this book will not wait so long to realise what treasures you have. In the Andes we lived heartbeat-to-heartbeat. Every second was a gift, glowing with purpose and meaning. I have tried to live that way ever since, and it has filled my life with more blessings than I can count. I urge you to do the same. As we used to say in the mountains, 'Breathe. Breathe again. With every breath, you are alive.' After all these years, this is still the best advice I can give you. Savour your existence. Live every moment. Do not waste a breath.

MIRACLE IN THE ANDES

Left page: 1 The crash site, seen from the helicopter in which Parrado flew with the rescue team. **2** Survivors sitting outside on the seats from the wreckage. **3** Darkness fell before all the survivors could be airlifted out, so six had to spend another night at the crash site. **4** Parrado's parents, Seler and Eugenia, in 1970. **5** Delgado (on fuselage roof) and Canessa (standing) stitch squares of insulation to make a sleeping bag for the climb to freedom. **6** Parrado, inside the tail section, drinking melted snow.

Right page: 7 Parrado in 1971 (left), with Canessa (right) and a team mate. **8** Roy Harley, Canessa and Vinzintín at the tail section. **9** Sergei Catalán waits with Canessa and Parrado for the helicopters to arrive. **10**. From left, Cecilia, Veronique and Veronica Parrado. **11** The author's sister, Susy. **12** First day back in Carrasco, on the beloved motorbike.

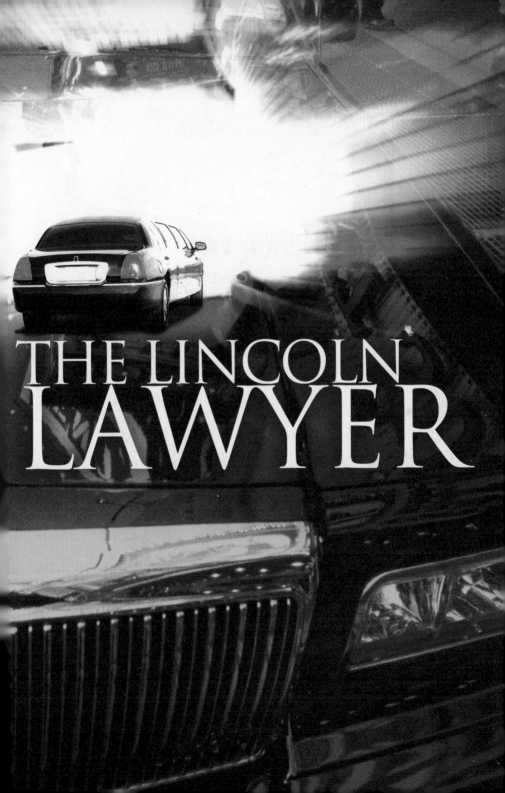

THE LINCOLN
LAWYER

When Mickey Haller acquires a wealthy new
client, he's convinced he's got a 'franchise'—a
case that will pay really big money if he wins.
And as the evidence for the defence starts to
stack up, he believes he may also be looking at
the easiest trial of his career.
Then someone close to him is murdered
and, chillingly, Haller discovers that all is
not as it seems . . .

ONE

Monday, March 7

The morning air off the Mojave in late winter is as clean and crisp as you'll ever breathe in Los Angeles County. It carries the taste of promise on it. When it blows in like that I like to keep a window open in my office. There are a few people who know this routine of mine, people like Fernando Valenzuela. The bail bondsman, not the baseball pitcher. He called me as I was coming into Lancaster for a nine o'clock calendar call. He must have heard the wind whistling in my cellphone.

'Mick,' he said, 'you up north this morning?'

'At the moment,' I said, rolling up the window. 'You got something?'

'Yeah, I got something. I think I got a franchise player here. But his first appearance is at eleven. Can you make it back down in time?'

Valenzuela has an office on Van Nuys Boulevard a block from the civic centre, which includes two courthouses and a jail. He calls his business Liberty Bail Bonds. His phone number, in red neon on the roof of his establishment, can be seen from the high-power wing on the third floor of the jail. His number is scratched on the wall next to every payphone in there.

You could say his name is also permanently scratched onto my Christmas list. At the end of the year I give a can of salted nuts to everybody on it. Planters holiday mix. Each can has a ribbon and bow on it. But no nuts inside. Just cash. I have a lot of bail bondsmen on my Christmas list. I eat holiday mix out of Tupperware well into spring.

'I think I can make eleven,' I said. 'What's the case?'

'Gotta be big money. They booked the guy on a half mil and his mother's lawyer came in here ready to sign over property in Malibu to secure it.'

'Booked for what?' I asked, keeping my voice even.

'The cops booked him last night for ag-assault, GBI and attempted rape. It sounds like a bar pick-up gone bad. The family lawyer said the woman's in it for the money. You know, the civil suit to follow the criminal case.'

'What's the family lawyer's name?'

'Cecil C. Dobbs, Esquire. Out of Century City. See, I told you. Money.'

Valenzuela was right. I knew of C. C. Dobbs by reputation and guessed that there wouldn't be more than one or two names on his entire client list that didn't have a Bel-Air or Holmby Hills address.

'Give me the client's name,' I said.

'That would be Louis Ross Roulet.'

He spelt it out and I wrote it down on a legal pad.

'Almost like the spinning wheel but you pronounce it Roo-*lay*,' he said. 'You going to be here, Mick?'

'Why me?' I asked. 'Was I asked for? Or did you suggest me?'

I had to be careful with this. I had to assume Dobbs was the kind of lawyer who would go to the California bar in a heartbeat if he came across a criminal-defence attorney paying off bondsmen for client referrals.

'I asked Roulet if he had a criminal-defence lawyer, and he said no. I told him about you. I didn't push it. I just said you were good.'

'Was this before or after Dobbs came into it?'

'Before. Roulet called me this morning from the jail. He saw the sign, I guess. Dobbs showed up after that.'

I wondered how truthful Valenzuela was being with me. A guy like Dobbs would have had his own man. If criminal defence wasn't his own forte, then he'd have had a specialist in the firm. But Valenzuela's story seemed to contradict this. Roulet came to him empty-handed.

I made a decision. 'I'll be there,' I said. 'I'll see you at eleven.'

MY CLIENT for the calendar call, Harold Casey, a member of the Road Saints motorcycle gang, had been charged with the cultivation and sale of marijuana. When the judge asked if we were ready to schedule the trial for later in the week, I told him I wanted to carry it over until the following week because I was having trouble locating an indispensable witness. In truth I was having trouble getting Casey to pay my fees. The judge agreed.

In the hallway outside the courtroom I turned my cellphone back on and called my driver to tell him I was coming out. I then checked voicemail and found a message from Lorna Taylor. I decided to call her back in the car.

Earl Briggs, my driver, had the Lincoln right out front. Earl didn't get out and open the door or anything. His deal was just to drive me while he worked off the fee he owed me for getting him probation on a cocaine sales conviction. I paid him twenty bucks an hour to drive me but held half of it back to go against the fee. It wasn't quite what he was making dealing crack but it was safer, legal and something that could go on a résumé. Earl said he wanted to go straight in life and I believed him.

I could hear the sound of hip-hop pulsing behind the closed windows of the car as I approached, but Earl killed the music as I reached for the door handle. I slid into the back and told him to head towards Van Nuys.

Then I called Lorna Taylor back. Lorna is my case manager. The phone number that runs on my half-page ad in the Yellow Pages and on thirty-six bus benches scattered through high-crime areas in the county goes directly to the office/second bedroom of her condo in West Hollywood. The address the California bar has for me is the condo as well.

Lorna is the first buffer. To get to me you start with her. My cell number is given out to only a few and Lorna is the gatekeeper. She is tough, smart, professional and beautiful. She's my bookkeeper, too.

'Law office,' she said when I called in.

'Sorry, I was in court,' I said, explaining why I missed her call. 'What's up?'

'You talked to Val, right?'

'Yeah. I'm heading down to Van Nuys now. I got that at eleven.'

'He called here to make sure. He sounds nervous.'

'He thinks this guy is the golden goose, wants to make sure he's along for the ride. I'll call him back to reassure him.'

'I did some preliminary checking on the name Louis Ross Roulet. Credit check is excellent. The name in the *Times* archive comes up with a few hits. All real-estate transactions. He works for an exclusive real-estate firm in Beverly Hills called Windsor Residential Estates.'

'That's good. Anything else?'

'Not on that. And just the usual so far on the phone.'

Which meant she had fielded the usual number of calls drawn by the bus benches and the Yellow Pages, from people who wanted a lawyer. Before the callers hit my radar they had to convince Lorna that they could pay.

'Nobody we know?' I asked.

'Gloria Dayton called from Twin Towers.'

I groaned. Twin Towers was the county's main lockup downtown. It housed women in one tower and men in the other. Gloria Dayton was a high-priced prostitute who needed my legal services from time to time. I first represented her ten years earlier, when she was young and drug-free and still had life in her eyes. Now she was a pro bono client. I never charged her. I just tried to convince her to quit the life.

'When did she get popped?'

'Last night. Or rather, this morning. Her first appearance is after lunch. There's also a complication. Cocaine possession as well as the usual.'

I knew that Gloria worked through contacts made on the Internet, where she billed herself on various websites as Glory Days. When she got popped, it was usually after an undercover vice officer penetrated her check system and set up a date. The fact that she had cocaine on her person when they met sounded like an unusual lapse on her part, or a plant from the cop.

'All right, if she calls back tell her I'll be there.'

We talked about my schedule for the rest of the week and I checked my diary against hers. I had a couple of hearings set for each morning and a one-day trial on Thursday. It was all South Side drug stuff. My meat and potatoes.

'One last thing,' I said. 'You said the place Roulet works handles pretty exclusive real-estate deals, right?'

'Yeah. Every deal his name was attached to in the archives was in seven figures. A couple into the eights. Holmby Hills, Bel-Air, places like that.'

I nodded, thinking that Roulet's status might make him a person of interest to the media. 'Then why don't you tip Sticks to it,' I said.

'Will do.'

I closed the phone. We were making good time getting to Van Nuys for Roulet's first appearance. I called Fernando Valenzuela to tell him.

'One thing,' Valenzuela said when I'd finished speaking. 'I found out his case was assigned to Maggie McFierce. Is that going to be a problem?'

Maggie McFierce as in Margaret McPherson, who happened to be one of the toughest and, yes, fiercest deputy district attorneys assigned to the Van Nuys courthouse. She also happened to be my first ex-wife.

'It won't be a problem for *me*,' I said without hesitation.

The defendant has the right to his choice of counsel. If there is a conflict of interest between the defence lawyer and the prosecutor, then it is the prosecutor who must bow out.

'You know what that means, though,' I said. 'She'll be going for no bail. She always does with crimes against women.'

'Shit, can she get it? I'm looking at a nice chunk of change on this, man.'

'I don't know. You said the guy's got family and C. C. Dobbs. I can make something out of that. We'll see.'

I ended the call. As we spoke I had watched two motorcycles glide by my window. Each rider wore a black leather vest with a skull and halo patch sewn on the back. Now they were in front of us, and there were three more Harleys behind us. One of them came alongside the Lincoln and signalled us towards the upcoming exit. I recognised him as Teddy Vogel, a former client and the highest-ranking Road Saint not currently incarcerated.

'Pull off, Earl,' I said. 'Let's see what he's got.'

We pulled into a parking lot and I lowered my window as Vogel approached on foot. The other four Saints killed their engines but remained on their bikes. Vogel leaned down to the window and put his arm on the sill.

'Counsellor, how's it hanging?' he said.

'Just fine, Ted. What's up with you?'

'I got a call from Casey over in the Lancaster pen. He said I might catch you heading south. Said you were stalling his case till you got some green.' He reached inside his vest, took out a thick envelope and passed it to me.

'This is the whole ten grand?' I asked. 'In cash?'

'That's right. What's wrong with cash?'

'Nothing. But I have to give you a receipt. It's an IRS requirement.'

I wrote out a receipt and gave it to Vogel, then watched him saunter back to his Harley. I told Earl to get back on the freeway, then I opened the envelope and counted out the money. It was all there.

LOUIS ROSS ROULET was in a holding tank with seven other men who had made the half-block bus ride from the Van Nuys jail to the Van Nuys courthouse. There were only two white men in the cell and they sat next to each other on a bench while the six black men took the other side of the cell.

I looked at the white men and it was easy to choose between them. One was rail-thin with the desperate eyes of a hype who was long past fix time. The other looked like the proverbial deer in the headlights. I chose him.

'Mr Roulet?' I said, pronouncing the name as Valenzuela had told me.

The deer nodded. I signalled him over to the bars so I could talk quietly.

'My name is Michael Haller. People call me Mickey. I will be representing you during your first appearance today.'

We were in the holding area behind the arraignment court where attorneys can confer with clients before court begins. Roulet grasped the bars in front of me. Like the others in the cage, he had on ankle, wrist and belly chains. They wouldn't come off until he was taken into the courtroom. He was in his early thirties and, though at least six feet tall and 180 pounds, he seemed slight. His eyes were pale blue and it was rare for me to see the kind of panic that was so clearly set in them. Most of my clients have been in lockup before and have the stone-cold look of the predator. Roulet looked like prey.

'This is a set-up,' he said loudly. 'You have to get me out of here. I made a mistake with that woman, that's all. She's trying to set me up and—'

I put my hands up to stop him. 'Be careful what you say in here,' I said in a low voice. 'In fact, be careful what you say until we get you out of here and can talk in private.'

He looked around, seemingly not understanding.

'You never know who is listening,' I said. 'And you never know who will say he heard you say something, even if you didn't say anything. Best not to talk to anyone about anything.'

He nodded, and I signalled him down to the bench next to the bars. There was a bench against the opposite wall and I sat down.

'I'm really here just to meet you and tell you who I am,' I said. 'We'll talk about the case after we get you out. I've spoken to Mr Dobbs, and we're going to tell the judge that we're prepared to post bail. Is that right?' I opened a leather Mont Blanc folder and prepared to take notes on a legal pad.

Roulet nodded. He was learning.

'Good,' I said. 'Tell me about yourself—how old you are, whether you're married, what ties you have to the community.'

'Um, I'm thirty-two. I've lived here my whole life—even went to school here. UCLA. Never married. No kids. I work—'

'Divorced?'

'No, never married. I work for my family's real-estate business. Windsor Residential Estates. It's named after my mother's second husband.'

'How much money did you make last year?' I asked quietly.

'Why do you need to know that?' Roulet asked.

'If I'm going to get you out of here today, I need to know everything about your standing in the community. That includes your financial standing.'

Roulet looked over his shoulder at the others in the cell, then whispered his answer. 'My income was a quarter million.'

One of Roulet's cellmates came up to the bars next to him. The other white man. He had an agitated manner, his hands in constant motion.

'Hey, man, I need a lawyer too. You got a card?'

'Not for you, pal. They'll have a lawyer out there for you.'

I waited a moment for the hype to move away. He didn't.

'Look, this is private,' I told him. 'Could you leave us alone?'

The hype shuffled back to the corner he had come from.

I looked back at Roulet. 'What about charitable organisations?' I asked. 'Are you involved in any charities? Do you give to any charities?'

'Yeah, the company does. We give to Make a Wish and a runaway shelter in Hollywood. I think it's called My Friend's Place or something like that.'

'OK, good,' I said. 'Now Mr Roulet, you've got some heavy charges on you and I have a feeling the DA is going to request no bail, but this is good stuff. I can work with it.' I indicated my notes.

'No bail?' he said in a loud, panicked voice.

'Calm down,' I said. 'I said that's what she's going to go for. I didn't say she would get it. When was the last time you were arrested?'

I always threw that in out of the blue so I could watch their eyes and see if there was going to be a surprise thrown at me in court.

'Never. I've never been arrested. This whole thing is—'

'I know, I know, but we don't want to talk about that here, remember?'

He nodded. I looked at my watch. Court was about to start.

'I'm going to go now,' I said. 'I'll see you out there in a few minutes. When we are out there, don't say anything until you check with me. OK?'

'Well, don't I say "not guilty" to the charges?'

'No, they're not even going to ask you that. Today all they do is read you the charges, talk about bail and set a date for an arraignment. Got that?'

He nodded and frowned.

'Just so you know,' I said. 'I charge twenty-five hundred dollars for a first appearance and bail hearing like this. Is that going to be a problem?'

He shook his head no.

'Good. We can talk about the rest of it after you're out of here.' I closed my leather folder and stood up. 'One last thing,' I added. 'There's a lot of lawyers out there. Why d'you pick me?' I wanted to test Valenzuela's veracity.

Roulet shrugged. 'I don't know,' he said. 'I remembered your name from something I read in the paper. It was a story about a case where the evidence got thrown out. I think it was drugs. You won the case.'

'The Hendricks case?'

It was the only one I could think of that had made the papers recently. Hendricks was another Road Saints client. The Sheriff's department had put a GPS bug on his Harley to track his deliveries. Doing that on public roads was fine. But when he parked his bike in the kitchen of his home at night, that bug constituted unlawful entry by the cops. The case was tossed by a judge during the preliminary hearing. It made a decent splash in the *Times*.

'I can't remember the client's name,' Roulet said. 'I just remembered yours. When I called the bail bondsman today I asked him to get you. Why?'

'Just curious. I appreciate the call. I'll see you in the courtroom.'

I put the differences between what Roulet had said about my hiring and what Valenzuela had told me into the bank for later consideration and made my way back into the arraignment court. I saw Maggie McFierce sitting at the prosecution table, along with five other prosecutors. A prosecutor assigned to the courtroom handled most of the routine appearances and arraignments that were paraded through each day. But special cases brought the big guns out of the district attorney's office on the second floor of the courthouse next door. They brought the TV cameras out, too.

As I stepped through the bar into the space assigned to lawyers, defendants and courtroom personnel, I saw a man setting up a video camera on a tripod next to the bailiff's desk, beside the bar railing. There was no network symbol on the camera. The guy was a freelancer who'd got wind of the case and would try to sell his footage to one of the local stations.

I walked up to my ex-wife from behind and bent down to whisper into her ear. She was looking at photographs in a file. She was wearing a navy suit with a thin grey stripe. Her raven-coloured hair was tied back with a matching grey ribbon. I loved her hair when it was back like that.

'Are you the one who used to have the Roulet case?'

She looked up, not recognising the whisper. Her face was involuntarily forming a smile but it turned into a frown when she saw me. She knew exactly what I had meant by using the past tense and slapped the file closed.

'Sorry,' I said. 'He liked what I did on Hendricks and gave me a call.'

'Son of a bitch. I wanted this case, Haller.'

'I guess this town ain't big enough for the both of us,' I drawled.

'All right. I'll go peacefully after this hearing. Unless you object to that.'

'I might. You going for a no-bail hold?'

'That's right. But that was a directive from the second floor.'

'He's connected in the community. And has never been arrested.'

'That doesn't matter,' Maggie said. 'What matters is what he did last night.' She opened the file and snatched out one of the photos. 'Here's what your pillar of the community did last night. I don't really care what he did before. I'm just going to make sure he doesn't get out to do this again.'

The photo was a close-up of a woman's face. The swelling round the right eye had forced it tightly closed. The nose was broken and pushed off centre. A gash over the right eyebrow had been closed with nine butterfly stitches.

The lower lip was cut and had a marble-size swelling. The worst thing about the photo was the eye that was undamaged. The woman looked at the camera with fear, pain and humiliation undeniably expressed in that eye.

'If he did it,' I said, because that is what I would be expected to say.

'Right,' Maggie said. 'Sure, if he did it. He was only arrested in her home with her blood on him, but you're right, that's a valid question.'

I changed the subject. 'So,' I said. 'How is she?'

'She's scared shitless and hurting like hell. How else would she be?' She looked up at me and I saw the immediate recognition and then judgment in her eyes. 'You weren't asking about the victim, were you?' she said.

I didn't answer. I didn't want to lie to her.

'Your daughter is doing fine,' she said perfunctorily. 'She likes the things you send her but she would rather *you* show up a little more often.'

That was a direct hit and it was deserved. It seemed as though I was always chasing cases, even on weekends. I knew I needed to start chasing my daughter round the back yard more. The time to do it was going by.

'I will,' I said. 'Starting right now. What about this weekend?'

'Fine. You want me to tell her tonight?'

'Uh, maybe wait until tomorrow so I know for sure.'

She gave me a knowing nod. 'Great. Let me know tomorrow.'

I was saved from any further sarcasm by the start of the court session. The judge came out of chambers and bounded up the steps to the bench. The bailiff called the courtroom to order. I left the prosecution table and went back to one of the seats along the bar.

The judge ordered the first group out. There was a large holding area for in-custody defendants. I got up and moved to the opening in the glass. When I saw Roulet come through the door I signalled him over.

'You're going first,' I said. 'I asked the judge to take you out of order as a favour. I want to try to get you out of here.'

This was not the truth. I hadn't asked the judge, and he'd have done no such thing as a favour if I had. Roulet was going first because of the media presence in the court. It was a general practice to deal with media cases first as a courtesy to cameramen who had other assignments to get to.

'Why's that camera here?' Roulet whispered nervously. 'Is it for me?'

'Yes, somebody must have tipped him to the case.'

Before he could respond, his case was called, his name mispronounced by the clerk. Maggie announced her presence for the prosecution, then I announced mine. She had upped the charges, in her usual ploy as Maggie

McFierce. Roulet now faced attempted murder along with the attempted rape count. It would make it easier for her to argue for a no-bail hold.

The judge informed Roulet of his constitutional rights and set an arraignment date for March 21. I asked to address the no-bail hold. This set off a spirited back-and-forth between Maggie and me. She listed the atrocities committed upon the victim, then I listed Roulet's ties to the community and charitable efforts, offering to put C. C. Dobbs on the stand to further discuss Roulet's good standing. Dobbs's stature in the legal community would certainly be influential with the judge.

'The bottom line, Judge, is that the state cannot make a case for this man being a flight risk or a danger to the community,' I said in closing. 'Mr Roulet is anchored in this community and intends to do nothing other than vigorously attack the false charges that have been levelled against him.'

'Your Honour,' Maggie responded, 'all grandstanding aside, what should not be forgotten is that the victim in this case was brutally—'

'I am aware of the victim's injuries,' the judge interrupted, 'as well as Mr Roulet's standing. I am setting bail at one million dollars.'

I glanced into the gallery, to where Dobbs was sitting. I waited for a signal as to whether I should take the judge's bail order or argue for a lower amount. Dobbs simply got up and started to walk out of the courtroom. I took that to mean that the Roulet family could handle the million.

I turned back to the bench. 'Thank you, Your Honour,' I said.

The clerk called the next case. I glanced at Maggie as she closed the file on the case she would no longer prosecute. She then stood up and walked out through the bar and out of the courtroom, without looking back.

'Mr Haller?'

I turned to my client. A deputy was coming to take him back into holding.

'I'll work with Mr Dobbs and get you out fast,' I told Roulet. 'Then we'll sit down and talk about the case.'

'Thank you,' he said as he was led away. 'Thank you for being here.'

'Remember what I said. Don't talk to strangers. Don't talk to anybody.'

'Yes, sir.'

After he was gone I walked to the bar. Valenzuela was waiting at the gate with a big smile on his face. Roulet's bail was probably the highest he had ever secured. That meant his cut would be the highest he'd ever received.

He clapped me on the arm as I came through the gate. 'What'd I tell you?' he said. 'We got ourselves a franchise here, Boss.'

'We'll see, Val,' I said. 'We'll see.'

AFTER FIFTEEN YEARS of practising law, I had come to think of it in very simple terms. The law was a large, rusting machine that sucked up people and lives and money. I was just a mechanic, expert at going into the machine and fixing things and extracting what I needed from it.

Every attorney who works the machine has two fee schedules. Schedule A lists the fees the attorney would like to get for certain services rendered. Schedule B refers to the fees he is willing to take because that is all the client can afford. A franchise client is a defendant who wants to go to trial and has the money to pay his lawyer's schedule A rates. From first appearance to arraignment to preliminary hearing and on to trial and then appeal, the franchise client demands hundreds if not thousands of billable hours. He can keep gas in the tank for two to three years.

And it was beginning to look like Valenzuela had been on the money. Louis Roulet was looking more and more like a franchise client.

C. C. Dobbs was waiting in the hallway outside the arraignment court when I got out. 'Sorry,' he said. 'I didn't want to stay in there another minute. It was so depressing to see the boy caught up in that cattle call.'

'The boy?'

'Louis. I've represented the family for twenty-five years. I guess I still think of him as a boy.'

'Are you going to be able to get him out?'

'It won't be a problem. I have a call in to Louis's mother to see how she wants to handle it, whether to put up property or go with a bond.'

To put up property to cover a million-dollar bail would mean that at least a million dollars in the property's value could not be encumbered by a mortgage. Additionally, the court might require a current appraisal of the property, which could take days. Conversely, a bond could be purchased through Valenzuela for a ten per cent nonreturnable premium.

'Can I make a suggestion?' I asked.

'Please do.'

'Louis looked a little frail when I saw him back in the lockup. If I were you I would get him out of there as soon as possible. To do that you should have Valenzuela write a bond. It will cost you a hundred grand but the boy will be out and safe, if you know what I mean?'

'I know what you mean. I will suggest we go with the bond,' Dobbs said.

Dobbs was a thin, balding man in his late fifties. He had a deferential presence that probably came from thirty years of taking care of rich people. My guess was that he had become rich himself in the process.

'If we're going to be working together,' I said, 'I guess I should ask what you want to be called. Cecil? C. C.? Mr Dobbs?'

'Cecil will be fine.'

'Well, my first question, Cecil, is whether we *are* going to be working together. Do I have the job?'

'Mr Roulet made it clear to me he wanted you on the case. To be honest, you would not have been my first choice, because frankly I had never heard of you. But you are Mr Roulet's first choice, and that is acceptable to me.'

'Good. Now, do you want to talk about fees and get it out of the way?'

'If you would like.'

I looked around the hallway to make sure there were no other lawyers hanging around in earshot. I was going to go schedule A all the way on this.

'I get twenty-five hundred for today and Louis already approved that. If you want to go hourly from here, I get three hundred an hour and that gets bumped to five in trial because I can't do anything else. If you'd rather go with a flat rate, I'll want sixty thousand to take it through a preliminary hearing. If we end it with a plea, I'll take twelve more. If we go to trial, I need another sixty on the day we decide that and twenty-five more when we start picking a jury. This case doesn't look like more than a week, including jury selection, but if it goes past a week I get twenty-five a week extra.'

I hesitated a moment. Dobbs showed no reaction so I pressed on.

'I'll need thirty thousand for a retainer and another ten for an investigator by the end of the day. I want to get an investigator onto this before it hits the media and maybe before the cops talk to some of the people involved.'

Dobbs slowly nodded. 'Are those your standard fees?'

'When I can get them. I'm worth it. What are you charging the family?'

'That's between me and my client. But don't worry. I will include your fees in my discussion with Mrs Windsor.'

'I appreciate it. And remember, I need that investigator to start today.'

I gave him a card I pulled from the right pocket of my jacket. It had my cell number. The cards in my left pocket had the number that went to Lorna.

'I have another hearing downtown,' I said. 'When you get him out, call me and we'll set up a meeting. Let's make it as soon as possible.'

'Perfect,' Dobbs said, pocketing the card. 'Should we come to you?'

'No, I'll come to you. I'd like to see how the other half lives in those high-rises in Century City.'

Dobbs smiled glibly. 'It is obvious by your suit that you know and practise the adage that a trial lawyer should never dress too well. You want the jury to like you, not be jealous of you. Well, Michael, a Century City lawyer can't have an office that is nicer than the offices his clients come from. And so I can assure you that our offices are very modest.'

I nodded in agreement. But I felt insulted. I was wearing my best suit.

The courtroom door opened and the videographer walked out, lugging his camera and tripod with him. Dobbs saw him and immediately tensed.

'The media,' he said. 'How can we control this? Mrs Windsor won't—'

'Hold on a sec.'

I called to the cameraman and he walked over. I immediately put my hand out. He had to put his tripod down to take it.

'I'm Michael Haller. I saw you in there filming my client's appearance.'

Using my formal name was a code.

'Robert Gillen,' the cameraman said. 'People call me Sticks.'

He gestured to his tripod in explanation. His use of his formal name was a return code. It let me know he understood that I had a play working here.

'How'd you hear about this thing?'

He shrugged as though he was reluctant to answer. 'A source. A cop.'

I nodded. 'What do you get for that if you sell it to a news station?'

'I take seven-fifty for an exclusive and five for a non exclusive.'

'How about we take it off your hands right now for an exclusive?'

Gillen hesitated like he was unsure of the ethics involved.

'In fact, make it a grand,' I said.

'OK,' he said. 'You got a deal.'

While Gillen took the tape out of the camera, I pulled a wad of cash from my pocket. I turned to Dobbs. 'I can expense this, right?'

'Absolutely,' he said. He was beaming.

I exchanged the cash for the tape and thanked Gillen. He pocketed the money and moved towards the elevators.

'That was brilliant,' Dobbs said. 'We have to contain this. It could literally destroy the family's business.'

'Well, I'll do my best to keep it off the radar.'

TRAFFIC HEADING downtown was slow. I spent the time in the car working the phone. First I called Raul Levin, my investigator, to put him on alert about the potential meeting with Roulet. I asked him to do a preliminary run on the case to see what he could find out. Levin had retired early from the LAPD and still had contacts and friends who did him favours from time to time. Next I called Lorna again.

'Did you check on Gloria Dayton's arraignment?' I asked her.

'Yes. It looks like they might hold her over until tomorrow on a medical.'

I groaned. Holding Gloria's first appearance over until the next day for medical reasons meant that she was probably drug-sick. I had not seen or spoken to her in seven months. Her slide must have been quick and steep.

'Did you find out who filed it?' I asked.

'Leslie Faire,' she said.

I groaned again. 'That's just great. OK, well, I'm going to go down and see what I can do. I've got nothing going until I hear about Roulet.'

Leslie Faire was a misnamed prosecutor whose idea of giving a defendant a break was to offer extended parole supervision on top of prison.

'Mick, when are you going to learn with this woman?' Lorna said. 'She's never going to get out of the life, and now you can bet she's never going to be anything less than a twofer every time she calls. That would be fine, except you never charge her.'

What she meant by 'twofer' was that Gloria's solicitation or prostitution charges would now always be accompanied by drug charges.

'Well, the bar requires that all lawyers practise some pro bono—'

'You don't listen to me, Mick,' she said dismissively. 'That's exactly why we couldn't stay married.'

I closed my eyes. What a day. I had managed to get both my ex-wives angry with me.

'Look, can we change the subject?' I told her about Roulet's first appearance, and that it looked like I'd got the job.

'And what about Roulet? Did he do it?'

'Who knows, Lorna? That's not the question. The question is whether or not he's a paying customer. The answer is, I think so.'

'Well, get the cheque,' she said. 'Oh, there's one other thing. Sticks called and said he owes you four hundred dollars next time he sees you.'

'Yeah, he does.'

'You're doing pretty good today.'

'I'm not complaining.'

We said our goodbyes on a friendly note, the dispute over Gloria Dayton forgotten for the moment. Lorna and I had shared a short and sweet marriage, both of us quickly finding out that we had moved too fast while rebounding from divorces. We ended it, remained friends, and she continued to work with me, not for me. The only time I felt uncomfortable with the arrangement was when she acted like a wife and criticised my choice of client.

I called the DA's office in Van Nuys next. I asked for Margaret McPherson and caught her eating at her desk.

'I just wanted to say I'm sorry about this morning,' I told her. 'I know you wanted the case.'

'Well, you probably need it more than me.'

'Yeah, it's been a while since I had a franchise case.'

'Well, you didn't get as lucky a few minutes ago,' she whispered into the phone. 'The case was reassigned to Ted Minton.'

'Never heard of him.'

'He's one of Smithson's young guns. Just brought him in from downtown. He didn't see the inside of a courtroom until he came up here.'

John Smithson was the ambitious head deputy in charge of the Van Nuys Division. He was a better politician than a prosecutor and had parlayed that skill into a quick climb over other more experienced deputies to the division chief's post. Maggie McPherson was among those he'd passed by. Once he was in the slot, he started building a staff of young prosecutors who did not feel slighted and were loyal to him for giving them a shot.

'I don't get it, Mags. If this guy's a trial rookie, why wasn't I lucky?'

'Because these guys Smithson picks are all arrogant. They think they can do no wrong and what's more'—she lowered her voice even more—'they don't play fair. And the word on Minton is that he's a cheater.'

'Well, thanks for the heads-up.'

But she wasn't finished. 'A lot of these new people just don't get it. They don't see it as a calling. To them it's not about justice. It's just a game—a batting average. They like to keep score and to see how far it will get them in the office. In fact, they're all just like junior Smithsons.'

A calling. It was her sense of calling that cost us our marriage. Intellectually she could deal with being married to a man who worked the other side of the aisle. But when it came down to the reality of what we did, we were lucky to have lasted eight years. *Honey, how was your day? Oh, I got a guy who murdered his roommate with an ice pick a seven-year deal. And you? Oh, I put a guy away for five years because he stole a car stereo to feed his habit . . .* It just didn't work. Four years in, a daughter arrived, but, through no fault of her own, she only kept us going another four years.

Still, I didn't regret anything about it. My daughter was the only thing that was really good about my life, that I could be proud of. I think that, deep down, the reason I didn't see her enough was that I felt unworthy of her. Her mother was a hero. She put bad people in jail. What could I tell her was good and holy about what I did, when I had long ago lost the thread of it myself?

'Listen, Mags, tell Hayley I'll see her this Saturday. We'll do something.'

'You really mean that? I don't want to get her hopes up.'

I felt something lift inside me, the idea that my daughter would get her hopes up about seeing me. The one thing Maggie never did was run me down with Hayley. I always admired that.

'Yes, I'm sure,' I said. Then we said goodbye and I closed the phone.

I am from a family of attorneys. My father was the dean of criminal law in LA for almost three decades. His clients always made the headlines. I was just an afterthought in his life, a surprise visitor to his second marriage to a B-level movie actress known for her exotic Latin beauty but not her acting skills. The mix gave me my black Irish looks. My father was old when I came, so he was gone before I was old enough to really know him or talk to him about the calling of the law. He only left me his name. Mickey Haller, the legal legend. It still opened doors.

My cellphone rang and I checked the screen before answering.

'What's up, Val?'

'We're processing him out now.'

'Dobbs went with the bond?'

'You got it.' I could hear the delight in his voice.

'Don't be so giddy. You sure he's not a runner?'

'I'm going to make him wear a bracelet. I lose him, I lose my house.'

Even though the court had not ordered it, Valenzuela was going to put an electronic tracking bracelet on Roulet's ankle. He was taking no chances.

'Where's Dobbs?' I asked.

'Back at my office, waiting. I'll bring Roulet over as soon as he's out.'

'OK, I'll call him there.'

I ended the call and hit the speed-dial combo for Liberty Bail Bonds. Valenzuela's receptionist answered.

'Maisy, it's Mick. Can you put Mr Dobbs on the line?'

'Sure thing, Mick.'

A few seconds later Dobbs got on the line. 'This is Cecil Dobbs.'

'This is Mickey Haller. I hear our boy is about to be released.'

'Our boy?'

'Mr Roulet. Should be out inside the hour. Do you want to meet this afternoon to go over the case with him or do you want me to take it from here?'

'No, Mrs Windsor has insisted that I monitor this closely. In fact, she may choose to be there as well.'

'I don't mind the meet-and-greet with Mrs Windsor, but when it comes down to talking about the case, it's just going to be the defence team. OK?'

'I understand. Let's say four o'clock at my office.'

'I'll be there.' I ended the call.

When I called Raul Levin next, he told me he was already on his way to the LAPD Van Nuys Division to pick up a copy of the arrest report.

'Just like that?' I asked.

'No, not just like that. In a way, you could say it took me twenty years to get this report.'

I understood. Levin's LAPD connections had come through for him. No wonder he charged $500 a day. I told him about the meeting at four and he said he would be there.

The Lincoln pulled to a stop when I closed the phone. We were in front of the Twin Towers jail facility, a sad and forbidding place that I spent too much time in. I got out of the car and went inside once again.

TWO

There was an attorney's check-in window that allowed me to bypass the line of visitors waiting to get in to see loved ones incarcerated in the towers. When I told the window deputy whom I wanted to see, he printed out a visitor's pass. He slid it into the plastic frame of a clip-on badge and told me to put it on. Then he told me to wait for an escort.

After twenty minutes, a large woman in a deputy's uniform came into the waiting area and collected me. 'Sorry it took so long,' she told me as we waited between the double steel security doors in the women's tower. 'She was up in medical getting fixed up.'

'Fixed up?'

'Yeah, she got hurt,' the deputy said. 'In a scuffle. She can tell you.'

The deputy led me to the attorney visiting area, a row of booths in which an attorney could sit on one side and confer with a client who sat on the other side, separated by an eighteen-inch sheet of clear Plexiglas.

I was led to a booth and waited another ten minutes before the same deputy appeared on the other side of the Plexiglas with Gloria Dayton. Immediately, I saw that my client had a swelling round her left eye and a butterfly stitch over a small laceration just below her widow's peak. Gloria had jet-black hair and olive skin. She had once been beautiful, the kind of beauty that leaves you stunned at the fact that she had decided that selling herself to strangers was her best option. Now she just looked hard.

'Mickey Mantle,' she said. 'You're going to bat for me again?'

She said it in her little girl's voice that I suppose her clients enjoyed. It sounded strange, coming from that hard face. She always called me Mickey Mantle, even though she was born long after the great slugger had retired.

'I'm going to try, Gloria,' I told her. 'What happened to your face?'

'There was a little disagreement with some of the girls in my dorm.'

'Are you getting high in there?'

She looked indignant. 'No, I'm not.'

I studied her. She seemed straight. Maybe she wasn't getting high and that was not what the fight had been about.

'I don't want to stay in here, Mickey,' she said in her real voice. 'You think maybe you could get me into one of those pretrial whatchamacallits where I can get myself right?'

'The problem is, Gloria, they only have so many spaces in the pretrial intervention programme and the judges don't like sending people back when they didn't take advantage of it in the first place.'

'What do you mean?' she protested. 'I went the whole damn time.'

'That's right. But after it was over you went back to doing what you do and here we are again. You have to be ready for them to be tougher this time.'

Her eyes drooped. 'I can't do it,' she said in a small voice.

'Look, they have programmes in the jail. You'll get straight and come out with another chance to start again clean.'

She shook her head; she looked lost.

'For now, let's worry about your case,' I said. 'Tell me what happened.'

'What always happens. I screened the guy and it all checked out. He looked legit. But he was a cop and that was that.'

'You went to him?'

She nodded. 'The Mondrian. He had a suite—that's another thing. The cops usually don't have suites. They don't have the budget.'

'Didn't I tell you how stupid it would be to take coke with you when you work? And if a guy ever asks you to bring coke, you know he's a cop.'

'I know all of that and he didn't ask me to bring it. I forgot I had it, OK? I got it from a guy I went to see right before him. What was I supposed to do, leave it in the car for the Mondrian valets to take?'

'What guy did you get it from?'

'A guy at the Travelodge on Santa Monica. He offered it to me, you know, instead of cash. Then after I left I checked my messages and I had the call from the guy at the Mondrian. So I called him back, set it up and went straight there. I forgot I had the stuff in my purse.'

Nodding, I leaned forward. I was seeing a glimmer of hope on this one, a possibility. 'This guy in the Travelodge, who was he?'

'I don't know, just some guy who saw my ad on the website. He was Mexican or Cuban or something.'

'When he gave you the coke, did you see if he had any more?'

'He had to have more, or he wouldn't have given it to me.'

It was a good point. The glimmer was getting brighter.

'Did you screen him?'

''Course.'

'What, his driving licence?'

'No, his passport. He said he didn't have a licence.'

'What was his name?'

'Hector something.'

'Come on, Gloria. Hector what? Try to re—'

'Hector something Moya. It was three names. But I remember "Moya" because I said "Hector give me Moya" when he brought out the coke.'

'OK, that's good.'

'You think it's something you can use to help me get out?'

'Maybe, if this guy's a trade-up. I'm going to go see the prosecutor now. Do you remember what room the guy at the Travelodge was in?'

Gloria thought a moment. 'Yeah, it's an easy one. Three thirty-three.'

ON THE QUICK DRIVE over to the Criminal Courts Building I called Raul Levin. He was back at his home office in Glendale, looking through the police reports on the Roulet investigation and arrest. I asked him to put it aside and see what he could find out about the man in room 333 at the Travelodge on Santa Monica, and to run the name Hector Moya.

As Earl pulled to a stop in front of the CCB, I gave him a twenty-dollar bill and told him to run over to Philippe's to get us roast beef sandwiches. I'd eat mine on my way out to Century City.

While I was waiting for Leslie Faire to grant me an audience, Levin called back and gave me some added ammunition to go in with. He told me that the man in room 333 at the Travelodge had checked in under the name

Gilberto García. The motel did not require ID, since he paid cash in advance for a week and put a fifty-dollar deposit on phone charges. Levin had also run a trace on the name I had given him and came up with Hector Arrande Moya, a Colombian wanted on a fugitive warrant issued after he fled San Diego when a federal grand jury handed down an indictment for drug trafficking. It added up to real good stuff.

Faire was in an office shared with three other prosecutors. Two were gone, probably in court, but the other was sitting at the desk opposite Faire. I pulled a chair away from one of the empty desks and sat down.

'You filed on Gloria Dayton this morning,' I said. 'I want to see what we can do about it.'

'Well, we can plead her guilty and she can do one to three years.' She said it matter-of-factly with a smile that was more of a smirk.

'I was thinking of a pretrial intervention programme.'

'She already got a bite out of that apple and she spit it out. No way.'

'What if she had something to trade?'

Faire snorted like it was a joke. 'Like what?'

'A hotel room number where a major dealer is doing business.'

'Sounds a little vague.'

It *was* vague but I could tell she was interested. Prosecutors like to trade up.

'Call your drug guys. Ask them to run the name Hector Arrande Moya on the box. He's a Colombian. I can wait.'

She hesitated. She clearly didn't like being manipulated by a defence attorney. But the hook was set. She turned to her desk and made a call.

I listened to her telling someone to give her a background check on Moya. She waited a while, listened to the response, then hung up.

'OK,' she said, turning back to me. 'What does she want?'

'She wants a PTI slot. All charges dropped on completion. She doesn't testify against the guy and her name is on no documents. She simply gives you his hotel and room number and your people do the rest.'

She worked it over for a few moments, moving her jaw back and forth as if tasting the deal and deciding whether to eat more.

'All right,' she said finally. 'Let me talk to my boss. But I'll tell you right now, if we go for it, she'll have to go to a lockdown programme at County–USC. We're not going to waste a residency slot on her.'

County–USC was a hospital with a jail wing where sick and addicted inmates were treated.

'Fine with me,' I said. I stood up and handed her a business card.

THE LAW OFFICES of Dobbs and Delgado were on the twenty-ninth floor of one of the twin towers that created the signature skyline of Century City. I was on time, but everyone was already gathered in a conference room with a long, polished wooden table and a wall of glass that framed a western exposure stretching across Santa Monica to the Pacific.

Louis Roulet sat at the head of the table. Out of his grey jail jumpsuit, he now wore a dark brown suit over a pale silk T-shirt. He looked like a confident young real-estate executive, not the scared boy I saw in the courthouse.

To Roulet's left sat Cecil Dobbs and next to him was a well-preserved, well-coiffed and bejewelled woman I assumed to be Roulet's mother.

To Roulet's right the first seat was empty and waiting for me. Next to it sat Raul Levin, with a file in front of him on the table.

Dobbs introduced Mary Windsor to me. She shook my hand with a strong grip. I sat down and Dobbs explained that she would be paying for her son's defence and had agreed to the terms I had outlined earlier. He slid an envelope across the table to me. I looked inside and saw a cheque for $60,000 with my name on it, drawn on Mary Windsor's account.

I closed the envelope and slid it back across the table. 'I'm going to need the cheque to come from Louis,' I said, looking at Mrs Windsor. 'I work for him and that's got to be clear from the start.'

It was a control issue. I knew I had to make sure that Mary Windsor and Cecil Dobbs knew that this was my case to manage, to win or to lose.

I wouldn't have thought it could, but Mary Windsor's face hardened. She reminded me of an old grandfather clock, her face flat and square.

'Mother,' Roulet said. 'It's all right. I'll write him a cheque. I should be able to cover it until you give me the money.'

She looked from me to her son, then back to me. 'Very well,' she said.

'Mrs Windsor,' I said. 'Your support for your son is very important. And I don't mean just the financial end of things. If we are not successful in getting these charges dropped and we choose the alternative of trial, it will be very important for you to show your support in public ways.'

'Don't be silly,' she said. 'I will back him come hell or high water. And these ridiculous charges must be removed.'

'Thank you, Mother,' Roulet said.

'Yes, thank you,' I said. 'I will inform you, through Mr Dobbs, where and when you are needed. It's good to know you'll be there for your son.'

I said nothing else and waited. It didn't take her long to realise that she had been dismissed.

'But you don't want me here right now, is that it?'

'That's right. We need to discuss the case and it is best for Louis to do this only with his defence team. The attorney–client privilege does not cover anyone else. You could be compelled to testify against your son.'

'But if I leave, how will Louis get home?'

'I have a driver. I will get him home.'

She looked at Dobbs, hoping he would overrule me. Dobbs smiled and stood up so he could pull her chair back. Finally she stood up to go.

'Very well,' she said. 'Louis, I will see you at dinner.'

Dobbs walked her through the door of the conference room to the hallway. Then she left and Dobbs came back, closing the door.

I told Roulet he would have to be arraigned in two weeks and submit a plea. He would have the opportunity at that time to put the state on notice that he was not waiving his right to a speedy trial.

'That's the first choice we have,' I said. 'Whether you want this thing to drag out or you want to move quickly and put the pressure on the state.'

'What are the options?' Dobbs asked.

'I'll be honest with you,' I said. 'When I have a client who is not incarcerated, my inclination is to drag it out. It's the client's freedom that is on the line—why not get the most of it before the hammer comes down?'

'You're talking about a guilty client,' Roulet said.

'On the other hand,' I said, 'if the state's case is weak, then delaying things only gives them time to strengthen their hand. If we refuse to waive our right to a speedy trial, it puts a lot of pressure on the prosecutor.'

'I didn't do what they're saying I did,' Roulet said. 'I don't want to waste any time. I want this behind me.'

'If we refuse to waive, then theoretically they must put you on trial within sixty days of arraignment. The reality is that the clock is reset to sixty days after the preliminary hearing, when a judge hears the evidence and decides if there is enough there to warrant a trial. However, we could always waive the prelim, too. That would really force their hand.'

'I like that idea,' Roulet said. 'I want this over with as soon as possible.' He had said it as though a not-guilty verdict was a foregone conclusion.

'Well, maybe it doesn't even get to a trial,' Dobbs said. 'If these charges don't hold muster—'

'The DA is not going to drop this,' I said, cutting him off. 'Usually, the cops overcharge and then the DA cuts the charges back. That didn't happen here. Instead, the DA upped the charges. That tells me two things. One is that they believe the case is solid and, two, they upped the charges so that when we start to negotiate they will deal from a higher ground.'

'You're talking about a plea bargain?' Roulet asked.

'Yeah, a disposition.'

'No plea bargain. I'm not going to jail for something I didn't do. If that is a problem for you, then we need to part company right here.'

Almost all of my clients make protestations of innocence at one point along the way. Especially if it is our first case together. But Roulet's words came with a fervour and directness I hadn't seen in a long time. Liars falter. They look away. Roulet's eyes were holding mine like magnets.

'There is also the civil liability to consider,' Dobbs added. 'A guilty plea will allow this woman to—'

'I understand all that,' I said, cutting him off again. 'I think we're getting ahead of ourselves. We don't have to make any moves for a couple of weeks. We just need to know at the arraignment how we're going to play it.'

'Louis took a year of law at UCLA,' Dobbs said. 'I think he has baseline knowledge of the situation.'

Roulet nodded.

'OK, good,' I said. 'Then let's just get to it. Louis, your mother said she expects to see you at dinner. Do you live at home? I mean at her home?'

'I live in the guesthouse. She lives in the main house.'

'Anyone else live on the premises? Any siblings, boyfriends, girlfriends?'

'Only the maid. In the main house. That's it.'

'And you work at your mother's firm?'

'More like I run it. She's not there too much any more.'

'What did you do yesterday, Sunday, during the day?'

'I played golf at Riviera, my usual foursome. Started at ten and finished at four. I came home, showered and changed, had dinner at my mother's.'

'What happened after dinner?'

'I told my mother I was going to my place but instead I went out.'

I noticed that Raul Levin had started taking notes in a small notebook.

'What kind of car do you drive?'

'I have two, a Range Rover for taking clients around in and a Porsche Carrera for myself, which is what I drove last night.'

'Where'd you go?'

'I went over the hill and down into the Valley.' He said it as though it was a risky move for a Beverly Hills boy to descend into the working-class neighbourhoods of the San Fernando Valley. 'Ventura Boulevard. I had a drink at Nat's North and then I went down the street a ways to Morgan's.'

'Those places are pick-up bars, wouldn't you say?'

'Yes. That's why I went to them. I was looking to get laid.'

'What happened at Nat's North?'

'It was a slow night, so I left. I didn't even finish my drink.'

'You go there often? Do the bartenders know you?'

'Yeah, they know me. A girl named Paula was working last night.'

'OK, so you left and drove down to Morgan's. They know you there?'

'They should. I'm a good tipper.'

I turned to Levin. 'Raul, what is the victim's name?'

He opened his file. 'Regina Campo. Friends call her Reggie. Twenty-six years old. She told police she's an actress working in telemarketing.'

'Louis, did you know Ms Campo before last night?' I asked.

Roulet shrugged. 'Sort of. I'd seen her around the bar scene. But I'd never been with her before. I'd never even spoken to her.'

'Had you ever tried?'

'No, I never could really get to her. She always seemed to be with some-one or more than one person. I don't like to have to penetrate the crowd, you know? My style is to look for the singles.'

'What was different last night?'

'Last night she came to me, that was what was different.'

'Tell us about it.'

'I was at the bar at Morgan's, having a look at the possibilities, and she was at the other end with some guy. She wasn't even on my radar because she looked like she was already taken. After a while the guy she was with got up to go take a leak or go outside for a smoke. As soon as he's gone she slides on down the bar to me and asks if I'm interested. I said I was but what about the guy she's already with? She says don't worry about him, he'll be out the door by ten and then she's free the rest of the night. She wrote her address down for me and said to come by after ten.'

'What did she write the address down on?'

'A napkin, but the answer to your next question is no, I don't still have it. I memorised the address and threw out the napkin.'

'About what time was this?'

'Between eight and nine. As soon as the guy came back in they left.'

'When did you leave the bar?'

'I stayed for a few minutes, then I left. Her apartment was in the Tarzana complex so I went up to the Lamplighter near White Oak. It was on the way.'

'Why?'

'I wanted to see what the possibilities were. You know, see if there was something better out there, something I didn't have to wait around for.'

'OK, so who'd you talk to at the Lamplighter?'

'I didn't talk to anybody. There wasn't anybody I was interested in.'

'The bartenders know you there?'

'No, not really. I don't go there all that much.'

'How long were you at the Lamplighter?'

'About an hour, I'd say. Maybe a little less.'

'At the bar? How many drinks?'

'Yeah, two drinks at the bar.'

'How many drinks in all did you have last night?'

'Um, four at the most. I left one drink untouched at Morgan's.'

'What were you drinking?'

'Martinis. Grey Goose.'

'OK,' I said. 'What time was it when you got to Ms Campo's place?'

'It was twelve minutes to ten. I looked at my watch. She'd said ten so I waited in the parking lot till ten.'

'Did you see the guy she left Morgan's with come out?'

'Yeah, I saw him. He came out and drove off, then I went up.'

'So he leaves and you go in. What happens?'

'I go in and her place is on the second floor. I go up and knock.'

'Hold on a second. You went up? How? Stairs, elevator, what?'

'Elevator.'

'Anybody else in it? Anybody see you?'

Roulet shook his head, then continued. 'She opened the door a crack, saw it was me and told me to come in. The hallway by the front door was kind of a tight space. I walked by her so she could close the door. That's how come she was behind me. And so I didn't see it coming. She had something. She hit me with something and I went down. It got black real fast.'

I thought about this for a moment. 'So she didn't say anything, yell anything. Just came up behind and knocked you out.'

'That's right.'

'OK, then what? What do you remember next?'

'I remember waking up and these two guys are sitting on me. And then the police came. And the paramedics. My hands were cuffed.'

'Where was Ms Campo?'

'She was sitting on the couch and another paramedic was working on her face. She was crying and telling the other cop that I'd attacked her. All these lies. That I'd surprised her at the door and punched her, that I'd said I was going to rape her and then kill her. I moved my arms so I could look at my hands behind my back. I saw they had my hand in a plastic bag and I could see blood on my hand. That's when I knew the whole thing was a set-up.'

'What do you mean by that?'

'She put blood on my hand to make it look like I did it. But it was my left hand. I'm not left-handed. If I was going to punch somebody, I'd use my right.' He made a punching gesture with his right hand to illustrate this.

'You said she opened the door a crack and then let you in,' I said. 'Could you see her face?'

'Not all of it.'

'What could you see?'

'Her eye. Her left eye.'

'So did you ever see the right side of her face? Like when you walked in.'

'No, she was behind the door.'

'That's it!' Levin said excitedly. 'She already had the injuries when he got there. They were to the right side of her face, and that dictated that she put the blood on his left hand.'

I nodded as I thought about the logic of this. 'OK,' I said. 'I think that'll work. Now, Louis, you've told us you'd never been with this woman. Why would she do this? Why would she set you up like you say she did?'

'Money.'

But it wasn't Roulet who'd answered. It had been Dobbs.

'It's obvious,' Dobbs continued. 'She wants money from him, from the family. The criminal charges are just the prelude to a civil suit.'

'I saw a picture of this woman in court today,' I said. 'Half her face was pulped. You are saying that's our defence, that she did that to herself?'

Levin opened his file and took out a piece of paper. It was a black-and-white photocopy of the evidence photograph Maggie had showed me in court. He slid it across the table to Dobbs and Roulet.

'We'll get the original photos in discovery,' I said. 'They look worse, a lot worse, and if we go with your story, then the jury—that is, if this gets to a jury—is going to have to buy that she did that to herself.'

I watched Roulet study the photocopy. If he had been the person who'd attacked Regina Campo, he showed nothing while studying his handiwork.

'You know,' I said, 'I like to think I'm a good persuader when it comes to juries. But even I'm having trouble believing myself with that story.'

IT WAS NOW Raul Levin's turn in the conference room. He had given me the basics of the case by phone while I'd been riding into Century City, enough to get me through the initial questioning of my client. Now he would go through the case in detail, using the police reports to show us what the prosecution would have. It was all material the defence was entitled to and would receive through the discovery process, but usually it took weeks to get it through court channels instead of the hours it had taken Levin to get it through his source. He looked down at these documents as he spoke.

'At ten eleven last night the LAPD received a nine-one-one emergency call from Regina Campo of 1760 White Oak Boulevard, apartment 211. She reported that an intruder had entered her home and attacked her. Patrol officers arrived on the premises at ten seventeen. They were met in the parking lot by Ms Campo, who said she had fled the apartment after the attack, and that neighbours Edward Turner and Ronald Atkins were in her apartment, holding the intruder. Officer Santos proceeded to the apartment, where he found Mr Roulet lying on the floor in the control of Turner and Atkins.'

'They were the two faggots who were sitting on me,' Roulet said.

'The officers took custody of the suspect,' Levin continued. 'Mr Atkins produced a folding knife, which he said had been found on the floor next to the intruder. The officers handcuffed the suspect, and paramedics were called to treat both Campo and Roulet, who had a head laceration and slight concussion. Campo was transported to Holy Cross Medical Center for treatment. Roulet was taken to Van Nuys jail. Ms Campo's apartment was sealed for crime-scene processing and the case was assigned to Detective Martin Booker of Valley Bureau detectives.'

Levin spread more photocopies of the police photos of Regina Campo's injuries out on the table. There were front and profile shots of her face and two close-ups of bruising round her neck and a small puncture mark under her jaw. All the facial injuries were on the right side of Campo's face.

'These were taken at the hospital, where Ms Campo gave a statement to Detective Booker. She said she came home about eight thirty Sunday night and was home alone when there was a knock at her door at about ten o'clock. Mr Roulet represented himself as someone Ms Campo knew, so she opened the door, and was immediately struck by the intruder's fist and driven backwards into the apartment. The intruder entered and closed and locked the door. Ms Campo was struck at least twice more and driven to the floor.'

'This is such bullshit!' Roulet yelled. He slammed his fists down on the table and stood up.

'Louis, sit down,' I said. 'These are just police reports. All we are doing is getting a first look at the case, seeing what we are up against.'

Roulet sat down. I nodded to Levin and he continued.

'Ms Campo reported that the man who attacked her had his fist wrapped in a white cloth when he punched her.'

I looked across the table at Roulet's hands and saw no swelling or bruising. Wrapping his fist would avoid such telltale injuries.

'Was it taken into evidence?' I asked.

'Yes,' Levin said. 'The blood and the cloth are being analysed.'

I looked at Roulet. 'Did the police look at or photograph your hands?'

'The detective looked at my hands but nobody took pictures.'

I nodded and told Levin to continue.

'The intruder straddled Ms Campo on the floor and grasped one hand round her neck,' he said. 'The intruder told Ms Campo that he was going to rape her and that it didn't matter to him whether she was alive or dead when he did it. She said she told him that she would cooperate.'

Levin slid another photocopy onto the table. It was a photo of a black-handled folding knife that was sharpened to a deadly point. It explained the earlier photo of the wound under the victim's neck.

Roulet slid the photocopy over to look at it more closely. He slowly shook his head. 'This is not my knife,' he said.

I didn't respond and Levin continued.

'The suspect and the victim stood up and he told her to lead the way to the bedroom. The suspect kept behind the victim and pressed the point of the knife against the left side of her throat. As Ms Campo entered a hallway leading to the apartment's two bedrooms, she turned and pushed her attacker into a large floor vase. As he stumbled back over the vase, she made a break for the front door. Realising that her attacker would recover and catch her at the door, she ducked into the kitchen and grabbed a bottle of vodka off the counter. When the intruder passed by the kitchen on his way to the front door to catch her, Ms Campo stepped out and struck him on the back of the head, knocking him to the floor. Ms Campo then stepped over the fallen man and unlocked the front door. She ran out of the door and called the police from the first-floor apartment shared by Turner and Atkins. Turner and Atkins returned to the apartment, where they found the intruder unconscious on the floor. They maintained control of him until police arrived.'

'This is incredible,' Roulet said. 'To have to sit here and listen to this. I *did not* do this. This is like a dream. She is lying! She—'

'If it's all lies, I'll tear her apart and throw her entrails into the sea. But we have to know what she has put on record before we can go after her.'

'Damn right you are going after her,' Roulet said, pointing across the table at my chest. 'I want you to go after her with everything we've got.'

'You have my promise I will,' I said. 'Now, have you finished, Raul?'

'For now. I'm still working on all the reports. I should have a transcript of the nine-one-one call tomorrow and there'll be more stuff coming in.'

'Good. Is there any mention of this guy who Louis saw her with?'

'No, none. He's not in the file.'

'And what about the knife?'

'Blood and prints on the knife. But nothing back on that yet. Tracing ownership is unlikely. You can buy those knives in any fishing store.'

'I'm telling you, that is not my knife,' Roulet interjected.

'We have to assume the fingerprints will be from the man who turned it in.' I turned to Roulet. 'But it wouldn't surprise me to find prints from you on it as well. If she put blood on your hand while you were unconscious, then she probably put your prints on the knife.'

Roulet nodded and was about to say something, but I didn't wait.

'Is there any statement from her about being at Morgan's earlier in the evening?' I asked Levin.

He shook his head. 'No, the interview with the victim was in the ER and not formal. They didn't get into what she had been doing in the early part of the evening. I'm sure that will all be covered in the follow-up investigation.'

'So what's our next step?' Roulet asked.

'The next step is for Raul to keep doing his thing, finding out what he can about this alleged victim and why she lied about being alone. We need to find out who she is and who her mystery man is too.'

'And what will you do?'

'I'll set something up with the prosecutor, try to see where he's going. I have no doubt that I'll be able to go to the DA and knock all of this down to something you can plea to and get behind you. But it will require—'

Roulet shook his head. 'I told you, I'm not going to plead guilty to something I didn't do. If we go to trial, can you win?'

I held his gaze for a moment before answering. 'I can't guarantee anything, but . . . yes, based on what I see now, I'm confident I can win this case.'

As I nodded to Roulet, I think I saw a look of hope enter his eyes.

I stood up. 'Louis, I'll take you home now.'

'Actually, I could take him, since I'm going there,' Dobbs said.

'Fine,' I said. 'But we'll meet you there. I want Raul to see his place and Louis needs to give me that cheque we spoke about earlier.'

'Sounds like a plan,' he said. 'We'll meet again there.'

Fifteen minutes later I was riding in the back of the Lincoln with Levin. We were following a silver Mercedes carrying Dobbs and Roulet. I was checking with Lorna on the phone. The only message of importance had come from Gloria Dayton's prosecutor, Leslie Faire: we had a deal.

'So,' Levin said when I closed the phone. 'What do you really think?'

'I'm not sure what to think yet,' I said. 'Whatever happened in that apartment happened quick. That's a break for us. No actual rape, no DNA.'

'It reminds me of Jesús Menéndez, only without DNA. Remember him?'

'Yeah, but I don't want to.' I tried not to think about clients who were in prison without appellate hopes or anything else left but years of time in front of them. 'You know what I do think?' I said putting us back on course. 'That there's a chance Roulet isn't lying. His story is quirky enough to be true.'

Levin whistled softly between his teeth. 'You think you might have found the innocent man?' he asked.

'That would be a first,' I said. 'If I had only known it this morning, I would have charged him the innocent man premium. If you're innocent you pay more because you're a hell of a lot more trouble to defend.'

'Ain't that the truth.'

'You know what my father said about innocent clients?'

'I thought your father died when you were, like, six years old.'

'Five, actually. They didn't even take me to the funeral.'

'And he was talking to you about innocent clients when you were five?'

'No, I read it in a book. He said the scariest client a lawyer will ever have is an innocent client. Because if he goes to prison, it'll scar you for life.'

THREE

On the morning of March 17, I was in the South Side of the city, in Compton courthouse, representing a crack cocaine dealer at his sentencing. Raul Levin was waiting for me in the crowded hallway outside the courtroom. We had arranged a meeting to go over his findings in the Roulet case. He'd had to come to Compton because I had a busy schedule.

'Where do you want to go to talk and look at what I've got?' he asked.

'I don't have time to go anywhere,' I said. 'We can go sit in my car.'

'Let's do it.'

When we were in the Lincoln I told Earl to drive around and see if he could find a place that had coffee. 'And Earl?' I added. Put on your earphones while we talk about a case back here for a while, OK?'

Earl fired up his iPod and plugged in the earbuds. He headed the Lincoln down Acacia in search of java. Levin opened his briefcase on the fold-down table built into the back of the driver's seat.

'OK, what do you have for me?' I asked. 'I'm going to see the prosecutor today and I want to have more aces in my hand than he does. We also have the arraignment Monday.'

'I think I've got a few aces here,' Levin replied. 'Let's begin with your client. Other than parking and speeding tickets—which he seems to have a problem paying—I couldn't find squat on him.'

'What's with the tickets?'

'Twice in the last four years he's let parking tickets—a lot of them—and a couple of speeding tickets accumulate unpaid. Both times it went to warrant and your colleague C. C. Dobbs stepped in to pay them off.'

'I'm glad Cecil's good for something.'

'Other than that, only one blip on the radar. At the first meeting when you were giving Roulet the drill about what to expect and so on, it comes out that he'd had a year at UCLA law and knew the system. Well, I checked on that and he's never been enrolled in the law school at UCLA.'

I thought about this. It was Dobbs who had brought up UCLA law and Roulet had just nodded. It was a strange lie for either of them to have told because it didn't really get them anything.

'So if he lied about something like that . . .' I said, thinking out loud.

'Right,' Levin said. 'But that's it on the negative side. He didn't lie about his story—at least the parts I could check out. I got wits in here who put him at Nat's North, Morgan's and then the Lamplighter, bing, bing, bing. He did just what he told us. Right down to the number of martinis. Four total and at least one of them he left on the bar unfinished.'

'They remember that he didn't even finish his drink?'

'No, I'm not relying on a bartender's memory. I've got something you're going to love, Mick. And you better love me for it because it cost me a grand.'

From his briefcase he pulled out a padded case containing a small DVD player, and loaded in a DVD. But before he could play it the car pulled to a stop and I looked up. We were in front of a place called the Central Bean.

'Let's get some coffee and then see what you've got there,' I said.

Levin and I got out and waited in line for coffee. Levin spent the time telling me about the DVD we were about to watch in the car.

'I'm in Morgan's and want to talk to this bartender named Janice but she says I have to clear it with the manager. So I go back to see him in the office and he tells me that last year they had a problem behind the bar. Pilferage from the cash register. He couldn't figure out who had sticky fingers.'

'He put in a camera.'

'You got it. A hidden camera. He caught the thief. But it worked so good he kept the camera in place. The system records on a timer from eight till two every night. He gets four nights on a tape and rotates two tapes so he always has a week's worth of film to look at.'

'He had the night in question on tape?'

'Right.'

'The cops don't know about it?'

'They haven't even come to the bar. They're going with Campo's story.'

'But we're interested in the bar, not the cash register,' I said.

'The cash register is against the wall behind the bar. The camera is above it in a smoke detector on the ceiling. And the back wall is a mirror, so you can see the whole bar in the mirror. It's just reversed. I had the tape transferred to a disk because we can manipulate the image better.'

It was our turn in line. I ordered a large coffee with cream and sugar and Levin ordered a bottle of water. We took our refreshments back to the car.

Levin started the DVD player. On the small screen was a view of the bar at Morgan's. The mirror on the wall behind the cash register displayed the customers sitting at the bar and the two bartenders. I saw Roulet sit down by himself in the centre of the frame. There was a time and date code in the bottom right corner. It said it was 8.11 p.m. on March 6.

'There's Louis showing up,' Levin said. 'And here is Reggie Campo.'

He manipulated buttons on the player and froze the image. On the short side of the bar to the right a woman and a man sat next to each other.

Levin zoomed in on them. 'And that's our Mr X. Now watch.' He widened the picture back to full frame, then moved it in fast-forward mode. 'Louis drinks his martini, he talks with the bartenders and nothing much happens for almost an hour.'

He checked a notebook that had notes against specific frame numbers. He slowed the image to normal speed at the right moment and shifted the frame again so that Regina Campo and Mr X were in the centre of the screen. I noticed that we had advanced to 8.43 p.m. on the time code.

On the screen, Mr X took a packet of cigarettes and a lighter off the bar and slid off his stool. He then walked out of camera range to the right.

'He's heading for the smoking porch,' Levin said.

Regina Campo watched Mr X go, then she slid off her stool and started walking along the front of the bar, just behind the patrons on stools. As she passed by Roulet she appeared to drag the fingers of her left hand across his shoulders. Roulet turned and watched her as she kept going.

'That's not how Roulet said it went down—'

'Hold your horses. She's heading to the bathroom.'

I waited and watched as Regina Campo came back along the bar line. This time she squeezed up to the bar between Roulet and a man on the next stool. She had to move into the space sideways and her breasts were clearly pushed against Roulet's arm. It was a come-on if ever I'd seen one. She said something to Roulet, and when he nodded she put what looked like a cocktail napkin into his hand. They had one more verbal exchange, then Campo kissed Roulet on the cheek and headed back to her stool.

'You're beautiful, Mish,' I said, using the name I gave him after he told me of his mishmash of Jewish and Mexican descent.

I knew that what was on the DVD was important. It could be cause for reasonable doubt. It seemed to show a familiarity between victim and alleged attacker that was not included in the state's case. More important, it also caught the victim in a position in which her behaviour could be interpreted as being at least partially responsible for drawing the action that followed. This was not to suggest that what followed was acceptable or not criminal, but what the video did was move a crime that might have been viewed through a black-and-white prism into the grey area.

Levin was fast-forwarding the image again. 'Now watch this,' he said. He had shifted the frame to focus on Campo and the unknown man. When the time code hit 8.59 he put the playback in slow motion.

'OK, they're getting ready to leave,' he said. 'Watch the guy's hands.'

The man took a final draw on his drink, then slipped off his stool, helped Campo off hers and they walked out of the camera frame.

'What?' I said. 'What did I miss?'

Levin slow-reversed the image until he got to where the unknown man was finishing his drink. He then froze the image and pointed to the screen. The man had his left hand down flat on the bar as he drank.

'He drinks with his right hand,' he said. 'And on his left you can see a watch on his wrist. So it looks like the guy is right-handed, right?'

'Yeah, so? The injuries to the victim came from blows from the left.'

'Think about what I've told you.'

I did. And after a few moments I got it.

'The mirror. Everything's backwards. He's left-handed.'

Levin nodded and made a punching motion with his left fist.

'This could be the whole case right here,' I said, not sure that was a good thing. If the case ended before it even got to trial, my client would simply walk away. And with him would go the big franchise payday.

Levin turned off the player and started to put it away.

'What else have you got?' I asked him.

'There's Reggie Campo,' he said. 'She's not Snow White.'

He handed me a professional photo collage that showed Regina Campo in different poses, the kind of photo sheet sent to casting directors all over the city. Campo was a very attractive woman and something about her face was familiar to me but I could not place it. I wondered if I'd seen her in a television show or a commercial.

'In the police reports she lists her current employer as Topsail Tele-marketing. They take the calls for a lot of the crap they sell on late-night TV. Workout machines and stuff like that. Anyway, it's day work. You work when you want. The thing is, Campo hasn't worked there for months.'

'So what are you telling me, she's been tricking?'

'I've been watching her the last three nights and—'

'You what?' I turned and looked at him.

If a private eye working for a criminal defendant was caught tailing the victim of a violent crime, the prosecution could claim harassment and intimidation and I'd be the one held in contempt.

'Don't worry,' Levin said. 'It was a very loose tail. And I'm glad I did it. Either the bruises and the swelling have gone or she's using a lot of make-up, because this lady's been getting a lot of visitors. All men, all alone.'

'You ran a check on her, right? No criminal record?'

'Right, she's clean. My guess is that she's new to the game. You know, these women who want to be actresses, it's a tough gig. It wears you down. She probably started by taking a little help from these guys here and there, then it became a business. She went from amateur to pro.'

'If she did that, she could've graduated to setting a guy like Roulet up. He drives a nice car, wears nice clothes . . . have you seen his watch?'

'Yeah, a Rolex. If it's real, then he's wearing ten grand right there on his wrist. Maybe that's why she picked him out of all the rest.'

'This is good,' I said. 'But it means Louis lied about more than UCLA.'

'Yeah,' Levin agreed. 'He knew he was going into a pay-for-play deal with her. He should have told you about it.'

'Yeah, and now I'm going to talk to *him* about it.'

I asked Levin where he was parked and he directed Earl to the lot. When we pulled up at the kerb, Levin took a file out of his briefcase. It had a rubber band round it that held a piece of paper to the outside cover. It was an invoice for almost $6,000 for eight days of investigative services and expenses. Based on what I had heard during the last half-hour, the price was a bargain.

'That file has everything we just talked about, plus a copy of the video from Morgan's on disk,' Levin said.

I took the file. 'I'll call this in to Lorna and we'll send out a cheque.'

He cracked his door open but didn't get out. 'Anything else?'

'The left-handed man. We have to figure out who Mr X is and whether he was part of this thing or just another customer.'

Levin nodded and pumped his left-handed fist again. 'I'm on it.' He put on his sunglasses, opened the door and slid out.

THE VAN NUYS Civic Center is a long concrete plaza enclosed by government buildings. Anchoring one end is the Van Nuys Division of the LAPD. Along one side are two courthouses sitting opposite a public library. At the end of the concrete and glass channel is a federal administration building. I waited for Louis Roulet on one of the concrete benches near the library. When I saw him crossing the plaza towards me I got up to meet him.

'Where've you been?' I said abruptly.

'I told you I'd get here as soon as I could. I was in the middle of a showing when you called.'

'Let's walk.'

I headed towards the federal building because it would give us the longest stretch before we would have to turn around to cross back. I had my meeting with Minton, the new prosecutor assigned to his case, in twenty-five minutes in the older of the two courthouses. I realised that we didn't look like a lawyer and his client discussing a case. Maybe a lawyer and his realtor discussing a land grab. I was in my Hugo Boss and Roulet was in a tan suit over a green turtleneck. He had on loafers with small silver buckles.

'There won't be any showings up in Pelican Bay,' I said to him.

'What's that supposed to mean? Where's that?'

'It's a super max prison where they send violent sex offenders. You're going to fit in there pretty good in your turtleneck and loafers.'

'Look, what's the matter? What's this about?'

'It's about a lawyer who can't have a client who lies to him. In twenty minutes I'm about to go up to see the guy who wants to send you to Pelican Bay. I need everything I can get my hands on to try to keep you out of there and it doesn't help when I find out you're lying to me.'

Roulet stopped and turned to me. He raised his hands out, palms open. 'I haven't lied to you! I did not do this thing. I don't know what—'

'You and Dobbs said you took a year of law at UCLA, right? You didn't go to UCLA law school for a year. You didn't even go for a goddamn day.'

He brought his hands down and slapped them against his sides. 'Is that what this is all about, Mickey?'

'Yeah, that's right, and from now on don't call me Mickey. My friends call me Mickey, not my lying clients.

'What does whether or not I went to law school ten years ago have to do with this case? I don't—'

'Because if you lied to me about that, then you'd lie to me about anything, and I can't have that and be able to defend you.'

'Look,' Roulet said in a weak voice. 'I lied because of my mother, OK?'

'No, not OK. Explain it to me.'

'Look, my mother and Cecil think I went to law school for a year. He brought it up with you and so I just sort of agreed. What is the harm?'

'The harm is in lying to me,' I said. 'I need to operate from the standpoint of having facts from you. Incontrovertible facts.'

'OK, OK.'

'If you weren't in law school, where were you?'

Roulet shook his head. 'Nowhere. I just didn't do anything for a year. Most of the time I stayed in my apartment and thought about what I really wanted to do with my life. I knew I didn't want to be a lawyer. I eventually went to work for Mother. She wanted me to.'

I calmed down. Most of my anger had been a show, anyway. I was trying to soften him up for the more important questioning. He was ready for it now.

'Well, now that you're coming clean and confessing everything, Louis, tell me about Regina Campo.'

'What about her?'

'You were going to pay her for sex, weren't you?'

'What makes you say—?'

I stopped and grabbed him by one of his expensive lapels. 'Answer the question!'

'All right, yes, I was going to pay.'

'Why didn't you tell me this? Don't you see how that changes the case?'

'My mother. I didn't want my mother to know I . . . you know.'

'Louis, let's sit down.' I walked him over to one of the long benches by the police station where no one could overhear us. 'Your mother wasn't even in the room when we talked about the case.'

'But Cecil was and he tells her everything.'

I nodded, making a mental note to cut Cecil Dobbs out of the loop in case matters from now on. 'OK, Louis, I think I understand. But let me tell you a little bit about how this works. You know what I am? I'm a neutraliser. My job is to neutralise the state's case. Take each piece of evidence and find a way to eliminate it from contention. Neutralise it. You follow?'

'Yes, I follow. I—'

'For almost two weeks, Louis, you've concealed from me the method by which I could neutralise the entire case. It asks the question why. Why would a guy with money at his disposal, a Porsche in the parking lot and a Holmby Hills address need to use a knife to get sex from a woman who sells it anyway? When you boil it down to that question, the case collapses, Louis, because the answer is: he wouldn't. And that's when you see the set-up, you see the trap, and now it's the defendant who starts to look like the victim.'

He nodded. 'I'm sorry,' he said.

'You should be,' I said. 'We probably wouldn't be sitting here right now if you had been up-front with me from the start.'

I realised now where my anger was truly coming from. It wasn't because Roulet had lied. It was because I saw the franchise slipping away. There would be no trial, no six-figure fee. The case was going to end today when I walked into the DA's office and told Ted Minton what I had.

'I'm sorry,' Roulet said again in a whiny voice. 'What do we do now?'

'I have a question to ask you about that night, then I'm going to go into that building over there and meet the prosecutor. By the time I come out, this may all be over and you'll be free to go back to showing your mansions.'

'Just like that?'

'Well, he may want to ask a judge to dismiss the case in court.'

Roulet opened his mouth in shock. 'Mr Haller, I can't begin to tell you—'

'You can call me Mickey. Sorry about all that before.'

'No problem. Thank you. What question do you want to ask?'

'What did the note say? The one she gave you at the bar in Morgan's.'

'It said her address and then underneath she wrote "four hundred dollars", and then under that she wrote "Come after ten".'

'Too bad we don't have that. But I think we have enough. I'll call you when it's all over.'

He put his hand out and I shook it.

'Thanks, Mick. I knew I had the best lawyer when I got you.'

I watched him walk back across the plaza towards the public parking garage. 'Yeah, I'm the best,' I said to myself.

I felt the presence of someone and turned to see a man sit down on the bench. He turned and looked at me and we recognised each other. It was Howard Kurlen, a homicide detective from the Van Nuys Division. We had bumped up against each other on a few cases over the years.

'Well, well, well,' Kurlen said. 'The pride of the California bar. You're not talking to yourself, are you? Could be bad for a lawyer if that got round.'

'I'm not worried. How are you doing, Detective?'

Kurlen produced a sandwich from a brown bag and unwrapped it. There was peanut butter in it and a layer of something else I couldn't identify. It wasn't jelly. I looked at my watch. I still had a few minutes before I needed to get in line for the metal detectors at the courthouse entrance but I wasn't sure I wanted to spend them with Kurlen and his horrible-looking sandwich.

'How's my man Jesús doin'?' the detective asked.

Kurlen had been lead detective on the Jesús Menéndez case. He had wrapped him up so tightly that Menéndez had no choice but to plead and hope for the best. He still got life.

'I don't know,' I answered. 'I don't talk to Jesús any more.'

'Yeah, I guess once they plead out and go upstate they're not much use to you. No appeal work, no nothing.'

I nodded. Every cop had a jaundiced view of defence lawyers.

'I was wondering,' he went on, 'do you sleep well at night?'

'You know what I was wondering? What the hell is in that sandwich?'

He held up what was left of the sandwich. 'Peanut butter and sardines. Lots of good protein to get me through another day of chasing scumbags. You didn't answer my question.'

'I sleep fine, Detective. How about you? You ever put your head on the pillow and wonder whether you've put innocent people away?'

'Nope,' he said, mouth full of sandwich. 'Never happened, never will.'

'Must be nice to be so sure.'

'A guy told me once that when you get to the end of your road, you have to look at the community woodpile and decide if you added to it while you were here or whether you just took from it. Well, I add to the woodpile, Haller. I sleep good. But you lawyers are all takers from the woodpile.'

'Thanks for the sermon. I'll keep it in mind next time I chop wood.'

'You don't like that, then I've got a joke for you. What's the difference between a catfish and a defence attorney?'

'Hmmm, I don't know, Detective.'

'One's a bottom-feeding scum sucker and one's a fish.'

He laughed uproariously. I stood up. It was time to go.

TED MINTON had scheduled our meeting to discuss the Roulet case at a time when he knew the deputy district attorney he shared space with had a court hearing. Minton met me in the waiting area and walked me back. He did not look more than thirty but he had a self-assured presence. I probably had ten years and a hundred trials on him, yet he showed no sign of deference. He acted as though the meeting was a nuisance he had to put up with.

When we got to his small, windowless office, he offered me his office partner's seat and closed the door. We sat down and looked at each other.

'OK,' he said. 'So we're here to talk about Louis Roulet. Let's see, I have some things for you here.' He picked up a file and handed it to me. 'I want to play fair. That's the up-to-the-minute discovery. I know I don't have to give it to you until after the arraignment but, hell, let's be cordial.'

My experience is that when prosecutors tell you they're playing fair you'd better watch your back. I fanned through the discovery file but didn't really read anything. The file Levin had gathered for me was at least four times as thick. I was suspicious that Minton was holding back on me.

'This is everything?' I asked.

'Everything I've got.'

I knew for a fact—having been married to a prosecutor—that it was not out of the ordinary for a prosecutor to tell the police investigators on a case to take their time getting all the paperwork in. They could then tell the defence lawyer they wanted to play fair and hand over practically nothing.

'And you're going to trial with this?' I waved the thin file.

'I'm not worried. But if you want to talk about a disposition, I'll listen.'

'No, no disposition on this. We're going to waive the prelim and go right to trial. No delays.'

'He won't waive speedy?'

'Nope. You've got sixty days from Monday to put up or shut up.'

Minton pursed his lips as though what I had just told him were only a minor inconvenience, but I knew I had landed a solid punch.

'Well, then, I guess we ought to talk about unilateral discovery. What do you have for me?' He had dropped the pleasant tone.

'I'm still putting it together,' I said. 'I'll have it at the arraignment Monday. But most of what I've got is probably already in this file, don't you think?'

'Most likely.'

'You have that the supposed victim is a prostitute who had solicited my client in here, right? And that she has continued that line of work since the alleged incident, right?'

Minton's mouth opened maybe a half inch and then closed. I had hit him with another solid shot, but he recovered quickly.

'I am aware of her occupation,' he said, 'But I'm surprised that you know this already. I hope you aren't sniffing around my victim, Mr Haller?'

'Call me Mickey. And what I am doing is the least of your problems. You better take a good look at this case, Ted. It's going to bite you on the ass.'

'Really? How so?'

I looked at the computer on his desk. 'Does that thing play DVDs?'

Minton nodded. 'What have you got?'

I realised that showing him the surveillance video from the bar at Morgan's would be giving an early reveal of the biggest ace that I held, but I was confident that, once he saw it, there would be no case.

'I don't have all my discovery together but I do have this.' I handed Minton the DVD I had got from Levin. 'This is from the bar at Morgan's on the night of the supposed attack.'

'And this could have been doctored.'

'But it wasn't. You can have it checked. My investigator has the original and I will tell him to make it available after the arraignment.'

Minton got the DVD to play. He watched as I pointed out the time code and all the details that Levin had pointed out to me, including Mr X and his left-handedness. When it was over he ejected the disk and held it up.

'Can I keep this until I get the original?'

'Be my guest.'

Minton put the disk on his desk. 'OK, what else?' he asked.

Now my mouth let some light in. 'What else? Isn't that enough?'

'Enough for what?'

'Look, Ted, that disk blows this case out of the water. Let's forget about arraignment and trial and talk about a joint motion to dismiss.'

Minton smiled and shook his head. 'Can't do that, Mickey. This woman was injured quite badly. She—'

'Quite badly? She's been turning tricks again all week. You—'

'How do you know that?'

I shook my head. 'Man, I am trying to help you here, save you some embarrassment, and all you're worried about is whether I've crossed some line with the victim. Well, I've got news for you. She ain't the victim. If this thing gets to a jury and they see that disk, your case is over, Ted, and you have to explain to your boss Smithson why you didn't see it coming.'

'Prostitutes can be victims too.'

I shook my head again. 'She set him up,' I said. 'She knew he had money and she laid a trap. She wants to sue him and cash in. She either hit herself or she had her boyfriend from the bar, the left-handed man, do it. No jury in the world is going to buy what you're selling. Blood on the hand or fingerprints on the knife—it was all staged after he was knocked out.'

Minton nodded as if he followed the logic, but said, 'It doesn't change the course I am taking. I do have an offer for you, though, and it will be good only until Monday's arraignment. After that, all bets are off. Your client takes his chances with a judge and jury.'

I felt I was underwater and everything I said was trapped in bubbles. No one could hear me. Then I realised there was something I was missing. The LA County DA's office got some of the best out of law school. Minton might be short on experience but it didn't mean he was short on legal intelligence. I realised I should be looking at myself, not Minton, for understanding.

I stared at him a moment and then knew. There was something in his thin file that was not in the thick one that Levin had put together. Something that would get the prosecution past the fact that Regina Campo was selling it. Minton had so much as told me already. *Prostitutes can be victims too.*

I wanted to look through the state's discovery file to compare it with everything about the case that I knew. But I could not do it in front of him.

'OK,' I said. 'What's your offer?'

'Well, he's got to do prison time. That's a given. We're willing to drop it down to assault with a deadly weapon and attempted sexual battery. We'll go to the middle of the guidelines, which would put him at about seven years.'

I stood up. 'I'll present it to him,' I said. 'But he won't take it.'

Minton and I shook hands and I said I would call him, then I headed out.

In the hallway leading to the reception area I ran into Maggie McPherson.

'Hayley had a great time Saturday,' she said about our daughter. 'She's still talking about it. She said you were going to see her this weekend, too.'

'Yeah, if that's OK.'

'Are you all right? You look like you're in a daze.'

'It's turning into a long week. I'm glad I have an empty diary tomorrow. Which works better for Hayley, Saturday or Sunday?'

'Either's fine. Were you just meeting Ted on the Roulet thing?'

'Yeah. I got his offer. Now I have to go try to sell it. That's going to be tough. Guy says he didn't do it.'

'I thought they all said that.'

'Not like this guy.'

'Well, good luck.'

'Thanks.'

We headed opposite ways in the hallway and then I remembered something and called back to her.

'Hey, Happy St Patrick's, by the way.'

'Oh.' She turned and came back towards me. 'Stacey's staying a couple of hours late with Hayley and a bunch of us are going over to Four Green Fields after work. You feel like a pint of green beer?'

Four Green Fields was an Irish pub not far from the civic centre. It was frequented by lawyers from both sides of the bar. Animosities grew slack under the taste of room-temperature Guinness.

'I don't know,' I said. 'I think I have to head over the hill to see my client, but you never know, I might come back.'

We parted again and I left the courthouse. The bench where I had sat with Roulet and then Kurlen was empty. I sat down, opened my case and pulled out the discovery file Minton had given me. I saw nothing to justify Minton's demeanour until I came to the weapon analysis report. The report I had got from Levin was completely different, as if from another case. As I read I felt perspiration popping in my hair. I had been set up. Worse, Minton had the video from Morgan's and all the time he would need to prepare for it in court.

I slapped the folder shut and pulled out my cellphone. Levin answered after two rings.

'How'd it go?' he asked. 'Bonuses for everybody?'

'Not quite. Do you know where Roulet's office is?'

'Yeah, on Canon in Beverly Hills. I've got the exact address in the file.'

'Meet me there in thirty minutes.'

WHEN THE RICH in Beverly Hills want to drop small fortunes on clothes and jewellery, they go to Rodeo Drive. When they want to drop larger fortunes on houses and condominiums, they go to Canon Drive, where the high-line real-estate companies roost. This is where I found Windsor Residential Estates and Louis Roulet.

By the time I got there, Raul Levin was already waiting on the pavement outside. 'You want to tell me what's going on?' he asked.

'Yeah, when we get in there with him.'

The showroom was lined on both sides with steel wires that ran from ceiling to floor and on which were attached frames containing the photographs and pedigrees of the estates offered for sale. Roulet was in a sitting area to the right of the reception desk, seated on a sofa with a cigarette in one hand and the phone in the other. It sounded like he was setting up a showing with another realtor. He looked shocked to see us.

'Lisa, I have to go,' he said into the phone. 'I'll call you back.' He put the phone down and stood up. 'What happened?' he said. 'Is it over?'

'Not by a long shot,' I said.

He led us past the receptionist and down a hallway into a plush office. I closed the door. I was carrying the state's discovery file. The weapon report was front and centre. I stepped over and dropped it onto the desk.

'The case against you still stands and we'll probably be going to trial.'

Roulet's face dropped. 'I don't understand,' he said, sitting down behind the desk. 'You said you were going to tear that guy a new asshole.'

'Turns out the only asshole in there was me. Because once again you didn't level with me.' I turned to Levin. 'And because you got us set up.'

Roulet opened the file. On the top page was a colour photograph of a knife with blood on its black handle and the tip of its blade. It was not the same knife that was photocopied in the records that Levin had got from his police sources and had showed us in the meeting in Dobbs's office.

'What the hell is that?' Levin asked, looking down at the photo.

'That is a knife. The real one, the one Louis had with him when he went to Reggie Campo's apartment. The one with her blood and his *initials* on it.'

Levin sat down opposite Roulet. I stayed standing and they both looked up at me. I started with Levin.

'I went in to see the DA to kick his ass today and he ended up kicking mine with that. Who was your source, Raul? Because the report they gave you on the knife being untraceable was bogus. It was put in there to trick us.'

'It was the runner,' Levin said. 'The guy who runs the reports between the police station and the DA's office. I tell him which cases I'm interested in and he makes extra copies for me.'

'Well, they're on to him and they worked it perfectly.' I turned to Roulet. 'And now I get the real weapon report and find out not only is the knife a custom-made job but it is traceable right back to you because it has your initials on it! You lied to me again!'

'I didn't lie,' Roulet yelled back. 'I tried to tell you. I said it wasn't my knife. I said it twice but nobody listened to me.'

'Then you should have clarified what you meant. Just saying it wasn't your knife was like saying you didn't do it. You should have said, "Hey, Mick, there might be a problem with the knife because I did have a knife but this picture isn't it." What did you think, that it was just going to go away?'

'Please, can you keep it down,' Roulet protested. 'There might be customers out there.'

'I don't care! You're not going to need customers where you're going. How can we claim she set you up when the prosecutor can prove you had that knife with you when you walked through the door?'

He didn't answer, but I didn't give him a lot of time to.

'No wonder they didn't bother with a follow-up investigation at the bar. Not when they've got *your* knife and *your* fingerprints in blood on it.'

'I didn't do it! It's a set-up. I'm *telling* you! It was—'

'Look, I don't care what you're telling me. I can't deal with a client who doesn't see the percentage in telling his own attorney what is going on. So the DA has made an offer to you and I think you better take it.'

Roulet took out a pack of cigarettes and lit one off the one he already had going. 'I'm not pleading guilty,' he said after a deep drag.

'Seven years. You'll be out in four. You have till court time Monday and then it disappears. Think about it, then tell me you want to take it.'

'I won't take it. I didn't do this thing, and if you won't take it to trial then I'll find somebody who will.'

'You didn't do it?' I said to Roulet, grabbing the discovery file. 'OK, if you didn't do it, then would you mind telling me why you went to see this prostitute with a custom-made Black Ninja knife with a five-inch blade, complete with your initials engraved on both sides of the blade?'

'Because I always carry it!'

'You always carry it,' I said, not a question.

'That's right. I'm a realtor. I drive expensive cars. I wear expensive jewellery. And I often meet strangers alone in empty houses.'

'You must have some sort of system for checking customers out, right?'

'Sure, we can run a credit report and we can ask for references. But it still comes down to what they give us and these kind of people don't like to wait. When they want to see a piece of property, they want to see it. If we don't act quickly, there'll be another realtor who will.'

I nodded. There might be something here I could work with.

'There have been murders, you know,' Roulet said. 'Over the years. Every realtor knows the danger exists when you go to some of these places alone. For a while there was somebody out there called the Real-Estate Rapist. He attacked and robbed women in empty houses. My mother . . .'

He didn't finish. I waited. Nothing.

'What about your mother?'

Roulet hesitated. 'She was showing a place in Bel-Air once. She was alone and she thought it was safe because it was Bel-Air. The man raped her. He left her tied up. When she didn't come back to the office, I went to the house. I found her.' Roulet's eyes were staring at the memory.

'How long ago was this?' I asked.

'About four years. She stopped selling after it happened. Just stayed in her office and never showed another property again. I did the selling. And that's when and why I got the knife. I carry it everywhere. It was in my pocket when I went to that apartment. I didn't think anything about it.'

I was seeing how the defence could work. It still relied on coincidence. Roulet was set up by Campo and the set-up was aided coincidentally when she found the knife on him after knocking him out. It could work.

'Did your mother file a police report?' Levin asked.

Roulet shook his head as he stubbed out his cigarette in the ashtray. 'No, she was too embarrassed. Afraid it would get into the paper.'

'Who else knows about it?' I asked.

'Uh, me, and Cecil. Probably nobody else. You can't use this. She would—'

'I won't use it without her permission,' I said. 'But it could be important. I'll have to talk to her about it.'

'No, I don't want you—'

'Your life and livelihood are on the line here, Louis. You get sent to prison and you're not going to make it. Don't worry about your mother. A mother will do what she has to do to protect her young.'

Roulet looked down and shook his head. 'I don't know . . .' he said.

I exhaled. 'I know one thing,' I said. 'I'm going to go back to the DA and say we're passing on the deal. We'll go to trial and take our chances.'

I DROPPED EARL off at the commuter lot where he parked his own car every morning and drove the Lincoln back to Van Nuys and Four Green Fields. It was a shotgun pub on Victory Boulevard with the bar running down the left side and a row of scarred wooden booths down the right. It was crowded as only an Irish bar can be the night of St Patrick's Day. My guess was that the crowd was even bigger than in previous years because the drinker's holiday fell on a Thursday and many revellers were kicking off a long weekend. I had made sure my own diary was clear on Friday.

I ran into Robert Gillen in the crowd. The cameraman reached into his pocket and pulled out four crisp hundred-dollar bills and handed them to me. They were probably four of the original ten I had paid him two weeks earlier in the Van Nuys courthouse as I tried to impress Cecil Dobbs with my media-manipulation skills. I had already expensed the $1,000 to Roulet.

'I thought I'd run into you here,' he yelled in my ear.

'Thanks, Sticks,' I replied. 'It'll go towards my bar tab.'

He laughed and slapped me on the shoulder as I squeezed by him and pushed on. I finally found Maggie in the last booth in the back. It was full of six women, all prosecutors or secretaries from the Van Nuys office. They had two pitchers of Guinness on the table and one was full. But my chances of getting through the crowd to the bar to get a glass were negligible. Maggie noticed my plight and offered to share her glass with me.

'It's all right,' she yelled. 'We've swapped spit before.'

I smiled and knew that the two pitchers on the table had not been the first two. I took a long drink and it tasted good. Still standing at the side of the booth, I raised the glass in toast to Maggie.

As I had her glass, she reached over and raised the pitcher. 'Cheers!'

She didn't go so far as to drink from the pitcher. She put it down and whispered to the woman on the outside of the booth, who got up to let her out.

Maggie stood up and kissed me on the cheek and said, 'It's always easier for a lady to get a glass in these sorts of situations.'

'Especially beautiful ladies,' I said.

She gave me one of her looks and turned towards the crowd, which was five deep between us and the bar. She whistled shrilly and it caught the attention of one of the purebred Irish guys who worked the tap handles.

'I need a pint glass,' she yelled.

A clean glass made its way back to us hand to hand over the heads of the crowd. She filled it from the fresh pitcher and then we clicked glasses.

'So,' she said. 'Did Minton sandbag you?'

I nodded. 'Him *and* the cops did, yeah.'

'With that guy Corliss? I told them he was full of shit. They all are.'

I tried to act like what she had just said was not news to me and that Corliss was a name I already knew. I took a long slow drink from my glass.

'I shouldn't have said that,' she said. 'But my opinion doesn't matter. If Minton's dumb enough to use him, you'll take the guy's head off, I'm sure.'

I guessed that she was talking about a witness. But I had seen nothing in my review of the discovery file that mentioned a witness named Corliss. The fact that it was a witness she didn't trust led me further to believe that Corliss was a snitch. Most likely a jailhouse snitch.

'How come you know about him?' I asked. 'Minton told you about him?'

She frowned. 'No, I'm the one who sent him to Minton. He was there in the pen at the first appearance. That's why he called me.'

Now I understood. Corliss must have been in the group of inmates taken into the courtroom with Roulet. He had seen Maggie and me arguing over Roulet's bail. He therefore thought that Maggie still had the case.

'When did he call you?' I asked. 'After the hearing that Monday?'

The case hadn't made any notice in the newspapers or on TV. So I was curious as to where Corliss would have got the information he was trying to trade. Then I remembered that Maggie had been specific in detailing Regina Campo's injuries because she was trying to impress the judge to hold Roulet without bail. If Corliss had been in court, he'd have been privy to all the details he'd need to make up a jailhouse confession from my client.

'Yes, he called me late Monday,' Maggie answered.

'So why did you think he was full of shit? He's done it before, hasn't he? The guy's a professional snitch, right?'

She shook her head. 'I am sure you will find out all you need to know during discovery. Can we just have a friendly pint of Guinness here?'

'Tell you what,' I said. 'You've probably had enough Guinness for one St Patrick's Day. How about we get out of here and get something to eat?'

'Why, so you can keep asking me about your case?'

'No, so we can talk about our daughter.'

'Where are you taking me to dinner?'

I mentioned an expensive Italian restaurant in Sherman Oaks and her eyes got warm. It had been a place we had always gone to for anniversaries. Our apartment, which she still had, was a few blocks away on Dickens.

'Think we can eat there in an hour?' she asked.

'If we leave right now and order without looking.'

'You're on. Let me just say some quick goodbyes.'

'I'll drive.'

A few minutes later I was steering the Lincoln down the narrow alley that led to the door of the restaurant. A valet took the car and we went in. The hostess recognised us and acted like it had been only a couple of weeks since the last time we had been in.

I asked for a bottle of Shiraz and we ordered pasta dishes without looking at a menu. We skipped salads and appetisers. After the waiter left I checked my watch and saw we still had forty-five minutes. Plenty of time.

The Guinness was catching up with Maggie. She smiled in a fractured sort of way that told me she was drunk. Beautifully drunk.

'You should probably lay off the wine,' I told her. 'Or you'll have a headache tomorrow.'

'Don't worry about me. I'll lay what I want and lay off what I want.' She smiled at me. 'So how you been, Haller? I mean really.'

I smiled back. 'Fine. You? And I mean really.'

'Never better. Are you past Lorna now?'

'Yeah, we're even friends.'

'And what are we?'

'I don't know. Sometimes adversaries, I guess.'

'We can't be adversaries if we can't stay on the same case together. Besides, I'm always looking out for you. Like with that dirtbag, Corliss.'

'Thanks for trying, but he still did the damage.'

'I just have no respect for a prosecutor who would use a jailhouse snitch. Doesn't matter that your client is an even bigger dirtbag.'

'He wouldn't tell me exactly what Corliss said my guy said.'

'That's not fair.'

'That's what I said. It's a discovery issue but we don't get a judge until after the arraignment on Monday. So there's nobody I can complain to yet. Minton knows that. It's like you warned me. He doesn't play fair.'

Her cheeks flushed. I had pushed the right buttons and she was angry. For Maggie, winning fair was the only way to win.

We were sitting at the end of the banquette that ran along the back wall of the restaurant. We were on both sides of a corner. Maggie leaned towards me but went too far and we banged heads. She laughed, then tried again.

'He said he asked your guy what he was in for,' she said in a low voice, 'and your guy said, "For giving a bitch exactly what she deserved." He said your client told him he punched her out as soon as she opened her door.'

She leaned back again, too quickly, bringing on a swoon of vertigo.
'You OK?'

'Yes, but can we change the subject? I don't want to talk about work.'

'Sure.'

Just then the waiter brought our wine and our dinners at the same time.
The wine was good and the food was like home comfort. Then Maggie hit
me with a pitch right out of the blue.

'You didn't know about Corliss, did you? Not till I opened my big mouth.'

'I knew Minton was hiding something. I thought it was a jailhouse—'

'Bullshit. You got me drunk so you could find out what I knew.'

'Uh, I think you were already drunk when I hooked up with you tonight.'

She was poised with her fork up over her plate, a long string of linguine
with pesto sauce hanging off it. She then pointed the fork at me. 'Good
point. So what about our daughter?'

I shrugged. 'I think what you said last week is right. She needs her father
more in her life. And I want to play a bigger part. I was thinking maybe we
should set up a schedule, you know? Like make it a regular thing. She could
even stay overnight sometimes—I mean, if she wanted.'

'Are you sure about that? This is new from you.'

'It's new because I didn't know about it before. When she was smaller I
didn't really know what to do with her. Now I like talking to her. Being with
her. I learn more from her than she does from me, that's for sure.

She smiled. 'Well, great,' she said. 'I'm really glad. But let's move slow.
We can work out some dates and see how it goes.'

We continued eating in silence until we both had almost finished. Then
Maggie surprised me again.

'I don't think I can drive my car tonight,' she said.

I nodded. 'I was thinking the same thing.'

'But you only had half a pint at—'

'No, I mean I was thinking the same thing about you. But don't worry,
I'll drive you home.'

'Thank you.' She reached across the table and put her hand on my wrist.
'And will you take me back to get my car in the morning?'

She smiled sweetly at me. I looked at her, trying to read this woman who
had told me to hit the road four years before. The woman I had never been
able to get by or get over, whose rejection sent me reeling into a relationship I knew from the beginning couldn't go the distance.

'Sure,' I said. 'I'll take you.'

FOUR

In the morning, I awoke to find my eight-year-old daughter sleeping between me and my ex-wife. I reviewed what had happened the night before and remembered that I had ended up drinking all but one glass of the bottle of wine at the restaurant. I remembered taking Maggie home to the apartment and coming in to find our daughter had already fallen asleep for the night—in her own bed.

After the babysitter had been released, Maggie opened another bottle of wine. When we finished it she took me by the hand and led me to the bedroom we had once shared. But I couldn't remember whether it had been a triumphant return to the bedroom or a failure. I also couldn't remember what words had been spoken, what promises had possibly been made.

'This is not fair to her.'

I turned my head on the pillow. Maggie was awake. She was looking at our sleeping daughter's angelic face.

'What isn't fair?'

'Her waking up and finding you here. She might get the wrong idea.'

'How'd she get in here?'

'I carried her in. She had a nightmare.'

'Do you want me to leave before she wakes up? I could get dressed and act like I just came by to get you and drive you back to your car.'

'I don't know. Get dressed for now. Try not to wake her up.'

I slipped out of the bed, grabbed my clothes and went down the hall to the guest bathroom. I quickly got dressed and went back up the hallway to the bedroom and peeked in.

Hayley was still asleep. With her arms spread across two pillows she looked like an angel with wings. Maggie was pulling a long-sleeve T-shirt over an old pair of sweats. I walked in and stepped over to her.

'I'm going to go and have some coffee and be back in an hour,' I whispered. 'We can all go together and get your car and then I'll take Hayley to school. I'll even pick her up later if you want. My diary's clear today.'

'Just like that? You're going to start driving her to school?'

'She's my daughter. Don't you remember anything I told you last night?'

She shifted the line of her jaw. 'Well, yes, but I thought you were just saying that to get into my head on your case or just plain get me into bed.'

I laughed and shook my head. Any fantasies about us that I'd had the night before were vanishing quickly.

'I wasn't the one who led the other up the steps to the bedroom,' I said.

'Oh, so it was really about the case.'

'Tell you what,' I said. 'I'll be back in an hour. If you want a ride to the car that you were too drunk to drive last night, be ready and have her ready.'

'It's OK. We'll take a cab. And keep your voice down.'

I looked over at my daughter, still asleep despite our verbal sparring.

'What about her? Do you want me to take her tomorrow or Sunday?'

'I don't know. Call me tomorrow.'

'Fine. Goodbye.'

I left her there in the bedroom. Outside the apartment building I walked a block down Dickens to the Lincoln. Fighting always made me hungry, and I realised I was starved. I drove to the Du-Par's by Laurel Canyon Boulevard and ordered a short stack of pancakes and coffee. I tried to forget about Maggie McFierce by opening up my briefcase and pulling out a legal pad and the Roulet files. Before diving into the files I made a call to Levin.

'I've got something for you,' I said.

'Can't this wait till Monday? I just got home a couple of hours ago.'

'No, it can't wait and you owe me one after yesterday. Besides, you're not even Irish. I need you to background somebody.'

'All right, wait a minute.' I heard him put down the phone while he probably grabbed pen and paper to take notes. 'OK, go ahead.'

'A guy named Corliss was arraigned right after Roulet back on the 7th. They were in the holding pen at the same time. He's now trying to snitch Roulet off, saying Roulet told him that he gave a bitch what she deserved. Words to that effect. I want everything there is to know about the guy.'

'OK, what else you got?'

'That's it, other than I got a tip that he's a repeat snitch. Find out who he's crapped on in the past and there might be something there I can use.'

I closed the phone just as my pancakes arrived. I doused them with maple syrup and started eating while looking through the state's discovery file. The weapon report remained the only surprise. Everything else in the file, except the colour photos, I had already seen in Levin's file.

I moved on to that. Levin had larded the file with everything found in the net he had cast. He even had copies of the parking tickets and speeding citations Roulet had accumulated and failed to pay in recent years.

I was nearly through it all when the waitress swung by my booth with a coffee pot, looking to refill my mug. She recoiled when she saw the battered face of Regina Campo in the photos I had put to the side of the files.

'Sorry about that,' I said. I covered the photo with one of the files. 'It's work,' I said in feeble explanation. 'I didn't mean to do that to you.'

'All I can say is I hope you get the bastard that did that to her,' she said as she poured the coffee.

I nodded. She thought I was a cop. Probably because I hadn't shaved.

'I'm working on it,' I said.

She went away and I went back to the file. As I slid the photo of Regina Campo out from underneath it, I saw the undamaged left side of her face first. A wave of familiarity came over me again. I knew this woman looked like another woman I knew or was at least familiar with. But who?

I also knew it was going to bother me until I figured it out. I took the face shot of Campo and folded it lengthways down the middle so that one side of the crease showed the damaged right side of her face and the other showed the unblemished left side. I then slipped the folded photo into the inside pocket of my jacket and got up from the booth.

There was no one in the restroom. I quickly went to the sink and took out the folded photo. I leaned over the sink and held the crease of the photo against the mirror with the undamaged side of Reggie Campo's face on display. The mirror reflected the image, creating a full and undamaged face. I stared at it for a long time and finally realised why the face was familiar.

'Martha Rentería,' I said.

Back at the booth, I gathered my files and photos and put them all back into my briefcase. I left a more than adequate amount of cash on the table for tab and tip and left the restaurant in a hurry. I felt like I was having a strange food reaction. My face felt flushed and I was hot under the collar. I thought I could hear my heart pounding beneath my shirt.

Fifteen minutes later I was parked in front of my storage warehouse on Oxnard Avenue in North Hollywood. Behind a double garage door I have a 1,500-square-foot space where I keep the boxes of files from dead cases, as well as two other Lincoln Town Cars. Last year when I was flush I bought four Lincolns at once so I could get a fleet rate. The plan was to use each one until it hit 60,000 miles on the odometer, then dump it on a limousine service. I was on the second Lincoln and it would soon be time for the third.

Once I got the garage door up I went to the archival area, where the file boxes were arranged by year on industrial shelving. I found the boxes from two years earlier and ran my finger down the list of client names until I found the name Jesús Menéndez.

I pulled the box off the shelf and squatted down and opened it on the floor. The Menéndez case had been short-lived. He took a plea early, so there were only four files and these mostly contained copies of the documents relating to the police investigation. I paged through the files, looking for photographs, and finally saw what I was looking for in the third file.

Martha Rentería was the woman Jesús Menéndez had pleaded guilty to murdering. She was a twenty-four-year-old dancer with a dark beauty and a smile of big white teeth. She had been found stabbed to death in her Panorama City apartment. She had been beaten before she was stabbed and her facial injuries were to the left side of her face. I found the close-up shot of her face contained in the autopsy report. Once more I folded the photo lengthways, one side of her face damaged, one side untouched.

On the floor I took the two folded photographs, one of Regina and one of Martha, and fitted them together. The half faces damn near formed a perfect match. The two women looked so alike they could have passed for sisters.

SITTING on the concrete floor of my warehouse, files fanned out around me, I reacquainted myself with the Menéndez case. Jesús Menéndez was convicted of killing Martha Rentería after following her home to Panorama City from a strip club in East Hollywood called the Cobra Room. He raped her, then stabbed her more than fifty times. There was so much blood that it seeped through the bed and through cracks in the wooden floor to the apartment below. That's when the police were called.

The case against Menéndez was formidable but circumstantial. He had also hurt himself by admitting to police—before I was on the case—that he had been in her apartment on the night of the murder. But it was the DNA on the fluffy pink towel in the victim's bathroom that did him in.

I had taken on the Menéndez case as what I would call a 'loss leader'. Menéndez had no money to pay for the time and effort it would take to mount a thorough defence, but the case had garnered substantial media coverage and I was willing to trade my time and work for the free advertising.

Just a few months before Menéndez's arrest I had successfully defended his older brother Fernando in a heroin case. I had got a possession and sales charge knocked down to a simple possession. He got probation instead of prison. Those efforts resulted in Fernando calling me on the night Jesús was arrested for the murder of Martha Rentería.

Jesús had gone to the Van Nuys Division voluntarily after his face had been shown on every TV channel in the city—a police artist's drawing of the Latin male believed to have followed Rentería from the club. He had told his family that he was going to straighten things out and be back. But he never came back, so his brother called me. I agreed to take the case pro bono.

By the time I got to Jesús Menéndez, he had already told detectives Howard Kurlen and Don Crafton that he had not followed Rentería home but had been an invited guest to her apartment. He explained that earlier in the day he had won $1,100 on the California lotto and had been willing to trade some of it for a little of Rentería's attention. He said that at her apartment they had engaged in consensual sex and that when he left she had been alive and $500 in cash richer.

The holes in Menéndez's story were many. There had been no state lotto on the day of the murder and the mini-market where he said he had cashed his winning ticket had no record of paying out a $1,100 win to Menéndez or anyone else. Also, no more than eighty dollars in cash had been found in the victim's apartment. Lastly, the autopsy report indicated that bruising and other damage to the victim precluded consensual sexual relations. The medical examiner concluded that she had been brutally raped.

No fingerprints other than the victim's were found in the apartment. The place had been wiped clean. No semen was found in the victim's body, suggesting that her rapist had used a condom during the assault. But in the bathroom off the bedroom where the murder had taken place, a crime-scene investigator using a black light found a small amount of semen on a pink towel hanging on a rack near the toilet. The theory that came into play was that after the attack the killer had stepped into the bathroom, removed the condom and flushed it down the toilet. He had then wiped his penis with the towel. When cleaning up after the crime and wiping surfaces he might have touched, he forgot about that towel.

Based on his lies and the admission that he had been in the victim's apartment, Menéndez was arrested on suspicion of murder. Oral swabs were collected from him and sent to the lab for DNA typing.

When I entered the case, unaware of the DNA comparison that was under way, I saw a glimmer of light for Jesús Menéndez. He was Mexican born and had come to this country at the age of eight. His family spoke only Spanish at home and he had attended a school for Spanish speakers until dropping out at fourteen. He spoke only rudimentary English, and Kurlen and Crafton made no effort to bring in a translator for his interview.

My plan was to attack the interview, which had been taped, as a violation of Menéndez's rights because he could not have understood the Miranda warning he had been read by Kurlen or the document listing these rights in English that he had signed at the detective's request.

This is where the case stood until the lab results came back matching his DNA to that recovered from the towel in the victim's bathroom. After that, the prosecution didn't need the interview or his admissions. The DNA put Menéndez directly on the scene of a brutal rape and murder.

The district attorney himself revealed the DNA findings at a press conference and announced that his office would seek the death penalty. He added that detectives had also located three eyewitnesses—Menéndez's three roommates—who had seen him throw a knife into the LA River, although the knife had not been recovered.

Using Fernando Menéndez as my translator, I went to the Van Nuys jail and told Jesús that his only hope was for a deal that the DA had floated by me. If Menéndez would plead guilty to murder, I could get him a life sentence with the possibility of parole. I told him he'd be out in fifteen years.

It was a tearful discussion. Jesús insisted that he did not kill Rentería. He said he had lied to the detectives to protect Fernando, who had given him the money after a good month selling tar heroin. He told me that Rentería had had other suitors that night in the Cobra Room. The reason he had paid her so much was because she had played him off another bidder.

Lastly, Jesús told me it was true that he had thrown a knife into the river but it wasn't the murder weapon. It was just a knife he used on day jobs he picked up in Pacoima. It looked like the knife they were describing on TV and he got rid of it before going to the police to straighten things out.

I listened and then told them that none of their explanations mattered. The only thing that mattered was the DNA. Jesús had a choice. He could take the fifteen years or go to trial and risk getting the death penalty. I reminded Jesús that he was a young man. He could be out before he was forty.

By the time I left the jailhouse meeting, I had Jesús Menéndez's consent to make the deal. I saw him only one more time after that—at his plea-and-sentencing hearing when I coached him through the guilty plea. He was shipped off to Pelican Bay initially and then down to San Quentin.

On the warehouse floor, I opened the report on the autopsy of Martha Rentería. I was looking for two things that had probably not been looked at very closely by anyone else before. The first was the part of the report that dealt with the stab wounds that Rentería had suffered. Under the heading

'Wound Profile', the unknown weapon was described as a blade no more than five inches long, an inch wide and one-eighth of an inch thick. Also noted were the jagged skin tears at the top of the victim's wounds, indicating that the top of the blade had an uneven line. The shortness of the blade suggested that the weapon might be a folding knife.

I opened my briefcase, pulled out the recovered-weapon analysis report from the state's discovery file for the Campo case, and went over the paragraph I had read the day before. The knife was described as a custom-made folding knife with a blade five inches long, one inch wide and one-eighth of an inch thick—matching the unknown knife used to kill Martha Rentería.

I tried not to let the burning feeling building up in my throat distract me. I needed to check for a specific wound but I didn't want to look at the photos of Martha Rentería's horribly violated body. Instead I went to the page on which the medical examiner had marked the wounds on a generic body profile, numbering them from 1 to 53.

I saw two dots marked on either side of the neck, numbered 1 and 2. I turned the page and looked at the list of individual wound descriptions.

The description for wound number 1 read: *Puncture on the lower right neck with ante-mortem histamine levels, indicative of coercive wound.*

The description for wound number 2 read: *Superficial puncture on the left neck with ante-mortem histamine levels, indicative of coercive wound.*

The descriptions meant that the wounds had been inflicted while Martha Rentería was still alive. The examiner had suggested it was likely that the wounds resulted from a knife being held to the victim's neck in a coercive manner. It was the killer's method of controlling her.

I turned back to the state's discovery file for the Campo case. I pulled the photographs of Regina Campo and the report on her physical examination at Holy Cross Medical Center. Campo had a small puncture wound on the left side of her neck and no wounds on her right side. I scanned her police statement until I found her description of how she got the wound. She said her attacker pulled her up off the living-room floor and told her to lead him to the bedroom. He controlled her from behind by gripping her bra strap with his right hand and holding the knife point against the left side of her neck with his left hand. When she felt him momentarily rest his wrist on her shoulder she made her move, suddenly pivoting and pushing backwards, knocking her attacker into a large floor vase, then breaking away.

I thought I understood why Regina Campo had only one wound on her neck, compared with the two Martha Rentería had ended up with. If

Campo's attacker had got her to the bedroom and put her down on the bed, he would have been facing her when he climbed on top of her. If he'd kept his knife in the same hand—the left—the blade would have shifted to the other side of her neck. When they found her dead in the bed, she would have had coercive punctures on both sides of her neck.

I put the files aside and sat on the floor without moving for a long time. In my mind I held the image of Jesús Menéndez's tear-streaked face when I told him that he must plead guilty. I told him he had no choice. And though it was from his mouth that the word *guilty* was uttered in front of the judge, it felt to me now as though it had been me, his own attorney, holding the knife of the system against his neck and forcing him to say it.

FIVE

I got out of the new rent-a-car facility at San Francisco International by one o'clock and drove the Lincoln they gave me north to the city. By the time I had got over the Golden Gate it was almost two.

San Quentin is over a century old and looks as though the soul of every prisoner who lived or died there is etched on its dark walls. It was as foreboding a prison as I had ever visited, and I had been to every one in California.

They searched my briefcase and made me go through a metal detector. As I had not formally scheduled the interview the required five days in advance, I was put in a no-contact room—a Plexiglas wall between us with dime-size holes to speak through. I sat down and didn't have to wait long until they brought Menéndez in on the other side of the glass.

Two years ago, when he was shipped off to prison, Jesús Menéndez had been a young man. Now he looked like he was already the forty years old I told him he could beat if he pleaded guilty. He looked at me with eyes as dead as the gravel stones out in the parking lot.

We didn't bother with hellos and I got right into it.

'Look, Jesús, I don't have to ask you how you've been. I know. But something's come up and it could affect your case. I need to ask you a few questions. You understand me?'

'Why questions now? You have no questions before.'

I nodded. 'You're right. I should've asked more questions back then. I didn't know then what I think I know now. I am trying to make things right.'

'What do you want?'

'I want you to tell me about that night at the Cobra Room. You told me that you had to impress the girl, that you had to spend more than you wanted to because another guy was trying to get with her. Remember that?'

'*Si*, he was there talking. She went to him but she came back to me.'

'OK. If you saw a picture of him, would you remember him?'

'The guy who talked big? I think I 'member.'

'OK.'

I opened my briefcase and took out six photos. They included the booking photo of Louis Ross Roulet and five other mug shots I had culled out of my archive boxes. One by one I held the photos up to the glass. Menéndez leaned forward. As I showed each of the first five he looked, thought about it, then shook his head. But on the sixth photo I saw his eyes flare.

'That one,' he said. 'Is him.'

I turned the photo towards me to be sure. It was Roulet.

'And you're sure?'

Menéndez nodded. 'He's the one.'

'What makes you so sure?'

'Because I know. In here I think on that night all of my time.'

I nodded.

'Who is the man?' he asked.

'I can't tell you that right now. But I am trying to get you out of here.'

'You were the one who tol' me to come here.'

'At the time I didn't think there was a choice.'

'How come you never ask me, did you murder this girl? You my lawyer, man. You din't care. You din't listen.'

I stood up and called for the guard. Then I answered his question.

'To legally defend you I didn't need to know the answer to that question. If I asked my clients if they were guilty of the crimes they were charged with, very few would tell me the truth. And if they did, I might not be able to defend them to the best of my ability.'

The guard opened the door, and I left Menéndez still in his chair on the other side of the glass. I had come 400 miles for five minutes, but those minutes had been devastating.

Back in the airport departure lounge I sat with my elbows on my knees and my face in my hands. It was the lowest point of my life and professional career. My greatest fear had been realised and I hadn't known it. Not until now. I had been presented with innocence but I had not seen it or grasped it. Instead, I had thrown it into the maw of the machine like everything else. Now it was a cold, grey innocence, as dead as gravel and hidden in a fortress of stone and steel. And I had to live with it.

There was no solace to be found in the knowledge that, had we rolled the dice and gone to trial, Jesús would probably be on death row right now. Because I knew as sure as I knew anything else in the world that Jesús Menéndez had been innocent and I hadn't recognised it. I had turned away.

The bottom line was that I believed that I had one client who was guilty of the murder another client was serving a life sentence for. I could not help one without hurting the other. I needed a plan. I needed proof. But for the moment I could only think of Jesús Menéndez's dead eyes, because I knew I was the one who had killed the light in them.

As SOON AS I got off the plane at Burbank I turned on my cellphone. I had not come up with a plan, but I had come up with my next step and that started with a call to Raul Levin. The phone buzzed in my hand, which meant I had messages. I decided I would get them after I set Levin in motion.

He answered my call and immediately asked if I had got his message.

'I just got off a plane,' I said. 'What was the message?'

'Just an update on Corliss.'

'What are you doing tonight?'

'Just hanging out. I don't go out on Fridays. Too many drunks on the road.'

'Well, I want to meet, to talk to somebody. Bad things are happening.'

Levin apparently sensed something in my voice because he agreed to meet me at the Smoke House over by the Warner Studios.

At the airport valet window, I gave my ticket to a man in a red jacket and checked my messages while waiting for the Lincoln. Three messages had come in, all during the flight from San Francisco. The first was from Maggie.

'Michael, I just wanted to say I'm sorry about how I was this morning. To tell you the truth, I was mad at myself for some of the things I said last night and the choices I made. I took it out on you and I should not have. Um, if you want to take Hayley out tomorrow or Sunday she would love it and, who knows, maybe I could come too. Either way, just let me know.'

I saved the message to listen to again sometime and went on to the next. I was expecting it to be from Levin, but the next voice I heard was Roulet's.

'It's me. Louis. I was just checking in. I was just wondering after yesterday where things stood. I also have something I want to tell you.'

I hit the erase button and moved on to the last message—Levin's.

'Hey, Bossman, I have some stuff on Corliss. Dwayne Jeffery Corliss. He's a hype and he's done the snitch thing a couple of other times here in LA. He was arrested for stealing a bike he probably planned to trade for a little Mexican tar. He has parlayed snitching off Roulet into a ninety-day lockdown programme at County–USC. So we won't be able to get to him. Shrewd move by the prosecutor. Anyway, I'm still running him down. Something came up in Phoenix that looks pretty good for us. Something that blew up in his face. I should be able to confirm it by Monday.'

I erased the message and closed the phone. 'Say no more,' I said.

Once I heard that Corliss was a hype, I understood why Maggie had not trusted the guy. Hypes—needle addicts—were the most desperate and unreliable people you could come across in the machine. They would snitch off their own mothers to get the next injection. Every one of them was a liar and could be shown as such in court.

I was puzzled, however, by what the prosecutor was up to. Corliss's name was not in the discovery material Minton had given me. Yet he had stuck Corliss into a ninety-day programme for safekeeping. Was he hiding him, or simply putting him on a shelf in the closet so he would know exactly where he was and where he'd be if his testimony was needed? Minton obviously believed that I didn't know about Corliss. And if it hadn't been for Maggie's slip, I wouldn't. It was a dangerous move, nevertheless. Judges do not look kindly on prosecutors who flout the rules of discovery.

It led me to a possible strategy for the defence. If Minton tried to spring Corliss in trial, I might not even object under the rules of discovery. I might let him put him on the stand so I could shred him in front of the jury.

Levin was wrong and so was Minton if he was thinking I couldn't reach his witness. By coincidence, my client Gloria Dayton had been placed in a lockdown programme at County–USC after she snitched off her drug-dealing client. It was likely that she shared group therapy sessions or even meal-times with Corliss. I might not be able to get directly to him but as Dayton's attorney I could get to her, and she could get a message to Corliss.

The Lincoln pulled up and I gave the valet a couple of dollars. I exited the airport and drove south on Hollywood Way towards the Smoke House. I got there ahead of Levin and ordered a vodka martini at the bar.

Levin came in and got himself a beer, then we walked over to a table. When the waitress came we ordered salads, steaks and potatoes. I also asked for an order of the restaurant's signature garlic cheese bread.

'So?' Levin finally said after she was gone. 'You called the meeting.'

I nodded. 'I want to tell you a story. Not all of the details are set or known. But I'll tell it to you in the way I think it goes and then you tell me what you think and what I should do. OK?'

'I like stories. Go ahead.'

'I don't think you'll like this one. It starts two years ago with—'

I stopped and waited while the waitress put down our salads and the cheese bread. I asked for another vodka martini even though I was only halfway through the one I had. I wanted to make sure there was no gap.

'So,' I said after she was gone. 'This whole thing starts two years ago with Jesús Menéndez. You remember him, right?'

'He's the client you always say is in prison because he wiped his dick on a fluffy pink towel.'

He smiled. It was true I often used the case to get a laugh when trading stories at Four Green Fields with other lawyers. That was before I knew what I now know. I did not return the smile.

'Yeah, well, it turns out Menéndez didn't do it. He was innocent.'

Levin's face grew serious. He nodded, putting something together. 'He's in San Quentin. You were up at the Q today.'

I nodded. 'Let me back up and tell the story,' I said. 'You didn't do much work for me on Menéndez because there was nothing to be done. They had the DNA, his own incriminating statement and three witnesses who saw him throw a knife into the river. It was a hopeless case. So basically all I did was walk him to a plea. He said he didn't do it but there was no choice. The DA was going for the death penalty. He'd have gotten that or life without parole. I got him life with and I made him take it.'

I looked at my salad. I didn't feel like eating. I just felt like drinking and pickling the cork in my brain that contained all the guilt cells.

Levin waited me out. He wasn't eating, either.

'The case, if you remember, was about the murder of Martha Rentería, a dancer at the Cobra Room on East Sunset. Instead of a stage, they have a pit in the centre of the club, and when the music starts these guys dressed like Aladdin come out carrying this big cobra basket between two bamboo poles. They put it down and the girl comes up out of the basket dancing.'

'It's Hollywood, baby,' Levin said. 'You gotta have a show.'

'Well, Menéndez liked the show. He had eleven hundred dollars his drug-dealer brother had given him and he took a fancy to Martha Rentería. After her set they sat and talked and then she circulated a bit and pretty soon he knew he was in competition with another guy. He trumped the other guy by offering her five hundred dollars if she'd take him home.'

'But he didn't kill her when he got there?'

'Uh-uh. He followed her car in his. Got there, had sex, flushed the condom, wiped his prick on the towel and then went home. The story starts after he left. The real killer knocks on the door, maybe fakes like it's Jesús and that he's forgotten something. She opens the door. Or maybe it was an appointment. She was expecting the knock and she opens the door.'

'The guy from the club? The one Menéndez was bidding against?'

I nodded. 'Exactly. He comes in, punches her a few times to soften her up and then takes out his folding knife and holds it against her neck while he walks her to the bedroom. Sound familiar? Only she isn't lucky like Reggie Campo was. He puts her on the bed, puts on a condom and climbs on top. Now the knife is on the other side of her neck and he keeps it there while he rapes her. And when he's done, he stabs her again and again.'

My second martini came and I took it right from the waitress's hand and gulped half of it down. She asked if we'd finished with the salads and we waved them away untouched. Then I got right back to the story.

'After she's dead, the killer wipes the place down to take care of any finger-prints he might have left. And in the process he wipes away Menéndez's prints. This will look bad for Menéndez when he later goes to the police to explain that he is the guy in the sketches but he didn't kill Martha. They'll say, "Then why'd you wear gloves when you were there?"'

Levin shook his head. 'Oh, man, if this is true . . .'

'Don't worry, it's true. Menéndez gets a lawyer who once did a good job for his brother but this lawyer wouldn't know an innocent man if he kicked him in the nuts. This lawyer is all about the deal. He never even asks the kid if he did it. He just assumes he did it because they got his DNA on the towel and because of the witnesses who saw him toss the knife.' I gulped down the rest of the martini. 'Jesús Menéndez goes off to prison a young man. I just saw him and he's twenty-six going on forty.'

I was looking down at the table when a platter with a sizzling steak and steaming potato was put down. I looked up at the waitress and told her to bring me another martini. Then I cut into my steak and ate a piece.

'Who was the second guy who came to her door?' Levin asked.

I opened my briefcase and reached into it. 'I went up to San Quentin today and showed Menéndez a six-pack. All mug shots of my clients. Mostly former clients. Menéndez picked one out in less than ten seconds.'

I tossed the mug shot of Louis Roulet across the table. It landed face down. Levin picked it up and looked at it, then put it back face down.

'Let me show you something else,' I said. I pulled out the two folded photographs of Martha Rentería and Regina Campo. 'It's like a puzzle. Put them together and see what you get.'

Levin put the one face together from the two and nodded as he understood the significance. The killer—Roulet—zeroed in on women who fitted a model or profile he desired.

'You know that video from the bar?' I asked. 'What it shows is a killer at work. Like you, he saw that Mr X was left-handed. When he attacked Reggie Campo he punched with his left and held the knife with his left. This guy saw an opportunity and took it. Reggie Campo is the luckiest woman alive.'

'You think there are others? Other murders, I mean.'

'Maybe. That's what I want you to look into. Check out all the knife murders of women in the last few years. Then get the victims' pictures and see if they match the physical profile.'

Levin leaned forward. 'Look, man, I'm not going to throw a net over this like the police can. You have to bring the cops in on this.'

I shook my head. 'Can't. He's my client.'

'Menéndez is your client, too, and you have to get him out.'

'I'm working on that. And that's why I need you to do this for me, Mish.'

I called him Mish whenever I needed something that crossed the lines of our professional relationship into the friendship that was underneath it.

'I'll do what I can, Mick, but this isn't the right way to go. Declare conflict of interest and dump Roulet. Then work on jumping Menéndez out of the Q.'

'Jump him out with what?'

'The ID he made on the six-pack. That was solid. He didn't know Roulet from a hole in the ground and he goes and picks him out of the pack.'

'Who is going to believe that? I'm his lawyer! Nobody from the cops to the clemency board is going to believe I didn't set that up. You know and I know this to be true, but we can't prove a damn thing.'

'What about the wounds? They could match the knife they got from the Campo case to Martha Rentería's wounds.'

I shook my head. 'She was cremated. All they have is the descriptions and photos from the autopsy and it wouldn't be conclusive. Besides, I can't be seen as the guy pushing this on my own client. I'll lose them all.'

'I think you're wrong. I think—'

'For now I go along as if I don't know any of this. But you look into it.

Keep it separate from Roulet so I don't have a discovery issue. Bill the time to me on the Menéndez case. You understand?'

Before Levin could answer, the waitress brought my third martini.

I waved her away. 'I don't want it. Just the bill.' I looked back at Levin. 'Some franchise I got, huh?'

'Yeah. So why did he pick you? I mean, why would he pick the one lawyer who might put this thing together?'

'I don't know. Maybe he was worried I might hear about the case and put it together anyway. He knew that if he was my client I'd be ethically bound to protect him. At least at first. Plus he knows how big a payday this is for me. Maybe he thought I'd look the other way to keep the money coming in.'

Levin nodded.

'One other thing,' I said. 'I want you to look at Roulet, too. Find out all you can without getting too close. And check out that story about the mother, about her getting raped in a house she was selling in Bel-Air.'

Levin nodded again. 'I'm on it.'

The waitress came back, put our bill down and walked off. I dropped a credit card on it without even looking at the damage. I just wanted to leave.

'You want her to wrap up your steak?' I asked.

'That's OK,' Levin said. 'I've kind of lost my appetite for right now.'

'What about that attack dog you've got at home? Ask for a box.'

'That's an idea. I forgot about Bruno.' He looked around for the waitress.

'Take mine, too,' I said. 'I don't have a dog.'

DESPITE THE VODKA GLAZE, I made it through Laurel Canyon without getting pulled over. My house is on Fareholm Drive, which terraces up off the southern mouth of the canyon. All the houses are built to the street line and the only problem I had coming home was when I found some moron had parked his SUV in front of my garage and I couldn't get in.

I found a space big enough for the Lincoln about a block and a half away. When I walked back I noticed that the SUV was a Range Rover. I put my hand on the hood and it was cool to the touch. I looked up above the garage to the windows of my house that I could see, but they were still dark. I started up the stairs to the front porch, half expecting Louis Roulet to be sitting there, taking in the twinkling view of the city, but he wasn't.

I walked to the corner of the porch and looked out on the city. It was this view that had made me buy the place. I had used money from the last franchise case for a down payment, more than two years ago. But once I was in and there wasn't another franchise, I took the equity out in a second mortgage, and struggled every month to pay the nut. I needed to get out from under it but that view paralysed me. I'd probably be staring out at the city when they came to take the key and foreclose on the place.

The phone started to ring from inside the house. I moved to the front door and fumbled with my keys to unlock it and get inside in time. Very few people had my home number. No clients and no other lawyers except for one. I got in and grabbed the phone off the kitchen wall before it went to message. The caller was that one other lawyer with the number. Maggie.

'I just wanted to see if you got my apology and I also wanted to find out if you were going to do something with Hayley tomorrow.'

'Yes and yes. But Maggie, no apology is necessary and you should know that. I'm sorry for the way I acted before I left. And if my daughter wants to be with me tomorrow, then I want to be with her. Tell her we can go down to the pier or to a movie if she wants. Whatever she wants.'

'Well, she actually wants to go to the mall.'

I suddenly noticed a foreign odour in the house. The smell of smoke. The phone wasn't cordless. I wanted to get off the line and explore the house.

'Fine. I'll take her. What time is good?'

'I was thinking about noon. Maybe we could have lunch first.'

'Sure. I'll come by at noon. See you then.' I hung up.

I owned a gun but it was a collector's piece stored in a box in my bedroom closet at the rear of the house. So I quietly opened a kitchen drawer and took out a steak knife. I then walked through the living room to the hallway leading to the rear of the house. Three doorways led off the hall, to my bedroom, a bathroom and another bedroom I'd turned into a home office.

The desk light was on in the office. I had not been home in two days but I did not remember leaving it on. I approached the open door to the room.

'Come on in, Mick. It's just me.'

I knew the voice but it didn't make me feel at ease. I stepped to the threshold and stopped. Louis Roulet was sitting in the black leather office chair. He swivelled round to face me and crossed his legs. On his left ankle I could see the tracking bracelet that Valenzuela had made him wear. If Roulet had come to kill me, at least he would leave a trail. I leaned against the door frame so I could hold the knife behind my hip.

'What are you doing here, Louis?'

'You didn't return my call. I wanted to make sure we were still a team.'

'I was out of town. How did you find out where I live, Louis?'

'I work in real estate, Mick. I can find out where anyone lives. I can also find out whether they've maxed the mortgage value out and even if they're making payments on time.' He gave me a knowing smile.

'How'd you get in?' I asked.

'Well, that's the funny thing, it turns out I had the keys. Back when this place was for sale—about eighteen months ago—I came to see it because I thought I had a client who might be interested. Got the keys out of the real-tor's combo box. I knew immediately it wasn't right for my client. And I forgot to put the keys back. I have a bad habit of doing that. Isn't that strange that all this time later my lawyer would be living in this house?'

I knew then that he had been keeping tabs on me since the Menéndez case. And that he probably knew I had been up to San Quentin visiting him.

'What do you really want, Louis? Are you trying to scare me?'

'No, no, I want to make you an offer. I've been thinking about our fee arrangement and the difficulties the case presents. Frankly, Mick, I think you are underpaid. So I want to add a performance bonus. When I am found to be not guilty of this ugly crime, your fee automatically doubles.'

'That's nice, Louis, but the California bar refuses to allow defence attorneys to accept bonuses based on results. I couldn't accept it.'

'We don't have to treat it as a performance bonus, Mick. Just part of the fee schedule. Because you will be successful in defending me, won't you?'

I read the threat. 'There are no guarantees in the courtroom. Things can always go badly. But I still think it looks good.'

Roulet smiled. 'What can I do to make it look even better?'

'Nothing,' I answered. 'Don't do anything. Just sit tight and wait.'

He didn't respond. I thought about Regina Campo, alive and ready to go to trial. I needed to get him away from thoughts about the threat she presented.

'There is one thing that has come up, though,' I said. 'I don't have the details. My source can't tell me any more. But it looks like the DA has a snitch from the jail. You didn't talk to anybody about the case in there, did you?'

'No, I didn't. Whoever they have, he's a liar.'

'Most of them are. I just wanted to be sure. One other thing. Have you talked to your mother about testifying about the attack in the empty house? We need it to set up the defence of you carrying the knife.'

'I will. But she'll be hard to convince. She never reported it.'

'We need her to testify. It's not as good as a police report but it will work. Did she ever tell you what the guy looked like or how old he was?'

He shook his head. 'She couldn't tell. He wore a ski mask and goggles.

He jumped on her when she came in the door. He'd been hiding behind it.'

I nodded. I didn't want to go further with him at the moment. I wanted him out of my house. 'Listen, thank you for your offer, Louis. Now if you would excuse me, I want to go to bed. It's been a long day.'

Roulet got up and came towards me. I backed into the hallway, keeping the knife behind me and ready. But Roulet passed by without incident.

'And tomorrow you have your daughter to entertain,' he said.

That froze me. He had listened to the call from Maggie.

'I didn't know you had a daughter, Mick. That must be nice.' He glanced back at me, smiling as he moved down the hall. 'She's beautiful.'

I followed him, anger building with each step. I gripped the knife tightly. 'How do you know what she looks like?' I demanded.

He stopped and turned. He looked down at the knife in my hand and then at my face. 'The picture of her on your desk.'

I had forgotten. A framed photo of her in a giant teacup in Disneyland.

He smiled, knowing what I'd been thinking, then turned and crossed the living room to the front door. He opened it and paused. 'Good night, Mick. Enjoy your daughter tomorrow. You probably don't get to see her enough.'

'Good night, Louis.'

I closed and locked the door behind him, then stood there, waiting to hear his steps going down the stairs to the street. But a few moments later he knocked on the door. Holding the knife at the ready, I opened it.

'Your keys,' Roulet said. 'I figured you should have them.'

'Thanks.' I took the keys off his outstretched palm, closed the door and locked it once again.

SIX

Tuesday, April 12

The day started better than any defence attorney could ask for. I had no courtroom to be in, no client to meet. I slept late, spent the morning reading the newspaper cover to cover and I had a box ticket to the home opener of the Los Angeles Dodgers baseball season. It was a time-honoured tradition among those on the defence side of the aisle to attend. My ticket had come from Raul Levin, who was taking five of the defence pros he worked for as a gesture of thanks for their business.

Louis Roulet's trial was set to begin in a month. A trial was a slingshot. The key was in the preparation. Pretrial is when the sling is loaded with the proper stone and slowly the elastic is pulled back to its limit. Finally, at trial you let it go and the projectile shoots forward, unerringly at the target. The target is acquittal. You only hit that target if you have properly chosen the stone and stretched the elastic back as far as possible.

Levin was doing most of the stretching. He had continued to dig into the lives of the players in both the Roulet and Menéndez cases. We had hatched a plan we were calling a 'double slingshot' because it had two targets.

The prosecution did its part to help us load the slingshot. In the weeks since Roulet's arraignment, the state's discovery file had grown thicker. New developments included the identification of Mr X, the left-handed man who had been with Regina Campo at Morgan's the night of the attack. LAPD detectives were able to identify him using a frame taken off the video from the bar, which they showed to known prostitutes. Mr X was identified as Charles Talbot, owner of a convenience store on Reseda Boulevard.

Nowhere in the state's discovery was there mention of Dwayne Jeffery Corliss, the jailhouse snitch who had contacted the prosecution about Louis Roulet. Minton had sequestered Corliss in the lockdown programme, so he was offstage but ready. This was fine with me. What Minton didn't know was that Corliss was the stone I was going to put into the slingshot.

The state's discovery also contained little on the victim of the crime, but Levin had located a website on which Reggie Campo advertised her services. The ad stated that she was 'very open-minded and liked to get wild' and was 'available for S&M role play—you spank me or I'll spank you.'

Levin was also digging deeper into the life of Louis Roulet. Two women who had known him while students at UCLA told Levin that they suspected Roulet had spiked their drinks at a fraternity party and then took sexual advantage of them. Neither reported their suspicions to authorities but one woman had her blood tested the day after. She said that traces of ketamine, a veterinary sedative, were found. Luckily neither woman had so far been located by prosecution investigators.

Levin took a look at the Real-Estate Rapist cases of five years before as well. Four women—all realtors—reported being raped by a man who was waiting inside when they entered homes they believed had been vacated by their owners for a showing. Levin could find little to confirm that Mary Windsor had been one of the unreported victims of the rapist. She had agreed to testify about her secret tragedy, but only if her testimony was vital. She provided an appointment book and other documentation showing she was indeed the realtor handling the sale of the Bel-Air home where she said she was attacked. But ultimately we only had her word for it.

Still, when Mary Windsor recounted her story, it matched Roulet's telling of it in almost all details. Afterwards, it had struck both Levin and me as odd that she'd shared so many details of her harrowing ordeal with her son.

'I think he knows all the details because he was there,' Levin had said.

'You mean he watched it without doing anything to stop it?'

'No, I mean I think he was the man in the ski mask and goggles. She's a tough lady and I can't see her not reporting this unless she was protecting the guy who did it. Unless that guy was our guy. I'm telling you, man, Roulet is evil. The more I look at him, the more I see the devil.'

All of this background had to be hidden from discovery, so little of what Levin found was put down on paper. But it was still information I had to know as I made my decisions and set up the trial and the play within it.

At 11.05 my home phone rang as I was fitting a Dodgers cap onto my head. I checked the caller ID before answering and saw it was Lorna Taylor.

'Why is your cellphone off?' she asked.

'Because I'm off. I told you, no calls today. I'm going to the ball game with Raul. Why are you bothering me?' I said it good-naturedly.

'Because I think you are going to want to be bothered with this. The mail came in a little early today and with it you got a notice from the Second.'

The Second District Court of Appeal reviewed all cases from LA County. At any given time I usually have four or five cases on appeal.

'Which case?' I asked.

'One of your Road Saints. Harold Casey. You won!'

'Man, what a day for the underdog! Anything else happening?'

'Just the usual. Did you get in to see Glory Days yesterday at County?'

'It's Gloria Dayton and, yes, I got in to see her. She looks like she's over the hump. She's still got more than a month to go.'

The truth was, Gloria Dayton looked better than over the hump. I hadn't seen her so sharp and bright-eyed in years. I'd had a purpose for going down to County–USC Medical Center to talk to her, but seeing her on the downhill side of recovery was a nice bonus.

As expected, Lorna was the doomsayer. 'And how long will it last this time before she calls your number and says, "I'm in jail. I need Mickey"?'

She said the last part with a whiny, nasal impression of Gloria Dayton. It was quite accurate but it annoyed me.

'I have to get going now,' I told her.

'Well, have a great time.'

I clicked off and headed for the front door.

Having given Earl the day off with pay, I drove myself to Dodger Stadium. The home opener is always a sellout but I was the first one to the seats. The plan was for Levin to get there early as well. He had called the night before and said he wanted some private time with me. Besides watching batting practice, we would discuss my visit with Gloria, and Levin would give me an update on his investigations relating to Roulet.

But Levin never made it for batting practice. The other four lawyers showed up, and we missed our chance to talk privately. The game started and still no sign of him. I turned my cellphone on and tried to call him, even though it was hard to hear. The call went to a message.

'Mish, where you at, man? We're at the game and we're waiting on you.'

I closed the phone, looked at the others and shrugged. 'He didn't answer.' I left my phone on and put it back on my belt.

During a lull in the game I heard my phone ringing. I grabbed it off my hip and flipped it open without looking at the screen. 'Raul?'

'No, sir, this is Detective Lankford with the Glendale Police Department. Is this Michael Haller?'

'Yes,' I said.

'Do you know a man named Raul Aaron Levin?'

'Yes, I know him. What's wrong?'

'I'm afraid Mr Levin has been the victim of a homicide in his home.'

My head dropped so low and so forward that I banged it into the back of the man seated in front of me. I then pulled back and held one hand to one ear and pressed the phone against the other. 'What happened?'

'We don't know,' Lankford said. 'That's why we're here. It looks like he was working for you recently. Is there any chance you could come here to possibly answer some questions and assist us?'

I tried to keep my voice calm. 'I'm on my way,' I said.

RAUL LEVIN'S BODY was in the back room of his bungalow a few blocks off of Brand Boulevard. The room had probably been designed as a sun room or maybe a TV room, but Levin had turned it into his home office. The uniformed cops made me wait in the front living room until the detectives could come from the back and talk to me.

I had decided on the drive from the stadium that I knew who had killed

Raul. I knew he had got too close to Roulet. And I was the one who had sent him. The only question left for me was what I was going to do about it.

After twenty minutes, two detectives came into the room. One of them identified himself as Lankford, the detective who'd called me. He was older, the veteran. His partner was a woman named Sobel. They wore rubber gloves and had paper booties over their shoes.

'OK, this is what we've got,' Lankford said. 'Mr Levin was in his office, sitting in his desk chair. The chair was turned from the desk, so he was facing the intruder. He was shot once in the chest. Looks like a .22 but we'll wait on the coroner for that. After the shot, he tried to get up or just fell forward to the floor, where he expired face down. The intruder ransacked the office.'

'Who found him?' I asked.

'A neighbour found his dog wandering around, recognised it and brought it back. She found the front door open, came in and found the body.'

'We haven't found anything that can lead us to next of kin,' Sobel said. 'Do you know if he had any family?'

'I think his mother lives back east. He was born in Detroit. Maybe she's there. I don't think they had much of a relationship.'

She nodded. 'We found his desk diary. Your name is on almost every day for the last month. Was he working on a specific case?'

I nodded. 'A couple of different cases. One mostly.'

'Do you care to tell us about it?' she asked.

'I have a case about to go to trial. Next month. It's an attempted rape and murder. He was running down the evidence and helping me to get ready.'

'You mean helping you back-door the investigation, huh?' Lankford said.

I realised then that Lankford's politeness on the phone was merely sweet talk to get me here. He was different now, more aggressive.

'Everybody is entitled to a defence, Detective.'

'Yeah, sure,' Lankford said. 'And they're all innocent, only it's their parents' fault for taking them off the tit too soon, right?'

'To get back to your case,' Sobel said, 'what's the defendant's name?'

'Louis Ross Roulet. The trial's in Van Nuys Superior.'

'Is he in custody?'

'No, he's out on a bond.'

'Any animosity between Roulet and Mr Levin?'

'Not that I know of.'

I had decided. I was going to deal with Roulet in the way I knew how. I was sticking with the plan I had concocted—with Levin's help. Drop a depth charge into the case and make sure to get clear. I felt I owed it to my friend Mish. He would have wanted it this way.

'Could this have been a gay thing?' Lankford asked.

'What? Why do you say that?'

'Prissy dog, and then all around the house he's only got pictures of guys and the dog. Everywhere. On the walls, next to the bed, on the piano.'

'Look closely, Detective. It's probably one guy. His partner died a few years ago. I don't think he's been with anybody since then.'

'Died of AIDS, I bet.'

I didn't confirm that for him. I just waited. I was annoyed by Lankford's manner, but I figured his torch-the-ground method of investigation would preclude him from being able to tag Roulet with this. I only needed to stall him for six weeks, and by then I wouldn't care if they put it together or not.

'Did this guy go out patrolling the gay joints?' Lankford asked.

I shrugged. 'I have no idea. But if it was a gay murder, why was his office ransacked and not the rest of the house?'

Lankford nodded. He seemed to be momentarily taken aback by the logic of my question. But then he hit me with a surprise punch.

'So where were you this morning, Counsellor?'

'What? Are you saying I'm a suspect?'

'No, it's just routine. The scene indicates the victim knew his killer. He let the shooter right into the back room. We're going to have to clear all acquaintances, professional and social. I'm just trying to tighten the focus.'

'I was home. I was getting ready to meet Raul at Dodger Stadium. I left for the stadium about twelve and that's where I was when you called.'

'What about before that?'

'Like I said, I was home. I was alone. But I got a phone call about eleven that will put me in my house and I'm at least a half-hour from here. If he was killed after eleven, then I'm clear.'

Lankford didn't rise to the bait. Maybe the time of death was still unknown. 'When was the last time you spoke to Levin?' he asked instead.

'Last night by telephone. He called to ask if I could get to the game early, so he could update me about the Roulet case. I said I would.'

Sobel spoke up. 'Is there anything else you can tell us, Mr Haller?'

'Yeah, there is one thing you should probably check out. A few weeks ago, Raul did some work for me on a case that involved one of my clients snitching off a drug dealer. He made some calls, helped ID the guy. I heard afterwards that the guy was a Colombian and he was pretty well connected.

He could have had friends who . . .' I left it for them to fill in the blanks.

'I don't know,' Lankford said. 'This was pretty clean. Doesn't look like a revenge deal. They didn't cut his throat or take his tongue. One shot, plus they ransacked the office. What would the dealer's people be looking for?'

'Maybe my client's name. The deal I made kept it out of circulation.'

Lankford nodded thoughtfully. 'What's the client's name?'

'I can't tell you. Attorney–client privilege.'

'OK, here we go with that bullshit. How are we going to investigate this if we don't even know your client's name? Don't you care about your friend in there on the floor with a piece of lead in his heart?'

'Yes, I care. But I am also bound by the rules and ethics of law.'

'Your client could be in danger.'

'My client is safe. My client is in lockdown. If you want the name of the dealer, it's Hector Arrande Moya. He's in federal custody.'

Sobel wrote it all down. I believed I had now given them sufficient reason to look beyond Roulet and the gay angle.

'Mr Haller, have you ever been in Mr Levin's office?' Sobel asked.

'A few times. Not in a couple months, at least.'

'Do you mind walking back with us anyway? Maybe you'll see something out of place or notice something that's missing.'

'Is he still back there?'

'The victim? Yes, he's still as he was found.'

I wasn't sure I wanted to see Raul Levin's body in the centre of a murder scene. But I decided that I must see him to fuel my resolve. 'OK,' I said.

'Then put these on and don't touch anything while you're back there,' Lankford said. From his pocket he produced a pair of paper booties.

I put them on. Then I followed them down the hallway to the death room.

The body was in situ—as they had found it. It was in an awkward posture, chest down on the floor, arms and hands underneath, face turned to the right. I immediately regretted my decision to come into the room. I knew that the final look on Raul's face would crowd out all other visual memories I had of him. My own face must have shown the horror I was feeling.

'Can you step over here to the desk and tell us if you see anything unusual?' Sobel asked. There was sympathy in her voice.

I was thankful to do it because I could keep my back to the body. As I walked over to the desk, my eyes lingered on Levin's computer. I wondered what he may have put on electronic files about Roulet. Sobel noticed.

'We don't have a computer expert here yet,' she said. 'But it looks to me like the whole drive was pulled out.' She pointed under the table at the PC unit. It had one side of its plastic cowling removed.

My eyes moved over the table. Papers and files were spread across it in a haphazard way. I looked at the tabs and recognised some of the names.

'Some of these are my clients but they're old cases. Not active.'

'They probably came from the filing cabinets in the closet,' Sobel said. 'The killer could have dumped them here to confuse us. To hide what he was really looking for or taking.'

'Hey, check this out,' Lankford said.

I turned with Sobel and saw that the medical examiner's people were slowly turning Levin's body over. Blood stained his shirt, but Lankford was pointing to the dead man's hands, which had not been visible before. The two middle fingers of his left hand were folded down against the palm while the two outside fingers were fully extended.

'Was this guy a Texas Longhorns fan or what?' Lankford asked.

Nobody laughed.

'What do you think?' Sobel said to me.

I stared down at my friend's last gesture and just shook my head.

'Oh, I get it,' Lankford said. 'He's telling us that the devil did it.'

I thought of Levin calling Roulet the devil, of having the proof that he was evil. And I knew what my friend's last message to me meant. As he died on the floor of his office, he tried to tell me. Tried to warn me.

I WENT TO Four Green Fields and ordered a Guinness but quickly escalated to vodka over ice. I didn't think there was any sense in delaying things. After the second vodka assault, I took out my cellphone and started making calls. First I called the four other lawyers from the game. We had all left when I got the word but they had known only that Levin was dead, none of the details. Then I called Lorna and she cried on the phone. I talked her through it, then decided to take a break before making another call.

I pushed my glass to the edge of the bar gutter and said to the bartender, 'Gimme a Guinness and give yourself one, too.'

I'd decided it was time to slow down, and one way was to drink Guinness, since it took so long to fill a glass out of the tap. When the bartender finally brought it to me I saw that he had etched a harp in the foam with the tap nozzle. An angel's harp. I hoisted the glass before drinking from it.

'God bless the dead,' I said.

'God bless the dead,' the bartender said.

The thick ale was like mortar I was sending down to hold the bricks together inside. I felt like crying. But then my phone rang. Without looking at the screen I said hello. The alcohol had made my voice unrecognisable.

'Is this Mick?' a voice asked.

'Yeah, who's this?'

'It's Louis. I just heard the news about Raul. I'm so sorry, man.'

I pulled the phone away from my ear as if it were a snake about to bite me. I pulled my arm back, ready to throw the phone at the mirror behind the bar, where I saw my own reflection. Then I stopped and brought it back.

'How do you already know what happened to Mish?' I asked.

'If by Mish you mean Raul, I just got a call from the Glendale police. A detective said she wanted to speak to me about him.'

I straightened up on my stool. 'Sobel? Is that who called?'

'Yeah, I think so. She said she got my name from you. She said it would be routine questions. She's coming here to my office.'

I didn't think Sobel was in any kind of danger, even without Lankford. My concern was that she and Lankford were already on to Roulet and I would be robbed of my chance to avenge Raul Levin and Jesús Menéndez.

'Don't talk to them without your lawyer present.'

'Won't they get suspicious if I don't talk to them?'

'It doesn't matter. They don't talk to you unless I give my permission. And I'm not giving it.' I gripped my free hand into a fist. I couldn't stand the idea of giving legal advice to the man I was sure had killed my friend.

'OK,' Roulet said. 'I'll send her on her way.'

'Where were you this morning?'

'Me? I was here at the office. Why?'

'Did anybody see you?'

'Well, Robin came in at ten. The receptionist. Not before that.'

I didn't know what to tell Roulet because I didn't know what the time of death was. 'Call me after Detective Sobel leaves. And remember, no matter what she or her partner says to you, do not talk to them. Consider anything they tell you to be a lie to trick you into talking to them.'

'All right, Mick. That's how I'll play it. Thanks.' He ended the call.

I closed my phone and dropped it on the bar like it was something dirty and discarded. 'Yeah, don't mention it,' I said.

I drained a quarter of my pint, then picked up the phone again. Using speed dial I called Fernando Valenzuela's cell number. He was at home.

'Do you still have a tracking bracelet on Roulet?'

'Yeah, he's got it.'

'How's it work? Can you track where he's been or only where he's at?'

'It's global positioning. It sends up a signal. You can track it backwards to tell where somebody's been. What's up?'

'I want to know where he's been today. You got it there or at the office?'

'It's on my laptop, man. Let me boot it up. Hold on.'

I held on, finished my Guinness and had the bartender start filling another before Valenzuela had his laptop fired up.

'Anything wrong, Mick?'

'Yeah, something's wrong. Do you have it up or what?'

'Yeah, I'm looking at it right here. How far back do you want to check?'

'Start at this morning.'

'OK. He, uh. . . he hasn't done much today. I track it from his home to his office at eight. Looks like he took a little trip nearby—a couple blocks, probably for lunch—and then back to the office. He's still there.'

I thought about this while the bartender delivered my next pint.

'Val, how do you get that thing off your ankle?'

'You mean if you were him? You don't. You can't. It bolts on and the little wrench you use is unique. It's like a key. I got the only one.'

'You're sure about that? There aren't any copies from the manufacturer?'

'Not supposed to be. Besides, it doesn't matter. If the ring is broken— like even if he did open it—I get an alarm on the system. It also has what's called a "mass detector". Once I put that baby round his ankle, I get an alarm on the computer the moment it reads that there's nothing there.'

I drank the top off my new beer. 'What if the battery's dead?'

'I got that covered too, Mick. He's got a charger and a receptacle on the bracelet. Every few days he's got to plug it in for a couple of hours to juice it. If the battery goes below twenty per cent I get an alarm on my computer and I call him and say plug it in. If he doesn't do it then, at ten per cent *he* starts beeping and he's got no way to turn it off. Doesn't make for a good getaway. And that last ten per cent still gives me five hours of tracking.'

'OK, OK.' I was convinced by the science.

'What's going on?'

I told him about Levin and told him that the police would have to check out Roulet, and the tracking bracelet would probably be our client's alibi.

Valenzuela was stunned. 'What do you think happened, Mick?' he asked.

I knew that he was asking if I thought Roulet was behind the killing.

'I don't know,' I said. 'But you should watch yourself with this guy.'

I closed the phone, wondering if Roulet had somehow found a way to take the ankle bracelet off or to subvert the tracking system.

The bartender sauntered over to my spot at the bar. 'Hey, buddy, did you lose your car keys?' he said. 'Somebody found keys in the parking lot.'

I reached into my jacket pocket, then brought my hand out, palm up. My key ring was displayed on my hand. 'No,' I said. 'There—'

In a quick and unexpected move, the bartender grabbed the keys. 'You're not driving, pal,' he said. 'When you're ready to go, I'll call you a taxi.'

I looked at my watch. It wasn't even five o'clock. Embarrassment burned through the alcohol padding. I picked up the phone and punched in a speed-dial number. Maggie answered right away. The courts usually closed by four thirty. The prosecutors were usually at their desks in that last hour of the day.

'Hey, is it quitting time yet?'

'Haller? What's going on? Are you drinking? Your voice is different.'

'I think I might need you to drive *me* home this time.'

'Where are you?'

'Four Green Fields. I've been here a while.'

'Michael, what's—?'

'Raul Levin is dead.'

'Oh my God, what—?'

'Murdered. So this time can you drive *me* home? I've had too much.'

'Let me call Stacey and get her to stay late with Hayley, then I'll be on my way. Do not try to leave there, OK? Just don't leave.'

'Don't worry, the bartender isn't gonna let me.'

AFTER CLOSING my phone I told the bartender I'd have one more pint while waiting for my ride. I took out my wallet and put a credit card on the bar. He ran my tab first, then got me the Guinness. He took so long filling the glass that I had barely tasted it by the time Maggie got there.

'That was too quick,' I said. 'You want a drink?'

'No, it's too early. Let's just get you home.'

'OK.' I got off the stool, and left with my arm round her shoulders.

We got to the car, Maggie helped me in and then we were off. It took almost forty-five minutes in end-of-the-day traffic to get to Fareholm Drive. Along the way I told her about Raul Levin and what had happened. She had never known Levin. Though I had used him as an investigator for years, he didn't become a friend until after Maggie and I had divorced.

My house keys were on the ring that had been confiscated by the bartender so we had to go down the side of the house to the back porch and get the spare set—the one Roulet had given me—from beneath an ashtray on the picnic table. We went in the back door, which led directly into my office.

'Ah, that's nice,' she said. 'Our little teacup.'

I followed her eyes and saw she was looking at the photo of our daughter I kept on the desk. I thrilled at the idea that I had inadvertently scored a point of some kind with her. 'Yeah,' I said, fumbling any chance of capitalising.

'Which way to the bedroom?' she asked.

'Well, aren't you being forward. To the right.'

'Sorry, Haller, I'm not staying long. I only got a couple of extra hours out of Stacey. I've got to turn around and head back over the hill soon.'

She walked me into the bedroom and we sat down on the bed.

'Thank you for doing this,' I said.

'One good turn deserves another, I guess,' she said.

'I thought I got my good turn that night I took you home.'

She put her hand on my cheek and kissed me.

'Guinness,' she said, tasting her lips as she pulled away.

'And some vodka.'

'Good combination. You'll be hurting in the morning. Call me tomorrow. I want to talk to you when you're sober.'

'OK.' I leaned back on the bed and kicked my shoes off. I then rolled over to the edge and opened a drawer in the bedside table. I took out a bottle of Tylenol and a CD that had been given to me by a client known on the street as Lil' Demon. He was killed in a drive-by shooting six months later.

I loaded the CD into the player on the bedside table and soon the rhythmic beat of Tupac Shakur's 'God Bless the Dead' started to play. The song was a salute to fallen comrades.

'You listen to this stuff?' Maggie asked, squinting at me in disbelief.

'Sometimes. It helps me understand a lot of my clients better.'

She shrugged. 'I've gotta go.'

'Just stay a few minutes.' I reached over and turned it down a little. 'Hey, I'll turn it off if you'll sing to me like you used to.'

'Not tonight, Haller.'

'Nobody knows the Maggie McFierce I know.'

She smiled a little and I was quiet while I remembered those times.

'Maggie, why do you stay with me?'

'I told you, I can't stay.'

'No, I don't mean tonight. I'm talking about how you stick with me, how you don't run me down with Hayley and how you're there when I need you. Like tonight. Not many people have ex-wives who still like them.'

She thought a little bit before answering. 'I don't know. I guess because I see a good man and a good father in there waiting to break out one day.'

I nodded and hoped she was right. 'Tell me something. What would you do if you couldn't be a prosecutor?'

'I'd be a teacher,' she finally said. 'Grade school. Little girls like Hayley.'

I smiled. 'You'd be a good teacher except when you're sending kids off to detention without bail.'

'Funny. What about you? What would you do if you weren't a lawyer?'

'I don't know. But I've got three Town Cars. I guess I could start a limo service, taking people to the airport.'

Now she smiled at me. 'I'd hire you.'

'Good. That's one customer. Give me a dollar and I'll tape it to the wall.'

But the banter wasn't working. I leaned back, put my palms against my eyes and tried to push away the day, to push out the memory of Raul Levin on the floor of his house, eyes staring at a permanent black sky.

'I used to be afraid that I wouldn't recognise innocence,' I said. 'That it would be there right in front of me and I wouldn't see it. But you know what I should have been afraid of? Evil. Pure evil.'

'What do you mean?'

'I mean, most of the people I defend aren't evil, Mags. They're guilty, yeah, but they aren't evil. You listen to them and you listen to these songs and you know why they make the choices they make. People are just trying to live with what they're given, and some of them aren't given a damn thing in the first place. But evil is something else. It's like . . . it's out there and when it shows up . . . I don't know. I can't explain it.'

'You're drunk, that's why.'

'All I know is, I should have been afraid of one thing but I was afraid of the complete opposite.'

She reached over and rubbed my shoulder. The next song was 'To Live And Die In LA', and it was my favourite on the homespun CD. I started to softly hum and then I sang along with the refrain when it came up.

Pretty soon I stopped singing and pulled my hands down from my face. I fell asleep with my clothes on. I never heard the woman I had loved more than anyone else in my life leave the house. She would tell me later that the last thing I had mumbled before passing out was, 'I can't do this any more.'

I wasn't talking about my singing.

I SLEPT ALMOST ten hours but I still woke up in darkness. It said 5.38 on the alarm clock when I rolled out of bed and hit the shower. I stayed under the spray until the hot-water tank ran cold. Then I got dressed.

I went into the home office to check my diary and the first thing I noticed was a dollar bill taped to the wall over the desk.

My adrenaline jogged up a couple of notches as I thought an intruder had left the money as some sort of threat. Then I remembered.

'Maggie,' I said out loud.

I smiled and decided to leave the dollar bill taped to the wall. I got the diary out of the briefcase and checked my schedule. All I had that day was an 11 a.m. hearing in San Fernando Superior.

For breakfast I had two Tylenols and chased them with fried eggs, toast and coffee. I doused the eggs liberally with pepper and salsa. It all hit the right spots and gave me the fuel to carry on the battle. As I ate, I turned the pages of the *Times*, which I had delivered every day. Inexplicably, there was no story on Levin's murder. Then I remembered that the *Times* put out several regional editions of the paper. I lived on the Westside, and Glendale was considered part of the San Fernando Valley. News of a murder in the Valley may have been deemed by *Times* editors as unimportant to Westside readers, who had their own region's murders to worry about.

I decided to buy a second copy of the *Times* from a newsstand on the way to the San Fernando courthouse. Thoughts about which newsstand I would direct Earl Briggs to reminded me I had no car. The Lincoln was in the parking lot at Four Green Fields. I didn't want Earl to pick me up at the house. I never let my drivers know where I live. So I decided to take a cab to my warehouse in North Hollywood and use one of the new Town Cars.

After cleaning the frying pan I decided it was late enough to risk waking Lorna with a call to confirm my day's schedule. When I picked up the house phone I heard the broken dial tone that told me I had a message waiting.

I called the retrieval number and was told by an electronic voice that I had missed a call at 11.07 a.m. the day before. When the voice recited the number that the missed call had come from, I froze. The number was Raul Levin's cellphone. I had missed his last call.

'Hey, it's me. You probably left for the game already and I guess you got your cell turned off. If you don't get this I'll just catch you there. But I've got another ace for you. I guess you'—he broke off for a moment at the background sound of a dog barking—'could say I've got Jesús's ticket out of the Q. I've gotta go.'

That was it. He hung up without a goodbye.

I replayed the message, then saved it. The first puzzle involved the time of the call. I didn't leave for the game until at least 11.30, yet I had missed the call from Levin that had come in more than twenty minutes earlier.

This made no sense until I remembered the call from Lorna. At 11.07 I had been on the phone with her. This meant that Levin's last call would have been kicked over to the voicemail system.

That explained the circumstances of the call but not its contents.

Levin had obviously found something he thought could help me get Menéndez out of prison. He had found Jesús's ticket out.

The last thing left to consider was the interruption of the dog barking and that was easy. I had been to Levin's home before and I knew the dog was a highly strung yapper that would start barking before I had even knocked on the door. The barking in the background on the phone message told me he had a visitor, and it may very well have been his killer.

I decided that the timing of the call was something I could not in good conscience keep from the police. I went into the bedroom and picked up the jeans I had worn the day before. In one of the back pockets I found the business card Sobel had given me at the end of my visit to Levin's house.

She answered the call right away and I decided to see what I could get from her before I gave her what I had.

'Anything new on the investigation?' I asked.

'Not a lot I can share with you. We got some ballistics back and—'

'You already did an autopsy?' I said. 'That was quick.'

'No, the autopsy won't be until tomorrow.'

'Then how did you get ballistics already?'

She didn't answer, but then I figured it out.

'You found a casing. He was shot with an automatic that ejected the shell.'

'You're good, Mr Haller. Yes, we found a cartridge.'

'I've done a lot of trials. And call me Mickey. It's funny, the killer ransacked the place but didn't pick up the shell.'

'Maybe that's because it rolled across the floor and fell into a heating vent. The killer would have needed a screwdriver and a lot of time.'

I nodded. It was a lucky break.

'So, was your partner right about it being a .22?'

She paused before answering, deciding whether to cross some threshold of revealing case information to me. 'He was right. And thanks to the markings on the cartridge, we even know the exact gun we are looking for.'

I knew from questioning ballistics experts in trials over the years that marks left on bullet casings during the firing process could identify the make and model of the weapon used, even without the weapon in hand.

'It turns out that Mr Levin owned a .22 himself,' Sobel said. 'But we found it in a closet safe in the house and it's not a Woodsman. The one thing we have not found is his cellphone. We know he had one but we—'

'He was talking to me on it right before he was killed.'

There was a moment of silence.

'You told us that the last time you spoke to him was Friday night.'

'That's right. But that's why I'm calling. Raul called me yesterday morning at eleven oh-seven and left a message. I didn't get it until today because after I left you people yesterday I just went out and got drunk. Then I went to sleep and didn't realise I had a message from him till right now. He called about one of the cases he was working on for me sort of on the side. Anyway, the content of the message isn't important but the call helps with the timing. And get this, while he's leaving the message, you hear the dog start to bark. It did that whenever somebody came to the door.'

'Mr Haller, you told us yesterday you were at home until around noon, when you left for the game. Why didn't you answer Mr Levin's call?'

'Because I was on the phone and I don't have call waiting. You can check my records; you'll see I got a call from my office manager, Lorna Taylor. I was talking to her when Raul called. Without call waiting I didn't know.'

'OK, we'll probably want your written permission to look at the records.'

'No problem.'

'Where are you now?'

'I'm at home.'

I gave her the address and she said that she and her partner were coming.

'Make it soon. I have to leave for court in about an hour.'

I closed the phone feeling uneasy. I had defended a dozen murderers over the years and that had brought me into contact with a number of homicide investigators. But I had never been questioned myself about a murder before. Lankford and now Sobel seemed to be suspicious of every answer I could give. It made me wonder what they knew that I didn't.

As I straightened up things on the desk it suddenly hit me. I sat back down as I remembered something Sobel had said. At first it had gone right by me. She had said that they had found Levin's .22 calibre gun but it was not the murder weapon. She said it was not a Woodsman.

I knew that the Woodsman was an automatic pistol manufactured by

Colt. I knew this because I owned a Colt Woodsman Sport Model. It had been bequeathed to me many years ago by my father. Upon his death. I had never even taken it out of its wooden box.

I got up and went to my bedroom. The polished wooden box was on the shelf in the walk-in closet where it was supposed to be. I reached up with both hands to bring it down and then walked it out to the bedroom.

I put the box down on the bed and flipped open the brass latch. I raised the lid and pulled away the oilcloth covering. The gun was gone.

SEVEN

Monday, May 23

Another cheque from Roulet had cleared. On the first day of trial I had more money in my bank account than I'd ever had in my life. Finally I had a franchise case and it had paid off. In terms of money, that is. Levin's murder would forever make this franchise a losing proposition.

We had been through three days of jury selection and were now ready to put on the show. The trial was scheduled for another three days at the most—two for the prosecution and one for the defence.

I sat next to Louis Roulet at the defence table. We were alone. I had no second and no investigator behind me—out of some strange loyalty to Raul Levin I had not hired a replacement. I didn't really need one, either. Levin had given me everything I needed. The trial and how it played out would serve as a last testament to his skills as an investigator.

In the first row of the gallery sat Cecil Dobbs and Mary Windsor. In accordance with a pretrial ruling, Roulet's mother was allowed to be in the courtroom during opening statements only. Because she was listed as a defence witness, she would not be allowed to listen to any of the testimony that followed. She would remain in the hallway outside, with her loyal lap dog Dobbs at her side, until I called her to the stand.

Also in the first row but not seated next to them was my own support section: my case manager and ex-wife Lorna Taylor. She was dressed up in a navy suit and white blouse. She looked beautiful and could have blended in easily with the phalanx of female attorneys who descended on the court-house every day. But she was there for me and I loved her for it.

The rest of the rows in the gallery were sporadically crowded. There were a few print reporters there to grab quotes from the opening statements and a few attorneys and citizen onlookers. No TV had shown up.

The courtroom clerk took a phone call, said a few words then hung up. 'Two minutes, people,' he said loudly. 'Two minutes.'

It was the judge calling ahead. I attempted to calm myself by rehearsing what I wanted to say to the jurors. I glanced over at Ted Minton at the prosecution's table and saw he was doing the same thing. I leaned forward and studied my notes. Then Roulet unexpectedly leaned forward and almost right into me. He spoke in a whisper, even though it wasn't necessary yet.

'This is it, Mick.'

Since the death of Raul Levin, my relationship with Roulet had been one of cold endurance. I put up with him because I had to. The three days of jury selection had been torture. Day after day I had to sit right next to him and listen to his condescending comments about prospective jurors. The only way I got through it was to pretend he wasn't there.

'You ready?' he asked me.

'Trying to be,' I said. 'Are you?'

'I'm ready. But I wanted to tell you something before we began.'

I looked at him. He was too close to me. It would have been invasive even if I had loved him and not hated him. I leaned back.

'What's wrong?'

'Nothing's wrong.' He leaned back next to me. 'As my lawyer you have to hold anything I tell you secret, even if it's a crime, right? It's covered by the attorney–client relationship, right?'

'Yes, Louis, that's right—unless you tell me about a crime about to be committed. In that case I can be relieved of the code of ethics and can inform the police. So what is it you want to tell me? We're about to start here.'

'I've killed people, Mick.'

I looked at him for a moment. 'What?'

'You heard me.'

He was right. I had heard him. And I shouldn't have acted surprised. I already knew he had killed people. I was just surprised he had decided to tell me two minutes before his trial was called to order.

'Why are you telling me this?' I asked. 'I'm about to defend you—'

'Because I know you already know. And because I know your plan.'

'My plan? What plan?'

He smiled slyly at me. 'Come on, Mick. It's simple. You defend me on this case. You do your best, you get paid the big bucks, you win and I walk away. But then, once it's all over and I'm not your client any more, you throw me to the cops so you can get Menéndez out and redeem yourself.'

I didn't respond.

'Well, I can't let that happen,' he said quietly. 'I am telling you I've killed people, and guess what! Martha Rentería was one of them. But if you go to the cops or use what I've told you against me, then you won't be practising law for long. Yes, you might succeed in raising Jesús from the dead. But I'll never be prosecuted because of your misconduct. I believe it is called 'fruit of the poisonous tree', and you are the tree, Mick.'

I still couldn't respond. Roulet had certainly thought it through. I wondered if he had got help from Cecil Dobbs.

At last I leaned towards him and whispered, 'Follow me.'

I got up and walked quickly through the gate and towards the rear door of the courtroom. From behind I heard the clerk's voice.

'Mr Haller? We're about to start. The judge—'

'One minute,' I called out without turning around.

I pushed through the doors into the dimly lit vestibule between the courtroom and the hallway. Then I waited for Roulet to step into the small space.

As soon as he came through the door, I grabbed him and spun him into the wall. I held him pressed against it with both of my hands on his chest.

'What the fuck do you think you are doing?' I hissed.

'Take it easy, Mick. I just thought we should know where we both—'

'You son of a bitch. You killed Raul and all he was doing was working for you! He was trying to help you!'

I wanted to bring my hands up to his neck and choke him on the spot.

'You're right about one thing. I am a son of a bitch. But you are wrong about everything else, Mick. Levin wasn't trying to help me. He was trying to bury me and he was getting too close. He got what he deserved for that.'

'How did you do it? How'd you beat the GPS? Your bracelet showed you weren't even near Glendale.'

He smiled at me, like a boy with a toy he wasn't going to share.

'Let's just say that is proprietary information and leave it at that. You never know, I may have to pull the old Houdini act again.'

In his words I heard the threat and in his smile I saw the evil that Raul Levin had seen.

'Don't get any ideas, Mick. As you know, I have an insurance policy.'

I leaned in closer. 'Listen, you piece of shit. I want the gun back. You think you have this thing wired? You don't have shit. *I've* got it wired. And you won't make it through the week if I don't get that gun back. Got that?'

Roulet slowly reached up, grabbed my wrists and pulled my hands off his chest. He started straightening his shirt and tie. 'Might I suggest an agreement,' he said calmly. 'At the end of this trial I walk out of the courtroom a free man. I continue to maintain my freedom, and in exchange for this, the gun never falls into, shall we say, the wrong hands.'

Meaning Lankford and Sobel.

I stepped back, using all my will not to raise my fists and attack. 'I promise you,' I said, in a voice that seethed with anger, 'if you fuck with me you will never be free of me. Are we clear on that?'

Roulet started to smile. But before he could respond the door from the courtroom opened and Deputy Meehan, the bailiff, looked in.

'The judge is on the bench,' he said. 'She wants you in here. Now.'

I looked back at Roulet. 'I said, are we clear?'

'Yes, Mick,' he said good-naturedly. 'We're crystal clear.'

I stepped away from him and entered the courtroom, striding up the aisle to the gate. Judge Constance Fullbright was staring me down.

'So nice of you to consider joining us this morning, Mr Haller.'

'I'm sorry, Your Honour,' I said as I came through the gate. 'I had an emergency situation with my client. We had to conference.'

'Client conferences can be handled at the defence table,' she responded.

'Yes, Your Honour. I apologise, Your Honour.'

'That's not good enough, Mr Haller. I am fining you five hundred dollars for contempt of court. Now, can we please have the jury.'

The bailiff opened the jury room door and the jurors started filing in.

I leaned over to Roulet and whispered, 'You owe me five hundred dollars.'

TED MINTON'S OPENING STATEMENT was a model of prosecutorial overkill. Rather than tell the jurors what evidence he would present and what it would prove, the prosecutor tried to tell them what it all meant. He was going for a big picture and this was a mistake. Any experienced prosecutor will tell you to keep it small. You want them to convict, not necessarily to understand.

'Now, you will hear testimony from the victim herself about her lifestyle being one we would not condone,' Minton told the jurors. 'The bottom line is she was selling sex to the men she invited to her home. But no matter what someone does for a living, the law does not allow them to be beaten, threatened at knife-point or put in fear of their lives. It doesn't matter what they do to make money. They enjoy the same protection that we all do.'

It was pretty clear to me that Minton didn't even want to use the word 'prostitute' for fear it would hurt his case. I planned to make up for the prosecutor's omissions. Minton had used all his challenges to try to keep the female content of the jury to a minimum because, I believe, he feared that once it was established that Regina Campo had been offering sexual services for money he might lose the females' sympathy and ultimately their votes on a verdict. I believed he was probably correct in that assumption and I worked just as diligently to get women on the panel. In the end I got three women and needed only one to head off a conviction.

Minton then gave a lengthy overview of the evidence. 'This is a very clear-cut and straightforward case,' he said as he was winding up. 'You have a man who attacked a woman in her home. His plan was to rape and then kill her. It is only by the grace of God that she is here to tell you the story.'

With that he thanked them for their attention and took his seat at the prosecution table. Judge Fullbright looked at her watch. It was 11.40 and she was probably weighing up whether to go to a break or let me proceed with my opener. One of the judge's chief jobs during trial is making sure the jury is comfortable and engaged. Lots of breaks is often the answer.

'Mr Haller,' she said, 'are you planning to reserve your statement?'

'No, Your Honour, but I believe I am going to be pretty quick.'

'Good,' she said. 'We'll hear from you and then we'll take lunch.'

The truth was I didn't know how long I would be. I had told the judge I'd be quick simply because I didn't like the idea of the jury going to lunch with only the prosecutor's side of the story to think about.

I got up and went to the lectern between the prosecution and defence tables. Fullbright ran her trials like a federal judge. Attorneys were not allowed to approach witnesses without permission and never allowed to approach the jury box. They were required to speak from the lectern only.

'Ladies and gentlemen of the jury,' I began, 'my name is Michael Haller and I am representing Mr Roulet. I am happy to tell you that this trial will most likely be a quick one. Probably it will have taken longer to pick all of you than it will take to present both sides of the case. The prosecutor, Mr Minton, seemed to spend his time this morning telling you about what he thinks all the evidence means and who Mr Roulet really is. I would advise you to simply sit back, listen to the evidence and let your common sense tell you what it all means and who Mr Roulet is.'

I kept my eyes moving from juror to juror, rarely looking down at my pad. I wanted them to think I was talking off the top of my head.

'In a criminal trial the defence has the option of making an opening statement at the start of the trial or right before presenting the defence's case, and I would normally take the second option. This case is different, because in essence the prosecution's case is also going to be the defence's case. But I guarantee that a version of the events and evidence very different from what Mr Minton just outlined is going to emerge in this courtroom. I think you will find that this whole case comes down to the actions and motivations of one person. A prostitute who saw a man with outward signs of wealth and chose to target him.'

Minton stood up and objected, saying I was going out of bounds in trying to impeach the state's main witness with unsubstantiated accusations. There was no legal basis for the objection. It was just an amateurish attempt to send a message to the jury. The judge responded by inviting us to a sidebar.

We walked to the side of the bench and the judge flipped on a sound neutraliser that sent white noise from a speaker on the bench towards the jury and prevented them from hearing what was whispered in the sidebar.

The judge was quick with Minton, like an assassin. 'Mr Minton, I know you are new to felony trial work, so I see I will have to school you as we go. But don't you ever object during an opening statement in my courtroom. This isn't evidence he's presenting. I don't care if he says your own mother is the defendant's alibi witness, you don't object in front of my jury.'

She rolled her seat back to the centre of the bench and flicked off the white noise. Minton and I returned to our positions without a further word.

'Objection overruled,' the judge said. 'Continue, Mr Haller.'

'Thank you, Your Honour.'

Knowing that Minton would have been intimidated to silence by the judge, I decided to raise the rhetoric up a notch and get directly to the wind-up.

'Ladies and gentlemen, in essence, what you will be deciding here is who the real predator was in this case. Mr Roulet, a successful businessman with a spotless record, or an admitted prostitute with a successful business in taking money from men in exchange for sex. You will hear testimony that the alleged victim in this case was engaged in an act of prostitution with another man just moments before this supposed attack occurred. And you will hear testimony that within days of this supposedly life-threatening assault, she was back in business once again, trading sex for money.'

I glanced at Minton and saw he was doing a slow burn. He had his eyes downcast on the table in front of him and he was slowly shaking his head.

I looked up at the judge. 'Your Honour, could you instruct the prosecutor to refrain from demonstrating in front of the jury? I did not object or in any way try to distract the jury during his opening statement.'

'Mr Minton,' the judge intoned, 'please sit still and extend the courtesy to the defence that was extended to you.'

'Yes, Your Honour,' Minton said meekly.

The jury had now seen the prosecutor slapped down twice and we weren't even past openers. I took this as a good sign and it fed my momentum.

'Finally, you will receive testimony from many of the state's own witnesses that will provide a perfectly acceptable explanation for much of the physical evidence in this case. The prosecution's own case will provide you with more than reasonable doubt about the guilt of my client. I guarantee you will find that you have only one choice at the end of this case. And that is to find Mr Roulet not guilty of these charges. Thank you.'

As I walked back to my seat I winked at Lorna. She nodded at me as if to say I had done well. My attention was then drawn to the two figures sitting two rows behind her. Detectives Lankford and Sobel. What were they doing in the courtroom? Watching me? Waiting for me?

I took my seat. The judge dismissed the jury for lunch and I walked over to the clerk's station so I could write out a cheque for $500. When I was finished, I checked the bench where the two Glendale detectives had been sitting a few moments before. They were gone.

THE PROSECUTION BEGAN presenting its case to the jury in the afternoon session and Ted Minton's strategy quickly became clear to me. The first four witnesses were a 911 dispatch operator, the patrol officers who responded to Regina Campo's call for help, and the paramedic who treated her before she was transported to the hospital. It was clear that Minton wanted to establish firmly that Campo had been brutally assaulted and was indeed the victim in this crime. It wasn't a bad strategy. In most cases it would get the job done.

The dispatch operator was essentially used as the warm body needed to introduce a recording of Campo's 911 call for help. There was no doubt that Minton had started out of the gate strong as the jurors sat listening raptly to Campo begging for help. She sounded genuinely distraught and scared.

The two patrol officers who followed offered different testimony because they did separate things upon arriving at the Tarzana apartment complex in response to the 911 call. One primarily stayed with the victim while the other went up to the apartment and handcuffed the man Campo's neighbours were sitting on—Louis Ross Roulet.

Officer Vivian Maxwell described Campo as dishevelled, hurt and frightened, even after being assured that the intruder had been caught.

When Minton was through with this witness, I stood up to conduct my first cross-examination of the trial.

'Officer Maxwell,' I asked, 'did you at any time ask Ms Campo what had happened to her?'

'Yes, I asked her what had happened and who did this to her.'

'What did she tell you?'

'She said a man had knocked at her door and when she opened it he punched her several times and then took out a knife.'

'Did she tell you who the man was?'

'No, she said she didn't know the man.'

'You specifically asked if she knew the man?'

'Yes. She said no.'

'So she just opened her door at ten o'clock at night to a stranger.'

'She didn't say it that way. She said, "I don't know who he is."'

Maxwell's partner, John Santos, testified next, telling jurors that Campo directed him to her apartment, where he found a man on the floor near the entrance. The man was semiconscious and was being held on the ground by two of Campo's neighbours, Edward Turner and Ronald Atkins. One man was straddling the man's chest and the other was sitting on his legs.

Santos identified the man being held on the floor as the defendant, Louis Ross Roulet, and described him as having blood on his clothes and his left hand. Santos had turned him over and cuffed his hands behind his back. The officer had then put a plastic evidence bag over Roulet's bloody hand.

Santos testified that one of the men who had been holding Roulet handed over a folding knife, which was open and had blood on its handle and blade. Santos told jurors that he had bagged this item as well and turned it over to Detective Martin Booker as soon as he arrived on the scene.

On cross-examination I asked Santos only two questions.

'Officer, was there blood on the defendant's right hand?'

'No, or I would have bagged that hand, too.'

'I see. So you have blood on the left hand only and a knife with blood on the handle. Would it then appear to you that if the defendant had held that knife, then he would have to have held it in his left hand?'

'It would seem that way to me,' Santos answered.

Arthur Metz was the paramedic who testified next. He told jurors about the extent of Campo's injuries when he treated her less than thirty minutes after the attack. He said that it appeared to him that she had suffered at least three significant impacts to the right side of her face. She also had a small puncture wound to her neck. He described all the injuries as superficial but painful. A blowup of the photograph of Campo's face that I had seen on my first day on the case was displayed on an easel in front of the jury.

When it was my turn to cross-examine Metz, I said, 'If she was hit three times on the right side of her face, the impacts would have come from the left side of her attacker, correct?'

'If the attacker was facing her, he would have punched her from the left, unless it was a backhand,' Metz said. 'Then it could have been a right.' He nodded and seemed pleased with himself.

'You are suggesting that Ms Campo's attacker hit her three times with a backhand and caused this degree of injury?' I pointed to the photo.

Metz shrugged. 'Anything is possible,' he said.

'Anything is possible,' I repeated. 'Well, is there any other possibility you can think of that would explain these injuries as coming from anything other than direct left-handed punches?'

Metz shrugged again. He was not an impressive witness.

'What if Ms Campo were to have hit her face with her own fist? Wouldn't she have used her right—?'

Minton jumped up immediately and objected. 'Your Honour, this is outrageous! To suggest that the victim did this to herself is an affront not only to this court but to all victims of violent crime everywhere. Mr Haller—'

'The witness said anything is possible,' I argued, trying to knock Minton off the soapbox. 'I am trying to explore what—'

'Sustained,' Fullbright said, ending it. 'Mr Haller, don't go there unless you are making more than an exploratory swing through the possibilities.'

'Yes, Your Honour,' I said. 'No further questions.'

I sat down and glanced at the jurors and knew from their faces that I had made a mistake. I had turned a positive cross into a negative. The point I had made about a left-handed attacker was obscured by the point I had lost with the suggestion that the injuries to the victim's face were self-inflicted.

Still, I tried to focus on a positive aspect. It was good to know the jury's feelings on this now, before Campo was in the witness box.

I scanned the courtroom. It was almost empty now. Lankford and Sobel had not returned to the courtroom, leaving a disparate collection of retirees, law students and lawyers resting their feet until their own hearings began. But I was counting on one of these onlookers being a plant from the DA's office. My guess was that Ted Minton's boss would have a means of keeping tabs on the case. I was playing as much to the plant as I was to the jury.

The afternoon dragged on and I could see that the jurors were growing bored with the prosecutor's linear presentation of events. Minton obviously wanted to save his most powerful stuff for day two. He would have the lead investigator, Detective Martin Booker, to bring all the details together, then the victim, Regina Campo, to bring it all home to the jury. It was a tried-and-tested formula, but it was making the first day move like a glacier.

Things finally started to pop with the last witness of the day. Minton brought in Charles Talbot, the man who had picked up Regina Campo at Morgan's and gone to her apartment on the night of the attack. Talbot was hauled in to testify that Campo had been uninjured when he left.

Talbot was fifty-five years old with dyed blond hair. He had been divorced for twenty years and owned a twenty-four-hour convenience store called Kwik Kwik. The business gave him a comfortable living, an apartment in the Warner Center, a late model Corvette, and a nightlife that included a wide sampling of the city's professional sex providers.

Minton established all this, then brought him to the night of March 6, asking him to describe how he hooked up with Regina Campo.

'I saw her ad on the website and I called her up and we made a date. We met at Morgan's and we had a couple of drinks and we talked and we liked each other and that was that. I followed her back to her place.'

'When you went to her apartment, did you engage in sexual relations?'

'Sure did. That's what I was there for.'

'And you paid her?'

'Four hundred bucks. It was worth it.'

I saw a male juror's face turning red and knew I had pegged him perfectly during selection. He had brought a Bible with him to read while other prospective jurors were being questioned. Minton had missed it and accepted him on the jury. So had I. I figured he would be easy to turn against the victim because of her occupation. His reddening face confirmed it.

'What time did you leave her apartment?' Minton asked.

'About five minutes before ten,' Talbot answered.

'Did she tell you she was expecting another date at the apartment?'

'No, she didn't say anything about that.'

'Mr Talbot, could you describe the physical state Ms Campo was in when you left her shortly before ten o'clock on the night of March the 6th?'

'Completely satisfied.'

There was a loud blast of laughter in the courtroom and Talbot beamed proudly. The Bible man looked like his jaw was tightly clenched.

'Mr Talbot,' Minton said. 'Was she hurt or bleeding when you left her?'

'No, she was fine. When I left her she was fit as a fiddle.'

'And you didn't strike her or physically abuse her in any way?'

'No. What we did was consensual and pleasurable. No pain.'

'Thank you, Mr Talbot.'

I stood up and moved to the lectern for the cross-examination. 'Mr Talbot, are you right- or left-handed?'

'I'm left-handed.'

'Left-handed,' I echoed. 'And isn't it true that, before leaving Ms Campo's apartment, she asked you to strike her repeatedly in the face?'

'That is not true. I've never hurt a woman in my life.'

'Do you know a prostitute named Shaquilla Barton? On the website where she advertises her services she uses the name Shaquilla Shackles.'

Talbot thought about it. 'Yeah, I think so.'

'Have you ever engaged in acts of prostitution with her?'

'One time, yes. A year ago. Maybe longer.'

'And did you hurt her on that occasion?'

'No.'

'And if she were to come to this courtroom and say that you did hurt her by punching her with your left hand, would she be lying?'

'She damn sure would be. I tried her out and didn't like that rough stuff.'

'Thank you, Mr Talbot.' I sat down.

Talbot was excused and Minton told the judge that he had only two witnesses remaining to present in the case but that their testimony would be lengthy. Judge Fullbright checked the time and recessed court for the day.

Two witnesses left. I knew that had to be Detective Booker and Regina Campo. It looked like Minton was going to go without the testimony of the jailhouse snitch he had stashed in the PTI programme at County–USC. Dwayne Corliss's name had not appeared on any witness list or any other discovery document associated with the prosecution of the case. I thought maybe Minton had found out what Raul Levin had found out about Corliss before Levin was murdered. Either way, it seemed apparent that Corliss had been dropped by the prosecution. And that was what I needed to change.

As I came out of the courtroom, I saw a number of jurors standing by the elevator. I went into the restroom next to the bank of elevators so I didn't have to ride down with them. As I washed my hands I looked at myself in the mirror for signs of stress. I looked reasonably sane for a defence pro who was playing both his client and the prosecution at the same time.

When I came out of the restroom, the jurors were gone. But standing in the hallway by the elevator were Lankford and Sobel. Lankford was holding a folded sheaf of documents in one hand.

'There you are,' he said. 'We've been looking for you.'

THE DOCUMENT Lankford handed me was a search warrant granting the police the authority to search my home, office and car for a .22 calibre Colt Woodsman pistol, serial number 656300081-52. The authorisation, signed by a Glendale municipal court judge I had never heard of, said that the pistol was believed to have been the murder weapon in the April 12 homicide of Raul Aaron Levin. I did my best to act like it was the kind of thing I handled every other day. The truth was, my knees almost buckled.

'Where do you want to start?' Lankford asked. 'You have your car here, right? That Lincoln you're chauffeured around in like a high-class hooker.'

I started to recover from the shock. 'This is bullshit,' I said. 'You don't have the probable cause for this. I could have it quashed in ten minutes.'

'It looked pretty good to Judge Fullbright,' Lankford said.

'Fullbright? What does she have to do with this?'

'Well, we knew you were in trial, so we figured we ought to ask her if it was OK to drop the warrant on you. She said after court was over was fine by her—and she didn't say shit about the probable cause or anything else.'

They must have gone to Fullbright's chambers during the lunch break, right after I had seen them in the courtroom.

I looked at Sobel, the more sympathetic of the two. 'I'm in the middle of a three-day trial,' I said. 'Can we put this on hold until Thursday?'

'No way,' Lankford answered. 'We're not going to give you the time to dump the gun. Now where's your car, Lincoln lawyer?'

I checked the authorisation of the warrant. It had to be very specific and I was in luck. It called for the search of a Lincoln with the California licence plate NT GLTY. I realised that someone must have written the plate down on the day I was called to Raul Levin's house from the Dodgers game. Because that was the old Lincoln—the one I was driving that day.

'It's at home. Since I'm in trial I don't use the driver. I got a ride in with my client this morning and I was going to ride back with him.'

I lied. The Lincoln I'd been driving was in the courthouse parking garage. But I couldn't let them search it because there was a gun in a compartment in the back-seat armrest. It wasn't the gun they were looking for, but after Levin was murdered and I'd found my pistol box empty I asked Earl Briggs to get me a gun for protection. I didn't know the gun's history or registration and I didn't want to find out through the Glendale Police Department.

But the Lincoln with the gun inside wasn't the one in the warrant. That one was in my garage, waiting for the buyer from the limo service to come by and look at it. And that would be the Lincoln that would be searched.

Lankford grabbed the warrant out of my hand and shoved it into an inside coat pocket. 'Don't worry about your ride. We're your ride. Let's go.'

Soon I was riding in the back of a Grand Marquis. Lankford did the driving and I sat behind him.

'Let me see the warrant again,' I said.

Sobel turned towards Lankford, but he made no move.

'I'm not letting you inside my house until I've had a chance to study the warrant. I could do it on the way and save you some time. Or . . .'

Lankford reached inside his jacket for the warrant and handed it over his shoulder to me. I knew why he was hesitant. Cops usually had to lay out their whole investigation in the warrant application in order to convince a judge of probable cause, so they didn't like the target reading it.

I opened the warrant to the summary section and read.

Lankford and Sobel had put my name into the state's Automated Firearm System and hit the lotto. The AFS computer said I was the registered owner of a pistol of the same make and model as the murder weapon.

It was a smooth move but it wasn't enough to make probable cause. Colt made the Woodsman for more than sixty years. That meant there were probably a million of them out there and a million suspects who owned them.

The application summary stated that I had hidden from investigators the fact that I owned the gun. It said I had fabricated an alibi when initially interviewed about Levin's death, then attempted to throw detectives off track by giving them a phoney lead on the drug dealer Hector Arrande Moya.

The probable cause summary stated that the victim—Raul Levin—had been extorting investigative assignments from me and that I had refused to pay him upon completion of those assignments.

The outrageousness of such an assertion aside, the alibi fabrication was the key point of probable cause. The statement said that I had told the detectives I was home at the time of the murder, but a message on my home phone was left just before the suspected time of death and this indicated that I was not home, thereby collapsing my alibi and proving me a liar.

'This warrant is a piece of shit and you know it,' I said. 'I told you that message came in when I was on the phone and that can be proved. You lied by omission and commission. It's a bad-faith warrant.'

Because I was sitting behind Lankford I had a better angle on Sobel. I watched her for signs of doubt as I spoke. 'And the suggestion that Raul was extorting business from me and I wouldn't pay is a joke. Extorted me with what? And what didn't I pay him for? I paid him every time I got a bill.'

'You lied about the gun,' Lankford said. 'And you owed Levin money. It's right there in his accounts book. Four grand.'

'I didn't lie about anything. You never asked if I owned a gun.'

'Lied by omission. Right back at ya. Four grand.'

'Oh yeah, I killed him because I didn't want to pay him four grand,' I said with all the sarcasm I could muster. 'You got me there, Detective. Motivation. But I guess it never occurred to you to see if he had even billed me for the four grand yet, or to see if I hadn't just paid an invoice from him for six thousand dollars a week before he was murdered.'

I saw the doubt creep into Sobel's face. But Lankford was undaunted.

'A blackmailer's never satisfied,' he said. 'You never stop paying until you reach the point of no return. That's what this is about. The point of no return.'

I shook my head. 'And what exactly was it that he had on me that made me give him jobs and pay him until I reached the point of no return?'

Lankford and Sobel exchanged a look and Lankford nodded. Sobel reached down to a briefcase on the floor, took out a file and handed it to me.

'You missed this when you ransacked his place. It was in a dresser drawer.'

I opened the file and saw it contained several photos. I was in each one of them, and they showed me with various individuals whom I recognised as clients. They were prostitutes, street dealers and Road Saints, including Teddy Vogel handing me a roll of cash through the window of the Lincoln.

'You're saying Raul came to me with that? He extorted me with that? Those are my clients. Is this a joke or am I just missing something?'

'The California bar might not think it's a joke. Levin knew that.'

I tried to place the photographs. It became clear they had all been taken between the morning I caught the Roulet case and the day Levin was murdered. Roulet must have planted them at the crime scene to set me up. The police would have everything they needed to put Levin's murder on me—except the murder weapon. As long as Roulet had the gun, he had me.

After a while, Lankford looked at me in the rearview. 'We ran the history on that Woodsman,' he said. 'You know who owned it once, don't you?'

'Mickey Cohen,' I answered matter-of-factly, staring out of the window.

'How'd you end up with Mickey Cohen's gun?'

'My father was a lawyer. Mickey Cohen was charged in a shooting and my father defended him. When he got a not-guilty verdict, Cohen gave the gun to my father. Sort of a keepsake. It came to me in his will.'

We started climbing the hill to my home. I then gave them the bad news.

'Thanks for the ride,' I said. 'But you're wasting your time. Not only am I the wrong guy for this, but you aren't going to find that gun.'

Lankford's head jogged up and he was looking at me in the rearview again. 'And why is that, Counsellor? You already dumped it?'

'Because the gun was stolen out of my house.'

Lankford started laughing. 'Uh-huh, stolen. When did this happen?'

'Hard to tell. I hadn't checked on the gun in years.'

'You make a police report on it or file an insurance claim?'

'No.'

'So somebody comes in and steals your Mickey Cohen gun and you don't report it. Doesn't that sound a little screwy to you?'

'It does, except I knew who stole it. A client told me he took it, and if I were to report it I would be violating a client trust because my police report would lead to his arrest. Kind of a catch twenty-two, Detective.'

'That sounds like bullshit, Haller,' Lankford said. He pulled up in front of my garage and looked back at me. 'Which client stole the gun?'

'I told you, I can't tell you.'

'Well, Roulet's your only client right now, isn't he? Maybe we should run the charts from his ankle bracelet and see if he's been to your place lately?'

'I have a lot of clients, but do whatever you want. Roulet actually has been here. We had a meeting here once. In my office.'

'Maybe that's when he took it.'

'I'm not telling you he took it, Detective.'

'Yeah, well, that bracelet gives Roulet a pass on the Levin thing, anyway. We checked the GPS. So I guess that leaves you, Counsellor.'

'And that leaves you wasting your time.'

I suddenly realised something about Roulet's ankle bracelet but tried not to show it. Maybe I had a line on the trap door to his Houdini act. It was something I would need to check into later.

'Are we just going to sit here?' I said.

Lankford turned and got out. He then opened my door because the inside handle had been disabled for transporting suspects.

'No, Counsellor,' Lankford said. 'We're going through this whole place. I'll take the car and Detective Sobel will start in the house.'

I shook my head. 'Your warrant is bent, Detective, so, as far as I'm concerned, you're bent. You stay together so I can watch you both or we wait until I can get an observer here. My case manager could be here in ten minutes. You could also ask her about calling me on the morning Raul Levin got killed.'

'Fine,' Lankford said angrily. 'We'll start with the car. Together.'

I walked over to a keypad on the wall outside the garage and I tapped in the combination. The garage door started to rise, revealing the Lincoln.

I decided to ease things a little bit. 'Hey, Detective,' I said. 'What's the difference between a catfish and a defence attorney?'

Lankford stared angrily at the licence plate on my Lincoln.

'One's a bottom-feeding shit sucker,' I said. 'And the other one's a fish.'

For a moment his face remained frozen. Then a smile creased it and he broke into a long and hard laugh.

IT TOOK THEM half an hour to search the Lincoln and then move into the house. I watched the whole time. They didn't talk much and it became clear that there was a rift between the partners over the direction Lankford had taken in the investigation. At one point Lankford got a call on his cellphone and went out onto the porch to talk privately, leaving Sobel in my office.

'Do you think you are being manipulated at all on this case?' I asked her.

'What are you talking about?'

'The photos stashed in the bureau, the bullet casing in the floor vent. Pretty convenient, don't you think?'

'What are you saying?'

'Nothing. I'm asking questions your partner doesn't seem interested in.'

I checked on Lankford. He was tapping in numbers on his cell, making a new call. I turned and stepped into the open doorway of the office.

'What about Raul's message to me?' I said in a low voice. 'About finding Jesús Menéndez's ticket out, what do you think he meant?'

'We haven't figured that out yet.'

'Too bad. I think it's important.'

'Everything's important until it isn't.'

I nodded, not sure what she meant. 'You know, the case I'm trying is pretty interesting. If you come back and watch you might learn something.'

She looked from the desk to me. Our eyes held for a moment. Then she squinted with suspicion. 'Are you serious?'

'Yeah, why not?'

'Well, you might have trouble getting to court if you're in lockup.'

'Hey, no gun, no case. That's why you're here, right?'

Lankford came in. Sobel told him she had finished searching the office.

'I'm telling you, it's not here,' I said. 'You're wasting your time.'

'Let's do the bedroom next,' Lankford said.

I backed up into the hallway to let them pass.

Lankford walked straight into the closet and spoke from inside it. 'Here we go.' He stepped back out holding the wooden gun box.

'Bingo,' I said. 'You found an empty gun box. You must be a detective.'

Lankford put the box down on the bed. Either he was playing with me or the box had a solid heft to it. I felt a charge go down the back of my neck as I realised that Roulet could have easily snuck back in to return the gun.

Lankford flipped the box's latch and lifted the top. He pulled back the oilcloth covering. The cork cut-out that once held Mickey Cohen's gun was still empty. I breathed out so heavily it almost came out as a sigh.

'What did I tell you?' I said quickly, trying to cover up.

'Heidi, you got a bag?' Lankford said. 'We're going to take the box.'

I looked at Sobel. She didn't look like a Heidi to me.

'In the car,' she said. 'I've got to get it.'

'You're taking an empty gun box?' I asked. 'What good does it do you?'

'It's evidence that you had Mickey Cohen's gun. Says it right on this little brass plaque your daddy or somebody had made.'

'So what?'

'Well, I just made a call, Haller. See, we had somebody checking on Mickey Cohen's self-defence case. Turns out that over there in LAPD's evidence archive they still have all the ballistic evidence from that case.'

I understood. They would take the slugs and casings from the Cohen case and compare them with the evidence from the Levin case. I doubted Roulet could have realised how the police would be able to make a case without even having the gun when he thought out his scheme to control me.

Sobel left the room and Lankford looked at me with a killer smile.

'How long will ballistics take?' I managed to ask.

'Hey, for you, we're going to put a rush on it. So get out there and enjoy yourself while you can. But don't leave town.' He laughed.

Sobel came back in with a large brown bag and a roll of red evidence tape. She put the gun box into the bag, then sealed it with the tape. I wondered if the wheels had just come off everything I had put into motion.

FERNANDO VALENZUELA lived out in Valencia, an hour's drive north in the remnants of rush-hour traffic, in a nice Spanish-style house with a red tile roof. It was almost nine by the time I got there. I pulled up to the garage, which had been left open. One space was taken by a minivan and the other by a pick-up. On the floor between the pick-up and a fully equipped tool bench was a large cardboard box for a fifty-inch plasma TV. I got out and went to the front door and knocked. Valenzuela answered after a long wait.

'Mick, what are you doing up here?'

'Do you know your garage door is open?'

'Holy shit! I just had a plasma delivered.'

He pushed by me and ran across the yard. I closed his front door and followed him to the garage. He was standing next to his TV, smiling.

'Oh, man, that would've never happened if we still lived in Van Nuys,' he said. 'That sucker woulda been long gone. Come on, we'll go in through here.'

He headed towards a door that would take us from the garage into the house. He hit a switch that made the garage door start to roll down.

'Hey, Val, wait a minute,' I said. 'Let's talk out here. It's more private.'

He came back over to me, concern in his eyes. 'What's up, Boss?'

'What's up is I spent some time today with the cops working on Raul's murder. They said they cleared Roulet on it because of the ankle bracelet.'

Valenzuela nodded. 'Yeah, they came to see me a few days after it happened. I showed them how the system works and I pulled up Roulet's track for that day. They saw he was at work. And I showed them the other bracelet I got and explained how it couldn't be tampered with. It's got a mass detector, so you can't take it off. It would know and then I would know.'

'So did those two cops ask where *you* were that day?'

'What did you say, Mick?'

My eyes lowered to the plasma TV box, then back up to his. 'Somehow, some way, he killed Raul, Val. I want to know how he did it.'

'Mick, I'm telling you, the machine doesn't lie.'

'Yeah, I know, the machine doesn't lie. So I'm asking you, Val, where were you on that Tuesday morning?'

'You son of a bitch, how could you ask me that?'

Valenzuela suddenly lunged at me and shoved me hard against his truck. I shoved him back harder and he went backwards into the TV box. It tipped over and hit the floor with a heavy *whump* and then he came down on it in a seated position. There was a sharp snapping sound from inside the box.

'You broke the screen!' he cried.

'You pushed me, Val. I pushed back.'

He scrambled to the side of the box and tried to lift it back up but it was too heavy and unwieldy. I walked over to the other side and helped him right it. As the box came upright we heard small bits of material inside it slide down. It sounded like glass. Valenzuela's mouth spread in shock.

'That was eight thousand dollars,' he whispered.

'They make TVs that cost eight thousand dollars?'

I was shocked. What was the world coming to?

'Val, where'd you get the money for an eight-thousand-dollar TV?'

He looked at me and the fire came back. 'Where the hell do you think? Business, man. Thanks to Roulet I'm having a hell of a year. But I didn't cut him loose from the bracelet so he could go out and kill Raul. I knew Raul just as long as you did. I did not do that. I did not put the bracelet on and wear it while he went to kill Raul. And I did not go and kill Raul for him for a TV. If you can't believe that, then get the hell out of here and out of my life!'

A flash thought of Jesús Menéndez came to my mind. I had failed to see the innocence in his pleas. I didn't want that to ever happen again.

'OK, Val,' I said. I walked over to the house door and pushed the button that raised the garage door. I walked past the TV box and out of the garage. 'I'll split it with you, Val,' I said. 'I'll have Lorna send you a cheque.'

'Don't bother. I'll tell them it was delivered this way.'

I got to my car door and looked back at him. 'Then give me a call when they arrest you for fraud. After you bail yourself out.'

I got in the Lincoln and backed out of the driveway.

EIGHT

The second day of trial began with a forthwith to the judge's chambers for Minton and me. Judge Fullbright wanted to speak only to me but the rules of trial made it improper for her to meet privately with me. 'Mr Haller,' she began, 'is there anything you need to bring up with me?'

'No, Judge, everything's fine. Sorry if you were bothered yesterday.'

I did my best to put on a rueful smile, as if to show that the search warrant had been nothing more than an embarrassing inconvenience.

'It is hardly a bother, Mr Haller. We've invested a lot of time on this case.

The jury, the prosecution, all of us. I hope it is not going to be for naught.'
She stood up. 'Very well. Let's get to it, gentlemen. We have a jury waiting.'

Minton and I left the chambers and entered the courtroom.

'What the hell was that all about?' Minton whispered to me.

'Just a problem with another case of mine. You going to wrap it up today?'

'Depends on you. The longer you take, the longer I take cleaning up the
bullshit you sling.'

'Bullshit, huh? You're bleeding to death and don't even know it.'

He smiled confidently at me. 'I don't think so.'

'Call it death by a thousand razor blades, Ted. One doesn't do it. They all
do it. Welcome to felony practice.' I went to the defence table.

Minton's first witness of the day was LAPD Detective Martin Booker. He
was a solid witness, clear and concise. Booker introduced the key piece of
evidence, the knife with my client's initials on it, and under Minton's questioning he took the jury through his investigation of the attack on March 6.

'Before you got to the hospital to interview Ms Campo,' Minton said,
'you had been briefed by Officers Maxwell and Santos on what the victim
had reported happened, correct?'

'Yes, they gave me an overview.'

'Did they tell you that the victim was engaged in selling sex for a living?'

'No, they didn't.'

'When did you find that out?'

'Well, I was getting a pretty good sense of it when I was in her apartment
and I saw some of the property she had there.'

'What property?'

'Things I would describe as sex aids, pornographic videotapes, and in a
bedroom closet there was clothing of a sexually provocative nature.'

'Did it change your opinion of her as a victim of this attack?'

'No, it didn't. Anybody can be a victim. Prostitute or pope, doesn't
matter. A victim is a victim.'

Spoken just as rehearsed, I thought. Minton made a check mark on his
pad and moved on. He continued to probe the investigation in such detail
that the jurors' attention clearly lagged under the weight of information.

Finally, it was my turn. My goal was only to get in and get out.

'Detective Booker, did Ms Campo explain why she lied to the police?'

'She didn't lie to me.'

'She told the first officers on the scene, Maxwell and Santos, that she
didn't know why the suspect had come to her apartment, didn't she?'

'I wasn't present when they spoke to her so I can't testify to that. I do know that she was scared, that she had just been beaten and threatened with rape and death at the time of the first interview.'

'So you are saying that under those circumstances it is acceptable to lie to the police.'

'No, I did not say that.'

I checked my notes and moved on. I wasn't going for a linear continuum of questions. I was potshotting, trying to keep him off balance.

'Did you catalogue the clothing you believed Ms Campo used for her prostitution business?'

'No, I did not. It was not important to the case.'

'Would any of the outfits you saw there have been appropriate to sado-masochistic sexual activities?'

'I wouldn't know that. I am not an expert in that field.'

'How about the pornographic videos? Do you recall if any of them involved sadomasochism or bondage or anything of that nature?'

'No, I do not.'

'Did you instruct Ms Campo to get rid of those tapes and the clothing before members of Mr Roulet's defence team could view the apartment?'

'I certainly did not.'

I checked that one off my list and moved on. 'Have you ever spoken to Mr Roulet about what happened in Ms Campo's apartment that night?'

'No, he lawyered up before I got to him.'

'Do you mean he exercised his constitutional right to remain silent?'

'Yes, that's exactly what he did.'

'In your opinion, Detective, was Ms Campo struck with great force?'

'I would say so, yes. Her face was very badly cut and swollen.'

'Tell the jury about the impact injuries you found on Mr Roulet's hands.'

'He had wrapped a cloth round his fist to protect it. There were no injuries on his hands that I could see.'

'Did you document this lack of injury?'

Booker looked puzzled by the question. 'No,' he said.

'So you had Ms Campo's injuries documented by photographs but you didn't see the need to document Mr Roulet's lack of injuries, correct?'

'It didn't seem necessary to photograph something that wasn't there.'

'Did you find the cloth he supposedly wrapped his hand in?'

'Yes, it was in the apartment. It was a napkin, like from a restaurant. It had her blood on it.'

'Did it have Mr Roulet's blood on it?'

'No.'

'Was there anything that identified it as belonging to the defendant?'

'No.'

'So we have only Ms Campo's word for it, right?'

'That's right.'

I scribbled a note on my pad, then continued. 'Detective, did you pursue other explanations for Ms Campo's injuries?'

'No, she told me what happened. I believed her. He beat her and—'

'Thank you, Detective Booker. Just try to answer the questions I ask. If you looked for no other explanation because you believed the word of Ms Campo, is it safe to say that this whole case relies upon her word and what she said occurred in her apartment on the night of March the 6th?'

'It's not just her word,' Booker said. 'There is physical evidence. The knife. Her injuries. More than just her word on this.'

'But doesn't the state's explanation for her injuries and the other evidence begin with her telling of what happened?'

'You could say that, yes,' he said reluctantly.

'She is the tree on which all of these fruits grow, is she not?'

'I probably wouldn't use those words.'

'Then what words would you use, Detective? How would you describe Ms Campo's position in this case?'

Booker raised his hands in a quick gesture of surrender. 'She's the victim! We have to rely on her to set the course of the investigation.'

'You rely on her for quite a bit in this case, don't you? Victim and chief witness against the defendant, correct?'

'That's right.'

'Who else saw the defendant attack Ms Campo?'

'Nobody else.'

I nodded, to underline the answer for the jury. I looked over and exchanged eye contact with those in the front row.

'OK, Detective,' I said. 'I want to ask you about Charles Talbot now. How did you find out about this man?'

'Uh, the prosecutor, Mr Minton, told me to find him.'

'And do you know how Mr Minton came to know about his existence?'

'I believe you were the one who informed him. You had a videotape from a bar that showed him with the victim a couple of hours before the attack.'

'Until that point you didn't think it was important to find this man?'

'No, I just didn't know about him.'

'So when you finally did know about Mr Talbot and you located him, did you have his left hand examined to determine if he had any injuries that could have been sustained while punching someone repeatedly in the face?'

'No, I didn't.'

'Is that because you were confident in your choice of Mr Roulet as the person who punched Ms Campo?'

'It wasn't a choice. It was where the investigation led. I didn't locate Charles Talbot until more than two weeks after the crime occurred.'

'So what you're saying is that if he'd had injuries, they would have been healed by then, correct?'

'I'm no expert on it but that was my thinking, yes.'

'Did you question Mr Talbot's coworkers about whether they saw bruising or other injuries on his hand around the time of the crime?'

'No, I did not.'

'So you never really looked beyond Mr Roulet, did you?'

'That is wrong. I come into every case with an open mind. But the victim identified Roulet as her attacker, and his initials were on the weapon that had been held to Ms Campo's throat.'

'How do you know that knife was held to Ms Campo's throat?'

'Because she told us and she had the puncture wound to show for it.'

'Are you saying there was some sort of forensic analysis that matched the knife to the wound on her neck?'

'No, that was impossible.'

'So again we have Ms Campo's word that the knife was held to her throat by Mr Roulet. Now, without any explanation for it, I guess you would consider the knife with the defendant's initials on it to be a highly important piece of evidence of guilt, wouldn't you?'

'Yes. He brought that knife in there with one purpose in mind.'

'You are a mind reader, are you, Detective?'

'No, I'm a detective. And I am just saying what I think.'

'Accent on *think*. I have no further questions at this time.'

I returned to my seat while Minton tried to bandage up Booker on redirect. The damage was in perceptions and he couldn't do a lot with that.

After the detective stepped down, the judge called for a break. In the hallway, Booker walked up to me and pointed a finger in my face.

'Your whole bullshit defence is going to crash and burn, Haller,' he said.

'We'll see.'

'Yeah, we'll see. You know, you have some balls trying to trash Talbot with this. You must need a wheelbarrow to carry them around in.'

'I'm just doing my job, Detective.'

'And some job it is. Lying for a living. Tricking people from looking at the truth. Living in a world without truth. Let me ask you something. You know the difference between a catfish and a lawyer?'

'No, what's the difference?'

'One's a bottom-feeding, shit-eating scum sucker. The other's a fish.'

'That's a good one, Detective.'

He left me, and I stood there smiling. Not because of the joke or the understanding that Lankford had elevated the insult from defence attorneys to all of lawyerdom when he retold the joke to Booker. I smiled because it was confirmation that Lankford and Booker were in communication. Things were moving and in play. My plan was holding together. I still had a chance.

EVERY TRIAL has a main event. A witness or a piece of evidence that becomes the fulcrum upon which everything swings one way or the other. In this case the main event was billed as Regina Campo, victim and accuser, and the case would seem to rest upon her performance. But a good defence attorney always has an understudy and I had mine, a witness secretly waiting in the wings upon whom I hoped to shift the weight of the trial.

Nevertheless, when Minton called Regina Campo to the stand after the break, it was safe to say that all eyes were on her slight, diminutive figure as she was led in and walked to the witness box.

Minton led her through her testimony, starting with her personal background. Regina Campo's story was of a fresh-faced young woman coming to Hollywood from Indiana a decade earlier with hopes of celluloid glory. There were starts and stops to a career, an appearance on a TV show here and there. But when she was no longer a fresh face, she found work in a series of straight-to-cable films that often required her to appear nude. She supplemented her income with nude modelling jobs and slipped easily into trading sex for favours. Then she skipped the façade and started trading sex for money. It finally brought her to the night she encountered Louis Roulet.

Regina Campo's version of what happened that night did not differ from previous witnesses' accounts. But it was dramatically different in the delivery. Campo, her face framed by dark curly hair, was like a little girl lost. She seemed scared and tearful during the latter half of her testimony. Her lower lip and finger shook as she pointed to the man she identified as her attacker.

Roulet stared right back, a blank expression on his face.

'It was him,' she said. 'He's an animal who should be put away!'

Minton continued the questioning, taking Campo through her escape, and then asking why she had not told the responding officers the truth about knowing who the man who attacked her was and why he was there.

'I was very scared,' she said. 'I wasn't sure they would believe me if I told them why he was there. I wanted to make sure they arrested him.'

'Do you regret that decision now?'

'Yes, because it might help him get free to do this again to somebody.'

Campo had testified for nearly an hour. It was almost 11.30 but the judge did not break for lunch as I had expected. She told the jurors she wanted to get as much testimony in as possible during the day and that they would go to a late, abbreviated lunch. I wondered if the Glendale detectives had called her during the break to warn of my impending arrest?

I went to the lectern. If I was engaged in a defence of a thousand razors, I had to use at least half of them on this witness. I was ready.

'Ms Campo, have you engaged the services of an attorney to sue Mr Roulet over the alleged events of March the 6th?'

She looked as though she had expected the question, but not as the first one out of the chute. 'No, I haven't.'

'Have you talked to an attorney about this case?'

'I haven't hired anybody to sue him. Right now, all I'm interested in—'

'Ms Campo,' I interrupted. 'I didn't ask whether you hired an attorney or what your interests are. I asked if you had *talked* to an attorney—any attorney—about this case and a possible lawsuit against Mr Roulet.'

She was looking closely at me, trying to read me. I had said it with the authority of someone who knew something, who could back up the charge.

'Talked to an attorney, yes. But I didn't hire him.'

'Is that because the prosecutor told you not to hire anybody until the criminal case was over?'

'No, he didn't say anything about that.'

'Why did you talk to an attorney about this case?'

'I talked to him because I wanted to know my rights.'

'Did you ask him if you could sue Mr Roulet for damages?'

'I thought what you say to your attorney is private.'

'If you wish, you can tell the jurors what you spoke about.'

There was the first deep slash with the razor. She was in an untenable position. No matter how she answered she would not look good.

'I think I want to keep it private,' she finally said.

'OK, let's go back to March the 6th, to Morgan's bar when you first spoke to the defendant, Mr Roulet. What were you doing there?'

'I was meeting someone.'

'You were meeting Charles Talbot there to sort of size up whether you wanted to lead him back to your place to engage in sex for hire, correct?'

She hesitated but then nodded. 'Yes.'

'You meet your prospective clients in a public place like Morgan's to test them out and make sure they aren't freaks or dangerous before you take them to your apartment. Isn't that right?'

'You could say that. But the truth is, you can never be sure.'

'That is true. So when you were at Morgan's you noticed Mr Roulet sitting at the same bar as you and Mr Talbot?'

'Yes, he was there.'

'And had you ever seen him before?'

'Yes, I had seen him there and a few other places before.'

'Had you ever noticed that he wore a Rolex watch?'

'No.'

'Had you ever seen him drive up or away from one of these places in a Porsche or a Range Rover?'

'No, I never saw him driving.'

'Had you ever spoken to him?'

'No, we never talked.'

'Then what made you approach him?'

'I knew he was in the life. The other times I had seen him I could tell he was a player. I'd seen him leave with girls who do what I do.'

'Leave to where?'

'I don't know. To a hotel or the girl's apartment.'

'Well, how do you know they even left the premises? Maybe they went outside for a smoke.'

'I saw them get into his car and drive away.'

'Ms Campo, you testified a minute ago that you never saw Mr Roulet's cars. Now you are saying that you saw him get into his car. Which is it?'

She realised her mistake and froze for a moment until an answer came to her. 'I saw him get into a car but I didn't know what kind it was.'

I paused a moment and decided I had milked her contradiction for all it was worth. 'These women that you saw leave with Mr Roulet, did they disappear? Did you ever see them again?'

'No, I saw them again.'

'Had they been beaten or injured?'

'Not that I know of, but I didn't ask.'

'But all of this added up to you believing that you were safe as far as approaching and soliciting him, correct?'

'I don't know about safe.'

'Well, can you tell the jury why it was that you did not have to sit with Mr Roulet like you did with Mr Talbot and subject him to a "freak test"?'

Her eyes drifted over to Minton. She was hoping for a rescue but none was coming. 'I just thought he was a known quantity, that's all.'

'You thought he was safe.'

'I guess so. I don't know. I needed the money and I made a mistake.'

'Did you think he was rich and could solve your need for money?'

'No, nothing like that.'

'You testified that on prior occasions you had seen Mr Roulet with other women who practise the same profession as yourself?'

'Yes.'

'And do you extend professional courtesy to these women in terms of alerting them to customers who might be dangerous or unwilling to pay?'

'Sometimes.'

'And they extend the same professional courtesy to you, right?'

'Yes.'

'How many of them warned you about Louis Roulet?'

'Well, nobody did, or I wouldn't have gone with him.'

I nodded and looked at my notes for a long moment. Then I led her in detail through the events at Morgan's, and introduced the videotape from the bar's surveillance camera. A TV was wheeled in and the video was played.

'What did the note say that you passed him?' I asked after the television was pushed to the side of the courtroom.

'I think it just said my name and address.'

'You didn't quote him a price for the services you would perform?'

'I may have. I don't remember.'

'What is the going rate that you charge?'

'Usually I get four hundred dollars.'

'Usually? What would make you differentiate from that?'

'Depends on what the client wants.'

I looked over at the jury box and saw that the Bible man's face was getting tight with discomfort.

'Do you ever engage in bondage and domination with your clients?'

'Sometimes. It's only play-acting, though. Nobody ever gets hurt.'

'At the time you gave Mr Roulet the napkin with your address and price on it, you were confident that he would not be a danger to you and that he was carrying sufficient cash funds to pay the four hundred dollars?'

'Yes.'

'So why didn't he have any cash on him when the police searched him?'

'I don't know. I didn't take it.'

'Do you know who did?'

'No.'

I paused. 'Now, you are still working as a prostitute, correct?' I asked.

She hesitated before saying yes.

'And are you happy working as a prostitute?' I asked.

Minton stood. 'Your Honour, what does this have to do with—?'

'Sustained,' the judge said.

'OK,' I said. 'Then isn't it true, Ms Campo, that you have told several of your clients that your hope is to leave the business?'

'Yes, that's true,' she answered without hesitation.

'Isn't it also true that you see the potential financial aspects of this case as a means of getting out of the business?'

'No. That man was going to kill me! That's what this is about!'

'Was Charles Talbot the man who punched your face on March the 6th?'

'No, he was not,' she answered quickly.

'Did you offer to split the profits you would receive from a lawsuit against Mr Roulet with Mr Talbot?'

'No, I did not. That's a lie!'

I looked up at the judge. 'Your Honour, can I ask my client to stand up?'

'Be my guest, Mr Haller.'

I signalled Roulet to stand at the defence table and he obliged.

I looked back at Regina Campo. 'Now, Ms Campo, are you sure that this is the man who struck you on the night of March the 6th?'

'Yes, it's him.'

'Ms Campo, on your ad on the web you list your weight at a hundred and five pounds,' I said. 'So if the jury is to believe your story, they must believe you were able to overpower and break free of Mr Roulet.' I pointed to Roulet, who was easily six feet and outweighed her by at least seventy-five pounds.

'Well, that's what I did.'

'And this was while he supposedly was holding a knife to your throat.'

'I wanted to live. You can do amazing things when your life is in danger.'

She used her last defence. She started crying, as if my question had reawakened the horror of coming so close to death.

'You can sit down, Mr Roulet. I have nothing else for Ms Campo at this time, Your Honour.'

I took my seat next to Roulet. I felt the cross had gone well. My razor work had opened up a lot of wounds. The state's case was bleeding.

Minton went back in for a redirect but he was just a gnat flitting around an open wound. There was no going back on some of the answers his star witness had given, and there was no way to change some of the images I had planted in the jurors' minds.

In ten minutes he was through and I waived a recross, feeling that Minton had accomplished little and I could leave well enough alone.

The judge excused the jury to lunch, and said court would recess until 1.30. She then left the bench.

I asked Roulet if his mother could join us for lunch so that we could talk about her testimony, which I thought would come in the afternoon. He said he would arrange it. I told him we had less than an hour and that his mother should meet us at Four Green Fields.

When I turned from the defence table, I saw that the gallery was empty. Everybody had hustled out to lunch. Only Minton was waiting by the rail.

'Can I talk to you for a minute?' he asked me.

'Sure.'

We waited until Roulet had left the courtroom before either one of us spoke. I knew what was coming. It was customary for the prosecutor to throw out a low-ball disposition at the first sign of trouble. Minton knew he had trouble. His main-event witness had been a draw at best.

'What's up?' I said.

'I was thinking about what you said about the thousand razors. And, well, I want to make you an offer.'

'Don't you need somebody in charge to approve a plea agreement, kid?'

'I have some authority.'

'OK, then give me what you are authorised to offer.'

'I'll drop it down to aggravated assault with GBI. And I'll go down to four.'

The offer was a substantial reduction, but Roulet, if he took it, would still be sentenced to four years in prison. The main concession was that it knocked the case out of sex-crime status. Roulet would not have to register with local authorities as a sex offender after he got out of prison.

I looked at Minton as if he had just insulted my mother's memory.

'I think that's a little strong, Ted, considering how your ace just held up on the stand. Did you see the juror who is always carrying the Bible? He looked like he was about to shit the Good Book when she was testifying.'

Minton didn't respond. I could tell he hadn't even noticed a juror carrying a Bible.

'I don't know,' I said. 'It's my duty to bring your offer to my client and I will do that. But I'm also going to tell him he'd be a fool to take it.'

'OK, then, what do you want?'

'A case like this, there's only one verdict, Ted. I'm going to tell him he should ride it out. I think it's clear sailing from here. Have a good lunch.'

I left Minton there at the gate, half expecting him to shout a new offer to my back as I went down the centre aisle of the gallery. But he held his ground.

'That offer's good only until one thirty, Haller,' he called after me.

I raised a hand and waved without looking back. As I went through the courtroom door, I was sure I had heard a note of desperation in his voice.

AFTER WE CAME back into court from Four Green Fields I purposely ignored Minton. I wanted to keep him guessing. When we were all seated and ready for the judge, I finally looked over at him, waited for the eye contact, and then just shook my head. No deal. He nodded, trying his best to give me a show of confidence in his case and confusion over my client's decision.

One minute later the judge took the bench. 'Mr Minton, do you have another witness?' she asked.

'Your Honour, at this time the state rests.'

Fullbright stared at him a moment then looked at me. 'Mr Haller, are you ready to proceed?'

I told the judge I was ready to proceed with a defence.

My first witness was Mary Windsor. She was escorted into the courtroom by Cecil Dobbs, who then took a seat in the gallery. Mary Windsor was wearing a powder-blue suit with a chiffon blouse. She had a regal bearing as she sat in the witness box. I quickly established her relationship by both blood and business to Louis Roulet. I then asked the judge for permission to show the witness the knife the prosecution had entered as evidence.

Permission granted, I went to the court clerk to retrieve the weapon, which was still wrapped in a clear plastic evidence bag. It was folded so that the initials on the blade were visible. I took it to the witness box.

'Mrs Windsor, do you recognise this knife?'

'Yes, I do,' she said. 'It's my son's knife.'

'And how is it that you would recognise a knife owned by your son?'

'Because he showed it to me on more than one occasion. I knew he always carried it and sometimes it came in handy at the office when our brochures came in and we needed to cut the packing straps.'

'How long has he had the knife?'

'Four years.'

'You seem pretty exact about that. How can you be so sure?'

'Because he got it for protection four years ago. Almost exactly.'

'Protection from what, Mrs Windsor?'

'In our business we often show homes to complete strangers. Sometimes we are the only ones in the home with these strangers. There has been more than one incident of a realtor being robbed, or even murdered or raped.'

'As far as you know, was Louis ever the victim of such a crime?'

'Not personally, no. But he knew someone who had gone into a home and that happened to them.'

'What happened?'

'She got raped by a man with a knife. Louis was the one who found her after it was over. He went out and got a knife for protection after that.'

'Why a knife? Why not a gun?'

'He told me that at first he was going to get a gun but he wanted something he could always carry and not be noticeable with. So he got a knife and he got me one too. Mine's exactly the same, only the initials are different, obviously. We both have been carrying them ever since.'

'So would it seem to you that if your son was carrying that knife on the night of March the 6th, that would be perfectly normal behaviour from him?'

Minton objected, saying I had not built the proper foundation for Mary Windsor to answer the question, and the judge sustained it.

Mary Windsor, being unschooled in criminal law, assumed that the judge was allowing her to answer. 'He carried it every day,' she said. 'March the 6th would have been no dif—'

'Mrs Windsor,' the judge boomed. 'I sustained the objection. That means you do not answer. The jury will disregard her answer.'

'I'm sorry,' Mary Windsor said in a weak voice.

'Next question, Mr Haller,' the judge ordered.

'That's all I have, Your Honour. Thank you, Mrs Windsor.'

I returned to my seat as Minton got up from his.

Mary Windsor's testimony had adhered perfectly to the choreography we had worked up at lunch. She had delivered to the jury the explanation for the knife, yet had left in her testimony a minefield for Minton to cross. She had covered no more than I had provided Minton in a discovery summary. If he strayed from it he would quickly hear the deadly *click* under his foot.

'This incident that inspired your son to start carrying around a five-inch folding knife, when exactly was that?'

'It happened on June the 9th, 2001.'

I turned in my seat so I could more fully see Minton's face. He thought he had something. Mary Windsor's exact memory of a date was obvious indication of planted testimony. He was excited, I could tell.

'Was there a newspaper story about this supposed attack on a fellow realtor? Was there a police investigation?'

'No, there wasn't.'

'And yet you know the exact date. How is that, Mrs Windsor? Were you given this date before testifying here?'

'No, I know the date because I will never forget the day I was attacked.'

She waited a moment. I saw at least three of the jurors open their mouths silently. Minton did the same. I could almost hear the *click*.

'My son will never forget it, either,' Mary Windsor continued. 'When he came looking for me and found me, I was tied up, naked. There was blood. That was the reason he took to carrying a knife.'

'I see,' Minton said, staring down at his notes. He froze. He didn't want to raise his foot for fear that the mine would detonate and blow it off.

'Mr Minton, anything else?' the judge asked, a not so well disguised note of sarcasm in her voice.

Minton gathered himself and tried to salvage something. 'Mrs Windsor, did you or your son call the police after he found you?'

'No. Louis wanted to but I thought it would only further the trauma.'

'So we have no official police documentation of this crime, correct?'

'That's correct.'

I knew that Minton wanted to carry it further and ask if she had sought medical treatment after the attack. But sensing another trap, he didn't.

'So what you are saying here is that we only have your word that this attack even occurred? Your word and your son's, if he chooses to testify.'

'It did occur. I live with it each and every day.'

'Mrs Windsor, you are here to help your son, correct?'

'If I can. I know him as a good man who would not have committed this despicable crime.'

'You would be willing to do anything and everything in your power to save your son from conviction and possible prison, wouldn't you?'

'I wouldn't lie about something like this, oath or no oath.'

'Thank you, Mrs Windsor.'

Minton quickly returned to his seat. I had only one question on redirect.

'Mrs Windsor, how old were you when this attack occurred?'

'I was fifty-four.'

I sat down and Mary Windsor was excused. I asked the judge to allow her to sit in the gallery for the remainder of the trial, now that her testimony was concluded. Without objection from Minton, the request was granted.

My next witness was an LAPD detective named David Lambkin, who was a national expert on sex crimes and had worked on the Real-Estate Rapist investigation. In brief questioning I established the facts of the case and the five reported cases of rape that were investigated. I quickly got to the five key questions I needed to bolster Mary Windsor's testimony.

'Detective, what was the age range of the known victims of the rapist?'

'The youngest was twenty-nine and the oldest was fifty-nine.'

'So a woman who was fifty-four years old would have fallen within the rapist's target profile, correct?'

'Yes.'

'Can you tell the jury when the first and last reported attacks occurred?'

'Yes. The first attack was October the 1st, 2000, and the last one was July the 30th, 2001.'

'So June the 9th, 2001, was within the span of the rapist's attacks, correct?'

'Yes, correct.'

'In the course of your investigation, did you come to a conclusion that there had been more than five rapes committed by this individual?'

Minton objected, saying the question called for speculation. The judge sustained the objection but it didn't matter. The jury had seen the prosecutor keeping the answer from them. That was the payoff.

Minton recovered enough from the misstep with Mary Windsor to hit Lambkin with three questions with answers favourable to the prosecution.

'Detective Lambkin, did the task force investigating these rapes issue any kind of warning to women working in the real-estate business?'

'Yes, we did. We sent out fliers to real-estate brokers on two occasions.'

'Did they contain information about the rapist's description and methods?'

'Yes, they did.'

'So if someone wished to concoct a story about being attacked by this rapist, the mail-outs would have provided all the information needed?'

'That is a possibility, yes.'

'Nothing further, Your Honour.'

Minton proudly sat down and Lambkin was excused.

I asked the judge for a few minutes to confer with my client and then leaned in close to Roulet. 'OK, this is it,' I said. 'You're all we have left. Unless there's something you haven't told me, there isn't much Minton can come back at you with. You should be safe up there unless you let him get to you. Are you still cool with this?'

'I want to do it,' he whispered. 'I can handle the prosecutor.'

I pushed my chair back and stood up. 'The defence calls Louis Ross Roulet, Your Honour.'

LOUIS ROULET moved towards the witness box quickly. He looked like a man anxious for the opportunity to defend himself.

Under my questioning, Roulet testified that he had no eye contact with Regina Campo before she approached him at Morgan's. She said she would be free after ten and he could come by if he was not otherwise engaged.

Roulet described his unsuccessful efforts made over the next hour at Morgan's and the Lamplighter to find a woman he would not have to pay. He then drove to the address Campo had given him and knocked on the door.

'Who answered?'

'She did. She opened the door a crack and looked out at me.'

'Could you see her whole face through the opening in the door?'

'No. She only opened up a crack and I couldn't see her. Only her left eye and a little bit of that side of her face.'

'How did the door open? Was this crack on the right or left side?'

'As I was looking at the door, the opening would have been on the right.'

'So if she were standing behind the door and looking through the opening, she would be looking at you with her left eye.'

'That is correct.'

'So if she had a bruise or a cut or any damage on the right side of her face, could you have seen it?'

'No.'

'OK. So what happened next?'

'She saw it was me and she said to come in. She opened the door wider but still sort of stood behind it.'

'You couldn't see her?'

'Not completely. She was using the edge of the door as sort of a block.'

'What happened next?'

'Well, it was kind of like an entry area, a vestibule, and she pointed through an archway to the living room. I went the way she pointed.'

'Did this mean that she was then behind you?'

'Yes, when I turned towards the living room she was behind me.'

'And then what?'

'Something hit me on the back of my head and I blacked out. When I opened my eyes, somebody was sitting on me. Somebody was sitting on my legs, too. One of them told me they had my knife and if I tried to move or escape he would use it on me. A few minutes later the police were there.'

'What about your hand? How did the blood get on your hand?'

'All I know is that somebody put it on there because I didn't.'

'Are you left-handed?'

'No, I am not.'

'You didn't strike Ms Campo with your left fist?'

'No, I did not.'

'Did you threaten to rape her?'

'No, I did not.'

'Did you tell her you were going to kill her if she didn't cooperate?'

'No, I did not.'

I was hoping for some of the fire I had seen that first day in Cecil Dobbs's office but Roulet was calm and controlled. I needed to push things a little.

'Are you angry about being charged with attacking Ms Campo?'

'Of course I am.'

'Why?'

He seemed outraged that I would ask such a question. 'Have you ever been accused of something you didn't do and there's nothing you can do about it but wait for months until you finally get a chance to go to court and say you've been set up? But then you have to wait even longer while the prosecutor puts on a bunch of liars and you have to listen to their lies. Of course it makes you angry. I am innocent! I did not do this!'

I looked at the judge. 'Nothing further, Your Honour.'

Minton moved to the lectern without breaking his steely glare away from Roulet. He gripped the sides of the lectern so hard his knuckles were white. It was all a show for the jury.

'You deny touching Ms Campo,' he said.

'That's right.'

'According to you she just punched herself or had a man she had never met before punch her lights out as part of this set-up, correct?'

'I don't know who did it,' Roulet retorted. 'All I know is that I didn't.'

'And are you telling this jury that the victim in this case somehow knew you had a knife and used it as part of the set-up?'

'I don't see how she could have known about it. I think that when she went into my pocket for the money she found the knife.'

'Oh, so now you have her stealing money out of your pocket as well.'

'I had four hundred dollars with me. When I was arrested it was gone.'

Minton didn't try to pinpoint Roulet on the money. Instead he held up the photo of Regina Campo's beaten and bruised face.

'So Ms Campo had this done to her or maybe even did it herself.'

'I don't know who did it. It wasn't me. I wouldn't do that to a woman.' Roulet pointed to the photo. 'No woman deserves that,' he said.

I leaned forward and waited. Roulet had just said the line I had told him to find a way of putting into one of his answers during testimony. *No woman deserves that*. It was now up to Minton to take the bait. He was smart. He had to understand that Roulet had just opened a door.

'What do you mean by *deserves?* Do you think crimes of violence come down to a matter of whether a victim gets what they deserve?'

'No. I meant that no matter what she does for a living, she shouldn't have been beaten like that. Nobody deserves to have that happen to them.'

Minton brought down the photo. He looked at it himself and then back at Roulet. 'Mr Roulet, I have nothing more to ask you.'

I FELT THAT I was still winning the razor fight. I had done everything possible to manoeuvre Minton into a position in which he had only one choice. It was now time to see if that had been enough. Roulet had held up well under Minton's attack and I felt the wind was in our sails.

I stood up and looked at the judge. 'Your Honour, the defence rests.'

She nodded and looked at the courtroom clock. It was three thirty. She told the jury to take the midafternoon break. Once the jurors were out of the courtroom, she looked at the prosecution table.

'Mr Minton? Does the state have rebuttal?'

Minton stood. 'Your Honour, I would ask that we adjourn for the day so that the state has time to consider rebuttal witnesses.'

'We still have at least ninety minutes to go today, Mr Minton. I told you I wanted to be productive today. Where are your witnesses?'

'Frankly, Your Honour, the case has moved faster than anticipated. I would be hard-pressed to get the rebuttal witness I am considering even into court before six o'clock tonight.'

I turned and looked at Roulet, who had returned to the seat next to mine. I nodded to him and winked with my left eye so the judge would not see the gesture. It looked like Minton had swallowed the bait. Now I just had to make sure the judge didn't make him spit it out. I stood up.

'Your Honour, the defence has no objection to the delay. Maybe we can use the time to prepare closing arguments and instructions to the jury.'

The judge first looked at me with a puzzled frown. It was a rarity for the defence not to object to prosecutorial foot dragging. But then the seed I had planted began to bloom.

'You may have an idea there, Mr Haller. If we adjourn early today I will expect that we will go to closing statements directly after rebuttal. No further delays. Is that understood, Mr Minton?'

'Yes, Your Honour, I'll be ready.'

'Very well, then. We have a plan. As soon as the jurors are back I will dismiss them for the day.' She got up and left the bench.

Twenty minutes later the jury was heading home and I was gathering up my things. Minton stepped over and said, 'Can I talk to you?'

I looked at Roulet and told him to head out with his mother and Dobbs. After he was gone I turned to look at Minton. He now had the gleam of desperation in his eye. He needed a conviction—any conviction—on this case.

'What's up?'

'I have another offer.'

'I'm listening.'

'I'll drop it down further. Take it down to simple assault. Six months in county. That way he probably won't do sixty days actual.'

I nodded. It was a good offer, and I knew it had to have come from the second floor. Minton wouldn't have had the authority to go so low.

'He takes that and she'll rob him blind in civil,' I said. 'He won't go for it.'

'That's a damn good offer,' Minton said, a hint of outrage in his voice.

My guess was that Minton was under orders to go as low as he needed to get a guilty plea. The Van Nuys office didn't like losing cases. It pleaded them out when the going got rough.

'Maybe from your side it's a good offer. But it still means I have to convince a client to plead to something he says he didn't do. And it still opens the door to civil liability. So from his angle, it's not so good. If it was left to me, I'd ride the trial out. I think we're winning. I know we've got the Bible guy, so we've got a hanger at minimum. But maybe we've got all twelve.'

Minton slapped his table. 'You know he did this thing, Haller. And six months—let alone sixty days—for what he did to that woman is a joke. It's a travesty that I'll lose sleep over, but they've been watching and think you've got the jury, so I have to do it.'

I closed my briefcase and stood up. 'Then I hope you got something good for rebuttal, Ted. Because you're going to get your wish for a jury verdict. And I have to tell you, you're looking like a guy who came naked to a razor fight. Better get your hands off your nuts and fight back.'

I headed through the gate. Halfway to the doors at the back of the courtroom I stopped and looked back at him. 'Hey, you know something? If you lose sleep over this or any other case, then you gotta quit the job and go do something else. Because you're not going to make it, Ted.'

Minton sat at his table, staring straight ahead at the empty bench.

I went back to Four Green Fields to work on my closing. I ordered a Guinness and took it over to one of the tables to sit by myself. I sketched out some basic notes but I knew I would largely be reacting to the state's presentation. In pretrial motions, Minton had already asked to use a PowerPoint presentation to illustrate the case to the jury. It was all the rage with young prosecutors to put up the screen and flash computer graphics on it, as if the jurors couldn't be trusted to make connections on their own.

I was strictly old school. When it came to my turn, if I couldn't convince them, then nothing from a computer could, either.

At 5.30 I called Maggie at her office. 'It's quitting time,' I said.

'Maybe for big-shot defence pros. Public servants have to work till dark.'

'Why don't you take a break and come meet me for a Guinness.'

'No, Haller. I can't do that. Besides, I know what you want.'

I laughed. There was never a time that she didn't think she knew what I wanted. Most of the time she was right, but not this time.

'Yeah? What do I want?'

'You're going to try to corrupt me and find out what Minton is up to.'

'Not a chance, Mags. Minton is an open book. But hey, let me ask you something. Have you ever put a rush on ballistics?'

'What kind of ballistics?'

'Matching casing to casing and slug to slug.'

'Depends on who is doing it or if the slug is damaged. But they could have something in twenty-four hours.'

I felt the dull thud of dread drop into my stomach. I knew I could be on borrowed time. 'OK, Maggie, put those bad guys away.'

'I will.'

'Good night.'

I closed the phone and thought about things for a few moments, then opened it up again and called the Sheraton to see if they had a room available. I had decided that as a precaution I would not go home that night. There might be two detectives from Glendale waiting for me.

NINE

After a sleepless night in a bad hotel bed, I got to the courthouse early on Wednesday morning and found no welcoming party, no Glendale detectives with a warrant for my arrest. A flash of relief went through me as I made my way through the metal detector. I was wearing the same suit I had worn the day before but was hoping no one would notice. I did have a fresh shirt and tie on. I kept spares in the trunk of the Lincoln.

When I got to the courtroom, I was surprised to find Minton already there, setting up the screen for his PowerPoint presentation.

He looked over. 'Did you talk to your client about the offer?'

'Yeah, no sale. Looks like we ride this one to the end.'

I put my briefcase down on the defence table and wondered if the fact that Minton was setting up for his closing argument meant he had decided against mounting any kind of rebuttal. I knew I could simply ask him, but I did not want to give away my appearance of disinterested confidence.

Instead, I sauntered over to the bailiff's desk to talk to Bill Meehan, the deputy who ran Fullbright's court. I saw on his desk a spread of paperwork. He would have the list of custodies bused to the courthouse that morning.

'Bill, I'm going to grab a cup of coffee. You want something?'

'No, man, but thanks. I'm set on caffeine. For a while, at least.'

I smiled and nodded. 'Hey, is that the custody list? Can I take a look and see if any of my clients are on it?'

'Sure.'

Meehan handed me several pages stapled together. It was a listing by name of every inmate now housed in the courthouse's jails, with the courtroom each prisoner was headed to. As nonchalantly as I could, I scanned the list and quickly found the name Dwayne Jeffery Corliss. Minton's snitch was in the building and headed to Fullbright's court, as I had hoped and planned.

I handed the list back to Meehan, then left the courtroom and went down to the cafeteria on the second floor for a coffee. After I'd paid I walked over to an empty table and pulled out my cell.

'Lorna, it's me.' I said. 'We're in play with Corliss. Are you set?'

'I'm ready. Good luck today, Mickey.'

'Thanks. I'll need it. You be ready for the next call.'

As I closed the phone I saw LAPD Detective Howard Kurlen cutting through the tables towards me. The man who put Jesús Menéndez in prison didn't look like he was stopping in for a peanut butter and sardine sandwich. He got to my table and dropped a folded document in front of my coffee cup.

'What is this shit?' he demanded.

I started unfolding the document, even though I knew what it was. 'Looks like a subpoena, Detective. I would've thought you'd know that.'

'You know what I mean, Haller. What's the game? I've got nothing to do with that case up there and I don't want to be a part of your bullshit.'

'It's no bullshit. You've been subpoenaed as a rebuttal witness.'

'To rebut what? I didn't have a goddamn thing to do with that case.'

I nodded like I wanted to be accommodating. 'I'll tell you what, go on up to the courtroom and take a seat. If it's a mistake I'll get it straightened out as soon as I can. I doubt you'll be here another hour.'

'How about I leave now and you straighten it out whenever you want?'

'I can't do that, Detective. That is a valid and lawful subpoena and you must appear in that courtroom unless otherwise discharged.'

'This is such bullshit.'

He stalked back through the cafeteria towards the doorway. Luckily, he had left the subpoena with me, because it was phoney. I had never registered it with the court clerk and the scribbled signature at the bottom was mine.

Bullshit or not, I didn't think Kurlen was leaving the courthouse. He was a man who lived by the law. He would be in the courtroom until discharged. Or until he understood why I had called him there.

At 9.30 THE JUDGE put the jury in the box. I glanced back at the gallery and caught sight of Kurlen in the back row, looking pensive if not angry. I glanced further around the room and saw that Lankford and Sobel were sitting on a bench next to the bailiff's desk designated for law enforcement personnel. Their faces revealed nothing but they still put the pause in me. As I turned back to the court, I wondered if I would get the hour I needed.

'Mr Minton,' the judge intoned, 'does the state have any rebuttal?'

Minton stood up and adjusted his jacket before responding. 'Yes, Your Honour, the state calls Dwayne Jeffery Corliss as a rebuttal witness.'

I stood up, and noticed to my right that Meehan, the bailiff, had stood up as well. He was going to go into the courtroom lockup to retrieve Corliss.

'Your Honour?' I said. 'Who is Dwayne Jeffery Corliss and why wasn't I told about him before now?'

'Deputy Meehan, hold on a minute,' Fullbright said.

Meehan stood frozen with the key to the lockup door poised in his hand. The judge then apologised to the jury but told them they had to go back into the deliberation room until recalled. After they filed through the door behind the box, the judge turned her focus onto Minton.

'Mr Minton, do you want to tell us about your witness?'

'Dwayne Corliss is a cooperating witness who spoke with Mr Roulet when he was in custody following his arrest.'

'Bullshit!' Roulet barked. 'I didn't talk to—'

'Be quiet, Mr Roulet,' the judge boomed. 'Mr Haller, instruct your client on the danger of outbursts in my courtroom.'

I was still standing. I leaned down to whisper in Roulet's ear. 'That was perfect,' I said. 'Now be cool and I'll take it from here.'

He nodded and leaned back. He angrily folded his arms across his chest.

I straightened up. 'I'm sorry, Your Honour, but I share my client's outrage over this. This is the first we have heard of Mr Corliss. I would like to know when he came forward with this supposed conversation.'

'Mr Corliss first contacted the office through a prosecutor who handled the first appearance of the defendant,' Minton said. 'However, that information was not passed on to me until yesterday, when in a staff meeting I was asked why I had never acted on the information.'

This was a lie but not one I wanted to expose. To do so would reveal Maggie's slip on St Patrick's Day and it might also derail my plan. I had to be careful. I needed to argue vigorously against Corliss taking the stand but I also needed to lose the argument.

I put on my best look of outrage. 'This is incredible, Your Honour. Just because the DA's office has a communication problem, my client has to suffer the consequences of not being informed that the state had a witness against him? This man should not be allowed to testify. It's too late now.'

'Your Honour,' Minton said, jumping in, 'I have had no time to depose Mr Corliss myself. Because I was preparing my closing I simply arranged for him to be brought here today. His testimony is key to the state's case because it serves as rebuttal to Mr Roulet's self-serving statements. To not allow his testimony is a serious disservice to the state.'

With his last line Minton was threatening the judge with the loss of the DA's backing should she ever face an election with an opposing candidate.

'Mr Haller?' the judge asked. 'Anything before I rule?'

'I just want my objection on the record.'

'So noted. Do you want to go back and talk to Mr Corliss? I'll allow it.'

'No, Your Honour. As far as I'm concerned, all jailhouse snitches are liars. Anything that comes out of his mouth would be a lie. Anything.'

'Then I am going to rule that he can testify.'

'Your Honour,' I said, 'if you are going to allow him into this courtroom, could I ask one indulgence for the defence?'

'What is that, Mr Haller?'

'I would like to step into the hallway and make a quick phone call to an investigator. It will take me less than a minute.'

The judge nodded. 'Go ahead. I will bring the jury in while you do it.'

'Thank you.'

I hurried through the gate and down the middle aisle. In the hallway I speed-dialled Lorna's cellphone and she answered right away.

'OK, how far away are you?' I asked.

'About fifteen minutes.'

I looked at my watch. It was a quarter to ten. 'OK, we're in play here. Don't delay getting here, but then I want you to wait out in the hall outside the courtroom. Then at ten fifteen come into court and give the tape to me.'

'Got it.'

I closed the phone and went back into the courtroom. The jury was seated and Meehan was leading a man in a grey jumpsuit through the lockup door. Dwayne Corliss was a thin man with stringy hair that wasn't getting washed enough in the lockdown drug programme at County–USC. I recognised him. He was the man who had asked me for a business card when I interviewed Roulet in the holding cell on my first day on the case.

Corliss was led by Meehan to the witness box and the court clerk swore him in. Minton took over the show from there.

'Mr Corliss, were you arrested on March the 5th of this year?'

'Yes, the police arrested me for burglary and possession of drugs.'

'Are you currently being held in jail?'

'I'm in a lockdown drug-treatment programme in the jail ward at Los Angeles County–USC Medical Center.'

'Do you recognise the defendant in this case?'

Corliss looked over at Roulet and nodded. 'Yes, I do.'

'Why is that?'

'Because after I got arrested we were both in Van Nuys jail. When we got bused over here to the courts, we were together, first in the bus, then in the tank, and then when we were brought into the courtroom. We stuck close because we were the only white guys in the group we were in.'

'Now, did you talk at all while you were together for all of that time?'

Corliss nodded his head and at the same time Roulet shook his. I touched my client's arm to caution him to make no demonstrations.

'Yes, we talked,' Corliss said. 'Mostly about cigarettes. We both needed them but they don't let you smoke in the jail.'

'Did you ever ask Mr Roulet what got him into jail?' Minton asked.

'Yes, I did.'

'What did he say?'

'Well, first he asked me why I was there and I told him. Then I asked him why he was in and he said, "For giving a bitch exactly what she deserved."'

'Those were his words?'

'Yes.'

'Now, Mr Corliss, have you been promised anything by me or anyone in the district attorney's office in return for your testimony?'

'Nope. I just thought it was the right thing to do.'

'What is the status of your case?'

'I still got the charges against me, but it looks like if I complete my programme I'll be able to get a break on them. The drugs, at least.'

'But I have made no promise of help in that regard, correct?'

'No, sir, you haven't.'

'I have no further questions.'

I sat unmoving and just staring at Corliss. My pose was that of a man who was angry but didn't know exactly what to do about it.

The judge prompted me into action. 'Mr Haller, cross-examination?'

'Yes, Your Honour.'

I stood up, glancing back at the door as if hoping a miracle would walk through it. I checked the clock and saw that it was five minutes after ten.

I turned to the witness. 'Mr Corliss, how old are you?'

'Forty-three.'

'And where did you grow up?'

'Mesa, Arizona.'

'Mr Corliss, how many times have you been arrested before?'

Minton objected but the judge overruled. I knew she would give me a lot of room here since I was the one who had supposedly been sandbagged.

'How many times have you been arrested, Mr Corliss?' I asked again.

'I think about seven.'

'So you know how the system works, don't you?'

'I just try to survive.'

'And sometimes that means ratting out fellow inmates, doesn't it?'

'Your Honour?' Minton said, standing to object.

'Take a seat, Mr Minton,' Fullbright said. 'I gave you a lot of leeway bringing this witness in. Mr Haller gets his share now. The witness will answer the question.'

The stenographer read the question back to Corliss.

'I suppose so.'

'How many times have you testified for the prosecution in a court proceeding against a fellow inmate?'

'I think this is my fourth time.'

I looked surprised and aghast, although I was neither. 'So you are a pro, aren't you? You could almost say your occupation is jailhouse snitch.'

'If people tell me things that are bad, then I feel obligated to report it.'

'But you try to get people to tell you things, don't you?'

'No, not really. I guess I'm just a friendly guy.'

'A friendly guy. So you expect this jury to believe that a man you didn't know would just come out of the blue and tell you—a perfect stranger—that he gave a bitch exactly what she deserved. Is that correct?'

'It's what he said.'

'So he just mentioned that to you and then you both just went back to talking about cigarettes after that, is that right?'

'Not exactly.'

'Not exactly? What do you mean by "not exactly"?'

'He also told me he did it before. He said he got away with it before and he would get away with it now. He was bragging about it because, with the other time, he said he killed the bitch and got away with it.'

I froze for a moment. I then glanced at Roulet, who sat as still as a statue with surprise on his face, and then back at the witness.

'You . . .'

I started and stopped, acting like I was the man in the minefield who had just heard the *click* come from beneath my foot. In my peripheral vision, I noticed Minton's body posture tightening.

'Mr Haller?' the judge prompted.

I broke my stare from Corliss and looked at the judge.

'Your Honour, I have no further questions at this time.'

MINTON CAME UP from his seat like a boxer coming out of his corner at his bleeding opponent. He stood at the lectern and looked at the jury, as if to underline the importance of the upcoming exchange, and then at Corliss.

'You said he was bragging, Mr Corliss. How so?'

'Well, he told me about this time he killed a girl and got away with it.'

I stood up. 'Your Honour, this has nothing to do with the case in hand and it is rebuttal to no evidence offered by the defence. The witness can't—'

'Your Honour,' Minton cut in, 'this is information brought forward by defence counsel. The prosecution is entitled to pursue it.'

'I will allow it,' Fullbright said.

I sat down and appeared dejected. Minton ploughed ahead.

'Mr Corliss, did Mr Roulet offer any of the details of this previous incident in which he said he got away with killing a woman?'

'He said the girl danced in some joint where she was like in a snake pit.'

I felt Roulet wrap his fingers round my biceps and squeeze. His hot breath came into my ear. 'What the fuck is this?' he whispered.

I turned to him. 'I don't know. What the hell did you tell this guy?'

He whispered back through gritted teeth. 'I didn't tell him anything. This is a set-up. You set me up!'

'Me? What are you talking about? I couldn't get to this guy in lockdown. If you didn't tell him this shit, then somebody else did.'

I turned and looked up at Minton. He checked his notes and nodded.

'Nothing further, Your Honour.'

The judge looked at me. I could almost see sympathy on her face.

'Any recross from the defence with this witness?'

Before I could answer, there was a noise from the rear of the courtroom and I turned to see Lorna entering. She started walking towards the gate.

'Your Honour, can I have a moment to confer with my staff?'

'Hurry, Mr Haller.'

I met Lorna at the gate and took from her a videotape with a single piece of paper wrapped round it with a rubber band. She whispered in my ear.

'This is where I act like I am whispering something very important into your ear,' she said. 'How's it going?'

I nodded as I took the rubber band off the tape and looked at the piece of paper. 'Perfect timing,' I whispered back. 'I'm good to go.'

She nodded and then left the courtroom. I went back to the lectern.

'No recross, Your Honour.' I sat down and waited.

Roulet grabbed my arm. 'What are you doing?'

I pushed him away. 'Stop touching me. We have new information we can't bring up on cross.' I focused on the judge.

'Any other witnesses, Mr Minton?' she asked.

'No, Your Honour. No further rebuttal.'

The judge nodded. 'The witness is excused.'

Meehan started crossing the courtroom to Corliss. The judge looked at me and I started to stand. 'Mr Haller, surrebuttal?'

'Yes, Your Honour, I'd like to call Dwayne Jeffery Corliss back to the stand.'

Meehan stopped in his tracks and all eyes were on me.

I held up the tape and paper Lorna had brought me. 'I have new information on Mr Corliss, Your Honour. I could not have brought it up on cross.'

'Very well. Proceed.'

'Can I have a moment, Judge?'

'A short one.'

I huddled with Roulet again.

'Look, I don't know what's going on, but it doesn't matter because I can still destroy him. It doesn't matter if he says you killed twenty women. If he's a liar, he's a liar. If I destroy him, none of it counts. Understand?'

Roulet seemed to calm down as he considered this. 'Then destroy him.'

'I will.'

'Mr Haller,' the judge prompted.

I looked up at her. 'Yes, Your Honour.'

Carrying the tape and the paper that came with it, I stood up to go back to the lectern. On the way I took a quick glance across the gallery and saw that Kurlen was gone. I had no way of knowing how long he had stayed and what he had heard. Lankford was gone as well. Only Sobel remained.

I turned my attention to the witness. 'Mr Corliss, can you tell the jury where you were when Mr Roulet supposedly made these revelations to you?'

'When we got to the courthouse we were in the same holding cell with about six other guys, and we sat together there and we talked.'

'And those six men all witnessed you and Mr Roulet talking, correct?'

'They woulda had to. They were there.'

'So if I brought them in here one by one and asked them if they observed you and Mr Roulet talking, they would confirm that?'

'Well, they should. But . . . '

'But what, Mr Corliss?'

'It's just that they probably wouldn't talk, that's all.'

'Is it because nobody likes a snitch, Mr Corliss?'

Corliss shrugged. 'I guess so.'

'OK, so let's make sure we have all of this straight. You talked to Mr Roulet when you were in the holding cell together. Anywhere else?'

'Yeah, we talked when they moved us on out into the courtroom. They stick you in this glassed-in area and you wait for your case to be called. We talked some in there, too, until his case got called. He went first.'

'Do you remember what he told you when you were in the courtroom?'

'I think that might have been when he told me about the dancer.'

'OK, Mr Corliss.'

I held the videotape up, described it as video of Louis Roulet's first appearance, and asked to enter it as a defence exhibit. Minton objected, citing the lack of authentication of the tape.

'I am just trying to save the court some time,' I said. 'If needed I can have the man who took the film here in about an hour to authenticate it. But I think that Your Honour will be able to authenticate it with just one look.'

'I am going to allow it,' the judge said. 'Once we see it, the prosecution can object again if so inclined.'

The TV and video unit I had used previously was rolled into the court-room. The tape was played. It lasted twenty minutes and showed Roulet from the moment he entered the courtroom custody area until he was led out after the bail hearing. At no time did Roulet talk to anyone but me.

When the tape was over I addressed the witness. 'Mr Corliss, did you see a moment anywhere on that tape where you and Mr Roulet were talking?'

'Uh, no. I—'

'Yet you testified under oath and penalty of perjury that he confessed crimes to you while you were both in the courtroom, didn't you?'

'He must have told me everything when we were in the holding cell.'

'You lied to the jury, didn't you?'

'I didn't mean to. That was the way I remembered it but I guess I was wrong. I was coming off a high that morning. Things got confused.'

'It would seem that way. Let me ask you, were things confused when you testified against Frederic Bentley back in 1989?'

Minton stood. 'Objection. Where is he going with this?'

'Your Honour,' I said. 'This goes to the veracity of the witness. It is certainly at issue here.'

'Connect the dots, Mr Haller,' the judge ordered. 'In a hurry.'

'Yes, Your Honour.' I picked up the piece of paper and used it as a prop. 'In 1989 Frederic Bentley was convicted of raping a sixteen-year-old girl in her bed in Phoenix, Arizona. Do you remember this?

'Barely,' Corliss said. 'I've done a lot of drugs since then.'

'You testified at his trial that he confessed the crime to you while you were together in a police holding cell. Isn't that correct?'

'Like I said, it's hard for me to remember back then,' Corliss said.

'The police put you in that holding cell because they knew you were willing to snitch, even if you had to make it up, didn't they?'

'I don't remember that,' Corliss responded. 'But I don't make things up.'

'Then, eight years later, the man who you testified had told you he did it was exonerated when a DNA test determined that the semen from the girl's attacker came from another man. Isn't that correct, sir?'

'I don't . . . I mean . . . That was a long time ago.'

'Do you remember being questioned by a reporter for the *Arizona Star* newspaper following the release of Frederic Bentley?'

'Vaguely. I remember somebody calling but I didn't say anything.'

I held the piece of paper up towards the bench. 'Your Honour, I have here an archival story from the *Arizona Star*, dated February 9th, 1997. A member of my staff came across it when she Googled the name D. J. Corliss on her computer. I ask that it be marked as a defence exhibit and admitted into evidence as a historical document detailing an admission by silence.'

My request set off a clash with Minton about authenticity and proper foundation. The judge ruled in my favour. She was showing some of the same outrage I was manufacturing, and Minton didn't stand a chance.

The bailiff took the computer print-out to Corliss, and the judge instructed him to read it out loud.

Corliss held up the paper, cleared his throat and read in a halting voice. '"A man wrongly convicted of rape was released Saturday from the Arizona Correctional Institution. Frederic Bentley, thirty-four, served almost eight years in prison for attacking a sixteen-year-old Tempe girl. The victim identified Bentley, a neighbour, and blood tests matched his type to semen recovered from the victim. The case was bolstered at trial by testimony from an informant who said Bentley had confessed the crime to him while they were housed together in a holding cell. Bentley always maintained his innocence, even after his conviction. Once DNA testing was accepted as valid evidence in the state, he hired attorneys to fight for such testing of the recovered semen. A judge ordered the testing earlier this year, and the resulting analysis proved that Bentley was not the attacker.

' "At a press conference yesterday, the newly freed Bentley identified the informant who had testified against him as D. J. Corliss, a Mesa man who had been arrested on drug charges. Bentley charged that Corliss was well known to the police as a snitch and was used in several cases to get close to suspects. Bentley claimed that Corliss's practice was to make up confessions if he could not draw them out of the suspects. The case—" '

'OK, Mr Corliss,' I said. 'I think that's enough.'

Corliss looked at me like a child who has opened the door of a crowded closet and sees everything about to fall out on top of him.

'Were you ever charged with perjury in the Bentley case?' I asked him.

'No,' he said forcefully, as if that fact exonerated him of wrongdoing.

'Was that because the police were complicit in setting up Mr Bentley?'

Minton objected, saying, 'I am sure Mr Corliss would have no idea what went into the decision of whether or not to charge him with perjury.'

Fullbright sustained it but I didn't care. I was so far ahead on this witness that there was no catching up. I just moved on to the next question.

'Did any prosecutor or police officer ask you to get close to Mr Roulet and get him to confide in you?'

'No, it was just luck of the draw, I guess.'

I stared at him for a long moment with disgust in my eyes.

'I have nothing further.' I carried the pose of anger with me to my seat and dropped the tape box angrily down in front of me before sitting down.

'Mr Minton?' the judge asked.

'I have nothing further,' he responded in a weak voice.

'OK,' Fullbright said quickly. 'I am going to excuse the jury for an early lunch. I would like you all back here at one o'clock sharp.'

She put on a strained smile and directed it at the jurors while they filed out. It dropped off her face the moment the door was closed.

'I want to see counsel in my chambers,' she said. 'Immediately.'

She didn't wait for any response. She left the bench so fast that her robe flowed up behind her like the black gown of the grim reaper.

JUDGE FULLBRIGHT had already lit a cigarette by the time Minton and I got to her chambers. After one long drag she put it out against a glass paperweight, exhaled the smoke towards a ceiling vent and then brought her eyes down to Minton's. Judging by the look in them I was glad I wasn't him.

'Who did the due diligence on this witness of yours?' she asked Minton.

'We only did a background on him in LA County. There were no cautions, no flags. Nothing about Arizona came up.'

'Nobody thought to check to see if this guy had been anywhere else?'

'I guess not. He was passed on to me by the original prosecutor on the case. I just assumed she had checked him out.'

'Bullshit,' I said.

The judge turned her eyes to me.

'The original prosecutor was Margaret McPherson,' I said. 'She had the case all of about three hours. She's my ex-wife and she knew as soon as she saw me at first appearance that she was gone. And you got the case that same day, Minton. Where in there was she supposed to background your witnesses, especially this guy who didn't come out from under his rock until after first appearance? She passed him on and that was it.'

Minton opened his mouth to say something but the judge cut him off.

'Putting that man on the stand was gross prosecutorial misconduct.'

'Your Honour,' Minton barked. 'I did—'

'Save it for your boss. He's the one you'll need to convince. What was the last offer the state made to Mr Roulet?'

Minton seemed frozen and unable to respond. I answered for him.

'Simple assault, six months in county.'

The judge raised her eyebrows and looked at me. 'You didn't take it?'

I shook my head. 'My client won't take a conviction. It will ruin him. He'll gamble on a verdict.'

'You want a mistrial?' she asked.

I laughed and shook my head. 'No. All that will do is give the prosecution time to clean up its mess, get it right and then come back at us.'

'Then what do you want?' she asked.

'What do I want? A directed verdict would be nice. Something with no comebacks from the state. Other than that, we'll ride it out.'

The judge nodded and clasped her hands together on the desk.

'A directed verdict would be ridiculous, Your Honour,' Minton said, finally finding his voice. 'We're at the end of trial, anyway. We might as well take it to a verdict. The jury deserves it. Just because one mistake was made by the state, there is no reason to subvert the whole process.'

'Don't be stupid, Mr Minton,' the judge said. 'It's not about what the jury deserves. And as far as I am concerned, one mistake like you have made is enough. I don't want this kicked back at me by the Second and that is surely what they will do. Then I am holding the bag for your miscon—'

'I didn't know Corliss's background!' Minton said forcefully. 'I swear.'

The intensity of his words brought a momentary silence to the chambers. But soon I slipped into the void.

'Just like you didn't know about the knife, Ted?'

Fullbright looked at me and then back to Minton. 'What knife?'

Minton said nothing.

'Tell her,' I said.

Minton shook his head. 'I don't know what he's talking about,' he said.

'Then you tell me,' the judge said to me.

'Judge, if you wait on discovery from the DA, you might as well hang it up at the start,' I said. 'Witnesses disappear, stories change, you can lose a case just waiting. I needed to move on this case. So I had my investigator go through the back door and get reports. It's fair game. But they were waiting for him and they phoneyed up a report on the knife so I wouldn't know about the initials. I didn't know until I got the formal discovery packet.'

The judge formed a hard line with her lips.

'That was the police, not the DA's office,' Minton said quickly.

'Thirty seconds ago you said you didn't know what he was talking about,' Fullbright said. 'Are you telling me that this did in fact occur?'

Minton reluctantly nodded. 'Yes, Your Honour. But I swear, I didn't—'

'You know what this tells me?' the judge said, cutting him off. 'It tells me that from start to finish the state has not played fair in this case. It doesn't matter who did what or that Mr Haller's investigator may have been acting improperly. The state must be above that. And as evidenced today in my courtroom, it has been anything but that.'

'Your Honour, that's not—'

'I've heard enough, Mr Minton. I want you both to leave now. In half an hour I'll take the bench and announce what we'll do about this. I am not sure yet what that will be but no matter what I do, you aren't going to like what I have to say, Mr Minton. And I am directing you to have your boss, Mr Smithson, in the courtroom with you to hear it.'

I stood up. Minton didn't move. He still seemed frozen to the seat.

'I said you can go!' the judge barked.

TEN

I followed Minton into the courtroom. It was empty except for Meehan. I took my briefcase off the defence table and headed towards the gate.

'Hey, Haller, wait a second,' Minton said from the prosecution table.

I stopped at the gate and looked back. 'What?'

Minton pointed to the rear door of the courtroom. 'Let's go out here.'

He headed to the door and I followed. In the vestibule Minton stopped to confront me. But he didn't say anything. He was putting words together. I decided to push him even further.

'While you go get Smithson I think I'll stop by the *Times* office and make sure they know there'll be some fireworks up here in half an hour.'

'Look,' Minton sputtered. 'We have to work this out. Just hold off on the *Times*, OK? Give me your cell number and give me ten minutes. I'll go down to my office and see what I can do.'

'I don't trust you, Minton.'

'Well, if you want what's best for your client instead of a cheap headline you're going to have to trust me for ten minutes.'

I looked away and acted like I was considering his offer. Finally I nodded. I gave him my cell number, and then he was gone. I waited in the vestibule for fifteen seconds before stepping through the door. Roulet was standing close to the glass wall that looked down at the plaza below. His mother and Cecil Dobbs were sitting on a bench against the opposite wall. Further down the hallway I saw Detective Sobel lingering.

Roulet noticed me and started walking quickly towards me. Soon his mother and Dobbs followed.

'What's going on?' Roulet asked first.

I waited until they were all gathered close to me before answering.

'The judge is considering a directed verdict. We'll know pretty soon.'

'What is a directed verdict?' Mary Windsor asked.

'It's when the judge takes it out of the jury's hands and issues a verdict of acquittal. She's hot because she says Minton engaged in misconduct with Corliss and some other things.'

'Oh my God!' Mary Windsor brought one hand to her mouth and looked like she might burst into tears.

'I said she's considering it,' I cautioned. 'It doesn't mean it will happen. But she did offer me a mistrial already and I turned that down flat.'

'You turned it down?' Dobbs yelped. 'Why on earth did you do that?'

'Because the state would come right back and try Louis again—this time with a better case because they'll know our moves. Even if the verdict goes against us today, we have solid grounds for appeal.'

'Isn't that a decision for Louis to make?' Dobbs asked. 'After all, he's—'

'Cecil, shut up,' Mary Windsor snapped. 'Stop second-guessing everything this man does for Louis. He's right. We're not going through this again!'

Dobbs looked like he had been slapped by her. I realised he must have been whispering sweet negatives about me in her ear all along.

'There's only one thing the DA's office hates worse than losing a verdict,' I said. 'That's getting embarrassed by a judge with a directed verdict, especially after a finding of prosecutorial misconduct. Minton went down to talk to his boss and he's a guy who is very political and always has his finger in the wind. We might know something in a few minutes. If not, then we go back into court in twenty minutes to see what the judge wants to do. So if you will excuse me, I'm going to go to the restroom.'

I stepped away from them and walked down the hallway towards Sobel. Roulet caught up with me and grabbed me by the arm.

'I still want to know how Corliss got that shit he was saying,' he demanded.

'What does it matter? It's working for us. So let it go,' I said.

He shook his head. 'No, I'm not going to let it go, Mick.' He poked a finger into my chest. 'Something else is going on here, and I don't like it. Remember I have your gun. And you have a daughter. You have to—'

I closed my hand over his hand and pushed it away from my chest. 'Don't you ever threaten my family,' I said in a controlled but angry voice. 'You want to come at me, fine, but if you *ever* threaten my daughter again I will bury you so deep you will never be found. You understand me, Louis?'

He slowly nodded and a smile creased his face. 'Sure, Mick. Just so we understand each other.'

I released his hand and left him there. I started walking towards the end of the hallway where the restrooms were and where Sobel seemed to be waiting. I was walking blind, my thoughts of the threat to my daughter crowding my vision. But as I got close to Sobel I shook it off.

'Can I ask why you're here, Detective. Are you going to arrest me?'

'I'm here because you invited me, remember?'

'Uh, no, I don't.'

She narrowed her eyes. 'You told me I ought to check out your trial.'

I realised she was referring to the awkward conversation in my home office during the search of my house.

'Oh, right, I forgot about that. Well, I'm glad you took me up on it.' I gestured up the hallway towards the courtroom. 'So what did you think?'

'Interesting.'

My cellphone started to vibrate. I pulled it off my hip. The caller ID read-out said the call was coming from the district attorney's office.

'I have to take this,' I said.

'By all means,' Sobel said.

I opened the phone and said, 'Hello?'

'Haller, this is John Smithson in the DA's office. How's your day going?'

'I've had better.'

'Not after you hear what I'm offering to do for you.'

'I'm listening.'

THE JUDGE did not come out of chambers for fifteen minutes on top of the thirty she had promised. We were all waiting, Roulet and I at the defence table, his mother and Dobbs behind us in the first row. At the prosecution table, Minton was no longer flying solo. Next to him sat John Smithson.

Minton looked defeated. With Smithson beside him he could have been taken as a defendant with his attorney. He looked guilty as charged.

I turned to scan the gallery. I saw Sobel sitting in the back row, but her partner and Kurlen were still nowhere to be seen. The row reserved for the media was empty. I had kept my side of the deal with Smithson.

Deputy Meehan called the courtroom to order and Judge Fullbright took the bench with a flourish.

'In the matter of the state versus Louis Ross Roulet, I understand from my clerk that we have a motion,' she said.

Minton stood. 'Yes, Your Honour. The state moves to dismiss all charges against Louis Ross Roulet.'

The judge nodded. I heard a sharp intake of breath behind me and knew it was from Mary Windsor. She had known what was going to happen but had held her emotions in check until she actually heard it in the courtroom.

'Is that with or without prejudice?' the judge asked.

'Dismiss with prejudice.'

'Are you sure, Mr Minton? That means no comebacks from the state.'

'Yes, Your Honour, I know,' Minton said.

The judge wrote something down and then looked back at Minton. 'I believe for the record the state needs to offer some sort of explanation for this motion. Why is the state doing this at this late stage, Mr Minton?'

Smithson stood. He was a tall and thin man with a pale complexion. He wore a charcoal grey suit and a maroon bow tie with matching handkerchief peeking from the suit's breast pocket.

'If I may, Your Honour,' he said.

'The record will note the appearance of Assistant District Attorney John Smithson, head of the Van Nuys Division. Welcome, John. Go right ahead.'

'Judge Fullbright, it has come to my attention that there were irregularities in the investigation and subsequent prosecution of Mr Roulet. This office is founded upon the belief in the sanctity of our justice system. I personally safeguard that in the Van Nuys Division and take it very seriously. So it is better for us to dismiss a case than to see justice compromised in any way.'

'Thank you, Mr Smithson. That is refreshing to hear.'

The judge wrote another note and then looked back down at us. 'The state's motion is granted,' she said. 'All charges against Louis Roulet are dismissed with prejudice. Mr Roulet, you are discharged and free to go.'

'Thank you, Your Honour,' I said.

'We still have a jury waiting to return,' Judge Fullbright said. 'I will gather them and explain that the case has been resolved. If any of you attorneys wish to come back then, I am sure they will have questions for you. However, it is not required that you be back.'

I nodded but didn't say I would be back. I wouldn't be. The twelve people who had been so important for the last week were now as meaningless to me as the drivers going the other way on the freeway.

The judge left the bench and Smithson was the first one out of the courtroom. He had nothing to say to Minton or me. His first priority was to distance himself from this prosecutorial catastrophe.

Roulet was at the rail, leaning over to hug his mother. Dobbs had a hand on his shoulder in a congratulatory gesture. When the hugs were over, Roulet turned to me and with hesitation shook my hand.

'I wasn't wrong about you,' he said. 'I knew you were the one.'

'I want the gun,' I said, deadpan.

'Of course you do.'

He turned back to his mother, and I began returning files to my briefcase.

'Michael?'

It was Dobbs reaching a hand across the railing. I turned and shook it.

'You did good,' Dobbs said. 'We all appreciate it greatly.'

'Thanks for the shot. I know you were shaky about me at the start.' I was courteous enough not to mention Mary Windsor's outburst in the hallway.

'Only because I didn't know you,' Dobbs said. 'Now I do. Now I know who to recommend to my clients.'

'Thank you. But I hope your kind of clients never need me.'

He laughed. 'Me, too!'

Then it was Mary Windsor's turn. She extended her hand across the bar. 'Mr Haller, thank you for my son.'

'You're welcome,' I said flatly. 'Take care of him.'

'I always do.'

I nodded. 'Why don't you all go out to the hallway and I'll be out in a minute. I have to finish up some things here with Mr Minton.'

As I turned back to the defence table, I noticed that Sobel had left the courtroom. Only Minton remained. He was gathering up his things.

'What are you going to do now?' I asked him.

'I don't know. See if I can ride this out.' He turned and gave me a hard stare. 'The only thing I know is that I don't want to cross the aisle. I don't want to become like you, Haller. I like sleeping at night too much for that.' With that he headed through the gate and strode out of the courtroom.

I picked up my briefcase and pushed through the gate. I looked back at the judge's empty bench and the state seal on the front panel. I nodded at nothing in particular and then walked out.

ROULET AND HIS ENTOURAGE were waiting for me in the hallway. I looked both ways and saw Sobel down by the elevators. She was on her cellphone.

'Michael, can you join us for lunch?' Dobbs said upon seeing me. 'We're going to celebrate!'

'Uh . . .' I said, still looking at Sobel. 'I don't think I can make it.'

'Why not? You obviously don't have court in the afternoon.'

I finally looked at Dobbs. I felt like saying that I couldn't have lunch because I never wanted to see him or Mary Windsor or Louis Roulet again.

'I'm going to stick around and talk to the jurors when they come back. It will help me to know what they were thinking and where we stood.'

Dobbs gave me a clap on the upper arm. 'Always learning, always getting better for the next one. I don't blame you.'

He looked delighted that I would not be joining them. He probably wanted me out of the way so he could work on repairing his relationship with Mary Windsor. He wanted that franchise account to himself again.

I heard the muted bong of the elevator and looked back down the hall. Lankford, Kurlen and Booker stepped out of the opening elevator and joined Sobel. They started walking towards us.

'Then we'll leave you to it,' Dobbs said, his back to the approaching detectives. 'We have a reservation at Orso and we're already late.'

'OK,' I said, still looking down the hall.

Dobbs, Roulet and Mary Windsor turned to walk away just as the four detectives got to us.

'Louis Roulet,' Kurlen announced. 'You are under arrest. Turn around, please, and place your hands behind your back.'

'No!' Mary Windsor shrieked. 'You can't—'

'What is this?' Dobbs cried out.

Kurlen didn't answer or wait for Roulet to comply. He stepped forward and roughly turned Roulet around.

As he made the forced turn, Roulet's eyes came to mine. 'What's going on, Mick?' he said in a calm voice. 'This shouldn't be happening.'

Mary Windsor moved towards him. 'Take your hands off of my son!'

She grabbed Kurlen from behind, but Booker and Lankford quickly moved in and detached her, handling her gently but strongly.

'Ma'am, step back,' Booker commanded. 'Or I will put you in jail.'

Kurlen started giving Roulet the Miranda warning. Mary Windsor stayed back but was not silent.

'How dare you? You cannot do this!'

'Mother,' Roulet said in a tone that carried more weight and control than any of the detectives.

Mary Windsor gave up. But Dobbs didn't.

'You're arresting him for what?' he demanded.

'Suspicion of murder,' Kurlen said. 'The murder of Martha Rentería.'

'Everything that Corliss said in there was proven to be a lie!' Dobbs cried. 'Are you crazy? The judge dismissed the case because of his lies.'

Kurlen broke from his recital of Roulet's rights and looked at Dobbs. 'If it was a lie, how'd you know he was talking about Martha Rentería?'

Dobbs realised his mistake and took a step back from the gathering.

Kurlen smiled. 'Yeah, I thought so,' he said. He grabbed Roulet by an elbow and turned him round. 'Let's go,' he said.

'Mick?' Roulet said.

'Detective Kurlen,' I said. 'Can I talk to my client for a moment?'

Kurlen looked at me, seemed to measure something in me and then nodded. 'One minute.' He shoved Roulet towards me.

I took him by one arm and walked him a few paces away from the others. 'This is it, Louis,' I said in a whisper. 'This is goodbye. I got you off. Now you're on your own. Get yourself a new lawyer.'

The shock showed in his eyes. Then his face clouded over with a tightly focused anger. It was pure rage, and I realised it was the same rage that Regina Campo and Martha Rentería must have seen.

'I won't need a lawyer,' he said. 'You think they can make a case off what you somehow fed to that lying snitch in there? You better think again.'

'They won't need the snitch, Louis. Believe me, they'll have more.'

'What about you, Mick? Aren't you forgetting something? I have—'

'That doesn't matter any more. They don't need my gun. They've already got all they need. And when they finally stick that needle in your arm, that will be me, Louis. Remember that.' I smiled without humour and moved in closer. 'This is for Raul Levin. You might not go down for him but make no mistake, you are going down.'

I let that register for a moment, then stepped back and nodded to Kurlen. He and Booker came up on either side of Roulet and started moving him, but he shook them off, putting his raging eyes right back into mine.

'This isn't the end, Mick,' he said. 'I'll be out by tomorrow morning. What are you going to do then? You can't protect everybody.'

They took a tighter hold of him and roughly turned him towards the elevators. Halfway down the hall, Roulet turned his head to look back over his shoulder at me. He smiled and it sent something right through me.

You can't protect everybody.

A cold shiver of fear pierced my chest.

As Louis Roulet was hustled into the elevator, my hope was that it would be the last I would ever see of him, but the fear stayed locked in my chest, fluttering like a moth caught inside a porch light. I turned away and almost walked right into Sobel. I hadn't noticed that she had stayed behind.

'You have enough, don't you?' I said. 'Tell me you wouldn't have moved so quickly if you didn't have enough to keep him.'

She looked at me a long moment before answering. 'The DA will decide that. Depends on what they get out of him in interrogation.'

I shook my head. I wanted to tell her that they had moved too fast. It wasn't part of the plan. I wanted to plant the seed, that's all. I wanted them to move slowly and get it right.

The moth fluttered inside and I looked down at the floor. I couldn't shake the idea that all of my machinations had failed, leaving me and my family exposed in the hard-eyed focus of a killer. *You can't protect everybody.*

It was as if Sobel read my fears.

'But we're going to try to keep him,' she said. 'We have what the snitch said in court and the ticket. We're working on witnesses and the forensics.'

My eyes came up to hers. 'What ticket?'

A look of suspicion entered her face. 'I thought you had it figured out. We put it together as soon as the snitch mentioned the snake dancer.'

'Martha Rentería. I got that. But what ticket are you talking about?'

'I don't know if I should tell you, Haller. You're his lawyer.'

'Not any more. I just quit.'

'Doesn't matter. He—'

'Look, you just took that guy down because of me. I might get disbarred because of it. I might even go to jail for a murder I didn't commit. What ticket are you talking about?'

She hesitated and I waited, but then she finally spoke.

'Raul Levin's last words. He said he found Jesús's ticket out.'

'Which means what?'

'We traced Mr Levin's most recent movements. Before he was murdered he had made enquiries about Roulet's parking tickets. He even pulled hard copies of them. We inventoried what he had in the office and compared it with what's on the computer. He was missing one ticket. One hard copy. We didn't know if his killer took it or if he had just missed pulling it. So we went and pulled a copy ourselves. It was issued two years ago on the night of April the 8th. It was a citation for parking in front of a hydrant in the sixty-seven-hundred block of Blythe Street in Panorama City.'

It all came together for me, like the last bit of sand dropping through the middle of an hourglass. Levin really had found Jesús Menéndez's salvation.

'Martha Rentería was murdered two years ago on April the 8th,' I said. 'She lived on Blythe in Panorama City.'

'Yes, but we didn't know that. We didn't see the connection until that snitch in there mentioned the snake dancer. That connected everything.'

I nodded. 'Did you check Raul's phones for a tap? Somehow somebody knew he found the ticket.'

'We did. They were clear. Bugs could have been removed at the time of the murder. Or maybe it was someone else's phone that was tapped.'

Meaning mine. Meaning it might explain how Roulet knew so many of my moves and was even conveniently waiting for me in my home the night I had come home from seeing Jesús Menéndez.

'I'll check them,' I said. 'Does this mean I'm clear on Raul's murder?'

'Not necessarily,' Sobel said. 'We still want to see what comes back from ballistics. We're hoping for something today.'

I nodded. I didn't know how to respond. Sobel lingered, looking like she wanted to ask me something.

'What is it?' I said. 'What do you want from me, Detective Sobel?'

'You know what I want. I want Raul Levin's killer.'

'Well, so do I. But I couldn't give you Roulet on Levin even if I wanted to. I don't know how he did it. And that's off the record.'

'So that still leaves you in the crosshairs.'

She looked down the hall at the elevators, her implication clear. If the ballistics matched, I could still have a problem on Levin.

'How long do you think before Jesús Menéndez gets out?' I asked.

She shrugged. 'Hard to say. But I know one thing. They can't prosecute Roulet as long as another man is in prison for the same crime.'

I turned and walked over to the glass wall. I felt a mixture of elation and dread and that moth still batting around in my chest.

'That's all I care about,' I said quietly. 'Getting him out. That and Raul.'

She came over and stood next to me. 'I don't know what you're doing,' she said. 'But leave the rest to us.'

'I do that and I'll probably go to jail for a murder I didn't commit.'

'You're playing a dangerous game,' she said. 'Leave it alone.'

I looked down at the plaza. 'Sure,' I said. 'I'll leave it alone now.'

Having heard what she needed to, she made a move to go. 'Good luck,' she said.

I looked at her again. 'Same to you.'

BY THAT NIGHT, word had spread. Not the secret details but the public story. The story that I had won the case, got a DA's motion to dismiss with no comebacks, only to have my client arrested for murder in the hallway outside the courtroom where I had just cleared him. I got calls from every defence pro I knew—call after call until my cellphone finally died. My colleagues were congratulating me. In their eyes, Roulet was the ultimate franchise. I got schedule A fees for one trial, then I would get schedule A fees for the next. And when I told them I would not be handling the defence of the new case, each one of them asked if I could refer him to Roulet.

It was the one call that came in on my home line that I wanted the most. It was from Maggie.

'I've been waiting for your call all night,' I said.

'Sorry, I've been in the conference room,' she said.

'I heard you were pulled in on Roulet.'

'Yes, that's why I'm calling. They're going to cut him loose.'

'What are you talking about? They're letting him go?'

'Yes. They've had him for nine hours and he hasn't broken. They got nothing and that means they don't have enough.'

'But they have the parking ticket and there have to be witnesses who can put him in the Cobra Room. Even Menéndez can ID him there.'

'You know as well as I do that Menéndez is a scratch. He'd identify anybody to get out. And if there are other wits from the Cobra Room, then it's going to take some time to run them down. The parking ticket puts him in the neighbourhood but it doesn't put him inside her apartment.'

'What about the knife?'

'They're working on it but that's going to take time, too. They're going to have to kick him loose and work the forensics and look for the witnesses. If Roulet's good for this, then we will get him, and your other client will get out. You don't have to worry. But we have to do it right.'

'They jumped the gun. Damn it, they shouldn't have made the move today. When exactly will they let him go?'

'I don't know. This all just went down. Kurlen and Booker have just left for the PD. When they get there, I assume they'll kick him loose.'

'Listen to me, Maggie. Roulet knows about Hayley.'

There was a horribly long moment of silence before she answered.

'What are you saying, Haller? You let our daughter—'

'He broke into my house and saw her picture. He wants to get back at me. So you have to go home right now. Get Hayley and get out of the apartment.'

'I'm leaving now,' she said. 'And we're coming to you.'

'No, don't come to me. *He* might come to me.'

'This is crazy. What are you going to do?'

'I'm not sure. Just get Hayley and get safe. Then call me on your cell, but don't tell me where you are. It will be better if I don't even know.'

'Haller, just call the police. Tell them you've been threatened.'

'A defence lawyer telling the police he feels threatened . . . Yeah, they'll jump all over that. Probably send out a SWAT team.'

'Well, you have to do something.'

'I thought I had. I thought he was going to be in jail for the rest of his life. But you people moved too fast and now you have to let him go.'

'I told you, it wasn't enough.'

'Then go to our daughter and take care of her. Leave the rest to me.'

'I'm going.' But she didn't hang up. It was like she was giving me the chance to say something more.

'I love you, Mags,' I said. 'Both of you. Be careful.'

I hung up the phone before she could respond. Immediately I picked it up again and called Valenzuela's cell. After five rings he answered.

'Val, it's me, Mick. I need your help.'

'My help? After what you accused me of the other night?'

'Look, Val, this is an emergency. What I said the other night was out of line and I apologise. I'll pay for your TV, I'll do whatever you want, but I need your help right now.'

After a pause he responded. 'What do you want me to do?'

'Roulet still has the bracelet on his ankle, right?'

'That's right. I know what happened in court but I haven't heard from the guy. One of my courthouse people said the cops picked him up again.'

'They picked him up but he's about to be kicked loose. He'll probably be calling you so he can get the bracelet taken off.'

'I'm already home, man. He can find me in the morning.'

'That's what I want. Make him wait.'

'That ain't no favour, man.'

'This is. I want you to open your laptop and watch him. When he leaves the PD, I want to know where he's going. I think he might head for the apartment where Maggie and Hayley live.'

After a long silence, Valenzuela responded. 'OK, Mick. You got it.'

'Thanks, Val. And call my home number. My cell is dead.'

I gave him the number, then hung up. I looked out of the window and noticed that it was raining hard.

On the table in the dining alcove was the gun Earl Briggs had given me. I contemplated the weapon and all the moves I had made. The bottom line was I had been flying blind and in the process had endangered more than just myself. I leaned forward until my forehead touched the wall. I was out of moves. I could only wait for Roulet to make the next one.

The phone's ring startled me and I jumped back. It was Valenzuela.

'He's moving.'

'*Where?*' I shouted it too loud into the phone. I was losing it.

'He's heading south on Van Nuys.'

I tried to build an image of Roulet driving. If he was going south on Van Nuys that meant he was heading directly towards Sherman Oaks and the neighbourhood where Maggie and Hayley lived. But he could also be headed right through Sherman Oaks on his way south over the hill and to his home. I had to wait to be sure.

'He just crossed under the 101. He might just be going home, Mick.'

'I know, I know. Just wait till he crosses Ventura. The next street is Dickens. If he turns there, then he's not going home.' I stood up and started pacing, the phone pressed tightly to my ear.

'He stopped.'

'Where?'

'Must be a light. I think that's Moorpark Avenue there.'

That was a block before Ventura and two before Dickens.

'I'll call you right back.'

I didn't wait for a response. I hung up and called Maggie's cell. She answered right away.

'Where are you?'

'You told me not to tell you.'

'You're out of the apartment?'

'No, not yet. Hayley's picking the books she wants to take.'

'Goddamn it, get out of there! Now! I'll call you back.'

I hung up and called Valenzuela back, 'Where is he?'

'He's turned on Ventura, heading west.'

He was now driving parallel to Dickens, one block away, in the direction of my daughter's apartment.

'He just stopped,' Valenzuela announced. 'It's not an intersection. It looks like he's in the middle of the block. I think he parked it.'

I ran my free hand through my hair like a desperate man. 'I've gotta go. My cell's dead. Call Maggie and tell her to just get out of there!'

I shouted Maggie's number into the phone, then dropped it and headed out of the kitchen. I grabbed the gun off the table and went to the door. I couldn't stand around shouting on the phone while my family was in danger. I shoved the gun into the side pocket of my jacket and opened the door.

Mary Windsor was standing there, her hair wet from the rain.

'Mary, what—?'

She raised her hand. I looked down to see the metal glint of the gun in it just as she fired.

THE SOUND WAS LOUD and the flash as bright as a camera's. The impact of the bullet was like how I imagine a kick from a horse would feel. In a split second I went from standing still to moving backwards. I hit the floor hard and was propelled into the wall next to the living-room fireplace. I tried to reach both hands to the hole in my gut but my right hand was hung up in the pocket of my jacket. I held myself with the left and tried to sit up.

Mary Windsor stepped forward and into the house. I had to look up at her. Through the open door behind her I could see the rain coming down. She raised the weapon and pointed it at my forehead.

'You tried to take my son from me!' she shouted. 'Did you think I could allow you to do that and just walk away?'

And then I knew. Everything crystallised. I knew she had said similar words to Raul Levin before she killed him. And I knew there had been no rape in an empty house in Bel-Air. She was a mother doing what she had to do. And I knew, too, that Levin's last gesture had not been to make the sign of the devil, but to make the letter *M* or *W*, depending on how you looked at it.

Mary Windsor took another step towards me. 'You go to hell,' she said.

She steadied her hand to fire. I raised my right hand, still wrapped in my jacket. She must have thought it was a defensive gesture because she didn't hurry. I could tell she was savouring the moment. Until I fired.

Mary Windsor's body jerked back with the impact and she landed on her back in the doorway. Her gun clattered to the floor. Then I heard the sound of running feet on the steps up to the front porch.

'Police!' a woman shouted. 'Put your weapons down!'

'Put your weapons down and come out with your hands in full view!' This time it was a man who had yelled and I recognised the voice.

I pulled the gun out of my jacket pocket, put it on the floor and slid it away from me. 'The weapon's down,' I called out, as loud as the hole in my stomach allowed me to. 'But I'm shot. I can't get up. We're both shot.'

The barrel of a pistol came into view in the doorway. Then a hand and then a wet black raincoat containing Detective Lankford. He moved into the house and was quickly followed by his partner, Detective Sobel.

Lankford kicked the gun away from Mary Windsor as he came in. He kept his own weapon pointed at me. 'Anybody else in the house?' he asked loudly.

'No,' I said. 'Listen to me.' I tried to sit up but pain shot through my body.

'Don't move!' Lankford yelled. 'Just stay there!'

Sobel shouted a command into a handheld radio, ordering paramedics and ambulance transport for two people with gunshot wounds.

'One transport,' Lankford corrected. 'She's gone.'

Sobel shoved the radio into her raincoat pocket and came to me. She knelt down and pulled my hand and my shirt away from my wound so she could see the damage. She then pressed my hand back onto the bullet hole.

'Press down as hard as you can. You hear me, hold your hand down tight.'

'Listen to me,' I said again. 'My family's in danger. You have to—'

'Hold on.'

She reached inside her raincoat and pulled a cellphone off her belt. She flipped it open and hit a speed-dial button. Someone answered straight away.

'It's Sobel. Bring him back in. His mother just tried to hit the lawyer. He got her first.' She listened for a moment and asked, 'Then where is he?'

She listened some more, then said goodbye and closed her phone. 'They'll pick him up. Your daughter is safe.'

I stared at her. 'You're watching him?'

She nodded. 'We piggybacked on your plan, Haller. We were hoping that if we kicked him loose he'd show us his trick, show us how he got to Levin. But the mother sort of just solved that mystery for us.'

'And Maggie?' I asked weakly.

'She's fine. She had to play along because we didn't know if Roulet had a tap on your line or not. She couldn't tell you that she and Hayley were safe.'

I closed my eyes. I didn't know whether just to be thankful they were OK or to be angry that Maggie had used her daughter's father as bait for a killer.

I tried to sit up. 'I want to call her. She—'

'Don't move. Just stay still.'

I leaned my head back on the floor. I was cold and on the verge of shaking, yet I also felt as though I were sweating. I could feel myself getting weaker as my breathing grew shallow.

'Hang on in there,' Sobel said to me. 'You'll be all right. Depending on what the bullet did inside, you should be all right.'

'Grey . . .' I meant to say 'great' with full sarcasm. But I was fading.

Lankford came up next to Sobel and looked at me. In a gloved hand he held up the gun Mary Windsor had shot me with. I recognised the pearl grips. Mickey Cohen's gun. My gun. The gun she shot Raul with.

He nodded and I took it as some sort of signal. Maybe that in his eyes I had stepped up, that he knew I had done their work by drawing the killer out. Maybe he wouldn't hate lawyers so much after this.

Probably not. But I nodded back at him and the small movement made me cough. I tasted something in my mouth and knew it was blood.

'Don't flatline on us now,' Lankford ordered. 'If we end up giving a defence lawyer mouth-to-mouth, we'll never live it down.'

He smiled and I smiled back. Or tried to. Then the blackness started crowding my vision. Pretty soon I was floating in it.

ELEVEN

Postcard from Cuba, Tuesday, October 4

It has been four months since I was in a courtroom. In that time I have had three surgeries to repair my body, been sued in civil court twice and been investigated by both the Los Angeles Police Department and the California Bar Association. My bank accounts have been bled dry.

But I have survived it all and today will be the first day since the shooting that I will walk without a cane. The cane is a sign of weakness. Nobody wants a defence attorney who looks weak. I must stand upright, stretch the muscles the surgeon cut through to get to the bullet, and walk on my own before I feel I can walk into a courtroom again.

Though I have not been in a courtroom, I am the subject of legal proceedings. Jesús Menéndez and Louis Roulet are both suing me for malpractice and violation of legal ethics. For all the specific accusations in his lawsuit, Roulet has not been able to learn how I supposedly got to Corliss at County–USC and fed him privileged information. And it is unlikely that he ever will. Gloria Dayton finished her programme, took the $25,000 I gave her and moved to Hawaii to start life anew. And Corliss, who probably knows better than anyone the value of keeping one's mouth shut, has divulged nothing other than what he testified to in court. My lawyer tells me that Roulet's lawsuit is without merit and that it will eventually go away. Probably when I have no more money to pay my lawyer his fees.

But Menéndez will never go away. He is the one who gets to me at night when I sit on the porch and watch the million-dollar view from my house with the million-one mortgage. He was pardoned by the governor and released from San Quentin two days after Roulet was charged with Martha Rentería's murder. But it was revealed that he contracted HIV in prison and the governor doesn't have a pardon for that. Nobody does. My father was right. There is no client as scary as an innocent man. And no client as scarring.

Menéndez wants to take my money as punishment for what I did and didn't do, and he is entitled. But no matter what my failings of judgment were, I know that, by the end, I bent things in order to do the right thing. I traded evil for innocence. Roulet is in because of me. Menéndez is out because of me. Despite the efforts of his new attorneys, Roulet will not see freedom again. From what I have heard from Maggie, prosecutors have built an impenetrable case against him for the Rentería murder. They have also connected him to another killing: the follow-home rape and stabbing of a woman who tended bar in a Hollywood club. For Roulet, the battle now lies in just staying alive. His lawyers are engaged in plea negotiations to keep him from a lethal injection. Whatever the outcome, he is surely gone from this world.

Maggie and I are attempting to mend our wounds, too. She brings my daughter to visit me every weekend and often stays for the day. We sit on the porch and talk. I hold no anger for being used as bait for a killer. I think Maggie no longer holds anger for the choices I have made.

The California bar looked at all of my actions and sent me on a vacation to Cuba. That's what defence pros call being suspended for conduct unbecoming an attorney. CUBA. I was shelved for ninety days. They could prove no ethical violations in regard to Corliss, so they hit me for borrowing a gun from my client Earl Briggs. I got lucky there. It was not a stolen or unregistered gun. It belonged to Earl's father, so my ethical infraction was minor. I didn't bother appealing the suspension. I served the ninety days during my recovery.

Neither the bar nor the police found ethical or criminal violation on my part in the killing of Mary Windsor. From a block away, Lankford and Sobel had watched her take that first shot at my front door. Self-defence, cut and dried. But the feelings I have for what I did are not so clear-cut. I wanted to avenge my friend Raul Levin, but not in blood. I am a killer now. Being state-sanctioned tempers only slightly the feelings that come with that.

All investigations and official findings aside, I think that in the matter of Menéndez and Roulet I was guilty of conduct unbecoming myself. And the penalty for that is harsher than anything the bar could ever throw at me. No matter. I will carry all of it with me as I go back to work. I know my place in this world, and on the first day of court next year I will pull the Lincoln out of the garage, get back on the road and go looking for the underdog. I don't know where I will go or what cases will be mine. I just know I will be healed and ready to stand once again in the world without truth.

MICHAEL CONNELLY

Born: 1956, Philadelphia
Home: Tampa, Florida.
Website: www.michaelconnelly.com

Even with sixteen hugely successful crime novels behind him, Michael Connelly is not a man to rest on his laurels. '*The Lincoln Lawyer* came out of my desire to test myself and write a legal thriller,' he explains, adding that it also grew out of a chance meeting five or six years ago, when he was invited by a friend to join a group going to see a Los Angeles Dodgers baseball match. He sat next to a man he had never met before and started chatting. 'I learned that he was a criminal defence attorney who worked out of his car,' Connelly remembers. 'He explained that in Los Angeles County there were so many courthouses spread so far and wide that it worked best to make your car your office. He had a driver and he sat in the back of a Lincoln Town Car working the phones and the computer. I thought that this might make an interesting character and give a unique angle on the legal thriller.'

Connelly's interest in crime and people on all sides of the law started with an incident he witnessed when he was sixteen. One night, when he was working as a dishwasher in a Florida hotel, he spotted a man throwing something into a hedge. It turned out to be the gun that had been used to kill someone during a robbery. Connelly, who was the only witness, was interviewed by investigating detectives. 'That night of being immersed in the police department, and being interviewed repeatedly by detectives who seemed to me very hardened individuals, really impressed something on me,' he recalls.

He studied journalism and went on to work as a reporter for local newspapers in Florida, eventually landing the job of crime writer for the *Los Angeles Times*, one of the largest newspapers in America. Connelly believes that the time he spent as a crime reporter helped make him the writer he is today.' Very simply, I would not be doing what I am doing now if I had not spent those years on the crime beat. They were research and they became the underpinning of the novels that would follow.' Being a journalist also helped him with his craft. 'Your editor tells you how much room you have for your stories and it is never enough, so you learn to be spare and that every word counts.'

Michael Connelly is particularly appreciative of his British readers. 'In the States, if people like the books, they love the twists and trying to guess the story. But in the UK and other European countries, they see them more as social novels, as a reflection of what is happening in society, which is a more fulfilling response to get.'

Fans of Mickey Haller will be pleased to know that Connelly plans to feature him in future novels. 'When I finished *The Lincoln Lawyer*, one of the first feelings I got was that I missed writing about Mickey. I think that is a good sign, and almost a guarantee that he will be back at some point.'

LEGAL AID

George Bernard Shaw once said, 'England and America are two countries separated by a common language.' This is even more true when it comes to legal language so, to help readers of *The Lincoln Lawyer,* here is a glossary of American legal terms.

- **Miranda warning:** A routine statement read to persons who are taken into police custody, informing them of their legal rights.
- **Bail bondsman:** A person who posts bail in exchange for a fee.
- **Plea bargaining:** Refers to the negotiations that take place between the district attorney's office and the accused in order to avoid the trouble and expense of a trial. The district attorney offers up a less serious charge to which the defendant might be willing to plead guilty, in exchange for a guaranteed lesser sentence than he might get if he went to trial.
- **Discovery:** The pretrial phase in a lawsuit in which each party can request documents and other evidence from the other party.
- **Probable cause:** Reasonable grounds for belief that a person or property is connected with a crime. Probable cause must exist for a police officer to make an arrest, search or seize property, or obtain a warrant.
- **Redirect:** The second round of questioning of a witness, after opposing counsel has had an opportunity, during cross-examination, to damage what the witness said under questioning. Redirect is followed by recross.

The
Wedding
Officer

Anthony
Capella

'. . . a splendid, linen suit, panama hat, distant lawnmower kind of a book; guaranteed to whisk you far from this drizzly island, soothe you, warm you and return you home again without losing any of your luggage.'

Actor Hugh Laurie, on Anthony Capella's first novel, The Food of Love

PART ONE

T he day Livia Pertini fell in love for the first time was the day the beauty contest was won by her favourite cow, Pupetta.

For as long as anyone in Fiscino could remember, the annual Feast of the Apricots had incorporated not only a competition to find the most perfect specimen of fruit from among the hundreds of tiny orchards that lined the sides of Monte Vesuvio, but also a contest to determine the loveliest young woman of the region. The former was always presided over by Livia's father, Nino, since it was generally accepted that, as the owner of the village *osteria,* he had a more subtle palate than most, while the latter was judged by Don Bernardo, the priest, since it was thought that as a celibate he would bring a certain objectivity to the proceedings.

Of the two competitions, the beauty contest was usually the more good-natured. This was partly because the girls of the village were remarkably similar in appearance—dark-haired, olive-skinned and voluptuous—and it was thus a relatively simple matter to decide which one combined these features in the most pleasing way. It was also because each variety of apricot had its ardent champion, and the thought of the honour going to the wrong sort of apricot provoked almost as much debate as the decision over which farmer had produced the finest specimen of fruit.

Livia was too busy to pay much attention to either contest. A feast day meant that the little *osteria* would be even more crowded at lunchtime than usual, and she and her sister Marisa had been up since before dawn preparing the dishes that would be spread out on the tables lining the terrace, where vines provided shade from the fierce midday sun. In any case, everyone knew that one of the Farelli sisters would win in the end.

'Hello?' a male voice called from the little room which doubled as a bar and a dining room. 'Is anyone here?'

Her hands were full of wet *burrata* and shreds of leaf. 'No,' she replied.

'Then I must be talking to an angel, or perhaps a ghost,' the voice suggested. 'If there's no one around, I don't usually get an answer.'

Livia rolled her eyes. A smart-arse. 'I meant, there's no one to serve you.'

'Too busy to pour a glass of *limoncello* for a thirsty soldier?'

'Too busy even for that,' she said. 'You can help yourself and put your money on the counter. It's what everyone else does.'

A pause. 'What if I don't leave the full amount?'

'Then I will curse you, and something very unpleasant will happen.'

She heard the sound of a bottle being uncorked, and the sound of her father's lemon spirit being poured into a glass. Then a young man in a soldier's uniform appeared in the kitchen. He was holding a full glass in one hand and some coins in the other. 'It occurred to me,' he said, 'that if I left my money on the counter and some other rogue came along later and stole it, you would think that it was me who was the dishonest one.'

She pointed with her elbow at the dresser. 'You can put the money there.'

He was, she noticed, quite extraordinarily handsome. The black, tailored uniform recently redesigned by Mussolini showed off his lean hips and broad shoulders, and his dark eyes grinned at her from beneath a soldier's cap that was set on a mass of curls. Caramel skin, very white teeth and an expression of confident mischief completed the picture.

'What are you doing in here?' he asked, leaning back against the dresser and watching her. 'I thought everyone was outside.'

'I shall pray to Santa Cecilia for you,' she said. 'Clearly, you are afflicted by blindness, or you are a cretin. What does it look like I'm doing?'

The young soldier didn't seem at all put out. 'You look like you're cooking,' he remarked.

'Brilliant,' she said sarcastically.

'You know,' he said, taking a swig from his glass, 'you're much prettier than any of those girls in the beauty contest.'

She ignored the compliment. 'So that's why you're here. I should have guessed. You came to stare at the girls.'

'Actually, I came because my friend Aldo wanted to come. I'm stationed in the garrison at Torre El Greco.'

'So you're a fascist?' she said disapprovingly.

He shook his head. 'Just a soldier. I want to see the world.'

'Well,' she said, 'you can start by seeing the world outside that door. I don't have time to chat to you.' As she spoke she was putting balls of *burrata* inside some asphodel leaves.

'I'll tell you what,' he said. 'I'll go away if you give me a kiss.'

She glared at him. 'Not in a million years. Now get out of here.'

'But my intentions are honourable,' he assured her. 'You see, I've fallen in love with you. What's wrong with kissing someone you're in love with?'

She couldn't help it. She smiled slightly, then put her stern expression back on. 'Don't be ridiculous. We don't know each other from Adam.'

'Well, that obstacle is easily removed. I'm Enzo. And you are—?'

'Busy,' she snapped.

'I'm very pleased to meet you, Busy. Would you like to kiss me now?'

'No.' She had finished the antipasto, and began to chop lemons to accompany the *friarelli*, a kind of bitter broccoli.

'Then I shall just have to use my imagination instead.' He leaned back and closed his eyes. A smile played across his face. 'Mmmm,' he said thoughtfully. 'Do you know, Busy, you're a very good kisser.'

'I hope that hurt,' she said pointedly. 'I just imagined kneeing you in the *coglioni*.'

Enzo clutched his privates and fell to the floor. 'Ow! Ow! What have you done? Now we'll never have those twenty *bambini* I was planning!'

'Get out of the way,' she said, laughing. 'I have to drain this pasta.'

He jumped up. 'Tell me one thing, Busy. Do you have a boyfriend? Am I wasting my time here?'

'The answer to one question is no,' she said, 'and to the other one, yes.'

For a moment his brow furrowed as he worked it out. 'Impossible,' he said firmly. 'Anyway, one good answer is sufficient to be going on with. *Aaargh!*' He leapt back in horror. 'What in God's name is that?'

Hearing an unfamiliar voice in the kitchen, Pupetta had put her head through the window. It was topped by two massive horns, backswept like bicycle handlebars. The horns were considerably wider than the window, but she had long ago worked out how to ease one in before the other. It was this horn which had just claimed Enzo's cap.

'That's Pupetta,' Livia said, reaching across to retrieve the cap. 'Haven't you seen a buffalo before?'

Enzo shook his head. 'Not this close. I'm from Naples, we don't have buffalo in the city.' He took the cap and arranged it on Pupetta's head, where it looked almost comically small.

'Then we certainly couldn't get married and have those twenty *bambini* you wanted. I could never leave Pupetta.'

'Hmm.' Enzo scratched his head. 'In that case,' he said to Pupetta, 'you'd better be the first buffalo to come and live in Naples.'

Suddenly serious, Livia said, 'Anyway, we shouldn't be talking like this. You're a soldier, you're going to go off and see the world.'

'Only for a little while. Then I'll come back and have *bambini*. And *bufale*, of course,' he added quickly.

There was the sound of a clock striking and Livia rushed over to the stove. 'Now look what you've done. It's almost lunchtime,' she said, pulling saucepans out of the cupboard. 'If you like, you can come back later, though, and we'll have a coffee together.'

He snapped his fingers with delight. 'I knew it!' He finished his drink and set the glass down by the sink. 'It's excellent *limoncello*, by the way.'

'Of course it is. Everything is good here.'

'I can see that,' he said. He kissed his fingertips and blew the kiss at her as he walked backwards out of the door. After a moment she noticed that Pupetta was still wearing his cap.

SOON AFTER MIDDAY a crowd of people surged across the dusty piazza towards the *osteria*. Within moments every place on the terrace was filled, and Livia began to serve the food.

Most of the ingredients she cooked with came from the tiny farm immediately behind the restaurant. Each time Vesuvius erupted, it covered its slopes with a deep layer of potash, enriching the soil and enabling it to support a wealth of vegetables, including tomatoes, courgettes, black cabbage, aubergines and several species that were unique to the region, including bitter *friarelli* and fragrant *asfodelo*. There was also a small black boar with his harem of four larger wives; an ancient olive tree through which a couple of vines meandered; a chicken or two; and the Pertinis' pride and joy, Priscilla and Pupetta, the two water buffalo, who grazed on a patch of terraced pasture no bigger than a tennis court. The milk they produced was porcelain-white, and after hours of work each day it produced just two or three *mozzarelle*, each one weighing around a kilo—but what *mozzarelle*: soft and faintly grassy.

As well as mozzarella, the one cheese the Pertinis were renowned for was their *burrata*, a tiny sack of the finest, freshest mozzarella, filled with thick buffalo cream and wrapped in asphodel leaves.

Business was always good, not least because of the prodigious appetites of the Pertinis' neighbours. Visitors from the city might come and go, but the mainstay of the *osteria*'s business was the villagers themselves. At noon each day every last one of them stopped work and strolled over to the Pertinis' vine-shaded terrace, where for two hours they ate like royalty.

The Vesuviani, labouring as they did under the ever-present threat of annihilation, were also much more superstitious than other Neapolitans, which was to say, extremely superstitious indeed. Every lunch began with a dual offering: a grace offered up to heaven by the priest, and a small libation of wine poured onto the earth by Ernesto, the oldest labourer in the village, a tacit recognition of the fact that here on Vesuvius the ground beneath their feet was considerably more threatening, and closer to their thoughts, than heaven. Like every other village on the volcano, Fiscino was protected by a little circle of shrines, some containing statues of the Virgin, others little effigies of St Sebastian, who had been protecting them for as long as there had been people on the mountain. However, there had been a catastrophic eruption as recently as 1929 and the Vesuviani were not above hedging their bets. Many of these protective shrines also bore a mark depicting a horn, a symbol already old when Christianity came to these parts.

Similarly, it was accepted that while doctors might be good for certain straightforward medical problems, more complex maladies required the intervention of a *maga*, or healer. The *maga* fulfilled many of the functions of a pharmacist, dispensing herbs and recipes to treat everyday ailments, as well as potions that would make a woman fall in love or a man stay faithful. Within each family it was a matter of some speculation as to who would inherit the gift. For the Pertinis, the matter resolved itself early on. Both Livia and Marisa helped their mother in the kitchen, but while it soon became clear that Livia had inherited her mother's ability at the stove, Marisa preferred to concoct herbal recipes of a different kind.

Livia could not remember learning to cook. By the time she was twelve she had graduated from helping out, to being in charge when her mother was ill—a circumstance that occurred increasingly often. She knew instinctively how to bring out the best in whatever ingredients she was using.

DURING THE MEAL, Livia noticed that Enzo was sitting with a group of other soldiers, and that he was easily the most handsome of any of them. She also noticed that the beauty pageant contestants were sitting nearby, shooting the soldiers limpid glances out of the corners of their eyes. The three Farelli sisters, of course, were flirting more than anyone. Livia sighed. It seemed to her unlikely that Enzo would come back for that coffee after all. Colomba, the eldest of the sisters, was clearly setting her cap at him—or rather, her bonnet, a ridiculous concoction covered with glass fruit and feathers. So that was that. It was Colomba who had coined the nickname *stecchetto*, little toothpick, for Livia, because she was so scrawny. She had filled out since her sixteenth birthday, but she would never have Colomba's curves.

As she was serving the huge platter of sliced apricots in wine, which was the inevitable *dolce* of the feast-day lunch, something rather remarkable happened. A row had broken out between Colomba and her two sisters, Mimi and Gabriella, and within moments it had progressed from name calling and screaming, to hair pulling and scratching, much to the amusement of the watching soldiers. It required the intervention of Don Bernardo himself to calm the warring parties.

'This is a disgrace,' he thundered, getting to his feet and thumping the table with an empty wine bottle. 'And as a consequence of your appalling behaviour, I shall not be awarding the prize to any of you. I shall give it to'—Don Bernardo's gaze came to rest on Livia—'I shall give it to someone who truly deserves it, because she provided us with all this food.'

Oh no, Livia thought. To enter and not win would have been bad enough, but not to enter and to win because the priest was angry with the Farelli sisters would be humiliating. Colomba, for one, would never let her forget it.

The same thought must have belatedly occurred to Don Bernardo, who was quailing before the ferocity of Livia's scowl. 'Um . . . er . . .' he said.

Enzo jumped to his feet. 'He means Pupetta,' he shouted. 'Pupetta the wonder-cow, who provided the milk for our wonderful *burrata*.'

'Exactly,' Don Bernardo said, relieved. 'I mean Pupetta.'

'*Viva* Pupetta,' someone shouted. There was a general shout of agreement and people started to clap. The Farelli girls rearranged their bonnets, and settled down again to flirt with the soldiers. After all, there was no shame in losing to a buffalo.

AFTER LUNCH the accordions and the castanets came out, as they always did on a feast day, and everyone began to dance.

'Will you dance the tarantella with me, Busy?' Enzo asked Livia, as she passed him with a pile of plates in her arms.

'Certainly not. People will gossip. Anyway, you can stop calling me that. My name is Livia.'

'Well,' he said reasonably, 'if you're not busy, you've got time to sit down and take that coffee with me.'

She came back and sat down. 'Thank you for getting Pupetta that prize.'

'Not at all. She was definitely the best cow in the whole contest.'

Livia's younger sister, Marisa, brought them two cups of espresso. When she had gone Enzo fixed Livia with his big dark eyes and said seriously, 'What do you want to do with your life, Livia?'

No one had ever asked her a question like that before. Taken by surprise— she had assumed that they were going to go on talking nonsense—she said, 'Is there a choice?'

'Every girl has a choice,' he said. 'Particularly one as beautiful as you. You must have dozens of men wanting to be your beau.'

She was pleased by the compliment, but chose to ignore it. 'There have been some,' she admitted. 'But having a choice of men to marry isn't the same thing as being able to choose what to do in life. Whoever I end up with, I'll have to keep his house and cook for him.'

'Then you must make sure you marry a man who loves you,' he said.

'Yes,' she said doubtfully. That hadn't been what she'd meant, exactly. She tried to explain. 'I've been used to cooking for a lot of people, here at the restaurant. It's going to be very different when I get married.'

'Ah,' he said. 'Now I've realised why you were so rude to me earlier. You don't want to get married, because it means leaving here.'

'Possibly.' She shrugged, amazed that he had understood her so quickly.

'I'm exactly the same,' he said, leaning forward. 'Only for a different reason. I don't want to get married, because I *do* want to leave here, and if I get married I'll have to leave the army and live at home with my wife.'

'This is very romantic,' she said, laughing. 'We hardly know each other, and already we're telling each other that we don't want to get married.'

He shook his head. 'I'm saying that I'm as surprised as you. I wasn't on the lookout for someone, but when you meet the right person, you have to grab the opportunity while you can.' He reached across and took her hand in his. 'You are the most beautiful girl I have ever met, Livia.'

It was the kind of remark that, had it been made by one of the young men she usually served at the *osteria*, she would have dismissed with a mocking comment. But now she felt a wave of heat rising from her neck to her ears.

'Wait here,' he said, jumping up. 'I'm going to buy you a ribbon from Alberto Spenza.' He went over to where a plump young man was hanging around with the soldiers. She saw Enzo offer him a coin. Alberto glanced across at Livia, then opened his jacket to reveal a dozen yellow and red ribbons. She was absurdly pleased when she saw Enzo coming back across the square towards her with a long red ribbon dangling from his fingers. 'For you,' he said, presenting it to her with a bow.

At that moment Pupetta lowed mournfully from her pasture behind the house. 'Thank you,' Livia said, taking the ribbon and tying it in her hair. 'But now I'm afraid I'm busy again. I have to go and milk Pupetta and Priscilla.'

'Then I'll come and help,' he said.

'Don't get any ideas,' she warned. 'Just because you've bought me a ribbon, it doesn't mean I'm going to kiss you.'

'On my honour as a soldier, I promise I won't try anything.'

'Hmm,' she said. She wasn't surprised when, the moment they were alone in the barn together, he did try to kiss her. But since she had rather been hoping he would, she allowed him to embrace her briefly, before she pushed him away firmly and said, 'The milking has to be done.'

'And I'm the man to do it,' he said, pulling up a milking stool. 'Show me what to do.' They were both rather out of breath.

She pulled up a bucket and another stool and sat down next to Priscilla, who was less patient than Pupetta and liked to be milked first. 'You've never done this before, have you?'

'No,' he said, scooting closer. He rested his head on the buffalo's flanks, taking the opportunity to study Livia's profile from very close quarters. 'But I'm very good with my hands.' With her hair pulled back by the red ribbon, he could see where the hairline around her ears became softer and more downy as it merged into the fuzz of her skin, soft as an apricot. Impulsively, he leaned forward and placed a kiss on her cheek.

That day poor Priscilla was not milked very effectively, although it was one of the longest milking sessions the buffalo had ever known.

SOMETHING UNPRECEDENTED had happened: Livia had burnt the onions. And not just any onions, but the ones in her famous *sugo genovese*, that wonderful sauce of reduced onions, flavoured with beef stock, celery and chopped parsley. The customers at the restaurant were all too aware of a faint, bitter aftertaste in the sauce as they forked the pasta into their mouths. They exchanged glances, but nobody said anything.

'How was the meat?' Livia said, coming out to collect some dirty plates.

'Livia,' an old farmer called Giuseppe said gently, 'we haven't had the meat yet.'

'Haven't you?' She looked surprised. 'Oh, nor have you. I'll get it.' She went back into the kitchen.

After ten minutes someone stopped Livia's father as he brought in more wine. 'Nino, what's wrong with Livia? She's acting very strangely. That pasta didn't taste right at all. And she still hasn't brought out the *secondo*.'

Nino sighed. 'I'll go and have a word.'

He went into the kitchen and found Livia staring out of the window as she absent-mindedly stirred a saucepan. 'Livia. Are you all right? There are people out there waiting for food.' He suddenly noticed that her hair, which was tied back with a red ribbon he had never seen before, smelt of rosemary. 'Are you waiting for that boy to come back?' he demanded.

Livia blushed. 'Of course not.'

'Livia,' he said gently, 'he's a soldier. He'll probably never come. And if he does, what happens when he gets posted somewhere a long way away?'

'Wherever he goes,' she said, 'he'll come back eventually.'

FISCINO ETIQUETTE was both very liberal and very strict. Once they were formally engaged, it was completely accepted that Livia and Enzo would sneak off to roll around in the hay barn, but it was also expected that they would both be virgins on their wedding night.

One of the many advantages of this arrangement was that it forced the young man to be more inventive than he might have been if he had simply been able to make love in the conventional way, and by the time Livia came to be married she was already sure she was going to enjoy that side of things.

A fortnight before their wedding, Enzo took her to Naples to meet his family. She had not realised from his descriptions quite how poor they were, or what cramped conditions they lived in. But she was in love, and she was determined to make the best of her new life.

Enzo's mother, Quartilla, was a typical Neapolitan, sharp-eyed and shrewd. The first time they met she asked Livia to help her by making a *sugo*, a tomato sauce, while they talked. She had been told that this country girl was good in the kitchen and she wanted to see if it was true. 'Help yourself to whatever you need,' she said, and sat down to peel some *fagiole*. So Livia cooked, and Quartilla watched her like a lizard watching a fly.

Livia could have made a *sugo* blindfold—she had been making it almost every day for years. The only difficulty was, there were as many different kinds of *sugo* as there were days in a month. She knew that whichever recipe she chose now would be taken by Enzo's mother as a kind of statement about her character. She decided to follow her instincts.

'Do you have any anchovies?' she asked.

Enzo's mother looked as if she was about to explode. 'Anchovies?' In Naples, anchovies were only added to tomatoes if you were making *puttanesca*, the sauce traditionally associated with prostitutes.

'Please. If you have some,' Livia said demurely.

Quartilla shrugged and fetched a jar of anchovies from a cupboard.

The sauce Livia made now was powerful and fiery. She tipped the anchovies, together with their oil, into a pan, and added three crushed cloves of garlic and a generous spoonful of chilli flakes. When the anchovies and garlic had dissolved into a paste, she put in plenty of sieved tomatoes, to which she added a small amount of vinegar. After three minutes Livia dropped a few torn basil leaves into the sauce. 'There. It's finished.'

Instantly Quartilla was standing next to the pan, dipping a spoon in to taste it, then smacking her lips thoughtfully.

'Well,' she said at last, grudgingly, 'It's a bit showy, and it's got too much heat in it—it needs to be reined in a bit. But it'll do.'

And you're an old witch, Livia thought. Quartilla must have read her mind, because she added, 'And if you don't make Enzo happy, girl, I'll put you over my knee and beat you with that wooden spoon myself.' Her life in Naples, Livia recognised, was going to be very different from life in the country.

THE NIGHT BEFORE the wedding Livia wore green, and when she walked to the church a veil covered her face, so that evil spirits would not see her happiness. Enzo, meanwhile, carried a piece of iron in his pocket to ward off the evil eye. Their families walked with them, the little children running alongside catching the sugared almonds that were thrown up into the air. Afterwards there was a big party, for which Livia had cooked all the traditional dishes. The happy couple were toasted by the families with the cry of '*Per cent'anni!*', and Enzo had to make a formal announcement that Livia was now no longer her father's daughter, she was Enzo's wife.

I'm Signora Pertini now, Livia thought—for in Italy a woman keeps her father's surname after her marriage, her change in status denoted instead by the fact that she is no longer called *signorina*.

It was the custom that when newlyweds went to bed, the wedding guests came into the bedroom with them and placed gifts around the room—money, mostly, but also cloth, chinaware and sweets—so that when Livia and Enzo were finally left alone, with many a ribald comment from the departing guests, they first had to clear all the coins and sugared almonds off the bed.

The next morning, Enzo told her he had to report back to the garrison the following week.

'*Next week?*' Livia had not realised their honeymoon would be so short. But Enzo reassured her that he would be home again after a fortnight.

WHEN HE CAME home, however, something seemed to be worrying him. He cross-questioned her about what she had been doing, and which of his male friends she had seen when she was out shopping in the market.

The next day Quartilla announced that from now on, one of her other daughters would be doing the shopping.

'But why?' Livia asked, appalled. Now she wasn't cooking for all the *osteria*'s customers, going to the market was the only real pleasure she had.

'People have been talking. Apparently you're too friendly.'

'Enzo,' Livia cried, 'This is ridiculous. I married you because it was you I wanted. What makes you think I'd even look at another man?'

He smiled briefly. 'But I'm not here most of the time.'

She wanted to explode, but she said, 'Believe me, I am quite capable of looking after my own honour. But, I tell you what. Why don't I do the shopping in the market and take your sister with me?'

Enzo agreed that this was a good idea and, on reflection, Livia decided that it had not been such a big matter. Things would be better once Enzo had left the army, as he had promised to do by the end of the year.

PART TWO

February 1944

'This is as far as we go,' the driver said, pulling the truck over to the side of the road. He pointed. 'The Riviera is down that way, if you can get through the rubble.' He watched as James climbed down from his perch on top of a pile of ammunition boxes, then gave a cheery half-salute before putting the big K60 into gear. 'Good luck, sir.'

James Gould picked up his kitbag and knapsacks and arranged them around his body, the heavy roll of the kitbag balanced on one shoulder. ''Bye,' he called, attempting to return the driver's salute. 'Many thanks.'

He had been warned about the smell. As they'd retreated from Naples the Germans had blown up the sewers—those that hadn't already been destroyed by weeks of British and American bombing. Burning braziers stood outside some of the buildings to counteract the stink, but they seemed to have little effect. In the gloom of the narrow streets, with half-destroyed ruins towering precariously on either side, he picked his way gingerly through the debris down the hill towards the seafront.

He nodded politely at the Italians he passed: an elderly man, who scuttled past with his eyes averted despite James's polite *'Buona sera'*; a couple of *scugnizzi*, street urchins, who stopped to stare at him; an ancient woman, with a lined face, dumpy body and shapeless black dress, who he asked for directions. *'Scusi, signora. Dov'è il Palazzo Satriano, per cortesia?'* He had been practising his Italian on the troop ship from Africa, but the flowing consonants still felt strange and chewy in his mouth. The woman gave him a glance in which terror mingled with incomprehension. He tried again. 'The Palazzo Satriano? It's on the Riviera di Chiaia.' It was no good. *'Grazie mille,'* he said resignedly, and pressed on.

All around him were signs of the city's recent history. On one wall a giant mural depicting Mussolini's *fascio* symbol, an axe surrounded by a bundle of sticks, had been overpainted with a German swastika, and on top of that, a hastily whitewashed panel bore a crude Stars and Stripes and the words *Vivono gli Alleati*, Long live the Allies. The mural was decorated with a spray of bullet holes.

He turned the corner and found that he was in a street crammed with bars and restaurants. It surprised him: the briefing notes had said such premises were still officially closed. 'Naples is the first major city to be liberated by the Allies. The free world will be watching to see how we conduct ourselves,' the notes had gone on to say. On the evidence before him now, James thought, the free world might be a little shocked. The street had narrowed even further, so that it was barely wider than a desk, and the ubiquitous braziers gave off a stifling heat. Even so, the little thoroughfare was thronged with people. Pressing past him were uniforms of every hue and nationality—British khaki and American olive green, but also a melee of Poles, Canadians, New Zealanders, Free French, Highlanders, even a few diminutive Gurkhas, all picking their way cheerfully through the rubble. And the girls—everywhere he looked there were dark-haired, dark-eyed young women with flowers tucked behind their ears, strolling in pairs, hanging on the arms of the soldiers, or leaning languidly against doors.

At an intersection a street trolley rattled past, unbelievably full, a trio of nuns hanging off the running boards. Trucks were being directed through a tangle of traffic by an American military policeman in a white tin helmet and, opposite him, an Italian *carabiniere* in an elaborate uniform.

Eventually a friendly British fusilier pointed him in the right direction. The way led down a side street barely larger than an alley, then followed a dizzying series of zigzagging stone staircases. At the bottom, he stopped, momentarily taken aback by the view. In front of him, a vast orange sun was setting over the Bay of Naples. Under the red sky the sea was as smooth as a saucepan of boiled milk. Along the seafront, palm trees nodded in the evening breeze. And on the other side of the bay, the vast bulk of Mount Vesuvius loomed abruptly out of a distant peninsula, like an egg in its eggcup. A tiny question mark of smoke hung over its summit.

'Gosh,' he said aloud. Then, conscious that one was not here to admire views but to finish a war, he descended the steps towards the large building he could see at the bottom.

THE FIELD SECURITY Service had done itself proud, that much was immediately apparent. His new headquarters was an ancient *palazzo*, somewhat dilapidated in appearance but still bearing signs of its former grandeur. James wandered through the imposing entrance and into an inner courtyard, which contained a lemon tree and four brand-new Jeeps.

'Hello?' he called cautiously.

Through one of the windows that gave onto the courtyard he spotted an orderly in an American uniform, bearing an armful of files. 'Excuse me,' James said, leaning through the window. 'I'm looking for FSS.'

'Try upstairs,' the orderly said over his shoulder. 'Third floor.'

James trudged up the huge staircase that filled one corner of the courtyard. On the third floor he opened a door and stepped into a large, barely furnished salon. It contained an elegantly dressed woman, who was sitting by the window in an equally elegant chair, to which a goat was tethered. '*Scusi*,' James muttered, withdrawing quickly. He had forgotten that when an American said the third floor, he actually meant the second.

On the floor below the tapping of a typewriter indicated that he was now in the vicinity of an office, an impression confirmed by a printed sign on the door: 312 FIELD SECURITY SERVICE (BRITISH ARMY). Beneath it a second notice said: WEDDING OFFICER. APPOINTMENTS ONLY. OFFICE HOURS 3.00–4.00. The information was repeated in Italian. James knocked.

'*Avanti,*' a voice said.

He opened the door and entered into a large room, with a long table running down the middle of it piled high with files and papers. A dark-haired man was perched on one side of the table. He had a coloured neckerchief pushed into the collar of his shirt. 'Yes?' he said, looking up.

'Hello. I'm Captain Gould.'

'Oh.' The man seemed surprised. 'We were expecting you tomorrow.'

'I got a lift from Salerno. A supply truck on its way to the front.'

'Ah.' The man gestured at the papers. 'I was just sorting things out for you, as a matter of fact. I'm Jackson.' He stood up and offered his hand.

James stepped forward to shake it. 'Looks like quite a job,' he suggested, eyeing the mounds of paper.

'It is that.' Jackson ran his fingers through his hair. 'I'm a bit behind, actually. I was going to write you a note. But shall we do it over dinner?'

James had not had anything that could properly be described as 'dinner' for a very long time. 'Do you have a mess?' he asked hopefully.

Jackson laughed. 'Not exactly. That is, there's a man called Malloni who cooks our rations for us, but his culinary skills aren't up to much. No, I was thinking more of a restaurant. There's a place called Zi' Teresa's, down in the harbour. Black market, of course, and priced accordingly, but that needn't worry us. It's one of the better perks of the job—just ask the owner to sign the bill, and he'll knock fifty per cent off straight away.'

'But isn't that just the sort of thing we're here to stop?'

'Believe me,' Jackson said with a lopsided grin, 'kicking out the Jerries is nothing compared to the job we'd have if we tried to separate the Neapolitans from their grub. How about it?'

'Your transport.' Jackson pointed to where a Matchless motorbike was propped underneath a faded fresco showing nymphs and satyrs pockmarked with bullet holes. 'Whatever you do, don't keep it in the street. The Yanks have had three Jeeps stolen already.'

'How come you're both in the same HQ?'

'The theory is that their Counter Intelligence Corps and our Field Security do pretty much the same job. Some bright spark thought we should do it together.'

'And do you?'

Outside the *palazzo* Jackson turned left, marching briskly along the seafront. Automatically, James fell in beside him, their arms and legs swinging in unison. 'Well, we try not to step on each other's toes. It's a marvellous set-up they've got—twenty-five staff to our three, and a filing system that takes up a whole room. How's your Italian, by the way?'

James confessed that so far, he had barely understood a word that had been spoken to him.

'That's probably because what you were hearing was Neapolitan—it's almost a separate language. Don't worry, you'll soon pick it up. But CIC are hampered by the fact that not one of them even speaks standard Italian.'

'That's rather odd, surely?'

Jackson gave a bark of laughter. 'Not so much odd as fortuitous. There are plenty of Italian-Americans in the Fifth Army, but they've wangled positions in the stores. The last thing they want is CIC sticking their noses in.'

'You mean—they're pinching their own supplies?' James said, appalled.

Jackson stopped. 'Do you know, I think we should take a detour. There's something I ought to show you.'

He took James up the hill into the old quarter, a mass of dark medieval buildings piled on top of each other. Zigzagging erratically through the middle of this labyrinth was an alleyway that seemed to have become the main street by virtue of its length rather than any claim to magnificence. It was unbelievably crowded, both with buyers and sellers. Market stalls were piled high with every conceivable item of army equipment—ration packs, blankets reworked into dresses and coats, boots, cigarettes, phials of penicillin, toilet paper, even rolls of telephone wire. The stallholders eyed the two officers warily as they pushed through the crush.

'We used to round them up occasionally,' Jackson was saying, 'but a different set of faces simply came and took their places the next day. Penicillin's where the real money is, of course. So much has gone missing our medics sometimes have to come here and buy it back from the black marketeers, just to keep the field hospitals supplied.'

James nodded. Penicillin: it was the word on everyone's lips. Before penicillin there had been no effective way to treat the infections caused by bullet wounds or bomb shrapnel, so that even a relatively minor injury could lead to the loss of a limb or death. An American company, Pfizer, had now found a way to manufacture the wonder drug in huge quantities.

'Why do the Italians want so much of it?' James asked. 'After all, it's not as if they're fighting now.'

'It's not injuries they want it for, it's venereal disease. It's rampant here.'

'Oh. Of course.' James remembered the girls with flowers tucked behind their ears, hanging on the arms of soldiers. 'There's a fair amount of . . . fraternisation, I take it?'

They had turned off the street market now and were walking down through the old town. As if to illustrate his words, a group of GIs rounded the corner. Each had a bottle in one hand and a laughing girl in the other.

Jackson shrugged. 'It's simple economics, I'm afraid. The Jerries conscripted all the able-bodied Italian men and shipped them off to labour camps or to fight in Russia. After that, the economy collapsed—prostitution and black marketeering are pretty much all that's left. If you exclude the very old or the very young, almost any woman you see here is on the game.'

'And there's nothing we can do about it?'

Jackson shot him a glance. 'Well, winning the war would be a start,' he said. 'Officially, prostitution is illegal and we don't tolerate it. But at the end of the day, all that concerns Allied Military Government is keeping the soldiers on their feet. After a couple of weeks here, most are headed back to the front. So long as they can stand up and fire a rifle, that's all that matters.'

BACK ON THE SEAFRONT Jackson ushered James through the doorway of a restaurant. Behind the blackout blinds it was packed with people. Most were officers, but there was a smattering of GIs entertaining local girls, and several tables of surprisingly prosperous-looking Italians, some of whom were eating with American or British staff officers.

'You'd hardly know there was a war on, would you?' Jackson said, enjoying James's surprise.

'Signore Jackson. How very nice to see you.' The maître d' was shimmying between the tables towards them.

'A quiet table please, Angelo. My colleague and I have business to discuss.' The Italian smiled and led them to a table at the back.

A waiter was passing through the tables with some fish on a platter, showing them to the diners. Jackson stopped him and spoke in fast Italian, then turned back to James. 'It seems they have sea urchins today, though I'd advise you against them.'

'Why's that?'

'They have a rather inconvenient effect.' Seeing James's incomprehension, he lowered his voice. 'On the libido. Unless you intend to visit one of the rooms upstairs later, I'd steer clear.'

'So this is a—well, a brothel?'

The other man shrugged. 'Not as such. But every black-market restaurant has a few girls hanging around. There's a rather notorious beauty at this establishment, as it happens, with a glass eye.' He sat back and regarded James anxiously for a moment. 'You got a girl back home, Gould?'

'Absolutely,' James said, taken off guard. Jackson seemed to be waiting for more details, so he added, 'Her name's Jane Ellis. She's a land girl.'

'Engaged to her?'

'Pretty much.'

'Good. You'll find that comes in useful. In the wedding interviews.'

'Yes, I was going to ask you—'

'My advice to you, Gould,' Jackson said, leaning towards him, 'is to steer clear of seafood, stay out of the sun and *think of your girl*.'

'Well, of course. But what I don't quite understand—'

'At the first sign of trouble, just tell them you're *fidanzato*. Engaged.'

'I'll bear it in mind,' James said, completely mystified.

'Got to set the right example. You're the wedding officer now, you see.'

'Actually, I don't see,' James said. 'The first I knew of it was that sign on your door—'

'Not *my* door, old thing. *Your* door, now.' Suddenly, Jackson's mood seemed to brighten. 'Do you know, I think I might have those sea urchins after all. Since it's my last night.' He gestured to the waiter. 'What about you? They do a perfectly acceptable sausage and egg.'

'That sounds wonderful.' When the waiter had taken their orders, James persisted, 'Tell me, though—what *is* a wedding officer, exactly?'

'Ah.' Jackson seemed unsure where to begin. 'Well, ever since the Allies arrived, there have been a large number of soldiers wanting to marry local girls. Of course, any serviceman who wants to marry has to get the CO's permission. So, in an attempt to stem the tide, the CO decided that every potential fiancée has to be vetted to confirm that she's of good character.'

'But what on earth does "good character" mean?'

'Basically, that she isn't a whore.' Jackson shrugged. 'The fact of the matter is that she's bound to be, given what we were saying earlier. Your job is simply to gather the evidence. If she's got enough food, or if there's any furniture left in her apartment, she's a tart. If she can afford soap rather than cleaning herself with charcoal, she's a tart. If she can afford olive oil, or white bread, or lipstick, she's a tart. Just ask her what she's living on. Nine times out of ten she'll tell you there's an uncle somewhere, but that story never stands up to much scrutiny.'

'Doesn't sound too difficult.'

Jackson stared at him. 'No, I suppose it doesn't.' A jug of red wine arrived, and Jackson poured them both large glasses. '*Per cent' anni.*'

'Cheers.'

As he set his glass down James noticed that a man at a nearby table was watching them with an amused expression on his face. From his expensive suit James deduced that he was both a civilian, and someone of importance. He was dining with a group of American staff officers.

'Who's that?' he asked.

'Who? Oh, him. His name's Zagarella. He's a pharmacist, though his real occupation is professional cockroach. He's the man behind most of the stolen penicillin.'

'Can't you arrest him?'

Jackson smiled mirthlessly. 'I did, once. It didn't get me anywhere. As you can see, he has some rather well-connected friends.'

Their food came. The sausage and egg was, as Jackson had promised, perfectly acceptable. After months of rations James devoured it eagerly.

Jackson picked up his sea urchins, avoiding the violet spikes, and spooned the brightly coloured insides into his mouth. As they ate he explained what James's other duties would involve. Notionally, FSS were responsible for anything that could affect the security of the Allied Military Government. 'In theory, that means intelligence gathering. But there isn't any intelligence in Naples any more, only wild rumour. Just last week the Americans produced half a dozen so-called reliable reports that a suicide Panzer division had holed up in Mount Vesuvius and was waiting to come out and pounce on our rear. It took me three days to verify what I knew all along, which is that it was all a piece of nonsense.'

'You don't seem very impressed by our allies.'

'Well, we do have more experience of this sort of thing. Africa and India and so on.' Jackson poured himself some more wine. 'We're just naturally better suited to running an empire.'

James murmured something about the Germans having had a similar notion, but Jackson was disinclined to pick up on any irony.

'Actually, the Krauts ran this place pretty well. They didn't have any trouble with VD, for example. They simply imprisoned any girl who passed on an infection and gave the soldier concerned a field punishment. We're supposed to be more civilised, which gets us into all sorts of trouble.'

There was a curious incident when Jackson asked for the bill. Before it could be drawn up, Angelo, the maître d', sidled over to the table and said that there would be no charge 'for the British secret policemen'. He bowed to James. 'A very warm welcome to you, Captain Gould. I hope we'll see you here often.'

'How does he know my name?' James asked when Angelo had gone.

Jackson shrugged. 'It's his business to know everyone.'

'I'm not really happy about this,' James said. 'I don't see that I can start off by accepting—well, what could be construed as a bribe.'

'That's the way it's done here. You grease my palm, I'll grease yours.'

'But, technically, this place shouldn't even be open. I still want to pay my half,' James said doggedly. He called to the waiter, who went to fetch a bill.

'*Il conto*,' he said, putting it on the table with a smile. James looked at it: it came to more than two weeks' army wages.

'Can I give you one last piece of advice, Gould?' Jackson said when James had finished paying.

'Of course.'

Jackson hesitated. 'This place isn't like home. There aren't any rules here, only orders. Just follow the orders, and you'll be all right.'

LIVIA PERTINI CRASHED the pans together and glared at her father. 'How can I cook without food?' she cried.

Her father shrugged. 'Alberto Spenza is here and he wants to eat.'

'That gangster! He's had his snout in the trough for so long, it's a wonder he can fit any more in his fat stomach.'

'Try not to shout,' Nino suggested, although the truth was that Livia was making so much noise banging pots and pans around that nothing either of them said could be heard outside. 'He's one of our best customers.'

Livia sighed. 'I could make a *sugo*,' she said reluctantly.

'And some *melanzane farcite*?' Nino said hopefully. 'You know how Alberto loves your stuffed aubergine.'

'I suppose.'

'Good girl. And perhaps a *budino* for afterwards?'

'No! I don't have time. And there's only one egg.'

'Then maybe—'

'And I don't have time to talk to you now,' Livia added bluntly as she started chopping tomatoes for the *sugo*. Nino smiled and withdrew. He knew full well that when the pasta was sorted, his daughter would make a *budino di ricotta*, a cheesecake, somehow cooked with only one egg. It had been three weeks since they had last been able to buy supplies. It was simply impossible to obtain what you needed legitimately.

The sauce that Livia cooked now was a simple one, but thanks to the quality of the ingredients it was also extremely good. She chopped up a handful of *pomodorini da serbo*, a tiny tomato unique to the slopes of Vesuvius. These she fried quickly with some garlic in a little of the Pertinis' own olive oil. At the last moment she threw in a few torn leaves of basil from the bush that grew just outside the kitchen door. In less time than it had taken to cook the pasta, the sauce was done.

Later, as she washed the dirty pans, Livia became aware that Alberto Spenza was watching her from the doorway. She was not surprised—the kitchen was always open to customers—but the former ribbon seller was a more frequent visitor than most.

Since Enzo had gone off to fight, four years before, Alberto had rarely passed up any opportunity to drop by. As the war progressed and he prospered—it was widely known that he was a gangster, and possibly even a *camorrista*, a member of the Mafia—the visits had become more frequent. Livia saw the way he looked at her, and it made her fearful.

Today, at least, he seemed to be on his best behaviour. 'A fine meal,' he said with a smile, easing his bulk into the room. 'Is there some coffee?'

'Only from acorns,' she said sharply, pushing pans around the stove. Pretending to be busy meant she didn't have to look at him as they talked.

'Then it's fortunate that I brought some myself.'

She did look up then, surprised. Alberto was taking a twist of paper out of his pocket and unwrapping it. An aroma, which Livia had not smelt since before the war, filled the kitchen. Despite herself, she inhaled the deep, rich flavour and her features softened.

'It's called Nescafé,' Alberto said. 'The Americans get it in their rations. It's not really coffee, to tell the truth, but it's better than acorns. You just add boiling water. So simple!'

She shrugged and put a pan of water on the stove.

'You know,' Alberto continued, 'my sources say this war is likely to last another year at least, perhaps three.'

Livia thought of Enzo. Dear God, would she really not see him for another three years? It had already been four years since they were together.

As if reading her mind, Alberto said, 'That's a long time to try to keep this place going. You must be losing money hand over fist.'

'We'll manage,' she said defiantly.

He picked at his teeth with a knife. 'Of course,' he said thoughtfully, 'you could always come and cook for me. The war has been good to me. I can afford a . . .' He hesitated. 'A housekeeper.'

She busied herself making the coffee, pouring it into two tiny espresso cups. It smelt delicious, but when she tried some it was thin and bitter, delivering far less taste than the smell had promised. 'A housekeeper,' she repeated. 'So I wouldn't only be a cook?'

He shrugged again. 'I have some other needs as well.'

She shot him a glance. 'Such as?'

'Some washing, some cleaning . . . the kind of things my wife would do, if I had one,' he said casually. 'The kind of things you did for Enzo. He told his friends that he had a nickname for you. *Vesuvietta*. His little volcano.'

'Enzo's my husband,' she said loyally, but her cheeks flushed with shame. That part of their life should be private.

'Of course. And he'll still be your husband when he comes back. In the meantime, though, you should be looking after his interests. Who knows— he could come back with no legs, or blind, or with his hands shot off.' Livia put her hands over her ears to block out the terrible words, but she could still hear him. 'Shouldn't he return to find you've managed to put something aside? I'll pay you enough to recoup everything you've lost.'

'It's quite impossible—'

He shook his head. 'It happens all the time now. The girls in Naples are selling themselves for a mouthful of bread.'

'This is ridiculous—'

'And if by some sad misfortune Enzo never does come back—well, you'll need a husband who can look after you.'

'Alberto Spenza,' she snapped, 'I wouldn't go to bed with you if you were the last man in Italy—which, given that you're already the fattest man in Italy and everyone else is starving, is a distinct possibility. Now get out.'

He shrugged, apparently unconcerned. 'We'll see if you're so fastidious when you've been hungry for a few weeks.' He opened the door and went outside. 'Nino, your stubborn daughter doesn't want my job,' she heard him saying. 'In fact, she's been so rude to me I doubt you'll see me for a while.'

THAT AFTERNOON a truck came up the road to Fiscino. It drove slowly round the village; so slowly that Livia could see the faces of the six soldiers sitting in the back, each one holding a rifle. Then it stopped outside the *osteria*. The soldiers jumped down. An officer wearing the khaki shorts and lopsided beret of an Australian regiment climbed out of the front.

'We've been told you're hoarding food here,' he said to Nino. 'I have to requisition it for my men.'

'Livia, Marisa, go upstairs to your room,' Nino said. 'Lock the door.'

Livia felt the stares of the soldiers following her hungrily. 'This is Alberto's doing,' she said bitterly to her sister. 'As if I'd agree to go with him after he did something like this. He's stupid as well as fat.'

'He's not stupid,' Marisa said quietly. 'He knows he disgusts you, so he's not bothering to try to make you like him. He's trying to make you so desperate that you'll have no choice.'

For three hours the soldiers went through the *osteria* and the farm methodically, picking it clean. They took all the tomatoes, courgettes and aubergines, even the tiny ones. They pulled potatoes out of the soil and tossed them into the back of the truck. They threw the chickens in as well, picking them up by the legs and tossing them in with the vegetables as casually as if they had been cabbages. At this Nino tried to protest. The officer drew his pistol without a word and casually pointed it at the old man.

The soldiers worked on. They broke down the door of the barn, and took all the fruit that was stored in the hay. In the dairy they found a day's worth of *mozzarelle* sitting in a bucket: they took those, too, and a pail of milk left over from the cheese making. Then Livia, watching from the upstairs window, saw one of the soldiers undoing the gate which led to the pasture.

'No!' she cried. Marisa put a warning hand on her arm.

The soldiers tried to herd Pupetta and Priscilla towards the truck, but the two buffalo were big, stubborn old milkers who had absolutely no desire to be manoeuvred into a vehicle. One of the men picked up his gun. Two others grabbed the nearest animal, Pupetta, and held her by the horns. The one with the gun steadied the muzzle against her forehead. 'Steaks tonight, boys,' he called.

'I can't stand this,' Livia said, breathless with horror.

'Wait,' Marisa said. 'Don't be stupid—'

But Livia had already unlocked the bedroom door and was running downstairs. As she came out into the yard she heard a shot and saw Pupetta sink to her knees, wearily, and then slump to the ground.

'We'll need a saw,' one of the men said to Nino.

'You bastards,' Livia sobbed, shaking her fist as she ran forward to kneel by Pupetta.

'Livia, go back inside,' her father said. But it was too late. One of the soldiers had already grabbed her, laughing as he lifted her off her feet and tossed her casually into the back of the truck along with all their stolen food. She yelled angrily, and the other men cheered. One of the pair who had tossed her in the truck climbed up after her and pulled her arms behind her back, pinning both her wrists in one of his hands.

'Let me go,' she screamed. But the soldiers only cheered more. For the first time she began to feel afraid.

'OK, boys, that's enough,' the officer said casually. 'Throw her out.'

'I'll only be five minutes,' the one holding her said.

'I doubt you'd be five seconds, but that's not the point. You want a girl, there are plenty in Naples. We've got work to do.'

Reluctantly, the soldier released her and the officer pulled out a pocketbook and peeled off some notes, which he handed to Nino without a word. It was a hundred lire—not remotely a fair price for everything they had taken.

The officer's hand hesitated over the pocketbook. 'How much for the girl?' he asked in a low voice.

'She's not for sale,' Nino said.

After a moment the man shrugged and put the pocketbook away. Saluting ironically, he climbed into the front of the truck.

'We were lucky,' Nino said when the truck had disappeared from view.

'You call that lucky?' Livia cried. 'They've taken everything we have.'

'Not everything.' Nino crouched down next to her and stroked her hair gently. 'Don't you understand? It could have been so much worse.'

IN JUST FOUR YEARS, everything had changed completely.

When Mussolini first declared war, some of the women said that he was just starting a fight to show off. But you couldn't say that to the men, most of whom believed *Il Duce* had rescued the country from collapse. Alliance with Hitler was simply yet more evidence that Mussolini knew which side his country's bread was buttered.

Enzo had left with a kiss and a wave, confident that he would be back within a couple of months. Then came the first reports of setbacks. From Africa, from Greece, and then from Russia, the news came back: *It is with the deepest regret that the government has the honour of informing you of the heroic sacrifice of* . . . Even worse, in some ways, was when the letters from your loved one simply stopped arriving, as they did in Enzo's case.

There were German soldiers in the garrison at Torre El Greco, the first blue-eyed men Livia had met. They seemed friendly at first, despite their uniforms and guns—after all, they were all on the winning side together.

But young men who failed to join up voluntarily were taken anyway, in huge *rastrellamenti*, labour round-ups.

The Germans searched from house to house in the small hours of the morning, kicking in doors with their jackboots. There were just four of them in Enzo's parents' apartment, once the men had gone, but all their ration coupons combined only got them one loaf of bread a week, together with some pasta and a few beans.

One night Livia had been woken by a strange light coming through the window, along with a deafening growl. Getting up from the bed she now shared with Concetta, Enzo's younger sister, she went to see what was happening. She gasped. Under a black cloud of aeroplanes the sky was full of a ghostly, silvery, sparkling luminescence that fizzed from hundreds of tumbling flares.

She knew what she was meant to do: get to the safety of the big road tunnel that ran through the hillside below Naples. She quickly pulled on a dress and shook Concetta awake, but the pathfinder flares had done their job and the first bombs were already falling as they ran up the hill to the tunnel. Buildings were spitting out mouthfuls of stone and timber, the sky was full of the whistle of falling objects, and down by the harbour the silvery light of the flares had been replaced by the orange of a dozen fires.

When they reached the tunnel they found it crammed with people. A few had brought blankets, but most simply stood there in the gloom. In the morning they found a city transformed. It was as if Naples had been pulverised by giant fists. Even streets that had not suffered damage were covered in thick red dust. In some places the road itself had caught fire and the blackened cobbles now smoked in the sunshine. Glass crunched underfoot.

After that, the four women had taken their mattresses to the tunnel every evening, as, night after night, the Allied planes came back, the throb of their engines penetrating deep into the tunnel, followed by thuds and waves of pressure as their bombs gradually reduced the city to ruins.

Quartilla's nerves had been stretched to breaking point by the constant bombardments and she told Livia that she should go home, back to Fiscino, where she would be safer. Livia suggested that Quartilla should bring her family and come with her, but she wouldn't hear of it. 'I was born in Naples,' she said firmly, 'and I'll die in Naples, if that's what God demands of me.'

The railway tracks had been bombed, and travelling was slow. But in the countryside it seemed they had not suffered as much as the Neapolitans had done. Dishes had to be cobbled together from poor ingredients, though, and

Livia often found herself serving meals she was frankly ashamed of.

The German soldiers, who were the *osteria*'s main customers now, were usually polite, although as the war continued, relations with them soured.

Then, at last, the day came that everyone had been waiting for. A mass of warships appeared in the bay, the bangs and flashes from their guns like a thunderstorm. At long last, the Allies had invaded.

But the British and Americans had to fight for every inch of ground. Earlier in the year there had at least been some food, but as autumn gave way to winter, people starved. The *osteria* stayed open only because of the patronage of a few well-connected men of business like Alberto, who often sent along the ingredients they wanted cooked.

It was clear that liberation was going to be no better than occupation by the Germans had been. Now Italy was a battleground in which neither side was Italian, and for both sides, the needs of the civilian population came a poor second to the importance of winning the war.

A TINY LIZARD, seeing that James was awake, scuttled into a crack in the wall. It was the first time in months that he'd had the luxury of sleeping in private, let alone in such an enormous bed, and for a moment he couldn't recall where he was. Getting out of the bed, he went to pull the shutters open. Across the Bay of Naples, Vesuvius puffed a tiny, perfect smoke ring.

He put on his uniform and shaved in a foxed, silvery mirror under the inquisitive gaze of a cherub. It annoyed him that he still needed to do this only once a week. When he had scraped the soap off, the face that stared back at him was that of a boy. It seemed to him, though, that the curly ginger-brown hair on the top of his head was already thinning. He couldn't be going bald, he thought, not yet: he was only twenty-two.

At school he had been a classicist. He found both the history and the language of ancient Rome reassuring. Latin was like cricket, only more so: once you had mastered a set of fixed grammatical rules, everything made perfect sense. When he was called up, his linguistic skills were enough to get him assigned to an intelligence corps—or, more exactly, to the Field Security Service—where he had been given a choice of learning Italian, French or Arabic. Italian seemed the most similar to Latin, so he had chosen that. Then, as was typical with FSS, he had been posted to Africa. It had taken the intervention of his commanding officer to get this transfer.

He went to see if Jackson was still around, but the other man had mentioned an early start and it looked as if he had already left. James decided to start by inspecting his new quarters. On this floor there seemed to be about a dozen large rooms, grouped around the courtyard below. The first room was a kitchen, which also contained a tin bath. Presumably this was the domain of Malloni, the orderly. He looked in the cupboards, which were empty apart from a few tins of army rations. His heart sank a little—they were all marked 'Meat and Vegetables', a tasteless slop he had become all too familiar with over the past eighteen months.

The next room was one of the larger ones. Two men in plain clothes looked up from their desks as James entered. 'Hello,' he said, somewhat surprised to see them—Jackson had mentioned a couple of civilian staff, but James hadn't expected them to start so early. 'I'm Captain Gould.'

The Italians did not seem particularly interested in this information. 'Carlo,' one of them said curtly. He nodded at his companion. 'And Enrico.'

According to James's watch it was not yet eight o'clock. 'What are you working on?' he asked politely.

Carlo seemed quite taken aback. 'Filing expenses,' he said economically.

'May I?' James took the piece of paper Carlo was writing on. '"Captain Teodor Benesti, informant, two hundred lire,"' he read. '"Marshal Antonio Mostovo, contact, two hundred lire. Carla Loretti, gift, one cheese and a blanket, value fifty lire." What are these?'

'Payments for information,' Carlo said, taking the paper back.

James experienced a sinking sensation. 'Bribes, you mean?'

Carlo shrugged. 'If you like.'

'I don't like,' James said firmly. 'I don't know how Jackson ran this show, but paying informants is completely against the rules.'

Carlo looked at him without expression. 'You are mistaken. These figures do not relate to the payment of bribes. They are a record of the bribes we have been *offered*.'

'Oh, I see,' James said, relieved.

'And the money we are given,' Carlo continued, 'goes into a tin in the cupboard. So we always know exactly how much there is.'

The sinking sensation returned. 'What happens to the money in the tin?'

'We use it for the bribes we give out,' Enrico said. The two men watched James impassively.

He took a deep breath. 'There must be no more payments. Of any kind, given or received. Is that clear?'

'*Si*,' Enrico muttered.

'Of course,' Carlo said. But he carried on writing out his list.

When James left the room, the two Italians said nothing more for several minutes, then Enrico murmured under his breath, '*Ogni scupa nova fa scrusciu.*' Every new broom makes a noise.

BY NOON JAMES had sorted the mess of papers on the table into three large piles, which he had mentally dubbed Fascists, Criminals and Madmen. Most important of all, he had located the Black Book, the log of known criminal elements in the area, which started with a neat list of names and addresses, and 'fascist' or 'mobster' written against them. Fascinated, despite himself, James had sat down to read further when the door opened and three men walked in. As one of them was a major, and presumably James's CO, he jumped to his feet and saluted sharply.

Major Heathcote was a harassed-looking man of about forty. 'Frankly, I don't give a duck's arse about the Eyeties,' he told James. 'I simply want to get this district under some semblance of control. We all thought we'd be in Rome by now, but unfortunately the Jerries have dug in about sixty miles north at Monte Cassino and it's getting pretty grim. Come to me if there's anything you can't handle, but I'm really hoping you won't have to.'

James agreed that he would probably need to bother the major very little, and the CO started to leave. 'Oh, and weddings,' he said, suddenly swivelling round and fixing James with a steely expression. 'Try not to let the men get married. It causes no end of resentment, and it makes the soldiers soft.'

'Don't worry, sir,' James said. 'Jackson briefed me very thoroughly on the marriage situation.'

'I'm glad to hear it.'

The major left, accompanied by one of the men. The other man, a captain with startlingly blue eyes, stuck out his hand.

'Tom Jeffries, A-force,' he said cheerfully. 'Jumbo to my pals. My office is just upstairs, though of course I'm not there much.' He winked.

A-force were the cloak-and-dagger boys. Presumably Jeffries meant that he was usually away doing top-secret work behind enemy lines. 'Oh, of course,' James said. 'Pleased to meet you.'

'Listen, do you fancy a spot of lunch? There's a place down the road which does a very nice veal chop.'

And so, for the second time in twenty-four hours, James found himself being ushered into Zi' Teresa's. If the maître d' was surprised to see him he didn't show it, through Jeffries looked a little nonplussed when Angelo showed them, with a hint of a wink, to 'Captain Gould's usual table'.

As they ate, Jeffries quizzed James about his combat experience, which up to that time had been limited, to say the least.

'Not to worry. We might be able to slip you into something of ours now and again,' Jeffries said. 'We've usually got a few people popping in and out of EOT, killing Jerries, and an Italian speaker's always welcome.'

James made some vague noises of enthusiasm intended to imply how much he regretted that he was too busy to pop into Enemy Occupied Territory alongside a bunch of bloodthirsty maniacs who didn't speak Italian. In an effort to change the subject he lowered his voice and said, 'Shame what Major Heathcote was saying about the advance being bogged down at this Monte Cassino place.'

Jeffries's eyes twinkled. 'That depends on how you look at it. Think about it. Why are we here?'

'To beat the Germans?'

Jeffries shook his head. 'To tie up as many Germans as possible while the main show gets under way in France, that's why. The last thing Churchill wants is for the Jerry divisions in Italy to nip back over the Alps and reinforce their defences over there. Look, this whole show is just a massive ruddy diversion, Gould. If I were you, I'd allow yourself to be diverted.'

A woman approached the table. She was tall and extremely beautiful, with long black hair artfully pinned and curled round her head, and a slim dress of some slinky material that wouldn't have looked out of place in a Mayfair dance hall. She also, James noticed, had a glass eye.

'Speaking of which—may I introduce Elena, my girl?' Jeffries said. 'Darling, this is Captain James Gould.'

'Pleased to meet you,' James said, getting to his feet.

'Actually, she doesn't speak much English,' Jeffries said. 'Completely charming, though. She's a schoolteacher.'

'*Buongiorno, signorina*,' James said. '*Molto piacere di conoscerla*.'

Elena smiled. '*Voi parlate Italiano*?'

'Not as well as I thought, it seems,' he said in Italian. 'Your local dialect takes some getting used to.'

'Well, you speak it a lot better than Jumbo does. Will you tell him I'm going to the ladies' room, please?'

'Of course.'

'What did she say?' Jeffries asked as Elena left them.

'She said she was going to powder her nose. Look, is she really a teacher?'

'Why shouldn't she be?'

James thought of mentioning what he had heard about Zi' Teresa's celebrated glass-eyed employee, but Jeffries was glaring at him fiercely. 'Perhaps I'm mixing her up with someone else,' he said lamely.

'Actually,' Jeffries said, 'I wanted to talk to you about Elena. There's a bit of a language barrier, you see. I need a few phrases translated. Only some of it's a bit delicate. For example, "I'm feeling a bit tired, actually."'

'*Mi sento stanco, veramente.*'

'And what about, ah, "That's very nice, but I'd really rather you didn't"?'

'*È molto bene ma non farlo, grazie.*'

'And "Please stop"?'

'*Smettila, per favore.*'

Jeffries's lips moved as he silently practised the unfamiliar phrases. 'Well, that should cover it,' he said at last.

Elena rejoined them and she and Jeffries smiled at each other coquettishly. 'Tell me, James,' she said in Italian, 'how do I tell him "*Aspetta!*"?'

'Er—"Wait", I suppose.'

'Wayt. And how do I say "*Non smettere!*"'

'Don't stop.'

'And "*Svegliati, per favore caro*"?'

'Wake up please, darling.'

'Wek erp plis dah'leeng. OK, I think I have everything.'

'Jumbo? Anything else I can assist with?'

'No, I think I'm fully kitted up now. Thanks.'

'In that case,' James said, 'I'd better be getting back. Can I pay my share?'

Jumbo rolled up his left sleeve. His forearm bore no fewer than six wristwatches. 'No need, old chap,' he said, unbuckling one and laying it on the table. 'I met some Germans recently, up in Abruzzo. This one's on them.'

As JAMES ENTERED the Palazzo Satriano he became aware of a commotion echoing down the marble staircase. He rounded the first-floor landing and found his way blocked by a mass of women—young women, all dressed to the nines. They appeared to be pushing and shoving with the intention of getting closer to the door of the FSS office. With some difficulty, James battled his way past waves of scent, screeching voices and glossy black hair.

'What on earth is going on?' he asked Carlo when he reached the safety of the office. 'Why are there so many women outside?'

Carlo shrugged. 'They are the *fidanzate*. The women who want to marry Allied servicemen. These are just the most recent ones, the ones who have not yet been given a time when they will be interviewed.'

'Then—Good Lord—how many have we already arranged to see?'

Carlo rummaged in a cupboard and produced a thick sheaf of papers. 'Forty? Fifty?'

No wonder Jackson had been unable to do anything about the black market, James thought. All his time must have been spent on processing would-be war brides. 'Right,' he said. 'The first thing to do is to make a list.'

It took nearly three hours just to take the girls' names and addresses, and by the end of it James was exhausted.

At seven o'clock precisely, a tiny Italian man entered James's office. He was wearing a very ancient tuxedo and a white bow tie, which was almost exactly the same size and shape as the moustache on his upper lip.

'Dinner she served,' he said darkly.

'Ah,' James said. 'You must be Malloni.'

'I 'ave the honour, yes. Wet there.'

Malloni vanished, only to reappear a moment later with a steaming tureen in his arms. 'Ees dinner.'

'Right. Where do you usually . . .?' James gestured at the table, which was still covered in Jackson's papers, albeit sorted into piles. He watched as Malloni pushed them haphazardly towards the centre of the table to make room for his tureen. From behind the door he produced a small bronze gong, which he struck with great ceremony three times.

One by one a handful of other British officers appeared and introduced themselves as his dining companions. Kernick, Walters, Hughes and French all occupied offices in various other parts of the building.

Malloni proceeded to lay the table, putting a plate in front of each person. There was also a candelabra, which he did not light, and a number of smaller dishes with lids.

Eventually Malloni wrapped a white cloth over his left arm like a matador's cape, and with his other hand triumphantly raised the lid of the tureen.

It contained, as James had suspected it might, several portions of 'Meat and Vegetables' removed from their tins, mixed together and warmed through. Surreptitiously, he lifted the lid on one of the side dishes. It, too, contained 'Meat and Vegetables'. He tried another. 'Meat and Vegetables' again. He looked up. Malloni was going round the table, standing next to the left side of each man and holding the tureen steady for them.

'Jackson warned me this fellow wasn't up to much,' he muttered to Kernick. 'Why do you keep him on?'

'He's a very good source of Scotch. And occasionally he can lay his hands on a few cigars.'

James was grateful to have filled up at Zi' Teresa's, and ate as little as possible. His companions, however, consumed theirs with enthusiasm, a haste later explained by the eagerness with which they pushed their plates aside to get on with the real business of the evening, playing cards.

'*Scopa*,' Kernick explained. 'Local game. Really quite addictive. You'll play, Gould, won't you?'

Before he could reply, there was a deafening crash from downstairs, followed by a squealing noise. A second crash echoed up the stone staircase, accompanied by more squealing. 'What on earth is that?' James asked.

'According to the Americans,' Walters said, 'it's called jazz.'

Now that James listened more closely, he could just make out a hint of a melody in the strangled squeaks, which were presumably coming from a clarinet, although the drums still sounded as if they were being used in the manner of a punch bag rather than a musical instrument.

'They've not been at it very long,' Walters added unnecessarily. 'Quite keen, though. They practise nearly every night.'

After he had lost half a crown at *scopa* James went to bed. The jazz continued late into the night, making sleep difficult. When he did finally drift off he found himself dreaming of Neapolitan fiancées.

He woke with a start, just as the clarinet downstairs gave a sudden squeal of excitement. Knowing that sleep was unlikely now, he reached for his shirt and undid the pocket, searching for a cigarette. He lit one, letting the smoke mingle with the scents of jasmine and bougainvillea that wafted through the open windows.

Next to the pack of cigarettes was a letter. James hesitated, then drew it out. The letter had been travelling with him so long that it had started to come apart along the seams, but the words were legible enough.

> *Wendover Farm,*
> *Wendover, Bucks*

14th November 1943

Dear James,

> *This is a beastly letter—beastly to write, and even more beastly to get, I suppose. I wish I could have said this to your face, but I've thought and thought about it and it seems to me that it's better to let you know how things stand now than to wait until I see you, which*

mightn't be for months. Besides, I don't want to do anything behind
your back, and it wouldn't be fair on Milo either to keep him waiting
for your next home leave, whenever that might be.

Dearest James, please don't be upset. Of course your pride will be
hurt at being jilted (hateful word, but I can't think of a better one) but
apart from that I have this feeling that you're going to absolutely
understand. Now that I'm away from home, and able to talk to other
girls about their boyfriends (I didn't gossip about you, I promise), I
realise that what we had together was really a lovely warm friendship
rather than a love affair. If it hadn't been for the war I would
probably never have met Milo, and you and I would have got married
without even thinking about it very much. We would have managed to
have some children and it would never even have occurred to us that
anything was missing. I suppose I'm talking about passion. But
please don't think I'm trying to reproach you, James . . .

There was more, three or four pages of it, but the gist was that she'd met
a Polish airman who was able to supply the passion James had not been able
to. She had never given any indication that she would be anything other
than mortified if he had raised the subject of making love. Indeed, the extraordinary frankness of the letter had itself been a shock. Perhaps it was being
a land girl that had done that. He put the letter away, and lay down again.

'Passion,' he said out loud, around a mouthful of cigarette smoke. But
what was passion, when it came down to it? These Italians were passionate,
he supposed, but as far as he could see that simply meant they were over-
excitable, talked too much, and treated women with a lack of respect.

He sighed. Sex was yet another thing that this war had turned on its head.
Many of the men saw anyone who was still inexperienced as simply need-
ing to be dragged to the nearest brothel. Even before his dinner with
Jackson, whenever James was asked if he had a girl at home, he said he had.
Having a girl at home got you out of all sorts of difficulties.

LIVIA HAD DECIDED that they should hold a *festa* to make use of what
remained of Pupetta.

'But how will anyone pay us?' her father wanted to know.

'We'll let them pay whatever they can afford. After all, it's better than letting good food go to waste.'

'And who will we dance with?' Marisa said. 'There are no men.'

'There are a few. And they'll all come if there's going to be meat.'

They levered Pupetta's carcass onto a huge spit made out of X-shaped pieces of wood that straddled a pile of oak kindling. The fire was lit at dawn, and by midday the unfamiliar smell of roasting beef was spreading through the village. Their neighbours helped them bring out tables and chairs, and there was no shortage of volunteers to stoke the fire.

Meanwhile Livia and Marisa prepared the other dishes. Vegetables were still in short supply but there were *cannellini* and whole bulbs of fennel, and plenty of *coccozza*, a pumpkin-like vegetable, and *tenurume*, the tender shoots of the courgette plant. And of course, there was fresh mozzarella, made with milk from poor Priscilla—so miserable since Pupetta's death.

All the men in the district came, just as Livia had predicted. There were precious few of them: the maimed, the sickly, the very old, the very young, those in protected professions, and those with enough influence or cash to avoid the *rastrellamenti*. Alberto and his fellow *camorristi* were there, of course, but of more interest to the villagers were Cariso and Delfio, the Lacino brothers, who had escaped from a prisoner-of-war camp in the north and walked the 200 miles home, right though the German and Allied lines.

The Neapolitans say that hunger is the best sauce, and it was not until all the food was eaten, and a respectful interval had elapsed to pay homage to its excellence, that the music began. Livia took off her apron, eager to dance, but to her surprise she found she had no partner. She looked around, hoping someone would try to catch her eye. But instead, all she caught were glances that shifted away from her.

'Who will dance with me?' she demanded, looking them straight in the face, one after another. 'Franco,' she asked one of her neighbours, 'what about you? You've danced with me a hundred times.'

'That was before Enzo went away,' Franco said quietly.

'What does that have to do with it?' She glared at him, but he too dropped his gaze. Continuing on, she came to Alberto. He was smirking.

'Alberto,' she said.

He nodded. '*Si?*'

She let him think she was going to ask him, then, 'Nothing,' she said, contemptuously. 'Marisa, you'll dance with me, won't you?'

There was a low chuckle from the other men as they glanced at Alberto's furious face.

'We have Alberto to thank for this,' she muttered in her sister's ear as they spun back and forth to the throb of the *tammurro*. Then, as they were walking back to their seats, another explanation suddenly struck her. Enzo.

She ran to where the Lacino brothers were sitting with their family. 'Please,' she begged them. 'If you know anything at all, you must tell me.'

Cariso looked embarrassed, but Delfio spoke up. 'In the camp, we asked anyone we met for news of people from round here. There were a few there who'd been with Enzo in Russia.'

'And?' she cried.

'I'm sorry, Livia,' Delfio said. He held her gaze. 'He was in a position that came under fire from a British fighter pilot. None of them survived.'

Thoughts tumbled into Livia's brain, one after the other. Why had no one told her earlier? And why hadn't Quartilla written? As Enzo's mother, she would have been sent the official notification.

She had seen the grief of women many times over the last few years. After the initial shock, the wife or mother usually collapsed, shrieking and howling. But she did not howl. Instead, a deep and murderous resentment filled her heart. This was the Allies' doing. Allied soldiers had killed Pupetta. Now an Allied pilot had, from the safety of the skies, shot her poor husband, while he fought in a war that was none of his making. And these people had the nerve to call themselves Italy's liberators.

She turned and walked away from the fire, into the darkness, so she could be alone. It was only then that her legs gave way and she fell into Marisa's waiting arms. She allowed her sister to help her into the house. She did cry then—she howled and wailed and cursed. But it was not only Enzo she was crying for. Until that day, she had been able to hope that when the war was over, and Enzo returned, things would be better. Now she knew that life was going to get harder than she had ever imagined it could be.

'DO YOU KNOW why I'm here?'

The girl nodded. '*Sì*. You're the wedding officer.'

'The Field Security Officer,' James corrected. He had already decided not to continue using the phrase 'wedding officer', which surely made it sound as if arranging other people's matrimonies was the sole extent of his job. 'I need to write a report saying whether you are a suitable person to marry Private'—James looked at his notebook—'Private Griffiths.'

The girl, whose name was Algisa Fiore, was very pretty. Now, as she gazed at him, her big, dark eyes were full of happiness. 'Do you know Richard?' she asked eagerly.

James admitted that he had not yet made Private Griffiths's acquaintance.

At this, a brief cloud of incomprehension crossed Algisa Fiore's lovely features. 'Then how will you know if we are suitable for each other? Never mind, I will tell you about him. I like talking about Richard. He is *molto gentile*,' she explained. 'He loves animals. As I do.' She folded her long, pretty fingers over her knee. 'And he's so brave. Once he killed three Germans with only his bare hands and a spoon.'

'I'm sure Private Griffiths is a wonderful chap,' James agreed. 'But I'm afraid I need to ask you some questions of a more practical nature.'

'Ask me anything.' She lay back in her chair and began to play with a small silver cross that hung at her neck.

'What does this mean?' Switching to English, he said, slowly and clearly, 'You appear to have given me the wrong change entirely.'

Algisa Fiore laughed delightfully. 'I've got absolutely no idea.'

'Does Private Griffiths speak Italian?'

'Not really, but he can make me understand what he wants,' she said.

James coughed. 'What do you know about England?'

'I know it's where Richard comes from.'

'Did you know, for example, that it's a lot colder than here?'

'I know the women are ugly. At least, that's what Richard says.'

James gave up. He was never going to get anywhere at this rate. What had Jackson said? 'Basically, your job is to discover whether or not she's a tart.' He looked around. Algisa Fiore's apartment was small, bare and spotlessly clean. 'What do you live on?'

She blew out her lips. 'I have an uncle in Sicily. He sends me money.'

Jackson, he recalled, had been particularly scathing about uncles. 'May I have your uncle's address?' James asked, his pen poised over his notebook. 'Then, you see, I can check with him.'

There was a long pause. Algisa Fiore tugged at the cross on her necklace, and tapped her foot in the air. 'I can't remember it. He moves around a lot.'

He said gently, 'Where does the money really come from, Algisa?'

'Soldiers,' she said at last.

He wrote in his notebook, 'A. F. all but admitted living off prostitution.' He stood up. 'I'll need to look round your apartment.'

'Of course,' she said, standing up too.

He made a quick tour of the apartment. It was so bare that it didn't take long. But he noticed the bar of soap in the bedroom. Returning to the main room, he found her waiting for him fearfully. 'You're not going to write me a good report, are you?'

'I'm afraid not.'

She slumped down into her chair. 'I'll be a good wife to him, I'll make him happy. Can't you help me?'

'I'm afraid I don't make these rules. If you really want to marry each other, you'll just have to wait until after the war.'

'What makes you think either of us will still be alive after the war?'

'I'll see myself out,' he said, closing his notebook. As he closed the door to the apartment he thought he heard her weeping.

DURING THE MORNING, as James wrote up his report from the day before, a dapper gentleman was shown into his presence.

'An informant,' Enrico said tersely.

The dapper man introduced himself as *Dottore* Lorenzo Scoterra. He was, he said, an *avvocato*, a lawyer, and he wished to give the British some information about known fascists in the area.

James made it clear that he was unable to pay for this information, at which Dr Scoterra became quite impassioned. He did not want money, he said. He was motivated, he explained, purely by his regard for justice and the rule of law—the calling in which he had spent his professional life—and his admiration for the British. Dr Scoterra indicated, however, that he would not say no if James wished to carry on their discussion over a glass of marsala.

Since it was by now quite late, and James had had no breakfast, this seemed a reasonable suggestion and they repaired to the bar at Zi' Teresa's, where Angelo the maître d' greeted James with the casual wave afforded to an old friend.

James duly ordered two glasses of marsala, a drink he had not tried before. It was sweet and rather fortifying. The barman broke a raw egg into each glass just before serving it—a remarkable thing, given the scarcity of fresh eggs. Dr Scoterra seized his even before the barman had finished stirring it, downed the egg in one swallow, before turning to James with a smile of gratitude. He was, James noticed, almost painfully thin.

He proceeded to give James an exhaustive list of people who had benefited from the Germans' presence. The more notes James took, the more details Dr Scoterra seemed to remember, and they consumed several more glasses of marsala before the lawyer finally ran out of information.

'Well,' James said, putting down his pen and gesturing to the barman for a bill, 'that's been extremely useful, *Dottore*. But I'm sure you've got clients to attend to.'

'Yes, of course,' the lawyer said, a little reluctantly. Then he brightened. 'But I forgot—there's something I haven't told you.' The lawyer leaned sideways so that he could whisper conspiratorially into James's ear. 'There is a division of German tanks hiding inside Vesuvius. They are going to attack you from the rear. They know they will all be killed, but it is a point of honour with them—they want to die for their Führer.'

James recollected how Jackson had specifically told him not to listen to any stories about German Panzer divisions holed up in Vesuvius. 'I'm afraid your source is misinformed,' James said. 'That's been looked into, and it isn't true.'

Dr Scoterra looked wistfully at the bottles behind the bar.

'There is just one other thing, though . . .' James said.

Dr Scoterra brightened. 'Yes?'

'This trade in black-market penicillin. Do you have any idea who's behind it?'

Dr Scoterra laughed. 'But of course. Everyone does.'

'Who is it?' James asked, nodding to the barman for two more glasses of marsala-and-egg.

'The pharmacist, Zagarella. He runs it on behalf of Vito Genovese.'

'Would you say so in court?'

Dr Scoterra looked alarmed. 'If I attempted to do anything of the kind, I would be killed long before I got to the courtroom.'

'Well, where can I find Signore Zagarella?'

'You are not considering arresting him?' Dr Scoterra was now so perturbed that he was getting to his feet, despite the fact that the barman had not yet finished pouring his marsala. 'I had no idea that you were thinking of such a rash course of action. Really, as a lawyer I must advise you against it.'

'But the man is a crook, surely?'

They stared at each other across an unbridgeable gulf of understanding.

'At least promise me that you'll keep my name out of it,' Dr Scoterra said, fumbling for his coat buttons.

'Since you're not prepared to give evidence, that shouldn't be too hard. But the penicillin market must be stopped. This stealing could put soldiers' lives at risk.'

Dr Scoterra sighed. 'When you've been in Naples a bit longer, you'll understand. To survive in this city, it is necessary to be *furbo*, crafty. That's the way things are around here.'

James went back to the Palazzo Satriano, his mind made up. Jackson had let things slide, clearly, but there was no reason for him to do the same.

'We are going to raid the pharmacist Zagarella,' he told Carlo and Enrico. 'I have reason to believe that he may be connected with the black market in penicillin.'

Carlo yawned and scratched himself. 'Of course he is connected with it. He runs it.'

'Then why haven't we put him in prison?'

Carlo shrugged. 'We are just three men and, with respect, if we were to start taking on the *camorra* we'd need an army.'

'This may have escaped your notice, Carlo,' James said stiffly, 'but as it happens, an army is just what we have.'

He went downstairs and knocked on one of the windows that looked out onto the central courtyard. As Jackson had said, the Yanks' set-up was impressive. Doors opened and closed busily, revealing a succession of bustling offices full of men in olive-green uniforms. James was suddenly rather ashamed of the comparative lethargy of his own operation upstairs. The surly indifference of Enrico and Carlo—he still had no real idea of what they actually did most of the time—was surely no match for this.

No one came to the window, so he wandered into what seemed to be the main office, where he stopped a passing orderly and asked if he could see someone in charge.

'Got an appointment?' the orderly snapped.

'No, I just—'

'I'll get the book.' He bustled off. James made a mental note to get FSS an appointment book as soon as possible.

'Hey, buddy.'

The voice had come from behind him. James turned. The speaker was a young man of about his own age, seated at one of the desks. He wore a pair of steel-rimmed glasses that had been mended with a piece of copper wire. Even though the American was seated, James could tell that he was tall and lanky, an impression confirmed when he got to his feet.

'Eric Vincenzo. You're the new guy at FSS, right?' He waved at a chair in the corner. 'What's up?'

James sat down. Behind Vincenzo, a clarinet was resting on a shelf. This, James deduced, must be the perpetrator of the insomnia-inducing jazz that drifted up the stairs at night.

Following James's gaze, Vincenzo looked alarmed. 'You're not here to complain, are you? Have I been keeping the neighbours awake?'

James assured him that he was not there to complain about the noise, and explained about his planned raid on the pharmacist.

The American stroked his chin thoughtfully. 'So you're thinking of a joint operation? Well, the first thing is to check out this informant of yours. Let's take a look.' He had pulled open the drawer of a filing cabinet and was leafing through some files. 'Would that be the same Dr Scoterra who was the secretary of the local fascist party?'

'I don't think that sounds right.'

'Hmm.' He pushed the drawer shut. 'Well, there's an easy way to check.'

James followed him through a succession of rooms until they reached an enormous salon, presumably once the palazzo's ballroom. In the centre of the room was an equally vast filing system, nearly eight feet high.

'Goodness,' James said enviously.

'Oh, it's not ours. We took this from the German consulate. I'll say this for the Krauts, they kept immaculate records.' As Vincenzo spoke he was locating the right drawer. 'Here we are.' He handed James a folder.

The first item was a letter in Italian from one *Dottore* Scoterra, addressed to the German consul. James quickly scanned it. Dr Scoterra wished, he said, to offer his services as an informant. He made it clear that he did not expect to paid. He was motivated purely by his regard for justice and the rule of law, the calling in which he had spent his professional life, and admiration for the Germans. There followed a long list of names, many of which were familiar to James from his own conversation with Dr Scoterra. The letter ended with a suggestion that the Germans might like to interview him further in a quiet place, such as a bar.

'The little prick,' he said, with some feeling. 'He's been trying to use us to settle his own scores. He even got me to buy him a glass of marsala.'

'That's the one where the barman puts an egg?'

James nodded. 'You know, I thought at the time he seemed rather emaciated. It was probably the first food he'd eaten all week.'

Vincenzo laughed. 'You've been *fottuto*, as they say here. That means—'

'I know what it means,' James said tersely. 'Screwed over.'

'Yeah—you speak Italian, don't you?' Vincenzo said, eyeing James carefully. 'I noticed that letter didn't give you any trouble.'

'Don't you?'

'I'm learning, but it's a slow business.'

'With a surname like Vincenzo?'

'I'm third generation. My folks wanted me to be a proper little American, so they refused to speak Italian at home. Not that it stopped them from being locked up for six months as enemy aliens when war broke out.' He offered James the file. 'Want to trade?'

'Trade what?'

'Well, I reckon that even though your informant's motives may be less than honourable, he could be useful. We'd need to clear it with our COs, but it seems to me a joint operation could benefit both of us. Call me Eric.'

BOTH COS ENDORSED the notion of a joint operation against the black marketeers, so long as it was under one command. Curiously, the American CO seemed to think this was a job for the British, while Major Heathcote had a strong feeling that it was a task better suited to the Americans. After some internal wrangling, it was decided that for the time being James and Eric would report to Major Heathcote.

The operation took place one morning at dawn, and was divided into two parts. The Italian *carabinieri*, under Carlo and Enrico, had been given the task of rounding up the black marketeers on the Via Forcella, while James and Eric were to search the pharmacist's premises.

Signore Zagarella was having his breakfast when they knocked on his door. He received the news that they intended to look for contraband penicillin with equanimity.

'Go ahead,' he shrugged. 'You'll find nothing here.'

They searched for an hour. The apartment was not only bare of penicillin, it was bare of contraband goods of any kind. With a sinking feeling James realised that they had been expected. At last, in a wastepaper basket under the sink, he found a single used phial of penicillin. He showed it to Zagarella, whose expression did not change.

'You'll have to come with us to the Poggio Reale, initially,' James said, naming the city prison. 'You'll be held there while we make our enquiries.'

The pharmacist shrugged and held out his hands for the handcuffs. 'You can put me in Poggio Reale, if you like, but I can assure you I won't be there for long.'

JAMES WAS STILL in a buoyant mood the next morning as he set off with Eric to interrogate the prisoners rounded up in the raid on the Via Forcella.

On their way they dropped in on Zagarella in the Poggio Reale prison, where they found him as imperturbable as ever, and working his way through an excellent breakfast. He had been given a cell, or rather a suite of cells, which was larger than Algisa Fiore's apartment. One of the warders was busy making up his bed with fresh linen. James noticed that the prisoner also appeared to be wearing a freshly laundered shirt.

'Have you come to release me?' he wanted to know.

'Our enquiries are not yet complete,' James said. 'You'll stay here until they are.'

Zagarella dabbed at his lips with a napkin. 'I doubt that very much,' he assured them. 'I must say, I am surprised that you are still here yourselves. I imagined that you would have been transferred out of Naples by now.'

'It will give me great pleasure,' James said to Eric as they left the prison, 'to put that man behind bars.'

'He already is behind bars,' Eric pointed out, 'and to be honest, it doesn't seem to be inconveniencing him that much.'

'They're only treating him so well because he's convinced them he'll be out soon. If we get a conviction, he'll be just another prisoner.'

'James,' Eric said, 'do you know how many mobsters we've actually managed to convict since we came to Naples?'

'How many?'

'Three.' Eric frowned. 'Papers go missing. Witnesses don't turn up, or change their stories at the last minute. And yes, there have been guys from CIC who have been transferred after a word in the right ear. This man Vito Genovese who runs it all, he's in with AMG at the highest level—I mean the very highest level. If someone like Zagarella is really under his protection, there won't be much we can do about it.'

At the Questura, the main police station, James explained that they wished to interview the suspects rounded up in the raid on the Via Forcella. After much paperwork they were taken to the cells, where they were shown a very old man who was sitting in the holding pen, completely alone.

'What's going on?' James demanded. 'Where are the others?'

The policeman who had brought them down to the cells shrugged. 'What others?'

'There must have been dozens of people trading on the Via Forcella yesterday. Where are they all?' Seeing that he would get nothing out of the policeman, he spoke to the old man. 'When you came in here, how many were with you?'

'Oh, twenty or thirty. They all went in the night,' the old man said sadly. 'I would have gone too, but I couldn't afford the fine.'

'What fine?'

'Fifty lire.' The old man spread his arms. 'I'm just a scrap metal dealer.'

James sighed. 'What's this man charged with?' he asked the policeman.

'Selling copper telephone wire.'

'Nothing to do with penicillin?'

'It would seem not.' The policeman left them briefly then returned with a roll of telephone wire. 'This was found on him.'

'I cut the German wire,' the old man said proudly. 'That's what I'm meant to do, isn't it? We don't like the Germans.'

James translated what the old man had said to Eric, who scratched his head. 'That was before the Allies arrived. We dropped leaflets telling the Italians to do as much damage as they could. But after we arrived, we obviously wanted the wires left alone so we could use them ourselves.'

'Here,' the old man said, producing a dog-eared leaflet from an inside pocket and unfolding it. 'See? It says to cut the wires. Will I get a medal?'

'Can't we just kick him out?' Eric suggested.

'That won't be possible,' the policeman said sternly. 'He has been charged with destruction of Allied military property.'

'YOU WANT TO DO *what*?' Major Heathcote stared at him.

'I want to ask the Italians to have the old man released, sir,' James said. 'Even if he has done something wrong, which is debatable, this man has been locked up for all the wrong reasons.'

'By his fellow Italians.'

'As a result of *our* operation—'

'Which, it seems, was an abject failure,' snapped the major.

James said nothing.

The major sighed. 'And you've absolutely nothing to charge this pharmacist Zagarella with?' He looked from one to the other of them.

'No, sir,' Eric muttered.

'Do I take it, then, that he has been released from his incarceration?'

'Yes, sir,' James said between gritted teeth.

'So you have at least ended one illegal imprisonment,' the major said pointedly.

'Yes, sir.'

'Whilst in the process making AMG a complete laughing stock.' The major gestured at the door. 'Get out of here, Gould. You too, Vincenzo. I don't want to see either of you again for at least six months.'

'Yes, sir.' James hesitated. 'About this wire-cutter, sir.'

The major glared. 'I'll make a phone call, though God knows I've got more important things to think about.'

LIVIA WROTE to Enzo's family in Naples telling them what she had learned about his fate, but there was no reply.

Once Pupetta had been eaten, the Pertinis had to face the fact that there was almost no food apart from the mozzarella that they made each day from Priscilla's milk.

The lack of a tractor preyed on Livia's mind almost daily. With a tractor, they could get their cheese to market. With a tractor they could work the fields and recoup some of their losses.

Alberto waited a week after the news about Enzo came through, then resumed his campaign with renewed vigour. As if to mock their lack of transport, he arrived one afternoon in a magnificent new Bugatti and presented Livia with a loaf of white bread. She wanted to refuse it, but the thought of her father and Marisa reminded her that she was no longer in a position to be so high and mighty. So she swallowed her pride and reached for the loaf, determined to accept it with good grace. Alberto smirked triumphantly. She said sharply, 'I want to be clear with you, Alberto. I'll take your bread because I have no choice, but I'll never share your bed.'

The smile on his face didn't falter. For a moment he pulled the bread away, out of her reach, the way a boy might tease a younger sister by withholding a toy. Then, seeing her hand follow it, he laughed and let her take it.

'One day you will realise you have no choice about that, either,' he said in a low voice. 'It's no different from catching a little bird. First you lay a trail of breadcrumbs, to get it used to eating from your hand. Then—pfft.' He mimed closing his fist.

'Alberto,' she said wearily, 'Why me? Surely you must be fed up with this. There must be a dozen girls you could have without difficulty.'

He put his face even closer, so close she could feel his breath on her cheek. 'Of course there are. But I've decided I want you, and what's more everyone else around here knows it. If I don't succeed now, I'll be a laughing stock. I have to have you, Livia.'

ON SUNDAY MORNING James was woken at six o'clock by the telephone. It was Major Heathcote, and he got straight to the point. 'What do you know about this mob at the cathedral?'

'I didn't know there was a mob at the cathedral.'

'The MPs are worried it could turn into a full-scale riot. Take a look, would you?' The line went dead.

James got dressed and went downstairs. Deciding that if there was really going to be a riot it would be more safely witnessed from a Jeep than a motorbike, he went to wake Eric.

The American came awake groggily, and James had some difficulty persuading him that attending to a potential riot was more important than having a cup of coffee. Even without the coffee, it was a good fifteen minutes before a grumbling Eric was finally driving the two of them towards the Duomo.

Near the cathedral their way was blocked by a solid mass of people. As Eric edged the vehicle forward, James became aware that the mood of the crowd was strangely fraught. Women were tearing at their clothes and sobbing. Elderly men were stabbing their hands at the sky. There was a high proportion of nuns and priests among the crowd, he noticed, and everywhere the sign of the cross was being made. It was all very mystifying.

Suddenly James saw a familiar face. Telling Eric to pull over, he swung the door of the Jeep open. 'Dr Scoterra,' he called. 'Get in.'

The lawyer looked slightly embarrassed, as if he had been caught doing something slightly disreputable. But he climbed into the Jeep and pulled the door closed quickly. 'You should go back,' he said.

'What's going on here?' Eric asked, putting the Jeep into reverse.

'It is the liquefaction of the blood.' They must have looked perplexed, because Dr Scoterra added, 'The blood of the saint. A famous relic, which is kept in a special chapel of the cathedral. Twice a year, absolutely regularly, the dried blood becomes liquid. If, as now, the blood starts to liquefy at the wrong time, it means a great tragedy is coming to Naples.'

'You mean, something worse than being occupied by the Germans, having your young men conscripted to fight in Russia, and having Naples blown up by three different armies?'

'It is, of course,' Dr Scoterra said stiffly, 'only a superstition, which an educated man such as myself would never give credence to.'

'You just happened to be up early?'

Dr Scoterra sniffed.

Eric pulled the Jeep over and turned off the ignition. 'We'd better go take a look, anyway.'

The two of them pushed their way through the crowd towards a side door of the cathedral. Inside, things were no calmer—a wailing sea of people surging from side to side. Eventually, they found a priest.

'It is the saint,' he sighed. 'The blood. For certain, a terrible fire is coming, in which many people will perish.' At these words, a great weeping arose from those near enough to hear. The priest brightened. 'However,' he said loudly, gesturing towards another priest who was emerging from the vestry with a tray round his neck, like a cigarette girl at a cinema, 'it may be that a relic from one of the Christian martyrs will offer the faithful some protection.' There was a rush towards the priest with the tray.

Fighting through the throng, Eric and James found that the tray was laden with small white objects. 'If I'm not very much mistaken,' Eric said, picking one up and examining it, 'these are human bones.'

'Relics, *signore*, relics of the early martyrs,' the priest confirmed. 'Free to anyone who makes a donation of fifty lire to the offertory.'

'Are there any catacombs around here?' James asked Eric.

'Miles of 'em. All stuffed to the ceiling with bones.'

They looked at the tray of bones again. 'I suppose even priests have to eat,' James said.

'Screw that,' Eric said. Taking a priest in each hand, he pulled them towards the vestry. 'See if you can locate this blood, will you?' he called over his shoulder.

The saint's blood was encased in the stem of a magnificent silver reliquary, which was in turn being clutched reverently by another priest.

'Tell them if this goes on they're going to have a riot on their hands,' Eric suggested.

James did so, but the priests just shrugged. 'It is the saint,' one repeated. 'He is trying to warn us.'

'I've had enough of this.' Eric pulled his pistol out and pointed it at the priest holding the reliquary. The other priests crossed themselves in unison. 'Tell him that if that blood hasn't unliquefied within two minutes, they're going to have another Christian martyr to sell off in little pieces.'

'Are you sure this is a good idea?' James asked. 'We came here to *prevent* a riot. And I think that by any measure shooting a priest, in a cathedral, might well not be the most effective way of achieving that. If the Italians choose to believe in this stuff, that's their business.'

'So how do you propose we deal with this situation?'

'It seems to me the priests have taken care of that already. They've allowed the crowd to get worked up into a frenzy, admittedly, but they've also provided a solution, in the form of these relics. So long as they don't run out of relics—and from the sound of it, they've got an inexhaustible stock—it looks as if everyone's going to be happy.'

Somewhat reluctantly, Eric put his gun away.

'My apologies,' James said to the priests. 'My friend has not had breakfast.'

One of the priests stepped forward and pressed a piece of bone into James's top pocket. 'It will protect you from the coming fire,' he whispered, 'just as you have protected us from the American with no breakfast.'

'WE APPEAR to be having,' Major Heathcote said slowly, 'an epidemic of miracles.' He turned his attention back to the report in his hand, pausing occasionally to look up at James and scowl.

James already knew the report's contents. What he had failed to anticipate in the Duomo was that there were many other priests in Naples, all equally hungry. As a result, all over the city, the city's saints were now bleeding, sweating, weeping, growing their hair, losing their hair, grinding their teeth, or in various other ways animating themselves, to the delight and enrichment of the priests who attended them.

At last Major Heathcote put down the report. 'But I'm sure you can explain all this,' he said with ominous mildness.

'Sir,' James said awkwardly. 'The Italians seem to believe there's some kind of great disaster on the way. The priests are simply taking advantage of their credulity. In the case of the Duomo, it didn't seem appropriate to intervene in what was clearly an internal Italian affair.'

'Well, quite,' the major said reasonably. 'The fact that the civilian population has now been whipped up into a state of hysterical delirium because they think the Allies are going to bring down some kind of unspecified catastrophe is clearly not something that causes *you* any concern.'

'Sir—' James began again.

'Don't interrupt me.' The major banged the table in an explosion of rage. 'Some people are saying the Germans are going to come back and raze the city to the ground—did you know that? Others are openly talking about a return to fascism. Meanwhile the black market is out of control, the only people who can't buy penicillin freely on the Via Forcella—thanks to you— are our own army medics and the streets are full of syphilitic girls spreading disease to our soldiers.' He glared at James. 'Have you any comment?'

'I'm very sorry, sir.'

'Captain Gould,' the major said heavily, 'the only thing that is preventing me from sending you to the front line immediately is the knowledge that they need decent soldiers up there, not gutless incompetents.' He sighed. 'I wish to God I'd never lost Jackson. Anyway, these are your orders. You will get a grip on the civilian population of this city, and use whatever means necessary to stop this shambles. You will impose the regulations and requirements of the Allied Military Government without exception or favour. Do you understand?'

'Yes, sir.'

'Then get out of here. And send in Second Lieutenant Vincenzo.'

AFTER HIS CARPETING by Major Heathcote, James was left in absolutely no doubt what was required of him, and he carried out his orders scrupulously. Troops were brought in each day to clear the Via Forcella of contraband. Miracles of all kind were ruthlessly suppressed, usually by the simple expedient Eric had proposed in the Duomo, namely producing a gun and waving it threateningly at the nearest clergyman. Meanwhile, a series of raids closing bars, brothels, restaurants and other unauthorised premises removed the black marketeers' main outlets, and brought an end to the carnival atmosphere that had become such a feature of occupied Naples.

James himself led the raid that shut down Zi' Teresa's. He felt a pang of guilt when he saw the reproach in the eyes of Angelo, the maître d', but he forced himself to be businesslike.

'Here,' he told him, handing over a proclamation in English and Italian. 'You must put this on your door.'

'May I ask how long we must be closed for?'

'I suppose until the end of the occupation.'

'Then I congratulate you, Captain Gould. In all these years of war, Zi' Teresa's has never closed, not once. You have done what the fascists, the Germans and the Allied bombers all failed to do. You have made me shut my doors to the people of Naples.'

'I'm sorry if it causes you any hardship,' James said stiffly.

'This isn't about profit,' Angelo said quietly. 'This is about our pride.'

However, the new regime was not actually as successful as it seemed. For one thing, James knew that the black market, although driven underground, had barely been inconvenienced. His informant, Dr Scoterra, told him with some pleasure that all James had succeeded in doing to the trade in penicillin was to raise the black-market price by half. Now that the brothels were off-limits, front-line troops spent their leave in noisy, drunken groups.

James was still working his way through the backlog of wedding vet-tings, but the work was made faster now that he had adopted a policy of turning all the applicants down unless there was a glaring reason not to.

'And so far,' he told Eric, 'I haven't found one. Basically, you now have to be a nun to marry a British soldier.'

Eric screwed up his face. 'How would that work, exactly?'

'Figuratively speaking.'

Eric sighed. 'You know, James, I don't think I like this.'

'Nor do I. But orders are orders.'

DESPITE THE OCCASIONAL setback, however, James was able to tell himself that he had at last got his district under a semblance of control. The backlog of paperwork he had inherited from his predecessor had been reduced to manageable proportions. The biscuit tin in the cupboard, once stuffed with small-denomination notes for the purposes of bribery and corruption, now contained only a collection of sharpened pencils. There was an appoint-ments book, which Carlo and Enrico still did their best to ignore. He had even managed to obtain a single grey metal filing cabinet, of which he was secretly rather proud.

And yet, as each day passed, he was conscious of feeling restless, almost bored. And when he walked by a lemon tree in blossom, or caught the scent of some unfamiliar, exotic herb wafting through an open window, he was aware of a strange sensation, like a sharp pang of hunger. Perhaps it *was* just hunger, he thought: Malloni's unvarying diet of tinned rations was so monotonous that he was often unable to bring himself to eat. Not that he would have dreamt of complaining. Compared with the sacrifices so many others were making just then, his life was ridiculously easy.

THE NEXT TIME Alberto came to Fiscino he brought a chicken, which he asked Livia to cook for him. 'It's not a young one,' he said, holding it by the neck and regarding it critically as it flapped and wriggled in his grasp. 'Or particularly plump. But you know what they say: *gallina vecchia fa buon brodo*. The older the chicken, the better the broth.' He pulled the chicken's neck to snap it before handing it to her with a bow.

She had not eaten since the last of the loaf was finished, and her mouth watered as the bird bubbled in the stockpot with an onion, celery and some carrots that Alberto had also brought. 'Will you eat with me?' he asked her.

'I can't. I'm the cook.'

'You don't have any other customers.' He laid two places on her kitchen table. 'It's a good chicken,' he said persuasively.

She went to stand over by the stove. 'Even so.'

When the broth was made, he watched as she took the bird out of the pan and placed it on a dish. The broth she served to him just as it came out of the stockpot, thickened only with a little pasta.

'Such a simple dish,' he said, sucking it down in great spoonfuls. 'Yet so difficult to cook well. It's wonderful, Livia. Won't you try some?'

'No.' She had decided that she would eat later, from the leftovers. Even Alberto, surely, could not devour a whole saucepan of broth and a chicken.

'Suit yourself.' He went back to the broth. 'It really is very good.'

She watched as he drained every drop of the broth.

'And now,' he said, reaching for the chicken, 'for the *secondo*.'

He broke it open with his thick fingers, deftly easing the breast meat away from the bone, twisting off the legs and thighs with well-practised movements until the bird lay dismembered on the serving dish. 'Please,' he said, indicating the other place at the table.

'I can't,' she said again. But as the aroma of cooked chicken filled the air, and she felt weak, she allowed herself to flop into a chair. Alberto pushed a sliver of breast meat into his mouth, and chewed it with an expression of rapture. Then he picked out a smaller piece and held it towards her.

She closed her eyes. She could feel his thick fingers, slick with chicken grease, pushing against her lips, but all she could taste was that chicken, the rich, thick meaty flavour of it, filling her mouth and her mind, blotting out everything else. Then it was gone, and she could not help it—she had opened her mouth for more, the way a baby bird opens its beak to be fed.

She heard his voice in her ear. 'When you asked me, last time, why it had to be you,' he said quietly, 'I told you a lie. It wasn't just that I can't afford to be laughed at. It's because I love you.'

It was easier to keep her eyes shut, to blot out what was happening, what she was hearing. She said nothing, and after a little while another sliver of chicken was pushed between her lips.

Later, after he had gone, she felt sick. But that evening she went to the kitchen, where she had collected all the chicken's blood into a saucepan.

'I've had an idea,' she said to Marisa. 'What about the tank?'

'Which tank?'

'The one that broke down after you made a spell against the *tedesco* soldier. If we could get it to work, we could use it instead of a tractor.'

Marisa considered. 'I would need some cock's blood.'

Livia held up her saucepan. 'How about a very old cooking hen?'

'Possibly. But, Livia, neither of us knows how to drive a tank.'

'So?' Livia shrugged. 'It can't be that difficult.'

That afternoon they went up to the field behind the village where the German tank had broken down. Marisa poured a foul-smelling concoction into the fuel reservoir from a bottle she had brought with her.

'Try it now,' she said.

Livia climbed inside. It was very dark—the only light came from a few slits in the armour. She sat in the driver's seat and saw that on either side of her were two large levers. They presumably controlled the two tracks. In front of the seat a tiny eye-slit showed a very limited view of the way ahead. On her right a black button looked as if it might be the starter motor. She pressed it. Nothing happened. She tried again. This time the whole tank shook. She pushed at the levers and the machine lurched forwards.

JAMES WAS by now accustomed to excitable officers ringing with wild reports of security threats, so when a captain from Sant' Anastasia phoned to say that there had been sightings of a German tank in the area around Boscotrecase, he remembered Jackson's warnings and said, 'Don't worry, that rumour's been looked into, and there's nothing in it.'

'Well, I don't know how hard you looked,' the captain's disembodied voice said, 'but the man who reported it to me is not given to exaggeration and what's more he's familiar with German tanks. Says he saw the outline of a Panzer quite clearly, driving along above Cappella Nuova.'

James checked a map. Cappella Nuova was on the slopes of Vesuvius, only a few miles from the Allied airfield at Terzigno. If there really was a division of Panzers holed up in the area, they could do a lot of damage.

He phoned Major Heathcote and explained the situation. 'I think we'd better phone the airfield and put them on an alert, sir,' he said. 'And perhaps a few of our own tanks should go and take a look.'

'Tanks? Where on earth do you suppose I'm going to get tanks from?' the major snapped. 'You'll have to do a recce yourself. Take a few *carabinieri*. And if anyone has to get blown up, try to make sure that it's you.'

IT WAS the first time James had been out to Vesuvius. It was not apparent, from the other side of the bay, just how vast the volcano was—not a single mountain at all, but a series of foothills and escarpments that suddenly resolved themselves into the gargantuan twin peaks of Monte Somma and Monte Conna, the volcano proper. The smoke that perpetually hung over its tip, which in Naples had seemed so delicate and ethereal, now loomed menacingly over their heads.

Driving in convoy—James had brought the motorbike, rather than travel in one of the Jeeps with the Italians—he saw a battered sign that indicated they were passing the ruins of Pompeii. He made a mental note to come back and explore them some time.

As they began to wind their way up the mountain, great tongues of cooled lava scarred the landscape, some of them shiny as if they were made of molten black glass. Yet despite this there were more than a dozen villages and towns scattered across the lower slopes—a triumph, James supposed, of optimism over forward planning. Surely Pompeii was all the reminder one needed of the folly of building here?

All morning they crisscrossed the slopes, occasionally stopping to question the villagers. In San Sebastiano he was shown where the lava from the 1929 eruption had broken into two streams and flowed right around the town—a miracle, according to the man who showed this to him, worked by a wooden statue of St Sebastian. The same statue, slightly scorched, now stood in the church just a few hundred yards from the lava's edge, where it had not been fixed to the wall in case the saint was needed at short notice.

On the far side of the mountain, a shepherd had seen a tank travelling at speed down a country lane just two days earlier. Several other people claimed to have seen a Panzer in the fields above Boscotrecase. 'Near Fiscino,' seemed to be the general consensus, and as the afternoon drew to a close that little village seemed a logical place to head towards.

They were still riding in convoy, so that James's view was mostly blocked by the forward Jeep. It was only when it suddenly veered off the road and screeched to a halt that he realised something was wrong. He looked up, to his left. Yes, there was a Panzer, the swastika on its side quite visible. It was in a field about fifty yards above him.

Already the *carabinieri* were piling out of the back of the Jeep, clutching their tommy guns and spraying shots in all directions as they hurried towards the tank. Sparks flew from the Panzer's body as bullets pinged off metal and James felt a sudden sharp pain in his left shoulder. 'Bugger,' he said, with feeling. A ricochet had just winged him. He felt the wound gingerly. It seemed to be nothing serious. He raised his voice. 'No! Fall back!'

Having realised that their bullets were useless against the tank's armoured sides, the *carabinieri* were only too happy to oblige. James became aware that he was the only person still standing in the tank's path, which weaved erratically as it lurched towards him, only coming to a standstill at the last moment, the gun pointing directly at him. The hatch opened and a face appeared. James could see that although it was streaked with oil it was a rather pleasing face, all big eyes, delicate cheekbones and dark eyebrows. At the moment, however, it was scowling fiercely.

'What in the name of all the saints are you doing, standing in the middle of the road like that?' the face yelled in Italian. 'I could have killed you!'

The woman put her hands on the top of the tank and pulled herself out of the hatch, revealing a length of slender brown leg. As she slid down over the tank's side to the ground, some of the quicker *carabinieri* leapt forward to offer her a hand.

Slightly bemused, James said, 'Is this your tank?'

'Well, obviously not originally,' she retorted. The *carabinieri*, their previous terror now apparently forgotten, laughed.

'So it's stolen,' James persisted.

She pulled her hair, which was long, glossy and very black, out of her collar, where she had tucked it out of the way. 'So what?'

'I'm afraid you can't keep it.'

The young woman looked from the tank to James and raised an eyebrow. 'You want me to find some Germans and give it back?' she said incredulously. The *carabinieri* chuckled delightedly.

'You need to give it to *us*.'

'But then *you* would have stolen it.'

'We're sort of allowed to,' James pointed out. 'As the winning side.'

She considered this. 'Very well,' she said. 'Make me an offer.'

'The penalty for being caught in possession of military weapons is ten years' imprisonment.'

'It is?' She looked astonished. 'Oh. But I don't have any weapons.'

James looked pointedly at the four-inch gun barrel above his head.

'Oh, that,' she said, appearing to notice it for the first time. 'There happens to be a gun attached to it, certainly, but as far as I'm concerned, it's a tractor. Look.' She pointed to the rear of the tank where, James now saw, some kind of primitive hoeing device had been fastened.

'May I ask whether you have a permit to run a vehicle?'

The woman seemed to be about to answer this question when she suddenly noticed his shoulder. 'You're bleeding.'

He looked. It was true. In the adrenaline of the moment, he hadn't noticed that his shoulder was soaked with blood. 'I'm all right,' he said. But the young woman had turned away and was berating the *carabinieri* for standing there doing nothing while their captain was bleeding to death.

Suddenly James found himself being ministered to by half a dozen *carabinieri*, working far more efficiently under the young woman's instructions than they had ever done for him. From one of the Jeeps a stretcher was produced. He was lifted onto it as delicately as if he were a baby, and then carried with infinite care over the rough ground and into a house.

He was placed on a kitchen table while another young woman, with similar features to the first, and almost as pretty, was fetched to look at the wound. Before James quite knew what was happening both women were peeling off his shirt and examining his shoulder. His wound was washed, and the younger woman pressed all around it with firm, cool fingers. She spoke to her sister in rapid dialect, and the older woman leaned over him and offered him her hand. 'Squeeze this,' she instructed. As he squeezed he felt the hard band of her wedding ring.

'I think it may be sprained as well,' the younger one said. She left the room. James was left on his back, staring up at the mass of fragrant black hair that tumbled over the tank driver's forehead. He realised he was still squeezing her hand. 'Sorry,' he said, withdrawing it.

'What's your name?' she asked.

'Captain Gould. James Gould.'

'Jems Goot?'

'Near enough.' Despite himself, he suddenly felt rather cheerful. He had thought he was about to be blasted to smithereens by a tank gun, and now here he was being ministered to by two of the prettiest girls he had ever met.

The younger sister returned with two small jars. 'Stay still,' she told him. Reaching carefully into the first jar, she took out a bee. The insect walked over her fingers as unconcerned as a ladybird. 'This will only hurt a little,' she said. She held the bee to his shoulder, and James felt a sudden sharp pain as it stung him.

'What in God's name—' he began, trying to get up.

'It will help the cut heal.' From the second jar she spooned what looked like honey, which she dabbed on the edges of the wound. 'This too.'

It was nonsense, of course, but he supposed they were only trying to help. And her fingers were really very deft, massaging away the pain . . . He lay back and closed his eyes.

When he opened them again, his shirt was being cut up to make bandages. 'Thank you,' he said. 'You're very kind.'

'It's not kindness,' the older sister said matter-of-factly. 'We don't want to go to prison, that's all. Marisa thinks that one of us should flirt with you, just in case. She thinks it should be me,' she added, 'because you like me better.'

How on earth did she know that? 'I hope you told her you're not that kind of girl,' he muttered.

She looked down at him. Her eyes, he noticed, were deep green in colour, and they regarded him with what looked like contempt. 'No,' she said. 'I told her that I would rather die than flirt with a British officer.'

'I'm glad to hear it,' James said, confused by the bitterness in her voice. But for once, he wasn't completely sure that he was.

By the time the wound was dressed, and a sling rigged up, the pain in his shoulder had turned into a fuzzy warmth. Perhaps the bee sting had helped after all, James thought.

A plate of small, round, white objects was placed in front of him, together with a fork. 'Eat,' he was commanded. He pushed the fork into one of the objects. It was as soft as a poached egg and, when he punctured it, oozed what appeared to be ivory-coloured cream. He tried some. Richness flooded his mouth. The taste was fresh, but slightly sweet.

'Gosh,' he said. 'What is this?'

'*Burrata*. We make it ourselves.'

It was not a word he knew. He said firmly, 'I'm afraid I'll have to impound the tank. And you'll have to come with us to the military compound in Naples,' he added to Livia.

'There may be a problem. The tank runs on my father's grappa. While you're sitting here chatting, your men outside are drinking all the fuel.'

James went to stop the *carabinieri*, who, as Livia had said, were making hefty inroads into the bottles of pungent, colourless alcohol the two sisters had been using to run the tank. It was only then that he realised that the house doubled as a bar and restaurant. 'And I'm afraid you'll have to close this place,' he told the women. 'All places of entertainment are off limits.'

'By whose stupid order?' Livia demanded.

'Mine, actually.'

'But we live here.'

'Well, you'll have to close the kitchen and dining room.'

'But it's *our* kitchen. And *our* dining room.'

James scratched his head. Rules that had seemed straightforward when drawn up in Naples seemed rather more complicated here. 'In that case you can stay open,' he said, 'until you have some customers, at which point you will have to close. Is that fair?'

The girls reluctantly agreed that this was acceptable, so long as they were recompensed for the grappa. There was a brief negotiation, which somehow resulted in James agreeing to pay them an extortionate amount, and Livia went off to get some things.

Upstairs she took Marisa and her father aside. 'Don't worry about me,' she said. 'I'll be fine. But since they're taking me to Naples, I think I should stay there.'

'Why?' Nino asked, aghast.

'While I'm here, Alberto will never leave us alone. If I go, perhaps things will be better. There's enough food for the two of you, if the neighbours help out. I'll go to Enzo's family and get work in a factory. His mother won't let me starve.' Fighting back tears, she said, 'It's for the best.'

Nino said, 'I don't like to think of you getting a lift from soldiers.'

'I'll be careful. Besides, if this officer was going to try anything it would have been before, when he could have threatened us with prison.'

'Livia's right,' Marisa said. 'He's not like the officer who took our food.'

There was almost a fight among the policemen for the honour of helping Livia up into the back of the Jeep, but as it turned out, none of the *carabinieri* knew how to drive the tank. When they finally left for the military compound it was in a convoy, with Livia driving the tank, James standing to attention in the command hatch and the other vehicles bringing up the rear.

As they drove down the foothills of Vesuvius, James was conscious of an unfamiliar sensation. He was enjoying himself. He was alive. And the young woman who was crouched in the driving seat was definitely contributing to this feeling of well-being.

'SO YOU SEE,' James explained to Major Heathcote on the telephone, 'this woman and her fellow partisans took part in a local resistance operation. The partisans captured this tank, but there was no fuel to drive it. Then, after the Germans had left, the women hit on the idea of refuelling it with grappa. The tank was spotted as they tried to deliver it to the Allies.'

None of this was strictly a lie, but neither was it strictly true. It was, he told himself, simply a matter of making sure that busy people such as the CO didn't spend time on things that really weren't all that important.

'These partisans,' the CO said thoughtfully. 'What are they known as?'

'Er—the Pertini band, I believe, sir.'

'Not communists, are they?'

James thought of those negotiations over the grappa. 'No, sir. From what I've seen of them, they are most definitely democratic capitalists.'

'Good. Tell 'em we're very grateful for their gallant efforts, et cetera, and send them on their way.'

BY THE TIME James found someone prepared to take receipt of an operational German Panzer it was late. Livia was still surrounded by a mass of attentive Italians, but she was yawning, and she had little choice but to accept James's offer of a lift.

With one of his arms in a sling, and the back of the bike weighed down by Livia's bag, they made unsteady progress on the Matchless as they set off from the compound. 'Sorry about that,' he called over his shoulder.

After a while he felt her head rest against his back. The contact was rather agreeable, and for a moment he wondered if she was showing some interest in him after all. Then he realised that she had simply fallen asleep, curled up against his back as lightly as a cat.

Naples was quiet, illuminated by a huge moon, and as he steered his way carefully through the cobbled streets James felt a pang of affection for the place; so unpredictable, so maddening, yet capable of springing surprises like putting a sleeping girl on your motorbike in the middle of the night, and in the middle of a war to boot.

IN FACT, NAPLES was not completely quiet that night. Behind the blackout curtains at Zi' Teresa's, the closed-down restaurant was the venue for a meeting of the disaffected.

Angelo, who had called the meeting, was there, as was the beautiful glass-eyed Elena Marlona. Among the other women in the room were several that James would have recognised.

'How can we work if the brothels are shut?' Algisa Fiore demanded. 'It's ridiculous. We have to operate from home, or slip out onto the streets when no one's looking.'

'It's worse for us,' a middle-aged man who ran one of the city's oldest pizzerias pointed out. 'At least you carry the tools of your trade around with you. Me, I can't do anything without my oven.'

'It's all down to this Englishman, Gould,' someone said. 'Surely we can do something?'

'We could have him killed,' a villainous-looking pimp suggested.

'A waste of time,' Angelo said. 'They'll just replace him with someone else and they'll clamp down even harder.'

'Then he must be seduced or bribed. There's always something that will corrupt a man.'

'Not this one,' Angelo said. 'He even pays for his own dinner. But come to think of it . . . there is something that he likes. Food.' Angelo looked thoughtful. 'Though I think he may not even have realised it himself.'

'Hardly surprising, if his cook is Ciro Malloni.' Those who knew Malloni chuckled.

'Malloni is there for a reason,' Angelo said. 'He works for Vito Genovese. But I hear the Genovese family aren't too happy about these restrictions either . . . Leave it with me. I'll think of something.'

PART THREE

Livia woke up as they reached the harbour. 'You can drop me here,' she said, tapping him on the back. He pulled up, and watched as she untied her bag from the pannier.

'Perhaps I'll see you again,' he said tentatively.

'Perhaps,' she said, in a voice that suggested she rather hoped not. 'Thank you for the lift.' She picked up her bag and walked away.

'Will you be all right?' he called after her. She didn't reply. He supposed she was still upset about having the tank confiscated. But really, she could hardly have expected him to let her keep it. With a sigh, he turned the bike back in the direction of the Palazzo Satriano.

Livia had not realised how much of a battering Naples had taken since she was last here. Picking her way through the dark streets was a precarious business. Worse, when she got to the street in which Enzo's family lived, she saw that there was only a huge gap where their house had once stood.

'Excuse me,' she said, stopping a woman who was entering a nearby doorway. 'Can you tell me where the Telli family are now?'

The woman crossed herself. 'In heaven, God willing. They were all killed in an air raid.'

Livia stared at the mass of rubble, shocked.

'It was after Enzo died in Russia,' the woman added. 'His family got a letter and that's when they stopped going to the shelters. His mother said that if God took her to join him, she wouldn't complain.'

Poor Quartilla, Livia thought. She had adored her son.

'You look upset,' the woman said. 'Did you know the family well?'

'I was married to Enzo,' Livia managed to say.

With the last of her money she rented a room in a shabby boarding house near the port, and the next morning she went to the munitions factory to see if they had any work. But the munitions factory was gone too. An old man who was picking through the rubble for scrap told her that it had been destroyed by the Germans before they left. 'You could try the big hotels on Via Partenope,' the old man suggested. 'They've reopened now for Allied officers. They must need chambermaids.'

The concierge at the first hotel where Livia asked for work was brutally dismissive. 'As a chambermaid, or a whore?' he asked. 'Not that it matters. I've got no vacancies for either.' It was the same everywhere she went. After a while she tried going directly to the hotel kitchens, but the message was identical: we have all the cooks we need, and more.

She returned to her room exhausted. She hadn't eaten all day, but she was so tired that even her hunger couldn't prevent her from sleeping.

The next day there was more of the same. She was told there was a job going unloading pallets in the harbour, but when she got there, the line of applicants stretched for 300 yards. She went back to trudging round kitchens. In many places her knock was not even answered: the restaurants were boarded up and silent, closed by the crackdown on black marketeering.

It was late when Livia tried the back door of Zi' Teresa's. To her surprise, the door opened a crack, and a man's face peered out. 'Yes?'

Livia repeated her litany. 'Please, I'm looking for a job.'

'Go away. We're closed, we have no work.' Angelo regarded the girl in front of him for a moment. She was swaying on her feet and her eyes had a blank, unfocused expression. Softening, he said, 'Have you eaten today?'

Livia shook her head.

'Perhaps I can find you something,' he muttered, holding the door open.

He gave her some cold beans and watched her as she devoured them. 'What kind of work are you looking for?' he asked.

'I'm a cook. My name is Livia Pertini. My family run the *osteria* at Fiscino, but there are no customers any more, and no food to cook with.'

'Ah, so that's who you are.' Angelo nodded. 'I ate at your *osteria* once. It was a few years ago, but I can remember the food as if it were yesterday. Do you still make that wonderful *burrata*?'

'Yes, but now we can't get it to the market.' She explained about the impounded tank, and the closing of her own restaurant.

'So you've met Captain Gould?'

She sighed. 'Yes, I've met him.'

'That young man,' Angelo said, 'is not as fierce as he seems. But I'm afraid you did the wrong thing coming to Naples. You'd be better off going back to Fiscino and finding someone to look after you until this is all over.'

Livia shuddered. 'There's someone who offered. But I'm not going to do that. There must be someone in Naples who needs a cook.'

Just then Angelo was struck by an idea. 'Actually,' he said, 'there is one person.' He nodded thoughtfully. The more he considered his idea, the better it seemed. 'Livia, I might just be able to get you some work after all.'

'SHE'S AS SWEET as bread,' he told Elena. 'A real country girl—honest, hard-working, passionate, and pretty with it. And she knows how to cook— not fancy stuff, but proper country cooking. I had her make me some *pasta e fagioli* and it was the best I've ever had.'

'So you want her to seduce him?' Elena asked sceptically.

'No.' Angelo shook his head. 'She's not like that, and in any case, it isn't necessary. At the end of the day, sex is only sex. A man can be sleeping with the most beautiful woman in the world, but when he gets up from her bed he's still exactly the same person he was before. But a man who has eaten well—he's at peace with the world, he's happy, and more importantly, he wants other people to be happy. In short, he starts to become a more gener-ous, civilised human being. You follow?'

Elena shrugged. 'And she's happy to do it?'

'Not very,' Angelo admitted. 'Her family have suffered at the hands of the Allies and she took a little convincing.' This was an understatement: it had taken all his considerable powers of persuasion to get Livia to consider working for the British officer, and in the end he had only succeeded because she realised that it was the only job she was likely to be offered. 'But I'm sure it will work out,' he said, more optimistically than he felt.

'ARRESTED?' James said, perplexed. 'But what on earth can Malloni have been arrested for?'

'Stealing Allied Government property,' Carlo explained. 'Your rations. It turns out he was taking all the good stuff and selling it up on the Via Forcella, leaving you with what he couldn't unload.'

'Good Lord. Though I have to say, I'm not completely surprised. There was always something a little unlikely about Malloni. I suppose this means we'll have to find a new cook?'

'I have already taken the liberty of advertising. I have spread the word that interviews will take place from ten o'clock tomorrow morning.'

'*Grazie tante*, Carlo. I'm very grateful.'

THE NEXT MORNING James woke up early. He sniffed the air. An unfamiliar aroma was wafting into his bedroom. He sniffed again. That was it: it was the smell of fresh bread, and it was quite delicious. His stomach groaned involuntarily as he pulled on his uniform.

Going into the kitchen, he saw the back of a woman's head peering into one of his cupboards. For a moment he thought it was Livia Pertini, which was ridiculous. Then she turned round, and he realised it *was* her. 'What on earth are you doing here?' he said, astonished.

'I'm your new cook,' she said.

'Oh.' He rubbed his head, trying to resist the temptation to grin inanely at her. 'I'm afraid you're early. The interviews aren't until ten o'clock.'

'Well, why don't I make you breakfast, then you can interview me?'

'Um.' James had a vague idea that there was something slightly improper about this, but he couldn't think exactly what it was. And it was really very nice to see her. 'I suppose that's all right.'

'What is this?' she asked, showing him the tin of 'Meat and Vegetables' in her hand.

'Oh, that. It's a kind of . . . *stufato*, I suppose. A stew. It's horrible.'

She put the tin back. 'Then why do you have so much of it?'

'It's a long story.'

'Anyway,' she said, 'I managed to swap some with the woman upstairs for bread and fresh goat's milk, and I have pastries and mozzarella cheese and some oranges. How does that sound?'

'It sounds rather nice,' he admitted.

'Where's your tablecloth?'

'We don't usually bother with a tablecloth for breakfast,' he said. 'As a matter of fact, we don't usually bother with a table.'

'Presumably you must have a clean sheet somewhere?'

'I suppose I—'

'Could you get it, please?'

When he returned with the sheet, he found that she had picked some blossom from the lemon tree in the courtyard and stuck it in a vase. She laid the sheet over the table and pointed to a seat. 'Go on, sit.'

He sat. He had to admit, it all looked rather splendid. The bread was on a wooden cutting board, and the milk was in a little pottery jug, with the vase of lemon blossom next to it. Livia placed a ball of wet newspaper on the table, and proceeded to unwrap it. 'What's that?' he asked.

'Mozzarella cheese, of course. It's like the *burrata* you had before, but different.'

'It's soft,' he said, pushing his fork into the piece she passed him.

'You've never eaten mozzarella?' she said incredulously.

'In England we only have three cheeses,' he explained. 'Cheddar, Stilton and Wensleydale.'

'Now you're making fun of me,' she sniffed.

'Not at all.' He put some of the milky white cheese into his mouth. 'Oh,' he said. 'That's rather good, isn't it?' It was so soft it melted in his mouth, but the taste was explosive—creamy, and cuddy, and faintly tart all at once.

The door opened and Hughes walked in. 'I say, something smells good.' He looked at the table. 'What's all this?'

'It's breakfast,' James explained.

'Excellent.' Hughes pulled up a chair.

There was a knock at the door and Jumbo Jeffries stuck his head round it. He brightened when he saw the table. 'Are those oranges? They're just the thing for a flagging constitution.' He pulled up another chair. Within a few minutes another four or five officers had also joined them.

Livia put a plate of pastries on the table. Each one was decorated with candied lemon, custard and marzipan flowers. James picked one up suspiciously and bit into it. Next to him, Hughes was on his second, and the others were fast catching up. Soon James was looking at a table that had been cleared of everything but a few crumbs.

'I'll make sure there's more tomorrow,' Livia said.

'If you get the job,' James pointed out.

'THE EXTRAORDINARY THING is,' he told Livia at eleven thirty, 'you seem to be the only applicant. Or at least, the only one who's shown up.'

She shrugged. 'You're obviously a very unpopular employer.'

'I suppose we ought to re-advertise,' James said. 'I mean, I can't really give the job to the first person who knocks on the door, can I?'

'How many cooks do you need?'

'Just one.'

'So how many applicants do you need?'

'Well—one, I suppose.'

'There you are, then. Why don't I cook you lunch, and you can keep me on if you like it?'

Just before noon, she came into the big room that they used as their main office. 'You can't eat in that kitchen,' she said. 'It's not big enough.' She looked at the dining table. 'Can you clear those papers off, please?'

'I'm afraid not,' James explained. 'This is our work.'

'It'll still be your work later. Lunch will be in fifteen minutes.'

In fact, it was half an hour before lunch arrived. Livia insisted that everyone had to be seated before she served the food. 'The people wait for the pasta, not the pasta for the people,' she said firmly. By the time the moment arrived, every British officer in the building was waiting to see what Livia would serve.

The door opened and she entered. She was bearing an enormous dish of steaming *fettuccine*, tossed in a sauce made with tomatoes, olive oil, chopped onion, celery and garlic, and decorated with torn basil leaves. As she filled each bowl, she grated a little hard cheese and some pepper over it.

'You're quite sure none of this food came from the black market?' James asked, eyeing the cheese warily.

'Of course not. I swapped it for your rations,' Livia said. This was the truth, although she did not mention that the person she had swapped with had been the maître d' of Zi' Teresa's.

Plunging his fork into the pasta, James twisted it until he had, with some difficulty, managed to get some of the wriggling, slippery mass to stay on the tines. Then he placed it in his mouth.

It was extraordinary. He had never tasted anything like it—certainly not in the long years of rationing, but not even before that. Come to that, he had never in his life eaten pepper that was freshly ground, nor cheese that coated one's food like this in a thick white snowfall . . . The long silence as the other men round the table concentrated on their food suggested that they, too, were experiencing similar epiphanies.

At last Hughes pushed his chair back and said, 'That was rather different from what old Malloni gave us.'

'I'm absolutely stuffed,' Walters ventured.

'Me too,' Kernick agreed. 'Oh well, back to work.' He had started to get to his feet when the door opened and Livia entered, holding a dish even larger than the one in which she had served the pasta.

'The *secondo*,' she said, putting the dish on the table. 'There aren't enough plates, unfortunately, so you'll have to use the same ones.'

'What's this?' French asked.

'*Melanzana alla parmigiana*. It's a typical Neapolitan dish.'

There was a short silence. Walters said, 'Well, I don't want to give offence. I'll just have a taste.' As he spooned some onto his plate the smell of aubergine, baked in layers with tomato, garlic and herbs and topped with grilled cheese, filled the room.

'I say,' Hughes said, looking at the way Walters kept on spooning more onto his plate. 'Leave some for the rest of us.'

Livia placed two jugs of red wine on the table. '*Nun c'è tavola senza vinu*,' she said reprovingly. 'It isn't a table without wine.'

James opened his mouth to protest, but thought better of it. He dipped his fork into the layers of aubergine and cheese. Moments later, it seemed to detonate in his mouth, teasing his appetite awake again. The cheese tasted so completely of cheese, the aubergine so rich and earthy, the herbs so full of flavour, requiring only a mouthful of wine to finish them off. He paused reverently and drank, then dug again with his fork.

The *secondo* was followed by a dessert of sliced pears baked with honey and rosemary. The flesh of the fruit looked crisp and white, but when he touched his spoon to it, it turned out to be as meltingly soft as ice cream.

By the time the pears were eaten, both jugs of wine had been emptied.

After lunch James went to the kitchen, and found Livia elbow-deep in a pile of dirty dishes.

'Here, let me help you with those,' he offered, reaching for a towel. 'That lunch was absolutely marvellous. We'd all be delighted if you'd take the job.'

She shrugged, waiting for the catch.

'If that's still acceptable to you? Of course, we'll need to sort out your sleeping arrangements,' he said. 'And I'm sure you'll want to talk about money too.'

Aha, Livia thought. So that's it. He wants me to be his whore as well as his cook, just like Alberto. She glared at him.

'How much were you thinking of?' he prompted.

'Whatever you try to offer me,' she said curtly, 'it will be an insult.'

'Well, some idea of what you would accept would be useful,' he ventured.

'I will never do it for money.'

'I can see that,' he agreed, completely mystified. Presumably she meant that she was some kind of artist. 'Er—how about if you get the same as Malloni? Not that his cooking was a patch on yours, of course,' he said quickly. 'And you can have his old room upstairs, if that's acceptable.'

'Malloni?' she said. She had just realised that this conversation was, in all probability, not about what she thought it was about. 'Well, I suppose that would be all right,' she conceded.

As JAMES SAT at his desk afterwards, trying to make sense of a long and largely irrelevant Bureau briefing, he felt his eyelids start to droop.

'Aren't you taking a siesta?'

He looked up. It was Livia, standing at the door.

'We don't really do siestas,' he explained. 'It's not really a British thing.'

'But how do you digest your food?'

James shrugged. 'We just—work through it, I suppose.'

'Ridiculous,' Livia said decisively. 'You'll never win the war that way.' Then she was gone.

James decided it would be churlish to point out that taking siestas had not, in fact, helped the Italian army win anything very much. Besides, he really was feeling rather sleepy. Perhaps, he thought, a very brief nap might not be a bad idea. When in Rome, and so on . . .

He woke feeling refreshed, and went to get himself a glass of water from the kitchen. Livia was chopping a big pile of courgettes.

'You were quite right,' he told her. 'My digestion is suitably grateful. What about you? Did you get any rest?'

She shook her head. 'Too much to do. It will be supper soon.'

'Then you must have terrible indigestion,' he said.

She glanced at him suspiciously. 'It's all right,' he assured her. What was the word for ribbing? 'I was taking you for a *giro*, a little ride,' he explained.

She sniffed. 'Well, don't.'

'Better get used to it. It's how the British flirt, I'm afraid.' She gave him a wary look. Instantly he felt a fool. The woman was married, and he was her employer. 'Not that I'm flirting with *you*, of course,' he said.

She carried more courgettes over to the chopping board. 'Do you have a girlfriend, Captain Gole?' she asked pointedly.

He hesitated. A part of him wanted to be honest with her, but he heard his own voice saying, 'Yes, as it happens.'

'Is she pretty?'

'Well—fairly.'

'Fairly?' Her eyebrows went up. 'And are you going to marry her?'

'I suppose we'll have to wait and see.'

'If you're not sure,' Livia said, 'you won't marry her.' She stopped chopping for a moment. 'I knew the first time Enzo kissed me that I would marry him.' A faint smile played across her face.

James felt a pang of envy. Of course, he told himself, it was a wonderful thing that she was so devoted to her husband. And it was fortuitous, too: it meant there was absolutely no chance that he would make a fool of himself with her. All the same, as he studied her profile as she bent over the chopping board, and the way her delicate hands sliced and chopped in a surprisingly energetic blur, he could not help regretting that the only woman he had met in Italy who so completely delighted him was already spoken for.

GINA TESALLI was pregnant. A crescent of taut brown belly peeped out between her skirt and the thin white shirt she was wearing. She put her hands on the bulge protectively and smiled at him.

'It's Corporal Taylor's, there's no doubt about it,' she said. 'I've never had another boyfriend.'

James scratched his head. Gina was proving a hard one to turn down. Before the war she had been a student. Now she lived with her family, or at least the female members of it, her four brothers and father all having been conscripted by the Germans. They were good, middle-class people.

If James refused to give Gina permission to marry, an Englishman's child would be born out of wedlock. But if he gave her permission on those same grounds, he knew that as soon as the girls of Naples realised that all they had to do to secure a wedding was to get themselves pregnant, there would be tens, if not hundreds, of babies born for no better reason than to guarantee their mothers a ticket on the promised war brides' ships to England.

It was a complicated problem, and between the conflicting demands of a well-intentioned, perfectly sensible policy on the one hand and the happiness of three human beings on the other, he faltered.

He told Gina he would have to make some further enquiries before he wrote his report. It was a lie—he was going to leave her case to one side for the moment, in the hope that a solution would eventually turn up.

'Of course,' Gina said, clearly trying not to sound disappointed. 'Our baby won't be born until the summer. There's plenty of time.'

THE HOUR BEFORE lunch had become James's favourite time of the day. It was the time when just enough work had been done to feel virtuous, but not so much as to induce fatigue. There was the anticipation of a wonderful meal, to be followed by a refreshing nap. Best of all, there was the sound of Livia bustling around the kitchen as she cooked.

This was itself an operatic performance, divided into five separate acts. First, there was a prelude, as she returned from the market with her purchases and went through each item, telling anyone within earshot what its particular qualities and defects were. Then came the preparation of pasta, which might be followed by a brief *intermezzo*, a conversation with Carlo or Enrico about the latest rumours in the market. After this came a quieter period, in which meat was prepared and vegetables chopped—a dramatic drum roll of knife blades on the board—before delicious smells rippled outwards from the kitchen, suffusing the whole apartment with the odours of cooking tomatoes, fresh basil and oregano. Finally, the big table would be cleared of papers and transformed with oil, vinegar, bread, and jugs of flowers and wine. People would gather, bread would be broken, and the contented silence of the well-fed would alternate with conversation.

Livia's manner towards him could still hardly be described as friendly, but if her attitude sometimes bordered on the downright hostile, he found that, for some reason, it only made him want to laugh. There was something delightful about her glares and stares; so much so that on occasion he even found himself teasing her, just for the simple pleasure of provoking them.

He was too unfamiliar with these symptoms to recognise them himself, but there was absolutely no doubt that James Gould was falling in love.

HE WAS WORKING at his desk one evening when he noticed that the glass of water he had by his left hand was behaving in a curious way. A series of concentric circles, pulsing inwards from the rim, rippled across its surface. He studied it, fascinated, then carried it into the kitchen. 'Livia,' he asked, setting it down, 'do you know why it does this?'

She glanced at it. 'An earthquake,' she decided. 'Just a little one. We get them all the time here, particularly when it gets warmer.'

He put his fingers to the wall. He could feel something now, a tiny vibration that hummed through the old stones of the building.

'Don't worry,' she said casually. 'These buildings are very strong.'

Outside, the air raid sirens went off. 'It's not a ruddy earthquake,' he said, 'it's a raid. We should get to the shelters.'

She indicated the pan. 'I can't, or this will be ruined. You go ahead.'

'I'll wait with you,' he said. He looked out of the window. He could see the German planes now, wave after wave of pencil-slim Junkers 88s. They were coming in from the north, very high, to avoid the guns on the warships.

'Keep away from the windows, then,' she said grudgingly. 'If the glass goes you'll be cut to pieces.'

He stepped back. A loud boom cut through the noise of the sirens.

'And it's better if the windows are open. That way the pressure won't shatter the glass.' She caught his look. 'We've had raids before.'

Suddenly, there was a deafening bang which seemed to lift the whole building, followed by the sound of cracking stone.

'That was close.' She was still chopping courgettes.

'Will you come here,' he snapped, pulling her into the doorway. She looked faintly surprised. 'The lintel,' he explained. 'Strongest part of the room.' He had his arm round her, but he had no intention of letting go now.

There was another bang, even closer. He felt the ground heave under his feet, as if the building were a ship riding a sudden swell. Livia gasped. They were so close he could feel the pounding of her heart. Then the loudest explosion so far slammed the wall into their backs. He felt his ears pop, but all he could think about was how wonderful it was to be this close to her, breathing in the heady rosemary aroma of her hair, feeling her fragile shoulders moving under his hand. He wondered if he dared kiss her, and he suddenly experienced a kind of delicious, dizzying terror that had nothing at all to do with German bombs.

You mustn't kiss her, he told himself. Of course you mustn't.

He felt something hard in his breast pocket, and took it out. It was the little piece of saint's bone the priest had pressed on him in the cathedral. He had almost forgotten it was there. 'What's that?' she asked.

'Just a lucky charm someone gave me.' He put it back. 'Livia?'

'Yes?'

'If you died right now, is there anything you would regret?'

She thought about it. 'No,' she decided. 'And you?'

There were so many things, and none of them could be spoken out loud. But he was intoxicated with her presence. 'Well, I won't regret this,' he said. 'It's been the best ten minutes of the best evening of my entire ruddy war. Though I would regret not having taken the opportunity to kiss you.'

He leaned towards her. He was aware of her eyes flashing, and her foot stamped hard on the floor. But at that moment, the air was sucked from the room and an enormous explosion buffeted him around the head. His kiss, cut off a moment before their lips touched, turned into a clumsy embrace as he stumbled against her. Dust poured through the doorway. Dimly, through the muffled aftermath, he heard a rattling sound as dozens of roof slates clattered into the courtyard, where they smashed on the flagstones.

THE EXPLOSION HAD caved in one wall of the Americans' HQ. James immediately offered his own floor as temporary accommodation. It was the least he could do, and, besides, he could hardly claim he was short of space.

Like a colony of ants moving nest, the CIC operation disgorged itself from the ground floor. Trunks of papers and crates of equipment were ferried up the stairs by purposeful, bustling orderlies. Desks, chairs, typewriters, document cabinets and endless lengths of telephone cable all moved themselves into the various nooks and crannies of James's offices.

There was another problem, however. The Americans' mess was temporarily unusable. 'Only for a few days,' Eric told James. 'And if your charming cook could see her way clear to helping us out as well . . .'

'There's far too many of you,' James said firmly.

'Is there a problem?' Livia's voice said behind him.

He turned. 'These people were asking if they could eat with us. I said it was too many.' He could not meet her eye. After the all-clear sounded he had made an excuse about inspecting the damage, and had hurried away before she could see how ashamed he was.

'It's how many—about thirty people?' She shrugged. 'I used to cook for that many every day at the *osteria*. And we can eat outside, in the courtyard. There's more room down there.'

'You'll need some help with serving, at least.'

'I can get some people in. There'll be no problem.' Angelo would know where to find temporary waitresses.

Eric bowed. '*La quinta forza armata è molto grata, Signora.* The Fifth Army is extremely grateful, Madam.' His Italian, James noted, was really quite good.

LIVIA, TO HER SURPRISE, was enjoying herself. She might dislike the Allies on principle, but she had to admit that, taken as individuals, they were fairly easy to get along with. And, above all, she was cooking with real ingredients again, and in the sort of quantities she had previously only dreamed of. Thanks to Angelo and his black-market contacts, she had a whole fresh tuna, a wicker basket of tomatoes, a crate of anchovies, a pale wheel of parmesan, great handfuls of parsley, dozens of new potatoes and an armful of mint. By the time darkness fell she had pulled together a feast that even she was proud of.

That night there was an extra brightness in everyone's chatter, and more wine was consumed than normal. And there was a kind of gaiety too in the setting, in eating on temporary tables in the courtyard under the lemon tree and the stars, with broken roof tiles still crunching underfoot. There were no candles, but someone had found a few paraffin lamps, and they made a bonfire out of broken roof beams. Angelo had supplied Livia with wine as well as food, all of which was served to the soldiers by half a dozen of the prettiest girls the maître d' could locate at such short notice.

After the meal was eaten, it was inevitable that there was going to be dancing. Eric picked up his clarinet, various other soldiers found instruments of one sort or another, and an impromptu jazz band struck up. Soon the Americans were showing the waitresses how to do-wop and jitterbug.

James took the opportunity to go and speak to Livia. 'Mrs Pertini,' he said formally, 'I want to apologise for what I said to you during the raid.'

'What did you say?' she asked curiously.

He hesitated. 'You didn't hear?'

'I heard the bomb falling and I shouted at you to get down. I couldn't hear what you were saying.'

'I was saying . . .' He paused. 'I was talking nonsense. I do apologise.'

'That's all right,' she said, giving him a strange look. Then one of the Americans approached her, asking for a dance.

Five minutes later she was back, her face flushed with pleasure at the exertion and all the compliments she had received for her cooking. On an impulse she said, 'Captain Gute, aren't you going to dance with me?'

'Very well,' he said. 'But it will have to be a proper dance.'

'I'm sure that everything you do is proper,' she said with a sigh.

'I was referring,' he said, standing up, 'to the foxtrot, king of dances.'

Livia did not know how to dance the foxtrot, and said so.

'Then it's fortunate that I do. Just follow my lead.' He interleaved the fingers of his left hand with her right, placed his other hand on her shoulder, and gently but firmly propelled her onto the dance floor.

'Captain Ghoul,' she said, surprised, 'you are a very good dancer.'

'I know,' he said, easing her into a box turn. 'And quick . . . and slow.'

She studied her own left hand, where it rested on James's shoulder. What am I doing? Livia thought. These are the people who killed my husband. These are the people who killed Pupetta. She was rather ashamed to realise that, in her mind, the two deaths were almost of equal significance. But after all, she had been present when Pupetta had been shot, whereas poor Enzo had been gone for almost four years when he died.

James led her back to the table, and an uncomfortable silence fell between them.

Eventually she jumped to her feet again. 'I'll show you how to dance the *tarantella*, if you like,' she said.

James shook his head. 'I'm all danced out.'

She shrugged. 'Carlo?' Instantly Carlo was in front of her, his shoulders squared as he began to move his body in time with hers. Enrico took a guitar from one of the Americans and strummed it meditatively.

'In most Italian dances,' Livia said over her shoulder to James, 'the man pursues the woman. But in the *tarantella* it is the woman who is possessed by passion. So the man stays where he is, and the woman approaches him.' Enrico's fingers moved more fluently over the strings of the guitar, picking up the pace as Livia danced sinuously towards Carlo, pirouetting round his barely moving body. The tempo of the guitar increased still further and everyone was watching her now, as she spun this way and that, writhing with the fluid, pulsating rhythm of the dance. With a final shout, the music ended. It was the most erotic thing James had ever witnessed.

The men at the tables were on their feet, clapping and shouting their appreciation. Enrico started another tune and Livia walked out of the ring of firelight. James stood up, hoping that she would come back and talk to him. She caught his eye and smiled. But then another man in uniform had intercepted her; was speaking to her. She cast James a rueful look, as if to say that he had had his chance and not taken it. He turned away, but not before he saw that the man who was so keen to have her company was Eric.

THE APPLICANT'S NAME was Vittoria Forsese, and she was demurely dressed in a black frock. Her first husband, she said, had died fighting in Greece. But now, a year later, she had been lucky enough to meet another man who cared for her, a corporal in the Engineers.

James could see why her fiancé had been attracted to her. She was extremely pretty and completely charming.

'And what have you been living off?' he asked.

There was just the faintest of pauses. 'Savings.'

'Is there anyone who can vouch for you? A neighbour?'

'I don't remember,' she muttered.

He glanced around the little apartment. It was spotlessly clean, and hardly opulent. But there were the usual telltale signs. 'The money comes from soldiers, doesn't it?' he said gently. She did not answer, but a tear rolled silently down her face.

He considered what to do next. She was beautiful; she seemed hardworking, loyal and sweet-natured. And she had had the ridiculous good fortune to meet someone she loved who loved her. Abruptly, he came to a decision. He got to his feet and held out his hand. 'Congratulations, Vittoria. I can see no reason why you shouldn't be married as soon as possible.'

MORE AND MORE often, James found himself making excuses to hang around the kitchen. 'Don't you have a war to fight?' Livia asked him once.

'I don't really do fighting,' he explained. 'I'm not fierce enough.' He gestured towards the tomatoes she was peeling. 'Let me help with those.'

'If you like.'

He loved to watch her slim fingers turning the vegetables this way and that, and then try to copy what she was doing.

'Tell me more about this girl of yours,' she said as they worked.

He glanced at her. The temptation to fantasise was irresistible. 'Well,' he said, 'she's quite small, and rather skinny. And she has dark hair. She teases me a lot. And she's rather . . . imperious. She likes to boss people around.'

'She sounds a little bit like me. Not the bossy bit, of course.'

'Yes,' he said. 'Yes, I suppose she is a little bit like you.'

They worked in silence for a few moments.

'Captain Gud?'

'Please,' he said, 'I'd much rather you called me James.'

'Joms?'

He smiled. 'Yes?'

'What's a "pot"?'

'It's a pan. Like that.' He indicated the saucepan on the stove.

'That's what I thought.' She put another handful of tomatoes into the saucepan. 'So how can I be a pot?'

'Who says you are?'

'Eric. He says I'm a sexy pot.'

'Does he?' he heard his own voice say. 'And when was this?'

'This morning. Did I tell you? He's teaching me to speak English.'

Well, he didn't waste any time, James thought. Bloody Yanks. Oversexed and over here, as the saying went. He speared a tomato angrily with his knife.

LIVIA HAD FINALLY realised why James was behaving in such an odd manner. The way he veered back and forth between friendliness and pomposity, the absence of any attempt to grope her, the hanging around in the kitchen chatting, the nonsense about the imaginary girlfriend and the fact that he was such a good dancer, all pointed to a very obvious explanation. Captain Gould was a *finocchio*, a piece of fennel—homosexual.

Livia's reaction to her own brainwave was interesting. First of all, she clapped her hands together, delighted at her own cleverness. Of course! Why hadn't she realised sooner? Her second reaction was a sense of disappointment. This took her by surprise, somewhat. It surely wasn't that she was interested in the captain for herself? No, she decided; it was just that homosexuals were by and large sad, unhappy people, doomed to live unfulfilled lives, and since she quite liked the captain, she decided to show him, by being pleasant, that she, for one, did not mind what his sexuality was.

Once she had settled this in her own mind she felt much better, and the sense of disappointment she had experienced was lessened by the new anticipation of having him as her friend.

JAMES WENT to find Eric, but found his way barred by an orderly. 'Restricted area, sir. CIC only.'

'Don't be ridiculous. I work here.'

'It's for security reasons.'

'James.' It was Eric, hurrying out as soon as he saw who it was. 'What's up, buddy?'

'I can't get into my own offices, for one thing.'

'It's just a temporary precaution,' Eric soothed him. 'There are a few sensitive files lying around, that's all.'

'So sensitive you can't show them to your allies?'

Eric shrugged. 'Bureaucracy. You know how it is, James. But what's bugging you?'

He had taken James by the arm and led him into another room. James said pointedly, 'Mrs Pertini.'

Eric raised an eyebrow. 'The beautiful Livia? What's the problem?'

'You've been teaching her English. Or rather,' he said sarcastically, 'American, which is not quite the same thing.'

Eric ignored the insult. 'Between you and me, James, I hope to teach her a great deal more than that,' he said with a grin. 'But so what?'

'You called her a sexpot.'

Eric laughed.

'It's hardly a proper way to behave,' James snapped. 'The clue is in the name, Eric. *Mrs* Pertini? She's married.'

'But her husband's dead.' Eric saw James's expression. 'You didn't know? He got himself killed in Russia, fighting for the Germans.'

'Oh,' James said.

'Although at that point she hadn't seen him for four years. As you'd know yourself if you'd taken the trouble to have her vetted.' He clapped James on the back. 'So now that your chivalrous Brit instincts have been reassured, presumably it's OK for me to give the lady language lessons? After all, it's not as if you're in the running.' His eyes narrowed. 'Unless it's something rather less chivalrous you had in mind for yourself?'

'Of course not,' James said stiffly.

'Well, there you are, then. Keep yourself pure for—what was her name?'

'What? Oh. Er, Jane.'

'Keep yourself pure for Jane.'

James strode back to his desk, a great feeling of elation sweeping over him. Livia wasn't married. All he had to do now was to remove the small impediment of his imaginary engagement to Jane, and then he would be able to court her—and the sooner the better, given that Eric had clearly stolen a march on him.

JAMES FOUND HIMSELF increasingly curious as to why CIC were reluctant to let him into their offices.

The Americans' offices were next door to his own bedroom. One night, he waited until everyone was asleep and climbed onto the ledge of one of the huge windows. A brief nerve-wrenching scramble from one window to another, and he was inside their inner sanctum.

The place was full of documents. Everywhere he looked, there were boxes of files. He rifled through them until he found one marked 'Top secret—CIC only'. It contained a single folder. This must be it, he thought. It was marked OPERATION GLADIO. He opened it and scanned the first page.

Background

After the war, the political situation in southern Italy is likely to be troubled. The British support the automatic restoration of the monarchy. However, this is by no means the only possible outcome. In the south, some wealthy individuals are agitating for an independent

'Kingdom of Naples'. The communists, who have the support of the majority of the poor, are content to let these fantasists exhaust themselves, and will attempt a Stalinist revolution as soon as the Allies withdraw, linking up with workers' movements in Greece and Yugoslavia in order to create a Europe-wide super-state.

At present, the only alternative to communist takeover in Italy is probably the remnants of Mussolini's fascists, who are more than willing to deal with the communists if they are given the means to do so.

The third most powerful grouping in southern Italy is the Mafia, known locally as the camorra. *They have no political allegiance, but are vehemently opposed to the communists, probably because they sense that the communists would make life difficult for them.*

The most unpredictable element in this are the partisans, many of whom are fighting the Germans in well-organised, effective groups run on communist lines . . .

There was more in a similar vein. It made no sense to James. Why were the Americans worrying about what happened after the war, when they couldn't even get a grip on the black marketeering and corruption that was going on right under their noses? And what on earth was so secret about a fairly obvious assessment of the political situation in southern Italy?

He replaced the folder and exited the way he had come in.

SPRING HAD ARRIVED, as hot as an English summer. The people of Naples did not look so gaunt now. The Allied Military Government had finally opened up the food markets again, and fresh produce began to pour into the city. Now, when James took a siesta, he had to close the shutters of his bedroom against the heat of the midday sun.

His feelings for Livia might be hidden, but they were no less intense. Every time he heard her in the kitchen, singing, his heart soared with her voice: every time she put a plate of food in front of him, his passion fed on the sight of her slender hand, just as ravenously as he devoured her cooking.

With the black market apparently under control at last, he spent hours sitting at his desk trying to think of reasons to go and talk to her. But there were only so many times each morning one could wander into the kitchen.

Then he had an inspiration. He asked her if she would teach him to cook.

She stopped what she was doing, taken aback. 'That's a big thing, to learn how to cook,' she said warily.

'Not everything you know, of course,' he assured her. 'Just the easy stuff.'

She considered. In Naples, there were very few men who cooked. In fact, there was no Neapolitan word for 'chef', it being assumed that all cooking was done by enthusiastic amateurs. But James, after all, was a *finocchio*, and given to womanly pleasures.

'Well,' she said, seeming to come to a decision. 'I'll show you a few things and we'll see what kind of pupil you are. How does that sound?'

But, since Livia had never actually learned to cook, but had simply assimilated the skill, teaching him what she knew proved to be as hard as explaining how to breathe. In the end they agreed that she would carry on doing what she usually did, and he would try to copy her.

'I NEED TO GO home,' Livia announced one evening. 'I have to get some more cheese and to see that my sister and my father are all right.'

'I'll give you a lift on the bike, if you like,' James said, trying not to sound too eager. 'And, er, we could make a day trip of it.'

'Thank you,' she said. 'That would be very nice.'

Dawn announced another hot day, and the countryside wafted wave after wave of scents at them as they headed towards Vesuvius—orange blossom, myrtle, flowering thyme, and the peculiar smell of warm dusty roads. They passed a sign to Pompeii. It was a few miles out of their way, but he asked if she minded him taking a look.

They followed the road towards Torre Annunziata, where another, smaller sign prompted them to turn up a narrow track that led towards a cluster of ramshackle buildings. The excavated Roman town was immediately behind them, over a slight rise.

James switched off the engine. There was no one about.

'Have you been here before?' he asked.

'No,' she said, looking around.

The sheer scale of the place was staggering. He hadn't expected it to be so large—a whole town, abruptly obliterated by the mountain at its back. The forum, the large buildings that were obviously municipal offices, the private houses that presented only a doorway to the street but opened into large column-lined courtyards—it was not so very different in layout from any of the other Italian towns he had visited, with a forum instead of a piazza and temples instead of churches.

Here and there they came across casts of the inhabitants. Even after so long, you could still sense the terror and despair in their postures. One had been frozen in the act of holding something to his face, presumably a piece of cloth to breathe through. Another had blundered into a wall, lying down to die with his arms curled over his head as if to ward off blows raining from the sky. Yet another had tried to shield his companion from whatever was happening, and had died with his arms curled protectively round her.

They walked back to the bike in sombre mood and James drove away from Pompeii up the winding roads towards Fiscino. Occasionally he found himself glancing up at the summit of the volcano. The plume of smoke was leaning out to sea today, like a quill propped in an enormous ink-pot. It would have looked much the same in the days before it destroyed Pompeii, he thought: there couldn't have been much in the way of warning.

When they reached Fiscino, Marisa and Nino greeted Livia with cries of delight. With James they were more guarded, and it seemed to him that there was suspicion in the glances which Livia's father shot at him.

'He thinks you might be my boyfriend,' Livia whispered as they were led to the kitchen to inspect the mozzarella. 'Don't worry, I'll tell him you're not, although I won't explain why. He's quite old-fashioned.'

'Fine,' James said, mystified.

Next, Livia took James to say hello to Priscilla. When the buffalo saw who had come to visit her she hurried over to the gate, nudging her massive black nose under Livia's arm, hoping for a handful of hay.

'We used to have two of these,' Livia explained as she scratched Priscilla's forehead. 'The poor thing gets lonely on her own.'

'What happened to the other one?'

Livia looked at him with a sudden frown that echoed her father's expression earlier. 'Some soldiers shot her.'

'You mean the Germans?'

She laughed sarcastically. 'Because, obviously, nothing bad is ever done by Allied soldiers? No, the Germans did many terrible things when they were here, but they never shot our *bufale*. It took Allied troops to do that.'

'When? How did this happen?'

She found herself telling him an edited version of Pupetta's death—how the soldiers had been tipped off by a neighbour who bore her a grudge because Livia didn't like him, and how they had taken everything, all the food the Pertinis had, before opening fire on Pupetta. By the time she was halfway through she had to stop because she was crying.

James found himself wanting quite desperately to take her in his arms and kiss her. It was a very different feeling from the time when he'd tried to kiss her during the air raid. He reached forward and slipped his arm round her shoulder, and then, because she so clearly needed the reassurance his arms could give her, and because in her misery she buried her face in his chest, he put both arms round her and hugged her. She lifted her face to his.

'And then they threw me in their truck,' she said. 'And the officer—'

'The officer what?'

'The officer tried to give my father money for me,' she said quietly.

James let her go. He was horrified, but more than that, he felt tainted by association. No wonder the Italians resented their liberators, he thought, if this was how they behaved.

'Livia,' he said grimly, 'I'm so sorry.'

'Why? You weren't there.'

'I'm sorry about what happened. More than that—I'm appalled. But we can trace him. Did you notice any regimental markings on his uniform? Or a number on the lorry? I'll make sure the brute's court martialled.'

It was the first time she had seen him really angry. 'Court martialled for what?' she pointed out. 'We were the ones breaking the law, not him. According to the military government's rules, what we were doing was hoarding, and that's a crime. If you're a soldier, you can proposition as many women as you like.' She shot him a glance. 'Or men, for that matter.'

'It's one thing to offer a prostitute money. But to offer money to a respectable girl . . .'

'Often there's not much difference, these days.'

'Oh, yes, there is,' he said hotly. But he was revisited by a thought that all his received notions of what constituted respectability in a woman might be too simplistic for the times he was living in.

James saw the wistful way Livia looked around her before they left and realised that this was hard for her. It must be wonderful, he thought, to love a place as much as she clearly loved it here. For most of his life, home had simply been where you went when you weren't away at school.

When he had started the Matchless, Livia climbed on the back and Nino and Marisa festooned the handlebars with canvas bags full of *mozzarelle* packed in water. The liquid dribbled over James's legs as they set off, making the steering decidedly erratic.

ON THE COAST ROAD near Sorrento they found a tiny restaurant. There was no menu, but the owner brought out plates of tiny sand eels fried in batter and soused in lemon juice, a couple of sea urchins and a plate of oysters.

Livia picked up an oyster and sniffed it. 'No smell,' she said approvingly. That's how you can tell it's fresh.' She took the lemon the owner had provided and expertly squeezed a few drops onto one before handing it to him. 'Have you eaten oysters before, Yames?'

'I don't believe I have,' he said dubiously, inspecting a grey-white puddle of flesh nestled in its shell amidst a little slimy-looking liquid.

'You'd know if you had. They say you never forget your first time,' she said mischievously, selecting a juicy one for herself. 'Like making love.'

He took a deep breath. 'Actually,' he said, 'I wouldn't know much about that either.'

She smiled. 'I know.'

He glanced at her. 'You could tell?' He hadn't realised his inexperience was so apparent.

'Of course. A woman has an instinct about these things.' She clanked the shell lightly against his, as if they were drinking a toast. 'It doesn't bother me, really. *Cincin.*'

'*Cincin.*' They tipped the shells against their lips in unison.

It was salty, it was sweet, it was fishy, it was liquor, it was like a deep breath of seaweedy air and a mouthful of sea spray all at once. He bit once, involuntarily, and felt the flavours in his mouth swell and burst like a wave. Before he knew what he had done he had swallowed, and he felt a sudden sense that nothing would be the same again. Eve in her garden had bitten an apple. James had eaten an oyster, sitting outside a tiny restaurant overlooking the sea by Sorrento. His undernourished heart swelled in the Italian sunshine like a ripening fig, and he laughed out loud. He felt a great flood of gratitude as he realised that he was having the time of his life.

'Another?' She handed him one, and took another for herself, as the restaurant owner brought them wine, pale and golden and cool.

There were just four oysters each, and when they were all gone they turned their attention to the sea urchins, which were another taste again, salty and exotic and rich. For dessert the owner gave them two peaches. Their skins were wrinkled and almost bruised, but the flesh, when James cut into it with his knife, was unspoilt and perfectly ripe.

He was about to put a slice into his mouth when Livia stopped him.

'Not like that. This is how we eat peaches here.' She put a chunk of peach into her wine, then held the glass to his lips. He took it, tipping the wine and fruit into his mouth. It was a delicious, sensual cascade of sensations, another undreamt of experience.

AFTER LUNCH they continued along the coast, the road skirting the green clear waters of the bay. It was hot now, and the combination of sun and moving air was burning them.

'I want to swim,' Livia said. She pointed. 'I think we can get down to the sea that way.'

He turned onto the track she had indicated, which led through a grove of lemon trees down to a rocky beach. The sea was the colour of a field of lavender, and so clear you could see every rock and seashell on the bottom. Apart from the yelling of crickets, and the faint soughing of the water as it sucked gently at the pebbles, everything was very still. The Matchless ticked and creaked quietly as it cooled.

'We can undress over there,' Livia said, indicating a group of rocks.

'You go in first, if you want,' he offered. 'I won't look.'

But he did. He couldn't help it—he heard the sound of her bare feet as she ran to the sea, and then a splash and a shriek, and he looked up just in time to see a brown flash of nearly naked Livia plunging headlong into the water. After a moment she surfaced, pushing wet hair out of her eyes.

'Aren't you coming?' she called.

'Just a moment.' Behind the rock he took a series of deep breaths before he climbed out of his uniform and then ran into the icy water.

Afterwards they lay in the shade of a lemon tree, looking up at the sunlight flickering through the branches.

'My father eats lemons straight from the tree,' Livia said idly.

'Aren't they bitter?'

'Not when they're warm from the sun.' She reached up and plucked one to show him. 'This is a good lemon. We have a saying: the thicker the skin, the sweeter the juice.' Experimentally she took a bite, and nodded. 'It's good.' She held the fruit towards his mouth.

He steadied her hand and tried it. She was right: it was sweet.

She took another mouthful herself and grimaced. 'Pip,' she said, spitting it into her hand. She smiled at him, and in that moment all his delusions of self-restraint evaporated. He took her head in his hands and desperately pressed his lips against hers.

'Jamus!' she exclaimed.

'Come here,' he gasped. He kissed her again.

After a while she pulled free, a puzzled expression on her face. 'So you're not a fennel after all?'

'What?' he asked, perplexed.

'A fennel. You know, a *finocchio*. A *ricchione*.'

'A big ear?' he said, his confusion mounting.

'I guess not,' she said. Then she laughed. 'I'd never have swum—I didn't realise—' Her eyes narrowed. 'So that was just a trick, was it, pretending to be a *culattina*? When we ate the oysters?'

'I never pretended to be a *culattina*, whatever *culattina* is. I told you that I wasn't experienced,' he said. 'Where's this . . . other thing come from?'

'Ah,' she said. She was beginning to realise that her feminine intuition might have been struggling with the translation from British body language to Italian. And the more she thought about that, the more a faint but persistent sense of disappointment that had been constantly present ever since she accepted the job at the Palazzo Satriano seemed to lift, leaving behind it only a pleasant feeling that being kissed by James was rather nice.

She leaned forward to be kissed again, and he quickly obliged.

But—he could have kicked himself—it was he who broke the spell. Pulling away, he said, 'What about Eric? Do you kiss him too?'

Livia's expression darkened. 'You've only just kissed me,' she said, 'and already you want to own me?'

'I just need to know where I stand.'

'I like you both,' she said simply. 'I didn't mean to kiss you, though I'm not sorry I did. But it doesn't mean anything.'

'Of course not,' he said, disappointed.

He tried to kiss her again, but she turned her head away. He had changed the mood.

THAT NIGHT, Livia announced that she needed a wood-burning oven if she was to do justice to the ingredients they had brought back from Vesuvius. After some thought, she had realised that James already possessed the perfect article—the *schedario*, his grey filing cabinet.

'We'll put the wood in the bottom drawer,' she explained. 'Then the middle drawer will become a very hot oven, where we can make pizza and roast meat. The top drawer will be cooler, for vegetables and mozzarella.'

'The flaw in your plan,' James pointed out, 'is that the *schedario* is already full of *archivi*, files.'

'But you can put the files somewhere else,' she said persuasively.

Strictly speaking this was true, he supposed. After all, they had managed perfectly well without a filing cabinet before.

For dinner they ate wood-roasted pizza with a sauce of fresh tomatoes and mozzarella, decorated only with salt, oil and basil. He had never eaten anything so simple, or so delicious. But when he finally went to bed it was another taste he dreamt of, the taste of some all-too-brief kisses in a lemon grove above Sorrento.

'YOU SEE,' James explained, 'love isn't just something you *feel*. Love is something you *become*. It's like—going to a new country and realising that you never particularly liked the place you left behind. It's like a sort of tingling and—look, I'd better shut up, I seem to be talking awful nonsense.'

The girl, who was called Addolorata, smiled. 'No, that's exactly right!' she exclaimed. 'That's just how I feel about Magnus, too.'

'Magnus is a lucky chap,' James said.

He realised that he had not, in fact, asked Addolorata very many questions so far about her fiancé, or her financial situation. It seemed inconceivable, however, that he should turn her application down, given the splendid way they were getting on. 'Look,' he suggested, 'I've got to write this report, but it'll probably help you a bit if I tell you first what the best answers to my questions are. For example, if I were to ask you what you've been living off . . .'

'An uncle sends me money,' Addolorata said quickly.

'. . . you might turn out to have stolen some money from a German. No Germans around now to check with, you see. Uncles have a tiresome habit of being contactable.'

'That's what I meant—I stole it from a German.'

'Excellent,' he said, beaming at her. 'This is going to go rather well.'

Later, as he typed up his report, Livia stuck her head round his office door. 'What are you doing?' she asked.

'Marrying someone.'

'Who's the lucky girl?'

'Addolorata Origo. It's not me who's marrying her, actually, it's a captain in the Highlanders. I'm just helping.'

'Well, if you're not going to be long, I thought we might go for a walk,' she said casually, producing a bonnet he had not seen before.

He had seen the young couples strolling arm in arm down the Via Roma, and he knew putting yourself on display like this was an integral part of Italian courtship.

'Livia,' he said, his heart suddenly heavy, 'I'm afraid a walk's not going to be possible.' He took a deep breath. 'The wedding officer simply can't be seen to have an Italian girlfriend.' He saw her thunderstruck expression. 'I should have told you earlier,' he said lamely. 'It's my position—'

The slam of the door closing left him in no doubt what her feelings about his position were.

HE HOPED that by dinner she might have cooled down, but from the hostile stare she gave him he saw it was not the case. His plate was banged down on the table in front of him, and it seemed to him that he was given a far smaller helping than anyone else. To make matters worse, after dinner she seemed to make a beeline for Eric's table, where she laughed uproariously at everything he said. After twenty minutes of this, James got up and went to bed.

The next morning he awoke at dawn and went to the market. Going from stall to stall he made some discreet enquiries. Eventually, someone indicated that he might be able to supply what James was after. He was made to wait for half an hour, and then the man came back with a small paper bag.

'Here,' he said, passing it over. 'There's an eighth of a pound in there.'

James opened the bag and checked the contents. The smell of coffee beans, charred and dark and rich, filled his nostrils.

A little further on he found someone selling freshly baked *sfogliatelle*—tiny pastries filled with ricotta, candied lemon zest and cinnamon, like the ones that Livia served for breakfast. A large bag of oranges and some fresh goat's milk, and his shopping expedition was complete.

Back at the apartment, he had just laid the table with a cloth, flowers and china, and pressed some juice from the oranges, when Livia emerged, yawning, from her sleeping quarters. She stopped and sniffed the air suspiciously.

'It's not Nescafé,' he said. 'It's real.'

Her eyes widened. '*Real* coffee?'

'I may not be able to cook, but I *do* know how to make a breakfast.'

'Oh, James—that's wonderful. This will be the first coffee I've had since the start of the war, and the first time anyone has ever made me a meal.'

'No one ever made you a meal before?'

She shook her head. 'I always wanted to do everything myself.'

When he had poured them each a tiny cup of dense black liquid, they both took a bite of *sfogliatella*, and drank.

'One day,' he said, watching her drink hers in three ecstatic gulps, 'I will cook us both dinner. Just for the two of us.'

She took a sudden interest in the bottom of her coffee cup. 'So you think you might want to step out with me after all?'

'I want to be with you more than anything else in the world. But, Livia, I can't be seen with you in public. I can't acknowledge you as my girl. I can't even let the other officers know how I feel about you, because the CO might find out, and then I think I'd get the sack and be transferred back to Africa. I know it's not ideal, but it's all I can offer.'

'And, of course, you can't ever marry me,' she said quietly.

He shook his head.

'Where I come from that's quite a big thing, to court someone you've got no intention of marrying. If my father knew . . .'

'The war won't last for ever.'

'It's lasted four years already. Who knows how much longer it will go on for?' She smiled ruefully. 'Besides, when the war is over you'll go home. You'll have had enough of me by then.'

'I will never have had enough of you.'

'As you know,' Major Heathcote was saying, 'it is the responsibility of A-force to come up with initiatives to destabilise the Germans' hold on northern Italy.'

James nodded. He still wasn't sure why the CO had asked to see him.

'And as you are also aware,' the major said slowly, 'with penicillin in such short supply, the spread of syphilis has been a big problem for our medical chaps. The Germans, on the other hand, don't seem to be nearly so troubled by it.'

James nodded again.

'A-force have a plan.' The major sighed. 'A sort of two birds, one stone scenario. The idea is that we round up women with syphilis and then ship them up north, behind the lines. Where, one presumes, they will spread their diseases among the German soldiers rather than our own.'

James found it hard to believe what he was hearing. 'Isn't that rather—well, unethical? Using sick women to do our dirty work for us?'

'It probably isn't ethical,' the major muttered. 'But it's been approved at the highest level. Your job is to arrange the detention of suitable women.'

'*Rastrellamenti*,' James said.

'What's that?'

'That's what the Italians called the German round-ups—*rastrellamenti*. They probably never expected to find their liberators doing exactly the same thing.' A further thought struck him. 'How are the women to be selected?'

'From among those with records of prostitution, presumably.'

'But that could mean we include the fiancées of some of our own soldiers. Women who haven't married only because we won't allow them to.'

'We can hardly show special favours to those who we've already decided are unfit to marry our troops,' the major pointed out. 'Really, Gould. I think you're failing to focus on the big picture.'

'It's only when one focuses on the small picture,' James said, 'that the full horror of this scheme becomes apparent.'

The major looked at him sharply. 'I hope you're not suggesting you won't carry out your orders, Gould?'

'No, sir.'

'I'm very glad to hear it.' The major waved him away. 'Dismiss.'

THEY SAT on the roof of the Palazzo Satriano, among the chimney stacks and the broken red roof tiles, as the sun set over the bay. Livia was plucking a pigeon. James nestled a tommy gun in his lap. Occasionally, when further pigeons landed on the rooftop, he would fire off a few shots in their direction. If he was successful, the bird got added to the pile at Livia's feet.

'I vould layk tu seets een dhe frond ro,' she said thoughtfully.

He grunted.

'Can iu tail may, vat time ees dhe intarval, pliss?' She switched to Italian. 'You know,' she said, 'English must be a very hard language. Because most of the time, English men would rather not speak at all.'

'Sorry,' he muttered. 'Tough day. Sometimes my work . . . there are things I don't like.'

She put down the pigeon she was working on. 'So tell me about it.'

She listened without comment until he had finished. 'It's not the most recent vettings I'm worried about,' he explained. 'I've been letting those weddings go ahead. It's the earlier ones, the ones I did when I first came to Naples. Any one of those girls is at risk.'

'Well, you have to make sure that none of those girls gets taken.'

'Livia, the round-ups will go ahead whether I'm involved or not.'

'But they will ask *you* whether the girls they have seized are really prostitutes. And then you must lie.'

'But in many cases, the files say that they are.'

'Files can go missing.'

'They'll ask the girls how they support themselves. It isn't hard to work out the truth.'

'You must speak to Angelo,' she decided. 'He will know what to do.'

'Angelo? What's he got to do with it?'

'Jims,' she said, 'who do you think got me this job?'

'Me?'

'You *gave* me the job,' she corrected. 'Which is not the same thing at all. I'm not meant to tell you this, but it was Angelo who made sure there were no other applicants. Angelo who sees we always have enough to eat.'

'But why should Angelo care what I eat?'

'I think,' she said vaguely, 'he was just a bit concerned that when you first came to Naples you weren't eating properly. And it's well known that a man who isn't eating properly can't do his job properly either. These days, apparently, you're much more—well, reasonable.'

'I see.'

'Although now you're angry.'

'No,' he said. And it was true, he wasn't. He was starting to see a possible way out of this mess, and Livia was right: Angelo might be just the person to help him do it. 'I'll go and talk to Angelo,' he promised.

HE WALKED OVER to the darkened restaurant. The notice announcing its closure was still displayed in the window, which in turn was draped in blackout blinds. He went round the back and knocked on the kitchen door.

Angelo opened it with a slight smile. 'Captain Gould. Will you take a glass of wine with me?'

'I'd be delighted, Angelo.' He had the feeling that he had been expected.

They sat either side of the empty bar, a bottle of Brunello between them. 'The last of my prewar stock,' Angelo said as he filled their glasses. 'I've been saving it for a special occasion.'

'Is this a special occasion?'

'Oh, I think so.' Angelo touched his glass gently to James's. 'To peace.'

'To peace.' They drank.

'Now then. How can I help you?'

'I think I can persuade my superiors to reopen the restaurants.'

Angelo raised an eyebrow. 'That would be very welcome.'

'The food shortages aren't so bad now, and they'll believe me if I tell them that there's no longer a risk to public order or security.'

Angelo nodded. 'But of course you want something in return.'

'Two things, actually. First, I need you to spread the word that every restaurant has to employ at least one girl. They can work as waitresses, cooks, maître d's, whatever.'

Angelo considered this for a moment. 'It's an excellent idea,' he said. 'The girls will have jobs, so they'll be able to show that they have a source of income when the *rastrellamenti* start.' He caught James's look. 'News travels quickly in Naples,' he said apologetically. 'Does this mean that the girls who are engaged to soldiers will be able to marry?'

'I don't see why not. After all, a girl who works in Zi' Teresa's can hardly be said to be of bad character.'

'Ah,' Angelo said. He raised his glass to James. 'Now you have become a true Neapolitan.' He inclined his head. 'And the second thing?'

'I want to know where Zagarella keeps his stolen penicillin.'

Angelo drew in his breath sharply. 'My friend, that is an altogether more dangerous undertaking. I'm not sure I can help you.'

'Of course you can. It isn't only Allied officers who eat in your restaurant, Angelo. The *camorristi* come here as well. You hear everything.'

'It is more difficult, and more complicated, than even you can imagine,' Angelo said. 'This trade in goods stolen from the Allies. Your predecessor, Jackson, thought that the Americans were simply too incompetent to stop it.' James nodded. 'Well, if I have learned anything in the past year, it is that your American friends are many things, but they are rarely incompetent.'

'What are you getting at?'

'Suppose you were the Americans and you wanted the Mafia to do you a favour—a big favour, something political. How would you persuade them to help you?' Angelo closed his fingers and rotated his wrist, the old Neapolitan gesture for corruption. 'Perhaps you would throw open your stores and say, "Help yourselves."'

'But what could the Americans possibly want from the Mafia?'

'I don't know. All I know is, there is a plan.'

James thought back to the document he had found in the Americans' offices. That, too, had implied that there was some kind of plan. But what?

'As you say, it's probably political,' he decided. 'In which case, it needn't concern us now. And they won't break cover to save Zagarella, not if the evidence against him is strong enough.'

Angelo considered. 'It will take money. A great deal of money.'

'That can be arranged.'

'There will be no receipts,' Angelo warned him. 'The kind of people I will need to pay will not want any record of their involvement.'

'Very well. But I want Zagarella himself. Not some underling.'

'I understand. Let me see what I can do.'

ALTHOUGH THE DAMAGE from the air raid had been repaired now, the court-yard had remained as the communal dining area. None of the Americans seemed keen to dispense with Livia's services, and James was beginning to realise the usefulness of a favour owed. It also meant he could eavesdrop on the Americans' conversations, although he had heard no more about any dealings with the Mafia. It worked two ways, however. That night, Eric came to sit next to him as he devoured a bowl of Livia's spaghetti.

'If I didn't know different, James, I'd say you've been avoiding me,' he said. 'How's tricks?'

James shrugged and waved a hand in the air. Conveniently, his mouth was full of spaghetti, and a shrug seemed to cover the situation anyway.

'You know, you've started to use Italian gestures,' Eric said mildly. 'That shrug was not the shrug of an Englishman.'

James swallowed his mouthful. 'Eric, it was just a shrug.'

'If you say so. By the way, I hear you're going after Zagarella again.'

'Where did you hear that?'

'So it's true?'

'If your sources told you it is,' James said, spinning another ball of pasta expertly onto his fork, 'then presumably it must be.'

'Oh, James.' Eric regarded him with amused disappointment. 'Such vagueness. Are we going to arrest him again? We're going to need some cast-iron evidence if we don't want to look like idiots.'

'As it happens,' James said casually, 'I was thinking I might take care of this one on my own. No need to tie up more manpower than we have to.'

'But last time,' Eric pointed out, 'we did it together, and we still didn't nail him.' A thought appeared to strike him. 'You're not suggesting that CIC had anything to do with him getting off?'

'I would never dream of suggesting any such thing.'

'But you're thinking it.'

James hesitated.

'If we weren't Allies, I'd take offence at that,' Eric said. 'I suppose you've heard this ridiculous theory that we're somehow in league with the Mafia.'

'I don't pay any attention to gossip.'

'James, we're intelligence officers. Gossip is our trade. But that one, I can assure you, has even less foundation than all the rest of the nonsense that gets talked around here.'

Livia was coming out with more pasta. Eric followed James's gaze and said, 'Speaking of gossip, there's been talk about Mrs Pertini.'

'What sort of talk?'

'They say she's stepping out with you.' Eric laughed mirthlessly. 'I'll tell you, that one did come as a bit of a surprise to me. Since I assumed from what you'd told me you had a girl back home in England.'

James couldn't think of anything to say.

'Didn't believe it at first,' Eric continued. 'I don't like to listen to gossip either, but Livia confirmed it herself. So I reckoned you'd either been lying to her, or lying to me.'

'Sorry about that.'

'That was when I realised that, underneath all that British candour, you're a lot more devious than you make out. I think we might have under-estimated you, James.'

'Who's "we"?'

'But you'll be pleased to know that mine is a lone voice,' Eric continued, ignoring the question. 'As far as most of CIC is concerned, you're still just the Brit who writes the wedding reports.'

'I'm glad to hear it. Since that is exactly who I am.'

'Anything you get, James,' Eric said softly, 'I strongly advise you to share it with your friends and allies.'

'You brute,' James snapped. A red mist descended, and he leapt to his feet, his fists clenched. 'Livia's no whore.'

Eric raised his own fists. 'I never said she was.'

'You were talking about sharing her—'

'I was talking about sharing intelligence, you stupid limey panty-waist.'

James had absolutely no idea what a panty-waist was, but that was beside the point. 'Take that back,' he spat.

The two of them circled each other furiously, their fists up, and soon they were hammering blows at each other.

'Stop it,' Livia screamed, running towards them. 'Stop it, both of you. You're behaving like children.'

Shamefaced, they stopped. There was blood on both their faces, but it was hard to say which of them had come off worse.

'They say all's fair in love and war,' Eric said, dabbing at his lip. 'Which is another way of saying all's unfair. Bear it in mind, James.'

THE MONEY IN THE TIN, which no longer held pencils, mounted daily. Most was put there by Carlo and Enrico—James thought it best not to enquire too directly into its provenance. Meanwhile, it seemed only appropriate that the filing cabinet, which had once held so many records of weddings refused, should in its new incarnation as an oven be responsible for their disappearance. James stuffed the bottom drawer full of papers, weighted them down with kindling, and set a match to them. For lunch that day he enjoyed a very good wood-roasted fish, served on a platter of salt and herbs.

The girls all had to be re-interviewed, and new reports written of a more positive nature. James was careful, however, not to go over the top. His approval was couched in a kind of subdued, dry officialese. No direct mention was made of Gina Tesalli's pregnancy, other than to her 'evident enthusiasm to become a good wife and mother'. Even Algisa Fiore was 'sober and demure', a fact she demonstrated by pulling him to her bosom and covering him with kisses when he explained what he was up to.

ONE DAY LIVIA cooked him a new dish for breakfast, a kind of spring omelette, filled with fresh peas and mint. Then she announced that she would go to the market while he worked. For lunch that day they ate borlotti beans with pancetta, and a fish James could not identify.

'My predecessor told me that seafood had an inconvenient effect on the libido,' James said thoughtfully as he wiped his plate with a piece of bread.

'That depends what you think is inconvenient,' Livia said enigmatically. 'There's a Neapolitan saying, too: fish for lunch, no sleep during siesta.'

It was certainly true that after lunch he felt no need for a nap. But that may also have been because Livia hadn't served any wine. He hung around the kitchen, trying to engage her in conversation, but she seemed disinclined to talk to him. Eventually he gave up and went and lay on his bed.

A sudden sound at the door made him open his eyes. It was Livia, slipping into his room.

She smiled. 'Hello.'

An Italian would have greeted her with a stream of compliments and effusive protestations of love. But his throat had gone dry. 'Livia . . .'

She was kicking off her shoes and climbing onto the bed. 'Such a huge bed,' she said, looking around. 'I've never slept in one like this before.' She glanced at him, to see that he had understood.

He reached for her, but she held his hand in hers, making him wait.

'Now, listen,' she said sternly, 'because this is something we need to be clear about. In the village I come from, it is forbidden to make love until you are married. And this is a good rule. Some things should be special.'

'Oh.' Had she not come to sleep with him after all? 'I don't understand.'

Her smile broadened. 'Don't worry, you will soon.' She slipped into his arms, wriggling against him, and her laugh—that delicious, throaty laugh, thick with promise—was suddenly very close to his ear.

HE TRIED TO WORK, but it was no use—his attention kept wandering as he experienced a series of delightful flashbacks to the afternoon's activities. Getting up from his desk, he went into the kitchen.

Livia was cooking. 'Hello,' he said, grinning at her.

'Hello.'

'I'm finding it hard to work.'

'Me too.'

'And I'm ravenous, too. What's for supper?'

'Wait and see. But since you're here, would you come and stir this for me, please?'

He took the bowl of egg whites she handed him and gave it a stir. She watched, rather critically, he thought.

'Yes,' she said, after a while. 'I see what you're doing.'

'Is something wrong?'

'Not enough wrist.' She put his hand on his and guided him. 'Like this. Move your hand around. It shouldn't always be in exactly the same place.'

'Does it really make that much difference?'

'Egg whites are funny things,' she said enigmatically. 'Sometimes they fold and sometimes they don't. You're just a little—well, over-enthusiastic.'

'Oh,' he said. He had just realised that this conversation was not actually about egg whites at all. He slowed his movements and tried to copy what she had just demonstrated. 'How's that?'

She watched him. 'Yes,' she nodded. 'That's really quite promising.'

As James continued to stir, Livia went to the larder and returned with a piece of beef.

'I'm wondering whether to grill it or stew it,' she announced. 'What do you think?'

He was flattered—she had never consulted him about a menu before. 'Well, a simple grilled steak is always nice,' he ventured.

'Yes,' she said thoughtfully. 'Yes, but it all depends how hot the stove is. If the stove is really, really high, you can just throw the meat on without thinking about it. But if the stove isn't quite so hot, you're better off going for a stew and simmering it slowly. Do you understand?'

He was becoming accustomed to this code by now.

'I think so, yes. So tell me, is the stove still hot today?'

'Today, the stove is still fairly fierce,' she admitted. 'But that won't always be the case. We should practise making a stew, just in case.'

'IT'S A DAMN STRANGE thing,' Major Heathcote said, 'but A-force seem to be having trouble finding any women of low repute for this disease-spreading scheme of theirs.'

'Really, sir?'

'Yes. Odd, when you consider we're putting over five hundred service-men through the VD hospital every week. Makes you wonder who they're all sleeping with.'

'Yes, sir.'

'I hear A-Force have handed over responsibility for the rastrallymenties to the Italian police now. Though, frankly, I'd be surprised if that produces any better results. These Eyeties are as tricky as a brass sixpence.'

'Some do seem to be less than scrupulous, sir.'

'Hmm.' The major looked at him shrewdly. 'How about you, Gould? No problems I should know about?'

'Everything seems to be under control, sir.'

'Good.' Major Heathcote paused. 'Between you and me, I'm not too upset that disease thing didn't come to anything. I'm not saying you had anything to do with that, but . . . just watch your step.'

WHEN THE TIN was full he took the money to Angelo. They had hit upon a simple way of transferring cash without arousing suspicion: James would eat a small meal, and Angelo would bring him an astronomical bill. James would then place a large pile of notes on the plate, thus reinforcing his own reputation as a fool who unnecessarily insisted on paying his own way.

Zi' Teresa's was fuller than ever these days. It might no longer be a place to secure a girl for your bed, but that was more than compensated for by the sheer beauty of the staff. From the sommelier to the cigarette seller, all were female and all were nice to look at, and, if they also seemed to leave quite soon after they arrived, no one minded very much, since they were quickly replaced by others who were just as lovely.

One night, as James was leaving, Angelo drew him to one side. 'A man will come and see you tomorrow,' he whispered. 'He has the information you require.'

The man who came to the Palazzo Satriano the next day was huge, a fat mountain of flesh who could barely fold himself into one of James's chairs. He did not introduce himself and he wasted no time on pleasantries.

'Zagarella has a mistress,' he said. 'She lives out at Supino, and that's where he keeps his stocks of penicillin. She has agreed to make sure he stays all night tonight, so you'll be able to arrest him in the morning.'

'Why is she doing this?'

The huge man shrugged. 'She has been shown a photograph of him with another woman.' He removed a piece of paper from his pocket and held it out to James. 'The house is isolated. I have drawn you a map.'

Something about the man made James's skin crawl, but he took the map and glanced at it. It seemed clear enough. 'Thank you.'

The man levered himself to his feet. 'Be very careful,' he said. 'Zagarella will certainly be armed.'

At that moment the door opened and Livia walked in. For a split second she and the fat man stared at each other. Then the fat man smiled.

'So this is where you have been hiding yourself, Livia,' he said.

'HIS NAME IS Alberto,' she explained. 'He's caused me trouble for years.'

'Well, he can't get at you here,' James said. 'You're under my protection.'

'You don't understand,' Livia said flatly. 'To a man like that, information is power. And you've entrusted him with the most dangerous information of all—the information that you are breaking the law.'

'He's in this just as much as I am.'

'But you have more to lose.' She shook her head. 'Alberto's a pig, but he's a clever pig. He'll find some way of twisting this to his own advantage.'

Seeing her looking so vulnerable stirred something deep in his heart. He took her in his arms. 'I swear you'll be safe,' he promised.

'Idiot!' she said, hitting him with her fist. 'It isn't me I'm worried about. It's you.'

He smiled at her. 'Then you really care about me?'

'*Porco dio!*' she fumed. 'Of course I do.'

'I wasn't sure.'

'Well, now you know. So now you can promise me that you won't try to arrest this man Zagarella tomorrow.'

'Livia,' he said, 'I have to. It's my duty.'

'How can it be your duty?' she shouted. 'Your superiors would absolutely forbid it if they knew.'

'Don't you see—unless I do this, I'm just another corrupt intelligence officer. It's the opportunity I've been waiting for.'

'Oh?' she said. 'I thought *I* was the opportunity you were waiting for.'

'Of course you are. But I still have to do this.'

She threw up her hands. 'Get out,' she cried. 'Go and get yourself killed.'

THEY SET OFF before dawn. The Italians were on less exuberant form than usual as the borrowed Jeep rolled through the dark streets and onto the coast road heading north. The sun was rising by the time they found the place, a farmhouse just as remote as Alberto had promised. It was very still.

Too still, James thought. He didn't have much experience of farms, but surely they were never this quiet. Why were there no dogs barking? He motioned for Carlo and Enrico to draw their weapons as he crept towards the front door. It was open. Stepping inside, he heard the muted half-cry of an infant. He relaxed a little. At least there were people here, and alive. Pushing open the door where the noise had come from, he hurried through into a bedroom.

The lifeless body of a man slumped against the wall was Zagarella, James was sure of that. The woman in the bed had been stabbed as she slept: there was blood all over the mattress, and—horror of horrors—there was the baby at her lifeless breast.

There was a movement beside him as Enrico crossed himself. James heard the rumble of an approaching truck. Carlo went to the window.

'Men,' he said economically. 'Men with guns.'

'Soldiers?'

Carlo peered out. 'I can't be sure.'

'Come out with your hands up,' an American voice shouted.

'*Si*, soldiers,' Carlo said resignedly.

IT WAS A DISASTER in every possible way. For a while he had wondered if Livia had sent the Americans after him, worried for his safety. But she swore she had not, and the Americans themselves said that they had simply received an anonymous tip-off. Even so, it required some fancy footwork to explain his own presence at the farmhouse in a way that satisfied the curiosity of his superiors. A search of the premises had not produced any clues and nor had it unearthed any penicillin.

Jumbo's view was that James shouldn't worry. 'He's dead. You won.'

'But who killed him? And how did they know we were coming?'

'Probably a falling out between thieves. And as for the timing, that must

382 | ANTHONY CAPELLA

be a coincidence. It couldn't have been the Americans, if you didn't tell them about the op in the first place.'

James knew he ought to feel triumphant, but he could not help feeling uneasy. It was all too neat. 'It's a mystery, Angelo,' he said gloomily at Zi' Teresa's later that day. 'Nobody knows anything.'

'You should ask yourself,' Angelo said thoughtfully, 'Who is better off because he is dead? Perhaps those who betrayed him were playing a double game. They get rid of Zagarella and they also get to keep his penicillin.'

HE WAS SORRY now that he had fought with Eric. The truth was, they had simply had a hot-tempered falling out over a woman. Slowly, they started to become friends again, although there remained a slight awkwardness whenever the subject of Livia came up.

The first batch of fiancées was now all married, but a backlog had built up, and the bellringers of Naples were kept busy. One of his new wedding vettings was rather different from the rest. About a fortnight after the weddings started up again, Jumbo Jeffries stuck his head round the door.

It turned out that he had come to see him about Elena. 'What with all these other girls getting married,' he said, stroking his moustache, 'it seems like a nice idea for us to tie the knot too. Actually, I was wondering if you'd like to be the best man.'

James assured him that he would be delighted, and said he would arrange for Elena to be vetted and receive the necessary papers forthwith—a mere formality, he promised his friend.

When the time for the interview came, however, Elena seemed a little preoccupied.

'Is something wrong?' James asked gently.

Elena shrugged. Then she burst out, 'I don't want to marry Jumbo. I love him, but I'm a whore, not a housewife. What will happen to me after the war is over? He'll want me to go back to England with him. It will be cold, and I've heard the food is disgusting. And I don't think Jumbo will ever be rich. I like my work here, and I like the freedom it gives me.'

It was a tricky problem. James asked her what she would do if a way could be found to avoid a marriage.

'I'd like to stay with Jumbo until the end of the war,' she said. 'After that, I should have another four or five years at the top, and with the money I save I'll open a whorehouse, the best whorehouse in Naples.'

'You could always tell Jumbo you don't accept his proposal.'

'But that will hurt his pride. He won't want to go on seeing me if I do that. Can't you help me somehow?'

It was hard to see how, but James promised to try to think of a solution.

After a few days he went back to see her. 'I've got it,' he said. 'We'll just have to pretend that you were married before, a long time ago, and you don't know what became of your original husband. This being a Catholic country, getting a divorce will take a long time—perhaps you'll need a dispensation from the Vatican, and of course you can't get that while Rome is in German hands.'

'You're a genius,' she said delightedly. 'I'll tell Jumbo this evening. Now, how can I repay you?'

James assured her that he wanted no payment.

'But I want to do something for you,' she said. 'I suppose you don't want to sleep with me?'

James explained that, quite apart from any awkwardness it might cause with Jumbo, Livia would probably not be too keen on this idea.

'JAMES, WHAT'S THIS?' she asked, pulling a piece of paper from the breast pocket of his shirt.

'Oh. It's a letter.'

'An important letter?' she asked, then answered her own question. 'Well, of course it must be, if you keep it next to your heart.' She started to unfold it, then glanced at him, suddenly serious. 'Is it from Jane?'

'Yes. She wrote that when she ditched me. I was in Africa.'

'You pretended you had a girlfriend when you met me,' she reminded him.

'Yes. That was stupid of me, wasn't it?'

'Very, because I knew you were lying, and that was what made me think there must be another explanation. What was she like, anyway?'

'I don't really know,' he said slowly. And it's true: everything about Jane had vanished, like an English mist exposed to the fierce Italian sun of Livia's vitality. 'I think she was quite brave, though. Because it probably took quite a lot of guts to write that letter.'

'She was in love.'

'That always makes it easier,' he agreed. 'Anyway, tear it up.'

'I can't do that,' she protested.

'Then I will.' He took the letter and ripped it into a dozen pieces, tossing them into the air like confetti. It felt good. He was with Livia, and nothing that happened in the past will ever matter again.

'One day you'll tear up my letters like that,' she said, suddenly sad.

'Never,' he said. 'Besides, we're never going to be apart, so you'll never need to write to me.'

JAMES WAS SHAVING when the seismologist came to see him. Or rather, he was trying to shave: the water supply, always spasmodic, appeared to have dried up again. Irritably, he started to wipe the shaving soap off. There wasn't really enough stubble on his cheeks to justify a shave, anyway, something which still irked him—although it had been a revelation that Livia actually seemed to like his hairless face and torso.

At the thought of Livia his irritation deepened. She'd gone back to her family for a few days, and although he would have liked nothing better than to go with her, conditions in Naples were too fraught for him to take leave just at present. At least she was safer where she was, away from the bombing. There had been a particularly unpleasant raid the previous night, and he was suffering from lack of sleep, to add to lack of Livia.

There was a knock on the bathroom door, and Carlo put his head around it. 'There's a professor here to see you. A man by the name of Bomi. He knows all about earthquakes, apparently. Shall I send him away?'

'No, I'll see him,' James said, wiping his hands with a towel. 'Put him in the office, will you?' It would be useful to get an idea of when the earth tremors that now passed through Naples almost every day, might stop. They were more frequent, the older Neapolitans said, than at any time in living memory. Although the tremors didn't seem to worry the Italian population, they certainly disturbed the servicemen, who were never sure if what they were experiencing was an earthquake or the first salvo of a German raid.

Professor Bomi was a short, distinguished-looking man in a state of some agitation. He had initially tried to speak to the commander of the airstrip at Terzigno, he explained, and since then had been sent round a dozen different departments, none of which had shown the slightest interest in what he was trying to tell them. He hoped James was going to do him the courtesy of actually listening to what he had to say.

With an inward sigh James settled himself in his chair and prompted, 'So this is about the earthquakes, I understand?'

Bomi shrugged. 'Possibly, yes. The earthquakes may be part of it, they may not. Pliny says that there were an unusual number before the eruption of AD 79. Essentially, Vesuvius is becoming active.'

'Are you sure?' James glanced out of the window. The mountain looked much as it always had, although he noticed that the little wisp of smoke that usually hung over the summit was absent. 'It looks all right to me.'

Professor Bomi made an impatient gesture. 'That's because we're eight miles away, and you can't see that part of the cone wall has collapsed right into the crater. It's completely blocked. That's why there isn't any smoke.'

'Is it dangerous?'

'You have heard of Pompeii, presumably?' the professor demanded.

'Hang on a minute here.' James stared at him. 'Are you saying there's going to be another eruption like the one that destroyed Pompeii?'

The *professore* became markedly less agitated. 'Well, of course one can't say *that* for certain. The last time Vesuvius became active, in 1936, we simply saw some new lava flows. But the time before that, in 1929, one flow reached almost to the sea and destroyed two towns. You must evacuate everyone within twenty miles of the volcano.'

'But that would mean evacuating Naples,' James said. 'Tens of thousands of people. Where would they all go?'

'That's not my concern,' Professor Bomi replied. 'I'm just telling you what might happen if they remain.'

'But what is it that makes you think that another Pompeii is more likely now than it was, say, six months ago?'

'Ah. A good question.' The professor took off his glasses and polished them. 'Well, we've seen some very interesting portents recently. Not just the earthquakes. There have been some unusual sulphuric emissions. Wells have run dry or been tainted. This may be a sign of tectonic movements.'

'And if the volcano does erupt, which way will the lava flow?'

The professor threw up his hands. 'Who knows? It depends on underground pressure, the way the land falls, even the winds. Do you have a map?'

James got hold of one and the professor showed him where previous lava flows had gone. 'San Sebastiano and Massa are the towns most frequently affected,' he explained. 'Then Terzigno, Cercola, Ercolano and Trecase.'

There was an airfield at Terzigno and Cercola was a military base. 'I'd better warn them,' James decided. 'Is Fiscino in any danger?'

'Not especially, but who can say?' The professor sighed. 'The one predictable thing about a volcano is its unpredictability. The best thing would be to keep the crater under close watch, but unfortunately my observatory has been taken over by the military.'

'Do you want me to see if I can get it back for you?'

The professor expressed such effusive gratitude that James began to suspect that a desire to observe any activity at close quarters, rather than the issuing of a warning, had been the main reason behind his visit. 'I'll see what I can do,' he said. 'But don't expect any miracles.'

When the professor had gone, James went to the window. He had become so used to Vesuvius as simply a picturesque part of the view that it was a shock to remember that it was, in fact, a vast bomb. Now that he thought about it, there was a kind of brooding malevolence in the way the volcano squatted over the city.

He felt a twinge of fear for Livia. If it did erupt, what would happen to her? He wished there were some way of getting a message to her, but so far as he knew there were no telephones in her village.

He could, however, telephone the airfield at Terzigno. Eventually he got through to the American commanding officer, who informed him that an entire wing of B-25 bombers—eighty-eight in all—had recently arrived there. James asked if there was anywhere else they could be moved to, and explained about the professor's warning.

'You're not seriously saying we should change our dispositions just because some Italian's got the wind up?' the man asked incredulously. 'Only last week someone wanted us to evacuate because a statue in the local church had started crying. These Italians are extraordinary.'

James had little more success with the troops stationed at the observatory, who informed him that the volcano was, if anything, less active now than it had been in the previous few months. 'Apart from a fairly unpleasant smell, all's quiet up here,' an officer told him.

'When you say a smell—is it sour, like something rotten?'

'That's right.' The officer seemed surprised. 'How did you know?'

'It's sulphur.' James managed to persuade the officer to let Professor Bomi have one room of the observatory back, but he felt increasingly uneasy about the situation.

He drafted a brief note, which summarised the professor's predictions, together with a suggestion that contingency plans should be made for a limited evacuation of both the military and the civilian population, and submitted it to Major Heathcote.

The major's response was one in which the words 'incompetent', and 'nothing better to do' featured several times.

To settle his mind, James spoke to Angelo, who smiled when he heard Bomi's name. 'Don't worry, my friend. That *professore* has been saying for years that a big disaster is overdue. But that's his job, isn't it? It's just like a priest saying that if you don't go to church the sky will fall in.'

'One day, statistically, he's going to be right,' James pointed out.

'Sure, but in the meantime he's worrying, so we don't have to.'

AS HE SAT ALONE in his room that night, James could not shake off the thought of Livia, perched up there on the mountain as if on the shoulder of a sleeping giant. If it woke, what would become of her? What would become of all the Vesuviani?

Abruptly, he pulled a notepad towards him. Bomi had said there would probably be two phases to the eruption, one in which the mountain spewed lava and ash, and another, potentially much more deadly, in which gases and smoke exploded into the air. That meant there would be a brief window of opportunity in which to deal with the situation. First there would have to be a reconnaissance to establish which towns and villages were directly threatened. Trucks would be needed to evacuate the population—no, not trucks, not immediately: the first thing would be fire engines, to deal with burning buildings. *Then* the trucks could come in—say a hundred of them. There would have to be military police to direct the traffic . . . He was making notes on his pad now; planning a battle, he realised, a battle in which the enemy was a force of nature rather than a division of Germans.

IF SHE WAS HONEST, Livia had to admit to herself that one reason she had gone back to Fiscino for a few days was because she needed to think about what was happening with James. Soon, inevitably, she would have to make a decision. Would she be one of the thousands of Italian girls crowded onto the war-bride ships, heading off for a new life in a cold, foggy country? And what would it mean for her father and Marisa if she did go to England?

She sat outside on the terrace and talked it over with Marisa, whose view was that she should make the most of it. 'You could always start another restaurant in England,' she suggested.

Livia was about to reply when her attention was distracted by a cloud of black, fluttering objects that poured out of the woods above the house.

'Bats,' she said, puzzled. 'Why are they coming out in the sunlight?'

Marisa followed her gaze. 'They've been doing that all week,' she said. 'During the day they come out in swarms and fly over the trees.' She paused. 'Livia, I've been seeing things. Fires. Burning. People. I can't see the faces, but I know they're terrified.'

Livia caught her breath. 'Vesuvius?'

'I don't know. But have you noticed the summit isn't smoking? And then there's Priscilla's milk.'

Marisa took her into the kitchen, where there was a bucket of water containing the previous day's *mozzarelle* and a pail full of the latest batch of milk. Livia tried the mozzarella first. It had a faintly sour taste.

'Sulphur,' she said at once. She tried the milk next. It had the same taint. 'It must be coming up into the grass.'

'What does it mean?'

'I don't know. Perhaps something is happening underground, something that has disturbed the bats' caves, and it's somehow making sulphur seep out of the ground as well. I'll try to get a message to James. He'll know what to do. We could go up to the observatory—there's a radio there.'

It was early evening by the time they reached the observatory. As the two women entered, a British officer got to his feet.

Livia explained why they had come and he listened attentively. 'So to summarise,' he said when she had finished, 'you think that the behaviour of the animals may be linked to an increased possibility of eruption?'

'Exactly,' Livia said.

Emboldened by his interest, Marisa said, 'And I've been seeing things—premonitions.' She explained what she had glimpsed.

The officer nodded. 'I see. Well, what do you think we should do?'

Livia asked if he could get a message to James at FSS headquarters, and he said that he would include it in his evening report.

When they had gone, the officer picked up his binoculars and followed their progress down the track. He had no intention of passing on their anxieties to HQ—he knew what the intelligence people would say if he started including that sort of nonsense in his report.

JUST BEFORE DAWN James woke to the sound of bombs falling. No, not bombs, he thought: there were no air-raid sirens. It must be a summer thunderstorm. A series of deep booming cracks were rolling across Naples, each one collecting its own echoes as it did so. He went to the window.

Yesterday, the top of Vesuvius had been round, like an egg in an eggcup. This morning the tip of the mountain had been sliced off, and a great bulbous cauliflower of ash-grey smoke sat on top of it, glistening in the first faint light of dawn. From here it appeared motionless, but the rolling waves of sound indicated the continuing force of the explosions within. Underneath the ash cloud, the top of the mountain was actually glowing red-hot, like a wick inside a candle. Two fiery trails spilled from the rim.

The phone was ringing. He ran through to the office and snatched it up.

'I don't suppose you did anything about those contingency plans?' Major Heathcote asked.

'As it happens, sir, I did.'

'Now might be a good time for me to take a look at them.'

James went and pulled on his clothes, his mind racing, then returned to the office, where Eric was now standing by the window. On hearing James, he turned round. 'Holy smoke,' he said. 'It's true.'

'The first thing is to get out there and find out which way the lava is heading,' James said. 'Then we'll need to evacuate the area. It's all in the plan.'

While James dug out his plan and organised a stenographer to make copies, Eric got on the telephone. 'They've got lava fountains in five different places,' he reported. 'Mainly around San Sebastiano and Massa.'

'Can we get trucks?'

'There are forty K60s at Cercola.'

'Let's get them moving towards San Sebastiano.'

'I'm onto it,' Eric said, dialling.

'And I'll go out there and see what's happening.'

'I'll come too. We'll take one of the Jeeps.'

'A Jeep will never get through the traffic,' James said. 'I'll take the Matchless—it's quicker.'

'I could get on the back.'

'It'll make it less manoeuvrable. And besides, if you come with me I won't have any room to bring Livia back.' He suddenly remembered. 'Oh Lord—there's a whole wing of B-25s at Terzigno.'

'Should we get them to take off?'

James shook his head. 'The eruption could last for days. We shouldn't move them unless we absolutely have to, or they might end up with nowhere to land. I'll take a look while I'm out there.'

He ran down the stairs and pulled the motorbike off its stand.

IT WAS THE MOST awesome thing he had ever seen. The sheer scale of it was breathtaking—nature's vast power effortlessly dwarfing the puny bombs and bullets of mankind's insignificant little conflict. At the foot of the mountain, he seemed to enter a dim fog, like an English winter's evening. For a moment he thought it was snowing; then he realised that the light grey flakes swirling all around him were not snow but ash. Already it was piling up on roofs, dusting the world with drifts of grey.

The nearer he got to the eruption, the stream of refugees became a rout, fear visible in their faces as they tried to flee the roaring cloud of smoke and ash that now hung directly overhead, like a giant pulsing coral, its underneath turned pink by the glow from the crater. Below it, it was quite dark.

At Ercolano he overtook a slow-moving procession of military trucks. They were the vehicles Eric had ordered from Cercola, hopelessly lost. He offered to guide them, and they followed him up the winding road.

He felt a light shower of sand. For a moment he thought it was being thrown up by the trucks. Then he realised that, in addition to the soft grey ash, tiny black fragments of grit were now falling from the sky.

As he rounded a bend he caught his first proper sight of the lava. There were at least two separate streams—tendrils of glistening fire, pushing down to the north and west, their progress through the pine woods marked by trails of burning, smoking vegetation. On its way downhill one of the streams had passed right over the road, completely blocking it. He pulled up about a hundred yards away. Even at this distance, the heat was immense. He had been expecting torrents of liquid rock, but this was more like a tumbling landslide of hot coals, nearly twenty feet high, juddering silently forwards, pushed down the slope by the pressure of yet more coals behind. The lava had a crust on top of it, like the skin on a rice pudding, and as it oozed slowly down the hill, veins of red, and occasionally brighter fissures of brilliant gold, opened up momentarily, revealing the vast heat underneath.

In San Sebastiano an extraordinary sight met his eyes. The inhabitants of the town were kneeling about fifty yards in front of a twenty-foot-high wall of lava, clustered around a priest who was holding aloft the statue of St Sebastian. Many of the congregation had flowerpots or saucepans tied to their heads. James soon realised why: the hail of sand was falling less densely now, but the individual fragments were getting bigger. A stone the size of a fist smashed to the ground in front of him, where it lay smoking fiercely. The airfield wouldn't have this rock-storm yet, he guessed. If he could get a message to them, they might still get the bombers to safety.

Behind him, the convoy of trucks pulled into the square. 'Evacuate everyone you can,' he called to the driver of the first one. 'Women and children first. I'm going on to the observatory.'

'Here, take this.' The man offered him a mess tin. James crammed it onto his head and stuck the handle down his collar to keep it in place. He waved his thanks and turned the bike round.

The stones were falling everywhere now. Several bounced off his makeshift helmet and it was a relief when the observatory finally loomed out of the greyness. Inside, a group of soldiers were crouching round a radio set. They stared at James. He supposed he must look a bit of a mess by now, covered in grey ash and with a tin clamped to his head. 'I'm an officer,' he said. 'Captain Gould. I need to get a message to Terzigno airfield.'

'Radio's down,' one of the men said. 'There's been no reception since this thing started.'

'Damn.' There was nothing for it: he would have to go to the airfield himself. 'Keep trying Terzigno. If you get through, tell them to get their planes into the air.'

He drove back through San Sebastiano, where the evacuation was proceeding, and took the road that led round the mountain. The column of cloud was directly above him now, clearly visible through the falling ash. In front of him, and a little higher than he was, another lava stream was oozing down the mountain. He lost sight of it momentarily as he rounded a corner, then slammed on the brakes. Just ten feet ahead, the road disappeared under a red river of smoke and fire. The Matchless skidded from under him. James rolled clear, but he heard the tyres burst and the petrol tank ignite as the bike came into contact with the hot coals. Desperately he crawled away from the heat, then slowly got to his feet. To get to Terzigno, he was going to have to outpace the lava on foot. He set off at a jog.

In Fiscino, eighteen hours after the eruption started, the anxious villagers could see the lava only a quarter of a mile above them, like a fiery golden road winding up to the summit of the mountain. Without doubt, it was heading directly for their village.

The sound of truck engines cut through the roar of the eruption. A line of Allied trucks was rumbling up the road from Boscotrecase. The front one stopped, its engine still running, and a soldier leaned out. 'We've come to evacuate you,' he yelled. 'Jump in, *capeesh*?' He gesticulated at the back of his lorry. '*Rapido, molto rapido*.'

A few of the villagers ran to the lorry, where willing hands hauled them up. 'Wait,' Livia cried. 'If we go now, the village will be destroyed.'

'There's nothing we can do,' Don Bernardo said gently, 'except pray. And we can do that just as well from a place of safety.'

'We can dig a trench.' Livia looked around. 'A moat to channel the lava away. It's worth a try, isn't it? It's either that or let our homes burn.'

'Livia's right,' Nino said. 'We can dig.'

'We can't hang around for you,' the truck driver warned. 'We have to get on to Cercola. If you want to be evacuated, it's now or never.'

'We'll take that risk,' Nino said. The driver didn't wait to be told twice.

The remaining villagers took their pickaxes and spades and climbed to the vineyards above the village. 'Here,' Livia said, pointing to a slight depression in the land. It followed the fall of the mountain, but at an oblique angle. 'If we can make that deep enough, and wide enough, it might just take the lava to one side of the houses.'

They used sticks to mark out a twenty-foot-wide ditch. As they dug, the sky bombarded them with a hail of tiny stones. Livia looked up to wipe sweat from her eyes and realised with a shock that the lava was now only a few hundred yards away, close enough for her to smell the burning pine trees. 'The channel isn't deep enough,' she said helplessly.

'Get some mattresses. Anything to hold it back,' her father called. She ran to the shed and harnessed Priscilla to a cart, then piled it high with mattresses and furniture. Forcing the terrified animal to haul the load towards the lava was no easy matter, and it was several agonising minutes before she was able to dump her load against the sides of the ditch.

Above them, the lava reached the fields on the outskirts of Fiscino. Fruit trees yards ahead of it ignited spontaneously, the flames roaring through the branches and stripping them, leaving only the blackened trunks for the lava itself to devour. One by one, as the wall of coal bulldozed everything in its path, the villagers were driven back from their places.

Sparks danced in the air, thousands of them, cascading onto the village like tiny burning arrows. The hay barn went up with a terrible crackling sound and sparks poured from the burning roof. On the ground, fires raced across the dry grass. The villagers ran to the well with buckets, forming a human chain to douse the fires, but after a few moments there was a shout from someone who had allowed some water from his bucket to splash onto his skin. It was scalding hot. A few minutes later the well itself was dry, a great hissing coming from its depths as the mountain sucked the liquid into its core and breathed back only steam and smoke.

Now we are defenceless, Livia thought to herself.

The wall of fire touched the ditch and paused, hanging there for a second, before spilling down into the narrow trench, filling it. A ragged, exhausted cheer went up from the villagers.

Moments later, a red ooze of fire appeared at the trench's nearest edge and spilled over it, a rivulet of lava pouring from its rim towards them.

'The cart,' Nino shouted. 'Get the cart.'

Livia helped her father to get the harness off the panicking Priscilla, then they put their backs to the cart and tried to push it towards the gap in the ditch. Others joined them. The cart rolled into the ditch and caught fire. The villagers leapt back—all except Nino, who held on a moment longer.

Suddenly, as Livia watched, flames sprouted from her father's back like wings and gathered round his head. Livia heard a terrible scream and realised that it was coming from her own mouth. She ran, together with Marisa, to drag Nino clear, forcing herself into the scorching heat as if into a solid wall. They pressed themselves against him to extinguish the flames.

And then that red bulge of fire was surging inexorably over the cart, gathering momentum as it headed straight for the centre of the village.

IT WAS ANOTHER HOUR before an exhausted James reached the airfield at Terzigno. It was only when he wiped some of the ash and mud from his uniform that he was able to make the guards understand that he was an officer, and that he needed to see the base commander urgently.

It was hard to make the commander believe that an incipient fall of rocks from the sky was really going to put all his aircraft out of action, and when he had succeeded, harder still to organise eighty-eight aircrew for take-off. By the time the first bombers taxied down the runway and took off, the hail of light stones had started, pattering down onto the tin roofs of the temporary airfield buildings like a torrential storm.

'Doesn't seem so very terrible,' the CO commented, giving James a sideways glance. 'Still, better safe than—'

His words were drowned out by a sudden cacophony as the patter of falling stones turned into a deluge. It felt, James thought, as if they were being buried alive—as though the Nissen hut they were standing in was a very small box in a very large hole, and some giant hand were shovelling huge quantities of gravel on top of them. Initially the stones bounced on the runway, then the first layer settled and provided a thick, black carpet that absorbed those which came after, rapidly increasing in depth. The remaining planes queuing for take-off ground to a halt. Across the airfield, the crews of the stranded B-25s sprinted for the safety of the buildings, their arms raised over their heads against the pummelling rocks.

'Do you have a vehicle I can take?' James yelled. 'I need to get back up the mountain. There are some civilians I have to check on.'

The base commander waved his arm at the black deluge of clinkers. 'You must be joking. You won't get ten yards. You're not going anywhere until this is over. That's an order.'

THERE WAS LITTLE the villagers could do now except wait for the lava's approach. They made a stretcher to carry Nino, mercifully unconscious, to safety. Even his breathing was painful, as though he had sucked the flames deep into his lungs. Then they organised a human chain to rescue the most precious possessions from the houses that were threatened.

It took twenty minutes for the lava to travel the last 200 yards. First the vines on the terrace caught fire, the leaves withering in the immense heat as if vaporised. Then the doors and window frames of their neighbour's house burst into flame. The lava nudged a corner of the *osteria*, and rolled up alongside it as if against a bank. For a moment it seemed as if the building might actually withstand the lava: then the juddering and jiggling of those hot coals, as big as boulders, seemed to pass into its fabric. The roof splintered and capsized; the lava wrenched the kitchen wall from its foundation as it continued on its inexorable way downhill.

Minutes later the hail of light stones from the sky suddenly turned heavier, carpeting everything with a thick layer of clinkers. Standing in the doorway of a neighbour's house, Marisa put her arm round Livia. 'We did all we could,' she said gently. 'Now we need to look after our father.'

IN FACT, the eruption of Vesuvius in 1944 caused fewer casualties than anyone had a right to expect. The evacuation of over 2,000 people from the area of Massa and San Sebastiano proceeded smoothly, thanks to the efficiency of the relief plans and the heroic efforts of hundreds of Allied volunteers who helped implement them. In San Sebastiano, the lava eventually came to a halt only yards from the church, a clear sign—to the inhabitants at least—that the saint had once again intervened to protect his own. Many smaller villages and farms, however, were not so fortunate.

The fall of lapilli—the technical name for volcanic hail—continued off and on for eight days and nights, like some biblical plague, closing roads and making the whole area impassable. Then, with a final deafening roar, a great cloud of gas and ashes exploded thousands of feet into the air. Ten days after it had started the eruption was over, the vast ash cloud drifting slowly southeast as far as Albania. The top of Vesuvius, which had been smoking gently for more than two centuries, was now completely still.

LIVIA AND MARISA applied a poultice to Nino's shredded feet and hands, but soon he was in shock, running a temperature and thrashing around, and there wasn't enough water to cleanse the wounds properly.

'I don't know what else to do for him,' Marisa confessed as they watched him shiver. 'He needs a proper doctor. Burns are difficult.'

There was no way of getting him to a doctor in Naples during the eruption. Even if there had been, the journey would have killed him.

'The only thing that can help him now is penicillin,' Marisa said. 'But I don't know where we could get hold of any.'

Livia smoothed a damp cloth over Nino. She knew someone who could supply her with penicillin, but it was too dreadful a prospect to contemplate.

All the next day, as her father's condition worsened, she sat up with him. Gradually she watched him weaken, his thrashing replaced by terrible juddering tremors as he drifted in and out of consciousness.

They were still effectively cut off from the outside world, marooned on their volcano by the endless expanse of grey clinkers.

'I think he's getting worse,' Marisa said. 'I'm sorry, Livia. All I can do now is make him more comfortable.'

Livia made a decision. She stood up. 'Wait here with him.'

'Where are you going?'

'To get him penicillin.'

THE ROCKS HAD STOPPED falling, but grey ash and black volcanic grit covered everything. It was like moving through a lunar landscape, utterly bereft of any features. I have no choice, Livia told herself as she trudged through the great grey drifts. For my father to live, I have no choice.

It was nearly a mile to the farmhouse where Alberto Spenza lived. It was an old place, very remote: a good place for the *camorra* to store contraband. She knew he would never have allowed himself to be evacuated, since it would have meant leaving all his black-market spoils behind. Sure enough, she saw his Bugatti parked in a barn, although even there it had not escaped the eruption unscathed. Stones had broken through the roof and dented the paintwork, and the bonnet was covered in ash.

Alberto was cleaning the car with a cloth. When he saw her approaching he straightened up, though he said nothing.

She stopped in front of him. 'I need some penicillin. Urgently.'

'Why?'

'That's my business.'

'Then it's my business too. Since it's my penicillin.'

'I need it for my father.'

His fleshy lips made an 'o'. 'It's expensive. You'll need enough for a couple of weeks, if he's very ill. How are you going to pay me?'

'We have some money saved up. You can have it.'

'Whatever you have saved, it won't be enough.' He was playing with her, drawing it out. 'But perhaps we could come to an arrangement.'

'Alberto . . .' She hated to beg, but she had no choice. 'Just let me have it, and I'll pay you back somehow.'

'I don't want your money, Livia.'

'What, then?'

He simply looked at her and waited.

She had known all along what his price would be, and she had come knowing she had no choice but to pay it. 'All right,' she said.

'Come inside.' He offered her his hand. After a moment's hesitation she accepted it, and they walked together into the house.

WHEN IT WAS OVER she went to the sink and rinsed her mouth out with his fancy French wine.

Alberto got to his feet and went to the larder. He took out a small package, and tossed it to her. 'Your penicillin.'

She looked at it. 'But this is only one ampoule,' she objected. 'You said yourself, I need enough for at least two weeks.'

Deep in his eyes, she saw a glint of triumph—the triumph of a man who knows he has come off best from a deal. 'Then you'll just have to come back tomorrow.'

'And tomorrow you'll give me the rest?'

'No,' he said. 'Tomorrow I'll give you one more. And the day after that, another one.'

'You pig,' she said furiously.

She was almost home when she felt the waves of nausea overwhelm her. She bent double beside the path and vomited into the volcanic grit and ash.

THE AIRFIELD WAS CUT off from the outside world for the duration of the eruption, with even the radio producing nothing but howling static and garbled, hiss-swallowed voices. Then, as the lapilli storm eased, contact began to be re-established. Faint voices from Naples promised that bulldozers had begun the job of clearing the roads, but the reports also made it clear that the job of getting back to normal was going to be a long one. An area of twenty square miles had been blanketed with clinkers.

James found himself in the unaccustomed position of being considered something of a hero. Quite apart from the fact that he had been ready with an evacuation plan, the story of his epic journey from San Sebastiano to Terzigno was, apparently, becoming the stuff of local legend.

'You know what these Eyeties are like,' Major Heathcote explained by radio link. 'It can only help our relations with the Italians to have saved so many civilians from Vesuvius. We're going to organise a little ceremony, with a news photographer there to picture the general shaking your hand.'

'Really sir, there's no need—'

'I know, Gould. Everyone hates a fuss, but the Bureau are insisting.'

It was gratifying, but the only thing he could think about was whether Livia was safe, and if so where she was. To begin with, he assumed that Fiscino must have been evacuated along with the other villages. Then he began to hear stories of one group of Vesuviani who had refused to leave.

Not knowing whether she was among them was agony. As he waited for the roads to reopen, the fear that she might be injured or even dead filled him with terror. He had been mad, he realised, to let her go from his side.

If she's all right, he promised himself, I will ask her to marry me. Even if we have to keep it a secret from the rest of the world, she needs to know how I feel.

NINO WAS no better, and no worse. The infection and the antibiotics struggled for supremacy, but gradually Marisa became more hopeful.

Every day that week, Livia went back to Alberto Spenza. Every day he handed her one more ampoule of penicillin. By the fifth day, she no longer felt sick afterwards. It was simply what she did.

She could barely even begin to think about what would happen when Nino did get better, and what the consequences of her deal with Alberto would be. It was, she suspected, going to change everything. That was part of the price. She had forfeited any right she might have had to be happy.

AT LAST a bulldozer from Naples reached the airfield, opening up the road to Vesuvius. James immediately applied for leave. His request was granted, and he was even loaned a four-wheel drive Jeep by the Fifth Army.

Most of the routes up the mountain were still blocked, and it was only when he gave a lift to some refugees returning to San Sebastiano, who showed him the hidden tracks that led through the woods, that James was able to get to Fiscino. As he neared the village he realised that one of the lava flows had come very close to it. Several of the houses had been damaged, and he felt a great pressure in his chest as he realised that one of them had been the *osteria*. But then he could see Livia, picking through the debris, and he was out of the Jeep and running towards her, calling her name.

'SO YOU SEE,' he explained, 'if it hadn't been for you, I would never have come up with the plan, and if it wasn't for the plan, hundreds—who knows, maybe thousands—of people would have been caught on the mountain.'

'Well done,' she said. 'You must be pleased.'

She seemed strangely subdued, even allowing for the fact that her home had been damaged. 'But you were really all right here?' he asked anxiously.

'As I told you, my father was the only one who was badly burnt. He had a fever, and for a while we thought we might lose him, but he's getting better now, thank God. Marisa's been looking after him.'

She was barely meeting his eye, and she hadn't even kissed him. He wondered if she was angry that he hadn't come to look for her. 'I tried to get here sooner,' he said. 'But then the rock-falls started, and no one could move.'

'We had them too.' She shrugged. 'We coped.'

'Livia,' he said gently, 'aren't you even a little pleased to see me?'

'Of course,' she said. 'But now I have to prepare my father's lunch. He's staying at our neighbour's house, over there.'

As he walked across to the other house with her he said, 'I've got a few days' leave. I could stay here and help. If you'd like me to, that is.'

'People would talk.'

'Does it really matter if they do?'

'Not to *you*, perhaps,' she snapped.

'You *are* cross with me. Livia, what's wrong?'

She shrugged miserably. 'You can stay if you like.'

'Really?' he said, confused. 'You do want me to?'

'I want you to.'

His heart lifted. She was just upset because of what had happened, not with him.

WHEN SHE HAD given her father his lunch, James took her for a walk. As he put his arm around her he felt her flinch. Hopefully, he thought, what he was about to say would give her something to be happy about.

'You know,' he said, 'it's possible that all this may turn out to be a blessing in disguise. I'm fairly sure there'll be compensation to rehouse your family somewhere else, because of this.'

'What do you mean, somewhere else?' she said with sudden anger.

'Well, now that the *osteria* has been damaged, you can consider where the best place to situate yourself really is—'

'We're already situated here,' she snapped. '*This* is where we live.'

'But if you simply repair the damage *here*,' he explained patiently, 'sooner or later there'll be another eruption, and next time your family might not be so lucky.'

She gazed out over the pine woods towards the sea. 'Yes, we have been lucky,' she said quietly, 'but not because we were spared. We were lucky because we lived here in the first place.'

'I understand,' he said, not understanding, 'but now there's the future to consider. Staying here would hardly be a sensible—'

'Why would I want to be sensible?' she cried. 'One life here is worth ten lived somewhere else. And if you don't see that, you're simply an idiot.'

He was flummoxed, and just a little angry, though he tried not to show it. 'Well, that's you Italians all over,' he said drily. 'Always choosing the grand gesture over common sense.' He searched for the most hurtful thing he could think of. 'Just bear in mind that, next time, the Allies might not be around to clear up your mess.'

She laughed scornfully. 'We managed perfectly well before you came.'

They were rowing now, and he couldn't understand the cause. 'Livia,' he said patiently, 'let's not quarrel. I'm desperately sorry about your father, and the damage to your restaurant, but you must surely see that it opens up choices you didn't have before—'

'You mean I could choose to come to England,' she snapped.

It was exactly what he meant, though he had been intending to work up to it gradually.

'So that's what this is about, is it?' he said stiffly. 'You were worried that I might use this eruption as an excuse to propose to you and drag you away from all this. Well, you needn't have any fears on that score.'

'Good. Because I can't think of anything worse.'

She had gone too far, and she knew it. But she was too miserable to tell him why she was so miserable, and she made no move to stop him as he strode angrily to the Jeep, climbed into the driving seat, and set off down the mountain in a spray of volcanic stones.

LIVIA SAT by a window, watching the sun set over the Bay of Naples and thinking. Despite her misery, she had been telling the truth when she told James that she couldn't be a war bride. She and James had, at best, until the end of the war together, and then he would go back to England without her. It was clear to her that her first duty was somehow to help her father rebuild the farm and the restaurant, and to provide for him in his old age.

But quite apart from that, the locked box in her mind, where she was shutting away her dealings with Alberto, was already refusing to stay locked. What she had done would always be there, seeping its poison into their relationship. She either had to tell James everything, or accept that it was over.

But to tell him everything was simply another way of ending it. However much James sympathised with the women he dealt with in Naples, the women who had prostituted themselves, she knew that he would never have allowed himself to fall in love with one of them.

No: it was going to end. The only choice she had now was of *how* it would end. Would she tell James about Alberto, and have it finish in anger and recrimination, or would she simply tell him it was over, and spare herself the added pain of a confession?

She watched the sun slipping under the sea, turning the sky to fire. Her eyes filled with tears, spilled, and filled again. She made a sudden decision. Jumping to her feet, she went in search of paper and a pen.

TWO LARGE FLAGPOLES had been erected on the outside of the Palazzo Satriano, from which the Stars and Stripes and the Union Jack fluttered side by side. In the entranceway, two military police stood on guard.

James spotted Hughes. 'What's going on?' he asked.

'The general's visit. Thanks to you, the Film Unit are going to make a newsreel about it. Apparently we're a wonderful example of Allied cooperation.'

James continued on to his own office. It was evidently being used as a receptacle for everyone else's junk. Boxes of papers were piled everywhere and a huge chandelier had been dumped on the table.

Major Heathcote strode in. 'Better get this place cleared up, Gould.'

'Yes, sir.'

'The general will be with us Thursday, at noon.' The major eyed James's uniform, which had barely been standard issue before the eruption and was in a considerably worse state now. 'Don't forget to draw a new uniform.'

'No, sir.'

The major hesitated. 'Incidentally, Gould, about this relief operation. It seems to have caught everyone's imagination. Anyway, the Bureau thinks it best to emphasise that it was a team effort. So as far as the public are concerned, you and Vincenzo came up with the plan together. And I, as the officer in charge, had overall responsibility.'

James found he did not care in the least who took the credit for the relief operation. 'Really, sir, it's perfectly all right.'

'That's the spirit, Gould. Of course *we* know it was mostly your work, but it looks better for the people back home this way.'

After the major had gone James began to tidy up. There was a lot to be done, and it was a couple of hours before he had made much impression.

Suddenly he smelt something. A wonderful, rich aroma was wafting through the apartment. He would have recognised it anywhere—it was the smell of Livia's *fettuccine al limone*. With a burst of happiness he rushed through to the kitchen.

The girl who was cooking turned round with a polite smile. 'Oh,' he said, disappointed. 'I thought you were Livia.'

Hughes was standing next to her, chopping a large pile of courgettes. 'I took the liberty of engaging Maria here on a temporary basis,' he explained. 'Just until Mrs Pertini comes back.'

'Yes, of course. Give me a shout when it's lunchtime, then.' Hughes and Maria were looking at him, clearly waiting for him to go. 'You probably want to slice those at slightly more of an angle,' he said to Hughes. As he closed the door there was a muffled giggle.

FOR FIVE DAYS Nino slept, occasionally opening his eyes to see who was washing his wounds or changing his bandages. Sometimes it was Livia, but more often he found Marisa sitting by his bed.

'*Dov'è Livia?*' he murmured. 'Where's Livia?'

'She'll be back later. Now sleep.'

Each day, Livia used up another of the ampoules of penicillin Alberto had given her. Then, suddenly, Nino was well enough to sit up. His daughters brought him broth made with the last of the chickens. They pulped the last of the precious tomatoes to make a *passata*, easily digestible and full of vitamins. He was weak, but it looked as if he was going to be all right.

That afternoon, she went back to Alberto's for what she hoped would be the very last time. The Bugatti was parked outside his farmhouse, its dents repaired and its bodywork gleaming.

She stepped inside his door. Alberto was waiting for her in the kitchen, but today he was wearing a suit. A dress hung from a hanger on the door.

'This is for you,' he said, taking it down and handing it to her. 'Put it on.'

He watched without comment as she took off what she was wearing and pulled on the dress. It was a short dress, pencil-thin, made of silk covered in hundreds of tiny black glass beads.

'I need a mirror,' she said, looking around.

'I'll be your mirror.' He adjusted the neckline. 'There. You look perfect, Livia.' He held out his clenched fists. 'Choose one.'

She frowned. Was he going to hit her? She tapped his left fist, and he opened it to show her a silver necklace.

'Turn round.'

As he fastened it she felt his breath on her neck, deep and regular. Then he stepped back and handed her a bonnet.

'Now we're going for a drive.'

The road to Massa was still covered with clinkers, which crunched under the car's wheels. Alberto drove slowly, careful not to damage the bodywork. The town was deserted, many of its buildings destroyed. But in the main square they found a truck parked with its engine running. Two men were carrying goods out of the houses that remained—candlesticks, mirrors, anything of value—and throwing them into the back.

'Those people are looting,' Livia said, horrified.

'It certainly looks like it.' Alberto stopped the car. 'Giuseppe, Salvatore,' he called. 'How's it going?'

One of the men shrugged. 'There's not much here.'

'Maybe you're not looking in the right places.' Alberto jerked his thumb at Livia. 'Look what *I* found.'

The men eyed Livia. With a laugh, Alberto put the car into gear and swept away from them.

Livia closed her eyes. Alberto was making it clear that until he handed over the penicillin, she was his, to dispose of as he wished.

When they reached Naples, Alberto drove into a quiet road at the back of the Questura, the main police station, and stopped the car. A *carabiniere* standing guard at the door nodded to him.

'A friend of yours?' Livia said at last.

'Yes. I do a lot of business with the people in this building.'

'And what's that got to do with me?'

'Today you're the business I'm here to do.'

She did not ask him to explain. Whatever he had in mind for her, it was bound to be unpleasant. She would shut it out of her mind until it was over.

'Livia,' he began, 'I want to ask you something.'

JAMES SAT at his desk, resplendent in a brand-new uniform. His boots were polished to a mirror finish, his brass belt-buckle shone, and his cap was hanging in readiness on the back of the door.

A howl of microphone feedback came from the courtyard. 'Testing,' an amplified voice said hesitantly. James went and looked out of the window. Even now, in the last few minutes of preparations, more bunting was being hung above the microphone where the general would deliver his speech.

He went back to his desk and picked up a letter from his in-tray. It was headed 'Commune of Cercola'.

Dear Sir,

The administration of this commune, in expressing the gratitude and thanks of the citizens of Cercola for the work done for the public benefit during the recent eruption of Vesuvius, feels bound to mention in particular the prompt intervention of the Allied authorities . . .

He added it to the pile of similar letters. The thanks were genuine, he had no doubt, but once those who had benefited from the Allies' help realised that they were being encouraged to make a song and dance about it for propaganda reasons, they had all tried to outdo each other in the effusiveness of their gratitude. Many of the letter writers were even now gathering on the raked seats downstairs, decked out in the robes and chains of office.

Eric put his head round the door. He at least had had the decency to be embarrassed by the suggestion that the idea for the operation had been anything to do with him.

'See you downstairs, buddy,' Eric said. 'General's car's on its way.'

James nodded. 'I'll be right down.' He opened another letter.

Dear Captain Gould,

I just wanted to let you know that Corporal Taylor and I have had our baby. He is a beautiful little boy, nine pounds, with blue eyes and dark colouring, very hungry. If you will let us, we would like to call him James, in recognition of all that you did for us.

Regards,

Gina Taylor (née Tesalli)

404 | ANTHONY CAPELLA

He smiled, and opened the next.

Dear James,

I am sorry that we parted on bad terms when you came to see me at Fiscino after the eruption. However, it doesn't matter now. What I am about to write has nothing whatsoever to do with our quarrel.

I have decided that I am not going to return to Naples to resume my position as your cook. My life has taken a different course now, one which, however much I regret, I cannot undo. It is probably for the best, in any case. I enjoyed our time together, but I would never have been happy in England with you. In fact, I could never be anywhere but here, looking after my father, and I have decided that I shall do that for the rest of my life rather than marry again. My reasons for this are complicated, but there is no chance whatsoever of persuading me otherwise. I ask only that you do not make it any more painful for me by trying to change my mind.

With best wishes for a happy life,

Livia

He stared at the letter. It was not possible. He read it again, twice. His first reaction was that she did not mean it, that she was simply angry with him. But the tone seemed resigned, even wistful, rather than furious.

Then the awful reality of it hit him. She was ditching him. He would never kiss her again, never see that mischievous smile or her eyes flashing with passion. She wanted him out of her life.

This is all wrong, he thought desperately. This is all completely wrong.

LIVIA WAS AWARE of Alberto looking at her in a strange way, but she kept her gaze fixed on the bonnet of the Bugatti. She shrugged. 'If there's something you want to ask, then ask.'

'Will you marry me?'

Her head did swivel then. '*What?* After everything you've done? You're even crazier than I thought.'

'It got complicated. I was angry. You're so beautiful, Livia, but so damn superior. No, wait.' She was trying to protest. 'Sometimes I wanted to cut you down to size. But everything I did, I did because I love you.' He paused. 'Even if it meant hurting you . . . Livia, after the war I'll be a rich man. I need a woman by my side. I need *you*. I'll give you everything you want. And I promise that I will never, ever harm you again.'

'What about . . .' She swallowed. 'What about the restaurant?'

'Of course we must rebuild it. More than that—I'll put money into it, we can build it up into a proper business. With me behind it it'll become successful again, you'll see. We'll make money there. There'll be jobs, good jobs, for Marisa and your father, and if your father wants to retire there'll be plenty left over to make him comfortable.'

She stared out of the windscreen with unseeing eyes. What Alberto was offering was more than she would ever be offered by anyone else, she knew. Logically, there was no alternative.

'GOULD.' IT WAS Major Heathcote, standing at the door. 'For heaven's sake, man, get a move on.'

'Yes, sir.' Despite his shock at the letter, he automatically fell into step beside the major as the CO hurried downstairs to the courtyard. Some of the Italian dignitaries, seeing the two British officers striding out together, broke into a round of applause. There were even a few shouts of 'Bravo.'

'Not yet, not yet,' the major muttered, glaring at the clappers. 'Wait for the general.'

They halted, then stood easy. The Italians applauded again, more politely this time. 'It's not a bloody parade,' the major muttered disgustedly.

The general's armoured car swung in from the Riviera di Chiaia, and two smartly dressed military policemen presented arms on either side of the entrance. A moment later, all the Allied servicemen in the courtyard snapped to attention as one. As the great man got out, Major Heathcote stepped forward and saluted.

'At ease, guys,' the general said through the din of cheering Italians. 'Is that camera rolling?'

The Army Film Unit director said that it was.

'Great. These the guys?' The general came around so that he was standing between Eric and James. Flashbulbs went off. Then he raised his hand for silence. An expectant hush fell on the crowd.

'ALBERTO,' SHE SAID, 'I'm sorry. It's a generous offer, but the answer's no.'

He sighed. 'I thought you might say that. Does this have anything to do with the Englishman?'

However afraid she was for herself, she was even more fearful for James, knowing that Alberto would have him killed without hesitation if he deemed it necessary. She shook her head. 'I'm not seeing him any more.'

She felt his eyes on her. After a moment he grunted and pointed towards the police station. 'In there,' he said, 'there are people who have been given the job of rounding up women with syphilis and sending them north, behind the German lines.'

She felt a cold spasm of fear closing around her stomach. 'What's that got to do with me?'

'I told them I've got a girl they can take.'

'But they'll find out—'

From an inside pocket he produced a piece of paper. As he unfolded it she saw that it was a certificate. 'An Allied army doctor has examined Livia Pertini and found that she is carrying the infection. It's already signed. All I have to do is fill in the date.' He paused. 'Unless, of course . . .'

'So that's the choice you're offering me?' she said. 'Marriage, or that?'

'I would rather you had agreed of your own free will. But everything I said still stands. Livia, I have to have you. Which is it to be?'

'WHAT WAS IT you guys did, exactly?' the general murmured as he ended his speech and turned to pin a ribbon to James's chest.

'Organised the civilian evacuation from Vesuvius, sir.'

'Oh, yes. Good work.' The general saluted them, and they saluted him back. 'Either of you speak Italian?'

'I do, sir,' James said miserably.

'Say a few words, would you?' He gestured at the crowd.

'Sir?'

'A few words of thanks. Though if you could mention the war on tyranny, that would be good.'

'Yes, sir.'

The general held up his hand for silence. Instantly, silence fell. James leaned towards the microphone. 'I just want to thank the general for his kind words. And to, er, reiterate that the war on tyranny is, er, very important to us.' He looked at all the expectant faces. Suddenly he knew that he could not go through with this nonsense any longer.

'Look,' he said, 'I'm not a hero. I'm not even a good soldier. The truth is I only came up with the evacuation plan because of a girl.'

The Italians gave a collective murmur of interest. Political speeches were all very well, but romance was much more fascinating.

'She lives on Vesuvius, you see. That was the point—I wanted her to be safe. But when it came to it, instead of seeing that she *was* safe, like a fool I went to Terzigno to make sure the aircraft were all right.'

As one man, his audience gasped with anguish at the thought of James's folly. Those in the back rows craned forward to get a better look.

'What's he saying?' the general said in Eric's ear.

'It's, uh, a little too fast for me to follow, sir.'

'I made the wrong decision,' James said slowly. 'I realise that now. Her house—her family's restaurant—was damaged. I still don't know exactly what happened during those ten days, or what she went through, but I know it was enough to somehow make her change her mind about me. And although I'm not going to take off this ribbon here and now, because the man standing beside me would have me shot, I would throw it in the sea tomorrow if I could only have her back.'

James looked at the crowd of Italian faces gazing sympathetically back at him. The emotions he had for so long been choking off suddenly, inexorably, welled to the surface, and his eyes filled with tears. 'I love her,' he said simply. 'I love her more than anything. And now she's asked me to forget her. But that's the one thing I can never, ever do.'

The Italians broke into applause. Many were openly weeping. One or two even got to their feet, running forward to hug James.

'Extraordinary,' the general said, looking around him with an air of bemusement. 'Quite extraordinary.'

ZI' TERESA'S was deserted apart from a barman polishing glasses.

'We're not open,' the barman began. But Angelo, seeing who it was, came out from the back and motioned for the barman to leave them.

'Would you like some company, James?' he asked.

James took Livia's letter out of his pocket and pushed it towards him. 'Here. You might as well read it.'

Angelo read the letter in silence. Then he reached under the counter for an unmarked bottle, which he unstoppered. He poured some of the pale brown liquid into two balloon glasses. James picked one up and sniffed it.

'What is it?'

'Grappa. Triple distilled, blended in the cask, and over a century old.'

James shrugged and knocked it back in one gulp. Even in his present mood, however, he could not ignore the unctuous, venerable fumes that caressed his sinuses and lingered as a rich, smoky aftertaste on his palate.

'So,' Angelo said thoughtfully, 'Livia has decided she will not marry you. She has chosen duty over love.'

James pushed his glass towards the maître d' for a refill. 'I let her down,' he said. 'I wasn't there when she needed me.'

'I see.' They drank in silence for a moment. 'You are being too hard on yourself,' Angelo said thoughtfully. 'You were simply doing *your* duty. Livia, I think, will forgive you for that.'

'Forgive me? She never wants to see me again.' He buried his head in his arms and groaned. 'Angelo, I've been such a fool.'

'That's true,' Angelo agreed. 'However, it may not matter.'

'What do you mean?'

'Simply this. Have you ever actually told Livia that you love her? That you want to spend the rest of your life with her? That no obstacle, however insurmountable it seems, will ever be enough to keep you apart?'

James sighed. 'No,' he admitted. 'It was a difficult situation—you know that. As the wedding officer . . .'

'James, James. Remind me why Britain is in this war.'

James shrugged. 'We decided that certain things were worth fighting for.'

'Such as?'

'Well—fair play. Sticking up for people who can't do it for themselves. Not letting ourselves be pushed around by some tinpot military dictator.'

'Yet when it comes to your own heart, you are prepared to have your life dictated to by the military, even at the expense of decency, of fair play—and yes, even of love.' Angelo nodded. 'You decided that our country was worth fighting for, and we're grateful. But what about Livia? Isn't *she* worth fighting for?' He placed his finger on the letter and pushed it back across the bar towards James. 'You can carry this letter round with you until it's faded and torn, or you can say that love renounced in circumstances like these has not been renounced at all, only tested. In short, my friend, if you really think the cause worth fighting for, then you can choose to fight.'

'By God, Angelo,' James said, staring at him. 'You're absolutely right.'

THE ROADS MIGHT be open, but the landscape was still eerily dead. Ash swirled around the wheels of his Jeep as James zigzagged up the mountain. When he got to Fiscino everything was quiet. He pulled up outside the ruin of the *osteria* and turned the engine off. There seemed to be no one about.

'Hello?' he shouted. Then he saw a face he recognised at one of the neighbours' windows. 'Marisa,' he called. 'It's me, James.' She came to the door. 'Where's Livia?'

'She's not here.'

'So where is she?' She hesitated, and he said, 'I have to speak to her.'

'She went to Alberto Spenza's house.'

'The gangster? What's she doing with him?' She hesitated again, and he said impatiently, 'Never mind. How do I get there?'

After a moment she pointed to an opening in the woods. 'Take that path, and follow it for about a mile.' Then, in a rush, she said, 'She went there yesterday, and she hasn't come back. I'm worried about her.'

'Don't worry, I'll find her,' he said, setting off at a run. He jogged along the track until he came to a farmhouse. There was a gleaming red Bugatti parked in the barn, and the front door was open. 'Livia?' he called.

There was no reply, so he stepped inside. In the kitchen, he saw the remains of a meal. Two half-full glasses of wine stood by two half-empty plates.

'Livia?' he said again. There were sounds coming from upstairs. A creaking bed. A woman's cry. He ran upstairs and kicked open doors.

There were two people in the bed, the fat man and a woman. He saw a mass of dark hair, a naked back and a dress thrown over a chair, but the woman with Alberto Spenza was not Livia.

Alberto wrapped himself in a sheet and lumbered to his feet.

'Where's Livia?'

Alberto crossed to the window and glanced out. 'So you came alone,' he commented. 'That was rash.'

With a snarl James advanced on the Italian. 'Tell me where she is, you bastard, or I'll—'

'Or you'll what? I have the ear of influential people. Do you think that one girl is more important to them than their war on tyranny?' He smiled mirthlessly. 'But if you have really lost something of value to you, you could always ask at the police station. Perhaps someone has handed it in.'

'What are you talking about?'

'She won't be coming back. But if you do ever find her, you might like to give her this.' He picked up the dress and threw it to James.

'I hope the Germans appreciate her,' Alberto said conversationally.

With a curse James ran towards him, and found himself looking down the barrel of a pistol. For a long moment they stared at each other. Then, without another word, James turned and left.

Seething and humiliated, he retraced his steps up the track to Fiscino. He could guess something of what Alberto had done now, although he still couldn't imagine how or why Livia had let herself get mixed up with him. And what had he meant about the Germans?

Marisa was waiting for him. 'Well?' she said anxiously. 'Was she there?'

'No,' he said curtly. He threw down the dress. 'Only this. Marisa, I think you'd better tell me everything.'

When she had finished he closed his eyes. 'I suppose there's no doubt,' he said, 'that she slept with that brute?'

She hesitated. 'I could lie, and say that perhaps she didn't. But we'd both know it isn't true. She did what she had to do.'

He took a deep breath. A basic, primal jealousy boiled in his veins.

'James,' Marisa said quietly, 'it's you she loves. Whatever she did, she never stopped loving you. You have to go on believing that.'

AT THE QUESTURA he was shown into the presence of the chief of police. The man called for the relevant files and looked through them lugubriously. Eventually he turned a file round and pointed. 'It's written here,' he said. 'There seems to be no doubt. Livia Pertini. Arrested in the act of soliciting and examined by a doctor the same afternoon. She was taken to the camp at Afragola to join the other girls.'

James's blood ran cold. 'So where is she now?'

The policeman glanced at his watch. 'I should imagine they will already have left by boat for the journey north.'

'We have to stop them. There's been a terrible mistake.'

The chief of police folded his hands over his stomach. 'Are you her boyfriend?'

'Yes, as it happens.'

'Ah.' The chief of police nodded thoughtfully. 'You were not aware that she was supporting herself in this way. This happens.'

'She is *not* a prostitute. Nor is there any question of her being diseased.'

'If you say so. But it's out of my hands now, it's a military matter.'

'There has been corruption. I demand a full investigation.'

The chief of police gave him a hard look. 'Be careful what you accuse us of, sir,' he said mildly. 'Unless your proof is absolutely cast iron.' After a moment he nodded. 'I thought not.' He started gathering the papers together. 'What will you do now?' he said conversationally.

'As matter of fact,' James said, 'I'm going to go and fetch her back.'

The chief of police smiled. 'I don't think you understand. She is being taken behind the German lines.'

'I understand perfectly.' James stood up. 'And however long it takes, I promise you I will find her.'

PART FOUR

The boat left from the harbour at Gaeta, speeding without lights through the water. There were about a dozen women on board, all of whom had been imprisoned together awaiting their fate. They were escorted by two men from A-Force, one British and one Italian. There was no shelter on board and the women, in their flimsy dresses, were soon drenched. Huddling together for warmth, they said little as the boat bounced and twisted over the waves.

The night was moonless, but the sea gave off a faint phosphorescent glow, and Livia could tell when they were nearing land again because the shoreline stood out black against the purple sky. The boat slowed to a walking pace, and the British officer went to the bow to peer into the water, looking for mines. For several minutes they proceeded like this, and then the officer was evidently satisfied, because he turned and raised his hand.

The boat accelerated: there was a 'chunk' sound as it hit something in the water, then a flash from under the boat—like underwater lightning, Livia thought: it flickered and was gone again. A great bulge of water seemed to rear out of the sea, barging the boat into the air. She heard screams, splintering wood, and only then, it seemed, the crack of an explosion. Cold water poured over her head and for ten agonising seconds, with her lungs bursting, she thought that she wasn't going to make it. But then, like a cork, she felt herself popping to the surface, where she gratefully sucked in the air.

Around her, others were coming to the surface too, grabbing onto bits of wreckage. Livia looked around. The shore was less than a hundred yards away. Wearily she turned onto her back and began kicking in that direction.

Eight of them made it to the beach, including the officer who had been standing in the bow when the mine exploded. It was a wonder, Livia thought, that he had possessed the strength to swim at all.

They made him as comfortable as they could, taking off his wet clothes and making a shelter from branches. It made no difference: the man died of his injuries before daybreak.

'What do you think we should do, Livia?' It was Abelina who spoke. She was a shy nineteen-year-old, who Livia had met in prison.

Livia thought for a moment. 'In my village, there were men who had walked back from prisoner-of-war camps in the north. They slipped through the German lines without any trouble. If they can do it, so can we.'

'We don't even know where we are,' another woman objected.

'And look at the way we're dressed,' someone else said.

'Well, I'm going to chance it,' Livia said. 'We know we have to go south. Who's coming with me?'

'I will,' Abelina said.

Then Renata, a woman from the slums in Naples who Livia had also spoken to in prison, said, 'Oh, all right. I might as well give it a try.'

The remaining women decided that it was too far, and too dangerous, to try to get back to Naples. Out of fear and inertia, Livia realised, they were probably going to end up doing just what the Allies had expected of them.

LIVIA, ABELINA AND RENATA walked inland until they came to a village, where it turned out they were just west of Rome. Hearing this, Livia's spirits lifted a little. They were probably only seventy miles from the front line, after which it was another seventy miles to Naples.

A few hours later, however, Renata was complaining of blisters and exhaustion. They all sat down on the grass and took off their shoes just before the sound of approaching vehicles filled the air. The trucks were on them before they could move—a convoy, each lorry filled with German soldiers. The men in the back of the trucks waved delightedly at the girls, the drivers tooted their horns. The last truck slowed down and stopped.

'What do you think?' Abelina said anxiously. 'Is it safe?'

'Well, I'm going with them.' Renata ran towards the truck. After a moment Livia and Abelina followed her.

As the truck began to move off, Livia felt hands pulling her up, and a huge soldier gently but firmly pulled her onto his lap. Opposite her, Renata and Abelina were already seated on two other soldiers. The one she was sitting on smiled at her and said '*Ich Heinrich.*' He pointed at Livia.

'Livia,' she said nervously.

'*Bella* Livia.' It seemed to be the only word of Italian he knew. '*Bella.*'

They sat on the soldiers' laps for twenty miles, and in return had to endure little more than the occasional shy kiss, some out-of-tune singing, and much raucous laughter. When the trucks finally pulled over and set the girls down, all of them were sorry to see the Germans go.

By the time the women arrived in the next village, it was getting late. They had nothing to lose, so they knocked on doors. The people were poor, their crops devastated by the war, but they gave the women a little bread before showing them to a barn where they could spend the night.

The next morning they were on the road again soon after dawn. Across the valley a pillar of smoke hung on the horizon, but there seemed to be no obvious dangers, so they kept on the way they were going. When they got much closer to the smoke they saw that it was coming from a village, where the church had been on fire. It was only then that Livia realised there was something acrid about the smell.

The door to the church had collapsed, blackened. Inside, the roof had burnt through, and the sunlight that streamed in made it easy to see what was there. There were bodies clustered round the altar, which had itself been reduced to a charred stump by the fire. Others were lying by the door, as if they had been trying to escape. Most were women and children.

As Livia turned away she saw an old woman sitting, rocking back and forth, by the roadside. 'What happened here?' she asked gently.

'Partisans,' the old woman said numbly.

'Partisans did this?'

'No. It was the Germans. They said that we let the partisans take our food.' The woman struck her own head. 'We asked the partisans to go away, but they kept coming back. So the Germans came and put everyone in the church. They threw grenades in. Then they set fire to the church.'

'How did you escape?'

'They left me here to tell the partisans what happened. I'm the only one they spared.'

The three women left the empty village and walked downhill in silence. When darkness fell, they huddled together under a tree, but none of them slept much that night.

The next day, they saw a convoy of German armoured cars on the road ahead, and decided to make a detour rather than risk being seen. Getting hopelessly lost, they spent the whole day negotiating a steep ravine. Livia's muscles felt like lead, and her head felt thick and groggy.

A man's voice said, 'Where are you going?'

Livia looked round. She could see no one, and for a moment she thought she must be hallucinating. Then two men stepped out from the bushes. They were wearing a faded uniform, but their feet were shod in the traditional sandals of mountain peasants, and at their throats were bright red neckerchiefs. Each had a rifle, and they were pointing them at the women.

Livia was too tired to be frightened. 'We're trying to get to Naples, but we need somewhere to rest,' she said. 'Is there somewhere we can stay?'

'What do you think?' the man asked his companion in a low voice.

The other man must have agreed, because the first one stepped forward onto the track and gestured for them to follow him. Eventually they reached a dense chestnut wood where their guide called a halt.

'Well, this is it,' he said, looking around him. 'Welcome to our *casa*.'

Looking around her, Livia saw that there were a number of wigwam-like tents dotted among the trees, each one camouflaged with leaves and branches. People were emerging to look at the newcomers. Some were in uniform, some wore peasants' clothes, and all of them wore a red neckerchief.

A young man detached himself from one of the groups and walked towards them. 'Welcome, comrades,' he called. 'My name is Dino, and you are now under my command.'

DINO WAS YOUNG, about twenty-two, but he had the confidence and charisma of a natural leader. Initially he was suspicious of the three women's sudden appearance in his camp.

Livia explained again that they were simply trying to get to Naples.

'Now is a bad time to try to cross the line,' Dino said. 'If the Germans don't get you, the Allied artillery will. You'd do better to wait a few weeks. Then the Germans will be forced to retreat past us.' He waved expansively towards the south. 'After that there'll be nothing between you and Naples.'

'Can we stay here while we're waiting?'

'We can't afford to keep visitors. If you eat, you work.'

'Of course.'

'What can you do? You look like whores, if you don't mind me saying.'

'Some of us are,' Livia admitted.

'Then you are the victims of capitalism and you will not be exploited here. Can you cook?'

Abelina and Renata nodded.

'I can,' Livia said. 'But at the moment I'd rather not.'

'Can you shoot?'

'Yes. I've been shooting hares in the countryside since I was a child.'

Dino unshouldered his rifle and handed it to her. 'Shoot that tree,' he said, pointing to a chestnut fifty yards away.

Livia's hand shook as she raised the gun to her shoulder, but she planted her feet properly, as her father had taught her, and a split second later she heard the crack as the bullet hit the trunk.

'Could you do that to a German?' Dino asked laconically.

She thought of the burnt, blackened bodies in the church. She could shoot the people who had done that.

'Yes,' she said, 'I could.'

Dino nodded. 'Good.' He took her to a tent, and she chose what uniform she could find—khaki trousers and a rough serge shirt.

He handed her a red neckerchief. 'Whatever else you wear, always wear this. We are *Garibaldini*, and we wear the revolutionary flag.'

'So you're communists?' Livia asked.

'Yes. Do you know anything about communism?'

'Nothing at all,' she confessed.

'We'll teach you. If you want to stay with us, that is.'

'I'll stay,' Livia said.

The men in the camp were of many nationalities. Some were local farm hands, forced to make a choice between joining the resistance or being taken by the Germans. Some were escaped prisoners of war—Russian, Polish and British—tired of walking south to rejoin the Allies. There were women, too, and these fell into two distinct groups. There were the girlfriends and the cooks, their long skirts grubby from the forest mud, who Renata and Abeline had joined. Then there were a smaller number who were fighters. They wore the same clothes as the men and were treated by them as equals. Like the men they had elaborate *noms de guerre*, which were sewn into their red neckerchiefs. It was this group of women that Livia had joined.

EVERY AFTERNOON, when the German patrols were at their most active, the partisans stayed in the camp and formed into small groups for seminars on communist theory. For Livia, it was a revelation. All her life, politics had been a subject for men, which women were kept well away from. Now, for the first time, someone actually sat down and explained the basic building blocks of society to her—the difference between the factory owner and the factory worker, and why the former was always trying to reduce the wages of the latter; why women were treated like property, and why the many always ended up working for the few. With a suddenness that took even her by surprise, Livia became a convert. At last there was an alternative to the poverty and exploitation she had been surrounded by all her life.

All her passion channelled into this new outlet, Livia drank in every word. One thing in particular continued to trouble her, though, and she took the opportunity to raise it with Dino privately.

'What about the reprisals?' she asked. 'On the way here, we saw some terrible things. The Germans are killing innocent people because of what you do.'

'Yes,' Dino said. 'They have committed many atrocities in this area.'

'Couldn't you . . .' Livia hesitated. She had no wish to be told to leave the only shelter she had, but she needed to ask. 'Couldn't you let the Allies do the fighting, and then there would be fewer reprisals against Italians?'

Dino's face darkened. 'This matter has been considered at the very highest level, and by the Allied commanders. Our orders come from them, and they say they need us to continue. Italy disgraced herself when we helped those fascists, now we have to be the ones to get rid of them.'

Despite their political differences with the Allies, the partisans regarded themselves as part of the Allied forces, subject to the same discipline and orders as any other unit. There was one endless topic of conversation among them: when would the Fifth Army arrive?

JAMES HUDDLED in a foxhole, his neck hunched against the shower of falling earth that trickled into his collar. The earth was falling because a shell had just exploded twenty yards from where he crouched. Every night, like some crazy game of tennis played with high explosives, the two sides bombarded each other's positions like this, shell for shell.

'Wish they'd shut up,' Roberts grumbled next to him. He was fiddling with a radio. 'It's almost time for Sally.'

'You shouldn't listen to that rubbish.'

'It's the only rubbish there is.' The radio whined as Roberts tuned it in. And then there she was, murmuring seductively through the static—the sweet voice of Axis Sally. 'Hi, boys,' she announced. 'How are we all tonight? There's going to be a thunderstorm later, I'm told. Me, of course, I'm nice and snug here in my little tent, but there's fifty thousand of you out there now, with nowhere to keep yourself dry. Fifty thousand. Heavens, that makes Anzio beach the largest prisoner-of-war camp in the world.' Then her husky voice became lower and more sympathetic. 'Did you hear about poor GI Ableman? We picked him up in no-man's-land a few hours ago. Seems he'd stepped on a Schuh mine, so there's not much hope for him. Anyway, here's a little song to cheer up his pals.' A foxtrot came on.

'What a bitch,' Roberts said with feeling.

'It's all written for her,' James said. 'The Germans have propaganda specialists, just like we do.'

'"The largest prisoner-of-war camp in the world." You've got to admit, she has got a point.'

James grunted. Of course she had a point. There was no two ways about it: Anzio was a hellhole. Of the 50,000 men Axis Sally had referred to, thousands were already dead. When he had volunteered for the front line he had imagined fighting his way towards Rome town by town to look for Livia. But in the three weeks he had been here, they had barely advanced 300 yards before being forced to retreat again.

Just as Axis Sally had predicted, it started to rain again: a heavy summer storm that swept more mud and debris into the foxhole. James strapped on a reel pack, a contraption like a rucksack that would play a telephone wire out from a spool on his back as he wriggled forward. It was his turn to go forward to the observation point. Gingerly he climbed up the firestep and slithered like a turtle over the edge of the trench into the mud.

He wriggled in the direction of the German lines for 100 yards or so, pausing every now and then as a shellburst illuminated the night sky and made movement even more dangerous than usual. He paused to check that his telephone wire wasn't snagging. He was so close to the German positions now that the enemy would be able to hear the faintest noise. It was not unknown for two men, one German and one Allied, both slithering forward in complete silence, to bash their heads against each other as they collided. Then it was a case of hand-to-hand combat until one of them was dead.

James rolled over onto his side and, careful not to raise his head, brought his binoculars up to his eyes. Soon an explosion to his left illuminated not only the sky but also the German position. They were fortifying the area known as Dusseldorf Ditch, he noticed. And Munich Mound looked as if it had taken a direct hit. To his right he heard whispering. A German patrol, he guessed, engaged on much the same mission as he was. He kept very still until the whispers appeared to have passed by, then he picked up the telephone handset and said very quietly, 'Twenty Jerries at Dusseldorf.'

A disembodied voice said, 'Roger that. Keep your head down.' A minute later, four mortar shells landed simultaneously on the ditch where James had noticed the refortification work.

He stayed where he was, phoning in every ten minutes with targets, and had just picked up the telephone to send in another one when he heard a voice at the other end saying, 'Time to come back, chum.'

'Already?'

'Change of plan. We're moving.' He could hear suppressed excitement in the man's voice. Perhaps it was true what everyone was saying, that the big breakout was going to happen any day now. James turned over onto his back again, wriggled round until his head was facing back towards his own lines, and began the long squirm back to his dugout.

WHEN JAMES HAD first put in for a transfer to the front line, Major Heathcote's initial reaction had been disbelief. Then disbelief had turned to shock when the captain had told him the real reasons for wanting to go north. The news that the wedding officer was intent on searching for a particular Italian girl so that he could marry her himself was proof of what the major had long suspected—that the man in front of him was possessed of an underlying streak of moral degeneracy. James was given just a few hours to pack his things and clear his desk. He barely had time to scribble a note for Jumbo, in which he explained what had happened, and asked his friend to make enquiries among his A-force contacts about Livia's whereabouts.

In the harbour he located the hospital ship that was to transport him the hour and half up the coast to Anzio. On arrival, the ship lingered a few miles off the coast, waiting for darkness, then, with a low throb, the engines picked up pace and they eased towards a tiny gap in the distant shore, framed by boats of all sizes. James stood on deck and watched as the shore grew near. There were no lights anywhere, and it was very quiet.

Suddenly a huge spume of water erupted from the sea 100 yards away, followed by another, like the blowing of some leviathan-sized whale.

'It's started,' the rating said. 'Always the same. That'll be a couple of 122s.'

As if in response to some invisible signal, the dusk became alive with lights—rockets streaking towards the beach from far inland and sparks dancing like fireflies in the darkness.

'Skirmish,' the rating said. 'Welcome to Anzio.'

As soon as the boat bumped the quayside James leapt for dry land. He spotted a subaltern standing by a stack of artillery shells and ran up to him.

'I've just arrived. Where do I go?'

The subaltern pointed towards a hole in the ground. 'Down there.'

James lowered himself into the hole and found that it led, via various stairs and ladders, to an underground room that was lit by a couple of hurricane lamps. From there he set off down a muddy track to join the unit of mortar men he had been assigned to.

Suddenly a Very light lit up the sky above him. A rattle of machine-gun fire, close by, made him start, and he ducked down automatically. He was only about 100 yards from the front now, he calculated, easily close enough to take a stray bullet in the neck. Then he saw a ladder going down into a trench, and a handwritten sign saying 'London Underground this way'. It led fifteen feet down to a narrow network of trenches, crowded with hollow-eyed, grime-encrusted men, along which he passed, until he found himself in a small, dimly lit dugout. A sergeant saluted him and a captain held out his hand. Roberts and Hervey had been here four weeks, and on one thing they were agreed: Anzio was the arsehole of the world.

As the weeks passed, and the promised advance kept being delayed, James's world shrank until the dugout, and his little patch of battlefield, became all that he could think about. His life with Livia was another life, and if he thought about her at all it was as a kind of vague, desperate yearning for laughter and gentleness and the smell of steaming *fettuccine al limone*—for anything, in fact, that was not covered in mud, lice and blood.

JAMES CRAWLED back to the dugout, where he found Hervey and Roberts packing up their equipment. 'You heard? We're off to Cisterna,' Roberts said.

James's heart quickened. Cisterna was on the way to Rome. 'So this is the breakout?'

'Looks like it. 'Bout bloody time, eh?'

They joined the rest of their company and headed towards the assembly point. Moving back from the line like this was a strange experience. By the time you reached the rear you were walking properly for the first time in weeks, a great elation sweeping over you as you realised that no one was actually, at that precise moment, trying to kill you.

At the rear a railhead had been set up, bringing ammunition up from the harbour. James whistled when he saw it. The last time he had been back here, the ammunition stack had been the size of a shed. Now it was as large as a church.

'It's the big one, all right,' Roberts muttered.

Eventually the order was given for their section to move forward and they stood two abreast in a crowded trench, waiting for something to happen. Then, just before dawn, the barrage started and for forty-five minutes every big gun in the beachhead pulverised the German positions.

Still they waited, shuffling forward now along the trench, their ears ringing. Ahead of them the fighting had already started, but the sheer pressure of numbers meant they couldn't all get into the battle at once. Meanwhile, the first wounded were already coming back along the line, looking dazed or relieved depending on the severity of their injuries.

'Doesn't look too bad,' Hervey muttered.

'Those are just the ones who can walk,' Roberts pointed out. 'The other poor bastards are still out there.'

Eventually they got to the front of the line, and then they were up out of the trench again and advancing at a run. All around there were thousands of others doing the same. Ahead of them, fighter planes circled over what was presumably the thick of the fighting.

A terrified German soldier ran towards them, his arms in the air as he tried to surrender. Someone pointed to the lines behind them and told him to keep running. Then shells started dropping nearby—small German 88s—and they flopped into a crater and waited for someone with a mortar to catch up with them. Somehow James and Hervey had got separated from the rest of their section. Eventually a mortar team turned up. 'Position?' gasped the mortar man as he wrestled with his weapon. Cautiously, Hervey raised his head to look, and as he did so, a shell took half of it away. He fell backwards without a sound, a look of wonder in his eyes. The mortar man got four mortars off and told them it was all he could do. Reluctantly, James left Hervey's body and climbed back onto the battlefield. They crawled towards the German lines, several more of them taking direct hits, until a Spitfire overhead spotted their predicament and managed to get close enough to fire directly into the gun emplacement. Someone else shouted an order, and then they were up again and running.

They were behind the German lines now. James passed a group of forty or fifty prisoners being guarded by a single GI. Then the inevitable counter-attack came—dozens of Tiger tanks cresting the brow of the hill and streaming down towards the advancing Allied infantry. He retreated to the German trench and helped a mortar man knock out two of the Tigers. Then, as abruptly as they had arrived, the tanks were retreating again, their guns swivelling round to continue firing to the rear as they left the scene.

That was the pattern for the whole day—advancing in a large, chaotic group; taking casualties; dropping into a foxhole until sheer pressure of numbers forced the Germans back.

To his enormous pleasure, he finally met up with Roberts, who although suffering from a shrapnel wound to the ear was still advancing. 'I'm not walking back through those bloody minefields,' he told James. 'I'm waiting until we take Cisterna and there's trucks to take me 'ome. Don't reckon it'll be long now.' He nodded to where the town could be seen ahead of them.

THREE DAYS LATER they were in Rome. The forward units drove into the city expecting fierce resistance, and were met instead by a relieved population throwing geranium flowers into their Jeeps.

James's first task was to discover the location of the German army brothel. Number 95 Via Nardones was a tall, stone building, presumably once a hotel. James ran up the steps and entered a large reception area. The desk was deserted, and the mess of scattered papers suggested that the occupants had left in a hurry.

'Hello?' he called up the stairs. He listened: it seemed to him that he could hear someone moving about.

He went up the stairs and caught a low murmur of voices. In the second room he looked into, four girls were cowering on a bed.

'It's all right,' he said in Italian. 'I'm just looking for someone. Was there a girl called Livia here?' he asked. The girls shook their shaven heads.

'There's a register,' one girl said. 'In the office. They kept a file on everyone. You can check there.' She led him to a room housing a large filing cabinet. Inside the cabinet, the files were still surprisingly ordered.

Hundreds of girls had passed through the brothel, but there were no Livias and no Pertinis among them.

WHEN JAMES GOT back to the barracks where his unit was billeted, Roberts told him a man had been looking for him. 'Big bloke. Said he was A-force.'

'Captain Jeffries?'

'I don't know, but he'd about a dozen Jerry watches down his left arm.'

'Yes, that'll be Jumbo,' James said fondly.

He found his way to the hotel in which A-force had set up a temporary headquarters. 'Ah, James, there you are,' Jumbo said, as if the breakout from Anzio had been little more than a hike. 'Say hello to my pal Buster.'

Buster was another Jumbo, though with a broken nose. 'Buster's responsible for the partisans in sector four,' Jumbo explained. 'That's this bit.' He pointed at a map on the wall. 'Tell him what you heard, Buster.'

'I've been asking all the partisan commanders for an update on their strength,' Buster said. 'One of them sent a message to say his motley crew was gathering more recruits all the time. He made a light-hearted reference to the fact that they even had a group of Neapolitan prostitutes with them.'

'Could one of them be Livia?'

'Of course,' Jumbo said confidently.

'If she *is* with Dino,' Buster said, 'she's done well. He's a good man.'

'Is there any way we can get her out of there?' James asked.

Buster shook his head. 'None whatsoever, I'm afraid. The whole sector's stiff with Jerries.'

'On the other hand,' Jumbo said cheerfully, 'we can probably get *you* in. Ever used a parachute?'

That night, the BBC's daily transmission of messages to the partisans contained some intriguing new material. Having told Mario his sister's cow needed milking and Piero that his wife thanked him for the hat, the clipped tones of the BBC presenter said, 'And finally a message for Livia, who is staying with Giuseppe. Please remain where you are. The tuna is on its way.'

High in the mountains, Dino's radio operator wrote down the message.

JAMES HAD NEVER done a parachute drop before, and as the B-17 banked and turned north towards the mountains, he felt his heart racing with excitement. Officially Jumbo was the one being dropped to liaise with the partisans, and James was merely there to assist with the unloading. According to the report the pilot would file later, James would overbalance and fall out of the plane while pushing out a crate. It was, Jumbo assured him, a fairly standard way of moving people around without getting official permission.

After twenty minutes James felt the plane start to descend. Jumbo got to his feet. 'Time to get this lot unloaded,' he yelled.

They cut the webbing and pushed the crates towards the bomb doors. As they swung open, a small bonfire on the ground flickered into life, tiny as a firefly. 'There's the signal,' Jumbo shouted. 'Heave.' They pushed the first crate out. It wobbled in the slipstream, then sprouted a khaki-coloured jelly-fish of silk, slowing its descent. Together they pushed the boxes out one by one, until Jumbo gave the signal to stop. Then the plane banked and came round again and this time Jumbo gave James a thumbs up and a firm shove, which sent him tumbling through the void.

There was a moment's panic, then he felt the blissful tug as his parachute filled with air. Beneath him, he could see dark figures already carrying crates out of the drop zone. And then a familiar skinny figure, running towards the place where he was going to land, and his heart soared way above the clouds. 'I love you,' he called down to her. 'I love you.' It sounded rather wonderful in Italian, so he shouted it again. 'Livia, I love you.'

Gently the ground came up to meet him and she was in his arms, the silk of the chute billowing around him as he held her, saying over and over, 'Livia, I'm so sorry. I let you go, but I'll never let you go again.'

THEY SAT on a tree trunk, a little away from the camp, his arm protectively around her shoulders.

'James,' she said with a sigh, 'there's something I need to tell you.'

'I know about Alberto. Marisa already explained.'

'But you still came?' she said, surprised. 'You'd be forgiven for wanting nothing more to do with me.'

'It isn't like that any more. This war's made everything different.'

She nodded. 'There's something you need to understand, though. Things are different for me now. Coming here—fighting—seeing what's been happening—here, I'm a communist first, and a soldier second, and a woman— well, probably not even third: being a woman comes way down the list.'

'But you won't always be a soldier.'

'I think perhaps I'll always be a communist now. And that means being a soldier, in a way. Who do you think is going to put it all back together, after the war is finally over and you people go back to where you came from?'

'Ah,' he said. 'Do I take it you still think England isn't the place for you?'

'I can't leave Italy. Not after this. Not after what the people here have been through. I'm sorry, James.'

'That's interesting,' he said. 'Because I won't be going back to England either. Or at least, not for any longer than it takes me to demob and get myself back over here.'

She looked at him, unsure that he really meant it.

'I want to stay in Italy,' he said gently. 'With you, if you'll have me. Without you, if you won't. A person can't choose where he's born. But he can choose where he spends his life, and I want to spend mine here.'

THE GERMAN RETREAT coincided with a heatwave. Even here in the hills the heat was oppressive. The leaders of the other partisan forces in the area were called to a meeting, at which Jumbo produced a map and, with James as translator, explained what each section was to do.

Dino, though, was fretting about the delivery of the big guns. 'We can dig the emplacements,' he told Jumbo, 'but when will we get the weapons to put in them? We've been asking for them for months.' The crates that had been airlifted in had contained only rifles and pistols for small-scale actions, whereas what the partisans required were Sten guns, grenades and semi-automatics.

'It's just an administrative cock-up,' Jumbo soothed the worried Dino. 'Probably someone else somewhere is complaining about an unwanted delivery of Stens. I'll get onto HQ and order up what you need.'

Privately, though, he was becoming anxious.

'I'm hearing some very odd stuff on the radio,' he confided to James. 'Apparently we've just withdrawn seven divisions from Italy to open up a new front in the Med.'

'But that makes no sense at all,' James said. 'Why let them outnumber us, just when they're almost finished?'

'It beats me too,' Jumbo admitted. 'I'm just hoping—well, that someone hasn't decided to make things more difficult for the Italians.'

'Why would anyone do that?' James asked. Then he was suddenly struck by a thought. 'Actually, I think I already know the answer to that. We need to get the commanders together. We need to tell them why those big guns they're waiting for might never arrive.'

'WHEN I WAS in Naples,' James explained, 'I saw a top-secret document. At the time I didn't understand why it was secret—it was just an assessment of what the political situation in Italy was likely to be after the war.'

He paused, gathering his thoughts. Dino, Jumbo and the commanders waited for him to continue.

'Basically, it said that among the Italians the most organised political group are the partisans. The writer thought that after the war the communists would take power. He wasn't very happy about this—he foresaw a communist super-state stretching from Moscow to Milan, as he put it.'

'So?' Dino asked. 'This is hardly a secret.'

'The report wasn't just an assessment,' James said. 'It was an action plan.'

There was a long silence while the partisans digested this. 'You're saying that we are being betrayed,' Dino said at last.

'I'm saying that it would suit some people if the partisans had their numbers and strength reduced by the Germans. As far as they're concerned, the war in Italy has already served its purpose—it's tied up twenty-five German divisions that otherwise might have ended up in France. Now the war is almost won, they're pulling Allied divisions out of Italy, leaving the communists to take care of the Germans—and vice versa.'

'Jumbo?' Dino said quietly. 'Can this be true?'

Jumbo nodded. 'It makes sense, I'm afraid. At the end of the day, the army commanders have to do what the politicians tell them.'

'You'd better call off your attack,' James said. 'Whatever supplies are dropped, I'll bet they won't include the big guns you need.'

'We can't call it off,' Dino said. 'Knowing that our deaths will serve some politician's purpose makes no difference. To our shame, we welcomed the fascists into this country. We can't simply sit back now and watch the German army go by without striking a blow against them.' He looked at the other commanders. 'Are we all agreed?'

One by one they nodded their heads.

'WHAT ARE YOU thinking?' Livia asked, her head nestled against his arm.

'I was thinking about Naples.' James was leaning against a cherry tree in the woods, where they had come to find some privacy. 'This is like living on Vesuvius, isn't it?'

'In what way?'

'Because we might get killed at any moment, and we don't know when.'

She moved her head so that she could look into his eyes. 'Yes. So how are you finding it?'

'I think,' he said, 'that a life like this is worth ten lived any other way. So long as it goes on including you, of course.'

She was silent for a moment. 'James?'

'Yes?'

'After the war, if you ask me to marry you, I'll say yes.'

He thought for a moment. 'But that doesn't make sense,' he objected. 'Why not say yes now?'

'You haven't asked me, for one thing.'

'Livia Pertini, will you marry me?'

'No.'

'But you just said—'

'I said ask me after the war. It's bad luck to say yes now.'

'How can it be bad luck?'

'Well, for one thing I'd need a piece of iron in my pocket, because bad luck doesn't like iron. And we'd need to have our heads covered, so that the evil spirits can't see how happy we are. And you should never make any decisions about who you marry on a Tuesday.'

'You made that last one up.'

'No, I didn't.'

'But it doesn't make sense to say—'

'If you're going to marry me, James,' she said sleepily, 'you're going to have to get a lot less attached to sense. Anyway, getting engaged the day before a fight with the Germans would just be tempting fate.'

ON THEIR WAY back to camp they passed Jumbo, who was busy cleaning the partisans' only machine gun. James gave him a thumbs up and later went back to give him a hand.

'So everything's all right with you and Livia?' Jumbo asked.

'Better than all right.' He couldn't help beaming. 'She wants to wait until after the war, but I think we're going to get married.'

'Congratulations, that's wonderful. I hope you'll be very happy.' Jumbo worked on his gun for a few minutes. 'You heard about Elena's little problem, I suppose? This long-lost husband of hers?'

'She did mention something along those lines,' James said awkwardly.

'Now Rome's free I suppose we'll be able to get it sorted out.'

'I suppose so. Though, er, it might take a while. Probably a backlog.'

'Thing is,' Jumbo said, 'she can't really go on being a whore if she marries me.' He caught James's look. 'I always had a pretty good idea. It's a shame this bloody war can't last a bit longer,' Jumbo said wistfully. 'Well, not from your point of view, but I've had the time of my life.'

TRAVELLING MOSTLY by night the German units swept through the mountains as if a dam had burst. The partisans, concealed, watched the endless procession of grey uniforms pass by, and waited. Two days later their spotters reported that a column of troops had been seen moving up from the south.

The partisans waited, hidden, until dusk. Then a growling sound, wafted on the still air, heralded the arrival of the convoy.

'Troops,' Jumbo said. 'Troops and trucks. Quite a lot of them.'

'Good luck, everyone,' Dino said. 'Wait for my order.'

The first trucks were almost past the partisans' position when Dino said, 'Now.' Immediately, rifle fire spat from the concealed trenches. The Germans scattered and took refuge behind what shelter they could. Only then did the second group of partisans, concealed on the ridge behind them, open fire, forcing the Germans to move back. But the disciplined and experienced German soldiers began to form into small fighting units.

If the start of the battle had been messy and noisy, now it was chaos. James looked anxiously for Livia, but couldn't see her. The partisans were in among the German position, fighting hand to hand.

He heard the sound of a heavy machine gun. The Germans were firing indiscriminately, mowing down their own men and the partisans alike in their desperation. James dived for a ditch, where he found Jumbo.

'That gun's going to be a problem,' Jumbo said. 'Think I've got the answer here somewhere.' He produced a German mine from his pocket. 'Any minute now, they'll need to change the barrel.'

'I'll come with you,' James said.

'Don't do that,' Jumbo said. 'You've got Livia to look out for. Give Elena my regards.' He heaved himself over the side of the ditch. James cursed, slammed another clip into his weapon, and followed, crouching low and firing in short bursts left and right. There was a sudden sharp pain in his left shoulder, knocking him backwards. He was just in time to see Jumbo coming under fire as he hurled the mine at the machine gun. Then there was a flash, and the gun truck exploded.

Within ten minutes it was over, the remaining German trucks either dashing back to the safety of the valley or captured. But the partisans had lost over half their men.

James went to find Livia, running from body to body to see if she was among the wounded. Eventually he found her sitting on the mountainside next to Jumbo's corpse. He sat beside her, and when at last she spoke, her voice cracked with exhaustion. 'I want to go home.'

THE NEXT DAY, as they were burying their dead, another column of men was seen moving up from the valley. But this time their uniforms were not grey but khaki, and Allied flags fluttered from the radio masts on their vehicles.

James went with Dino to act as interpreter, his arm in a sling where the bullet wound had been dressed. He explained what had happened, and the commanding officer thanked them.

'By the way,' he added to James, 'where did you learn your English? You speak it pretty well, for an Italian.'

James opened his mouth to explain, then for some reason he heard himself say, 'Well, I was born in England. But I grew up in Naples.'

'Thought so. Anyhow, we'd best be getting after the Jerries. Thanks for everything.'

As they walked back up the hill, with its lines of neat crosses, Dino said, 'You didn't tell him you were British.'

'No,' James said shortly.

Dino gave him a thoughtful look. Then he stopped by the line of graves. 'So many crosses. But you know, there's room for another one.'

'Where?' James asked, not understanding.

Dino pointed. 'On the end. Perhaps you could be buried there yourself, next to your friend Jumbo. What do you think? "Here lies James Gould, an officer of the British Army, who gave his life in gallant action with the partisans," et cetera, et cetera.'

'Dino,' James said, 'Are you saying I should just—go missing?'

Dino took something out of his pocket. 'Look,' he said, unfolding it. It was a partisan's red neckerchief. Embroidered in the corner was the name 'Giacomo'. 'He was a good man,' he said quietly. 'One of many good men who died here. I don't think he would mind you having it. It's almost as good as a set of identity papers, don't you think? One of these, and a letter from me thanking you for your help, will open many doors in Italy after the war.' Dino pressed the red neckerchief into James's hand. 'Take her home, Giacomo. Take Livia back to Naples.'

EPILOGUE

Time passes. Time passes, but people do not forget. Every year, on the anniversary of victory, they gather in the places that are special to them—an airfield, a war memorial, a café on a French bridge, a landing beach where they survived but others who were with them did not.

One of the places where they gather is a little *osteria* on the flanks of Mount Vesuvius, in a tiny village called Fiscino. They come from all over Europe, and from the US too, for those who live on the other side of the Atlantic are glad of a chance to fly back and visit their families in Naples.

The men have names like Bert and Ted and Richard. The women . . . the women have names like Algisa, Silvana and Gina. They are the war brides, the Italian girls who married Allied soldiers, thanks to a dispensation given with great reluctance by the men's commanding officers.

Others are here too, of course. There is Angelo, the former maître d' of Zi' Teresa's, long since retired, along with his wife and his sixteen grandchildren. There is Eric Vincenzo, who when asked what he is doing now is always somewhat evasive, but who is based in Langley, Virginia, the home of the CIA. And there is the elegant middle-aged lady who is always dressed, however unseasonably, in the finest furs. She has one eye, the other being made of glass, and she answers to the name Elena.

Marisa is here, or *Dottore* Pertini, as we must now learn to call her. She has long had a thriving medical practice in Boscotrecase, where it is known that for certain ailments beyond the reach of conventional medicine, she will be able to prepare you a compound not found in any pharmacy.

And her sister is here. She too is known as *Dottore* Pertini these days, though in her case it signifies that she has completed a university degree in political science. However, the fiery local councillor will always find time to cook, particularly when it is a feast for family and friends.

And here is her husband, moving a little slowly as he works his way down the long trestle table under the trees on the shady terrace, checking that everything is as it should be. It is he who took over the management of the restaurant and farm after Nino's death, and it is under his direction that it has become celebrated by all the food guides. The antipasto today will be *burrata,* creamy balls of mozzarella wrapped in asphodel leaves, made with milk from his own much treasured water buffalo.

There are children here too—dozens of them, for in the period immediately after the war there was an explosion of procreation. As the meal goes on, and on, and the adults show no sign of wanting to do anything other than talk, these youngsters slip from their chairs, gathering in small groups to play, or to look moody, or to flirt, depending on their age and sex.

And if they see Livia Pertini reach out a hand to touch her husband's arm as he passes, or see him bend his head for a fleeting kiss—habitually, almost unconsciously, breaking off his conversation to touch his lips to hers—they will, naturally, screw up their faces in mock-disgust, or pass some smart remark. For if they know little of war, they know even less of love. That is as it should be: each generation must be allowed to believe that it makes these discoveries for itself.

Besides, they have more important things to think about. Look, here comes another course, the long-awaited apricot *dolce,* carried to the table in triumph by the cooks.

ANTHONY CAPELLA

Born: December 6, 1962
Home: London
Website: www.anthonycapella.com

RD: What inspired *The Wedding Officer*?

AC: I went to Naples, and while I was there decided to read Norman Lewis's wonderful wartime memoir, *Naples '44*. It just seemed like the perfect time, and place, in which to set a story about food—partly because food was so scarce, and partly because all the themes that food invokes—family, continuity, security—were in a state of flux.

RD: Is it true that Jamie Oliver provided the idea that it's possible to use a filing cabinet as an oven, and are you an admirer of his cookery?

AC: That trip to Naples was made in the company of a whole bunch of people who like food, including the director of the Naked Chef programmes and Jamie Oliver. Over lunch one day, Jamie happened to mention he'd once made a wood oven out of a filing cabinet (the wood goes in the bottom drawer, the food in the top.) It seemed like just the thing for my lead character. I love all Jamie's books—the feeling he communicates that so long as you love food and care about ingredients you're on the right track, and the way he celebrates passion and enjoyment above perfection and formality. Those are things I absolutely believe in too.

RD: What is it that you love about Italy?

AC: How long have you got? Partly it's the sunshine, of course, partly the food, and the scenery, and the way that Italians seem to be able to enjoy life. But even if you took all those things away, there's still the incredible loyalty to the traditions of whichever tiny area they grew up in. Italians call it *campanilismo*, 'love of your own bell tower', and it's one of the reasons their food is so good: they're fiercely passionate about, and protective of, doing things the old way.

RD: Imagine you're going to be served the most wonderful Italian meal of all time. What would you choose as starter, main course and dessert?

AC: Well, it depends where I am, because every region of Italy has its own cuisine. In Campania the antipasto would be *burrata*, a ball of mozzarella containing a mouthful of liquid buffalo cream. The pasta and main course would have to be *ragù*, cooked in the traditional manner—'from sunrise to sunset', as the Neapolitans say. Dessert would be a peach grown in the volcanic soil of Vesuvius, eaten the Neapolitan way—you slice a chunk into your wine glass, then roll both wine and fruit into your mouth. That's typically Neapolitan: a simple pleasure elevated to sensual perfection.

RD: How do your three young sons rate your cooking?

AC: Not very highly. But then I'm not a great cook—I'm a foodie, which is completely different. I'm always burning things, because I tend to daydream. Daydreaming's not a problem when you're writing, of course.

RD: You tried pig-farming for a while, but it didn't work out. Would you like to have another go at agriculture of any kind?

AC: No. It's very, very hard—the damn brutes always seemed to need feeding or, even worse, the slurry pit needed emptying. And it was just impossible to make money. It's a shame because we need organic, non-intensive farms in Britain if we're ever to have good food.

RD: Can you name five goals, serious or trivial, personal or professional?

AC: No. I've never been that organised. Can anyone answer a question like that?

RD: And what three adjectives would you pick to describe yourself?

AC: Weedy, sybaritic, thoughtful . . . ?

RD: Last but not least, what's your biggest indulgence?

AC: At last, an easy one! Food.

CAMPANIA'S CUISINE

Many dishes native to Campania have been adopted by the rest of Italy. The fertile soil on the lower slopes of Vesuvius (right) nurtures some of the country's finest fruit orchards and vegetables, including the deep red, richly flavoured San Marzano tomato, and *pomodorini da serbo*, a tiny variety of tomato unique to this region.

The most celebrated local cheese is *Mozzarella di bufala Campana*, made from the milk of water buffalo that graze in the marshy lowlands. Of ancient origin, its name derives from part of the production cycle when the curd, after being stretched, is *mozzata*, or 'lopped off' into snowball-like rounds, before being cooled in cold water and then salted.

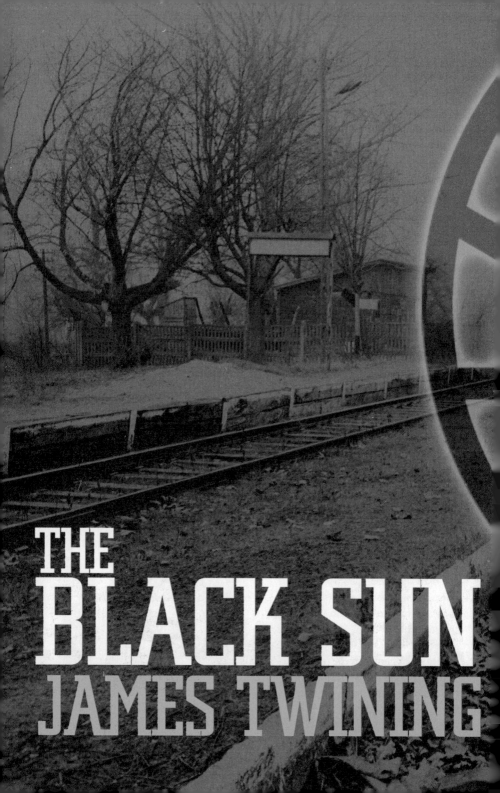

THE
BLACK SUN
JAMES TWINING

When a painting by an obscure artist called Karel Bellak is stolen from a synagogue in Prague, it's hardly headline news.
But for former art thief Tom Kirk, it turns out to be the first in a series of clues that point back to a fabled treasure lost during the chaos of the Second World War.

PROLOGUE

Ash cash. That's what medical students call it. Every cremation or burial release form requires a doctor's signature, and every signature earns its donor a small fee. Death could be good business for a doctor who happened to be in the right place at the wrong time.

To Dr John Bennett, however, as he walked onto the dark ward, the prospect of a few extra quid was small compensation for being paged at 3 a.m.

'Doctor?' A woman's voice rang out through the gloom.

'Morning, Laura,' Bennett greeted the approaching figure with a warm smile. 'Don't tell me you've killed another one of my patients?'

She shrugged helplessly. 'I've had a bad week.'

'Who was it this time?'

'Mr Hammon. He was fine when I came on duty. But when I looked in . . .'

'He was in a pretty bad way,' Bennett said gently, sensing she was upset. She smiled at him gratefully.

'Anyway, I'd better take a look. Have you got the paperwork ready?'

'It's in the office.'

The windowless room was about halfway down the ward, the only light coming from the glow of two surveillance monitors and the LED of a video recorder beneath them. One monitor showed the corridor, the other flicked between the patients' rooms.

Bennett was reaching for the light switch when something caught his eye. The roving camera had settled in one of the patients' rooms where two dark figures were silhouetted against the open doorway, one slight, one tall.

'Who's that?' Bennett said, frowning. He switched the system to manual.

'It's Mr Weissman's room,' Laura said in a low voice.

The two figures were now standing on either side of the bed looking down at the sleeping patient.

'What the hell are they playing at?' Bennett said. 'I'm calling security.'

As Bennett reached for the phone, the tall man on the left snatched a pillow from under the sleeping man's head. He awoke immediately, his eyes wide with surprise and then fear. His mouth moved to speak but any sound he made was smothered as the pillow was pushed down onto his face.

'Jesus Christ!' Bennett gasped. He jammed the phone to his ear, tapped the hook switch a few times, then locked eyes with Laura. 'It's dead.'

On screen, the tall man nodded to his companion, who lifted a black bag onto the bed and reached in. The teeth of a surgical bone-saw sparkled in the light. The figure slid back the man's left pyjama sleeve and placed the blade on his arm, just below the elbow. The man jerked his arm but to no avail, his strength clearly ebbing away in his attacker's strong grasp.

Bennett glanced at Laura. 'Don't make a sound. We'll be fine as long as they don't know we're here. Just stay calm.'

The saw expertly amputated the arm at the elbow. The struggling had stopped. The figure wiped the saw on the bedclothes then returned it to his bag. The arm, wrapped in a towel snatched from the foot of the bed, soon joined it. The heart-rate monitor showed a flat line, an alarm sounding in the empty nurses' station down the corridor.

The two men moved away, across the room. But as he was about to shut the door, the tall man looked up into the camera lens and smiled.

'Oh my God,' Bennett breathed. 'They're coming for the tapes.'

He jerked his head towards the other monitor. The thin man was walking slowly up the corridor towards them, the knife in his hand glinting.

1

Pinkas Synagogue, Prague, January 2, 10.04 a.m.

The shattered glass crunched under the leather soles of Tom Kirk's shoes. He glanced up to see where it had come from. High in the wall above him, white plastic sheeting had been taped across a window frame.

He lowered his gaze to the man opposite him. 'Is that how they got in?'

'No.' Rabbi Spiegel shook his head, his eyes burning with anger. 'They came in through the back. Broke the lock. The window was just for fun.'

Tom's handsome, angular face set into a grim frown. In his mid-thirties and six feet tall, he had the lithe, sinewy physique of a cross-country runner.

'And then they did this?' he asked, indicating the devastation around them.

Rabbi Spiegel nodded and a tear ran down his right cheek.

There were 80,000 names in all—Holocaust victims from Bohemia and Moravia, each painstakingly painted on the synagogue's walls and now covered in bright yellow graffiti.

Tom walked towards it and took a picture with his digital camera.

'They are evil, the people who did this. Evil,' Rabbi Spiegel said quietly.

'Why have you asked me here, Rabbi?' Tom asked gently.

'I understand that you recover stolen artefacts?'

'We try to help where we can, yes.'

It was just over six months since Tom had gone into business with Archie Connolly. The idea was simple—they helped museums, collectors, governments even, recover stolen or lost art. What made their partnership unusual was that, after a stint working for the CIA, Tom had spent ten years as an art thief—the best in the business, many said. Archie had been his fence and front man, finding buyers, identifying targets, researching security set-ups. This new venture represented a fresh start on the right side of the law that they were both still coming to terms with.

'Then come upstairs. Please.' The rabbi pointed towards a narrow staircase in the far corner. 'I have something to show you.'

The staircase emerged into a vaulted room, the morning light filtering in from high windows onto a series of shattered wooden display cases and a tiled floor strewn with drawings. Some were torn to pieces, others screwed up into balls, still more covered in dirty bootprints.

'This was an exhibition of children's drawings from Terezin, a transit camp not far from here,' the rabbi explained in a half whisper. He gave a sad smile. 'Come,' he said, crossing to the far wall, 'here's what I wanted to show you.'

A gilt frame, perhaps two feet across and a foot wide, hung empty on the wall, whitewashed stonework visible where the painting should have been.

Tom edged towards it. 'What was there?'

'An oil painting of this synagogue completed in the early thirties. It's been cut out,' the rabbi said. 'They could have left it in its frame if all they wanted to do was damage or destroy it. Do you think they took it with them?'

Tom frowned. 'The people who did this don't strike me as art lovers.'

'Especially not a painting by this artist,' the rabbi agreed grudgingly.

'Why, who was it by?'

'A Jewish artist. Not well known, but dear to us because he lived here in Prague—until the Nazis murdered him. He was called Karel Bellak.'

'Bellak?' Tom drilled him with a questioning look.

'You've heard of him?' the rabbi asked, clearly surprised.

Tom nodded slowly. 'I've heard the name. I'm just not sure where. I'll need to speak to my colleague in London to be sure I'm thinking of the right person. Do you have a photo of the painting?'

'Of course.' Rabbi Spiegel produced a photograph from his pocket and handed it to Tom. 'We made several copies a few years ago for the insurance company, so you can keep this one. They told us the painting wasn't worth much, but to us it was priceless.'

National Cryptologic Museum, Fort Meade, Maryland: January 3, 2.26 a.m.

It was a little game he played, to pass the time on his rounds. At each exhibit he would test himself against the information card to see how much he could remember. After twenty years he was pretty much word perfect.

Al Travis had been a guard at the National Cryptologic Museum since it opened. He liked it there. He felt he was part of something important. After all, technically he worked for the National Security Agency, which was right in the thick of things with this whole War on Terror.

First there was the Myer flag system, a line-of-sight communication tool devised in the Civil War by an army doctor who formed the Signal Corps. The next exhibit was the Cipher Wheel, a series of rotating wooden discs which, according to the card, was used by European governments for hundreds of years to encrypt messages. Then there was his favourite exhibit—the Enigma machine. The museum had several on display in two large glass-fronted cases. He found it incredible that, in 'breaking' the Enigma code, Polish and then British mathematicians had helped win the war for the Allies in Europe. But that's what the card said, and who was he to argue?

A sudden noise made Travis stop. He checked over his shoulder and then peered into the semidarkness ahead of him. 'Anyone there?' he called out.

As he waited for an answer, a steel wire shaped into a noose was lowered from above him until it was hovering just over his head, like a silver halo. Then, as Travis was about to move on again, it snapped past his face, the wire tightening round his neck and pulling him three feet off the ground.

Travis's hands leapt to his throat as he scrabbled at the wire, his legs thrashing beneath him. Two dark shapes materialised out of the shadows and a third man dropped down from the roof space. One of the men pulled a chair over from the wall and positioned it under Travis's flailing legs.

Perching on tiptoe, Travis was able to relieve the pressure on his throat. Teetering unsteadily, his mouth dry with fear, he watched the three masked figures approach the left-hand display cabinet. They unscrewed the frame, levered the glass out and leant it against the wall. Then one of the men took out one of the Enigma machines and placed it in his accomplice's backpack.

Travis tried to speak but all that came were choked grunts and moans.

The noise, though, made the men turn. One of them approached Travis. 'Did you say something, nigger?' The voice was thin and mocking.

Travis shook his head, though his eyes burned with anger at the insult.

The man kicked the chair from under Travis, who plunged towards the floor, the steel wire twanging under tension and snapping his neck.

Clerkenwell, London: January 3, 5.02 p.m.

Tom was sitting at his desk with the *Times* cryptic crossword in front of him. Much to his frustration, he hadn't yet filled in a single word.

There was a knock at the door. 'Yeah?' Tom called.

The door opened and a woman wearing jeans and a tight black jacket walked in, her right arm looped through the open visor of a black motorcycle helmet. 'Catch,' she called.

Tom looked up in time to see a tennis ball flashing towards his head. Without thinking, he shot a hand out and snatched it from the air.

'How was your game?' Tom asked with a smile.

Dominique de Lecourt hitched herself up onto the side of his desk. Her mass of blonde hair and pale, oval face had the remote beauty of a silent-movie star, though her blue eyes shone with energy and confidence.

'Didn't play. Decided to go to that auction instead.'

Tom laughed. 'I knew you wouldn't be able to resist. See anything good?'

'A pair of Louis XV porphyry and gilt-bronze two-handled vases.' Her English was excellent, with just a hint of a Swiss-French accent.

'Yeah, I saw those in the catalogue. What did you think?'

'I think two million is a lot to pay for a couple of nineteenth-century reproductions. They're worth twenty thousand at most.'

Tom smiled. Sometimes he found it hard to believe that Dominique was still only twenty-three. She had an instinct for a deal and a memory for detail that rivalled all but the most seasoned pros. Then again, Tom reminded himself, she'd had a good teacher. Until he died last year, she'd spent four years working for Tom's father in Geneva. When Tom had relocated the antiques dealership to London, she'd readily accepted his offer to move with it and help run the business.

The antiques shop was a double-fronted space with large arched windows, vital for attracting passing trade, although most visitors to Kirk Duval Fine Art and Antiques called ahead for an appointment. At the rear were two doors and stairs to the upstairs floors—the first floor empty, the second floor Dominique's apartment, the top floor Tom's.

The left-hand door opened onto a warehouse accessed via an old spiral staircase, while the right-hand door gave on to the office. The office was not a big room, perhaps fifteen feet square, the space dominated by the partners' desk Tom shared with Archie and two comfortable leather armchairs.

'When's Archie back?' Dominique asked.

'Tomorrow, I think. That's twice he's been to the States in the last few weeks. For someone who claims to hate going abroad, he's certainly putting himself about a bit.'

'What's he doing there?'

'God knows. Sometimes he just gets an idea into his head and takes off.'

'That reminds me,' she said, slipping off the desk. She crossed to Harry's desk and gathered up a pile of newspapers, then returned and placed them in front of him. 'I wanted to show you something. Only you might not like it. It's about Harry.'

'Harry Renwick?' Tom sprang up. Harry Renwick had been his father's best friend, a man Tom had known and loved since his childhood. That was until it transpired that dear old Uncle Harry had been living a double life. Operating under the name of Cassius, he had masterminded a ruthless art-crime syndicate that had robbed and murdered and extorted its way around the globe for decades. The betrayal still stung.

'You told me he'd disappeared after what happened in Paris.'

'Yeah,' Tom said. 'He just vanished.'

'Well, someone's looking for him.' Dominique unfolded the previous day's *Herald Tribune*. She turned to the Personals section and pointed at an ad.

Tom began to read the first paragraph. '*Lions may awake any second. If this takes place alert me via existing number. If chimps stop their spelling test within one or so hours, reward through gift of eighty bananas.*' He laughed. 'It's nonsense.'

'That's what I thought at first, but you know how I like a challenge.'

'Sure.' Tom smiled. Among her many attributes, Dominique had an amazing aptitude for word games and other types of puzzles.

'It's a jump code. Jewish scholars have been finding them for years in the torah. If you take the first T in the Book of Genesis, then jump forty-nine places to the fiftieth letter, then another forty-nine places, and so on, it spells the word "torah". The next three books do the same.'

'And this works in the same way?'

'It's a question of identifying the jump interval. In this case, it's every eighth letter, starting with the first.'

'So that makes this L . . .' Tom counted seven spaces, 'then A . . .' He grabbed a pen and began to write down each eighth letter: 'Then S . . . then T. Last!' he exclaimed triumphantly.

'*Last seen Copenhagen.* I decoded it earlier. After I found this, I looked through earlier editions. There have been coded messages using the same method every few weeks for the last six months or so. I've written them out here.' She handed Tom a piece of paper.

'*HK cold, try Tokyo,*' he read. '*Focus search in Europe . . . DNA sample en route . . . Reported sighting in Vienna . . .*' He looked up at Dominique. 'OK, someone seems to be looking for someone or something. But there's nothing to say it's Harry.'

Dominique took a newspaper from the bottom of the pile and opened it at the Personals page. 'This was the first message.' She pointed at a lengthy ad she'd circled in red. '*Ten million dollar reward. Henry Julius Renwick, aka Cassius, dead or alive. Publish interest next Tuesday.*'

Tom tried to digest this news. 'Did anyone reply?' he asked eventually.

'I counted twenty-five replies in all.'

'Twenty-five!'

'Whoever's behind this has got a small private army out there trying to track Harry down. The question is why.'

'No,' Tom reflected, 'the question is who.'

FBI Headquarters, Salt Lake City: January 4, 4.16 p.m.

Where had it all gone wrong? When had he passed from being a high achiever to an average Joe? How was it that people half his age were accelerating past him so fast he barely had time to spit out their dust before they were a speck on the horizon? Special Agent Paul Viggiano, forty-one, slipped a bullet into each of the five empty chambers of his shiny silver Smith & Wesson Model 342 AirLite Ti. The gun loaded, he raised it to eye level and took a deep breath. Then, breathing out slowly, he emptied the gun into the target at the far end of the indoor shooting range as fast as he could.

'Sounds like you really needed that,' the woman in the booth next to him said with a smile.

He managed a tight grimace in response as she turned to take aim.

One small oversight, that's all it had been. One little slip in an otherwise spotless career. And here he was, drowning in mediocrity.

He shook his head and hit the button to retrieve the target from the other end of the gallery. It whirred towards him and jerked to a halt. He examined it for holes. There were none. Not a single one.

The woman next to him squeezed off her shots with rhythmic monotony. Then she carefully placed her gun down and retrieved her target.

Viggiano couldn't help but peer over. Eleven holes. She had eleven holes in her target. How was that possible unless . . . unless it was her six and his five? He'd been so worked up he'd fired at the wrong target.

The woman had obviously come to the same conclusion. She looked up at him, her eyes dancing. He threw his ear protectors down on the bench and stalked out of the room before she could show anyone else.

'Oh, sir, I was kinda hopin' I'd find you down here.'

Byron Bailey was an African American from South Central LA, a bright kid who'd made it the hard way, winning a scholarship to Caltech on the back of good grades and an evening job packing shelves. His tail-wagging enthusiasm served to make Viggiano feel even older than he already did.

'So, you found me.'

'Er, yessir. We got a tip-off about the murder of the guard and the heist at the NSA complex in Maryland. It sounds like it might be for real.'

'What are you babbling about?'

'You ever heard of the Sons of American Liberty?'

'Nope.'

'They're a fringe group of white supremacists. Our mystery caller fingered them as the people behind the theft of the Enigma machine.'

'Did you get a trace?'

'No. The call was made right here in Salt Lake, but that's all we know. He had the sense to ring off before we could get a fix on his location.'

'Where are these jokers based?'

'Malta, Idaho, sir. Carter said that he wanted you to head up the investigation at our end.'

'Regional Director Carter?' A flicker of interest in Viggiano's voice now.

'That's right. Apparently you dealt with a similar situation a couple of years back. He suggested I help you out too, if that's OK, sir.'

THE BLACK SUN | 443

'Well, for once Carter's right,' Viggiano said, running a hand through his hair to check the parting. 'Saddle up, Bailey. You're coming along for the ride. Paul Viggiano's gonna show you a short cut to the big time.'

Borough Market, Southwark: January 5, 12.34 p.m.

The market stalls were tightly packed under the rusting cast-iron railway arches, their shelves groaning with fresh produce. Shoals of eager shoppers, wrapped up against the cold, battled their way along the aisles.

'What are we doing here?' Archie snapped as he squeezed between two pushchairs and then past a long queue in front of one of the flower stalls.

In his mid-forties and of average height, Archie had the stocky build of a bare-knuckle boxing champion, his crumpled, unshaven face reinforcing the image. So there was a certain incongruity about his tailored beige overcoat over an elegant dark blue suit, and his neatly clipped blond hair.

'You're meant to be coming to dinner tonight, remember?' Tom said. 'I thought I'd splash out.'

'Oh shit. I'm sorry, mate, but I'd completely forgotten.'

'Archie!' Tom remonstrated. 'We spoke about it last week. You promised.'

'I know, I know,' Archie said sheepishly. 'I just forgot and now . . . well, Apples has a game at his place tonight. Invitation only. I can't get out of it.'

'More like you don't want to get out of it. This gambling thing's getting a bit out of control, isn't it?'

'No, it's just a laugh,' Archie said, a little too emphatically.

Throughout the ten years that Archie had been his fence, Tom had known him only as a voice at the end of a phone line. Then Archie had broken his own rule the previous year, back when they were both still in the game, tracking him down to convince him to follow through on a job. From that meeting, a friendship had developed. It was one Tom increasingly valued.

'Besides, I need a bit of excitement now and then,' Archie continued. 'The art-recovery game, well, it's not got the buzz of the old days, has it?'

'I thought you got out because you'd had enough of the old days.'

'I did,' Archie conceded. 'It's just, you know . . . sometimes I miss it.'

'I know what you mean,' Tom mused. 'Sometimes, I miss it too.'

'Dom told me about those ads in the paper, by the way.'

Tom nodded. 'Seems the FBI aren't the only ones looking for Renwick.'

They had left the market and were making their way to Archie's car. 'How was Prague?' he asked. 'Worth following up?'

'Maybe. You ever heard of a painter called Bellak?'

'Karel Bellak? Yeah, course I have. What do you want to know?'

'Is this one of his?' Tom reached into his pocket and withdrew the photograph Rabbi Spiegel had given him.

Archie studied it for a few seconds. 'Could be. Bleak palette, heavy brush strokes, slightly dodgy perspective.' He handed it back. 'Of course, I've never actually seen one. As far as I'm aware, they were all destroyed. Bellak was a competent artist, but no great talent. Then in 1937 an ambitious SS officer commissioned him to paint Himmler's daughter Gudrun as a gift for his master.'

'But wasn't Bellak Jewish?'

'As it turned out, yes. But by then Himmler had hung the portrait in his office and commissioned a second painting. When he discovered the truth, he had the SS officer shot and Bellak sent to Auschwitz. Then he ordered that every last one of Bellak's works be tracked down and disposed of.'

'Clearly, some survived,' Tom said. 'This one was stolen a few days ago.'

'Why bother pinching that?'

'Maybe because he was Jewish,' Tom said. 'You should have seen the place. Someone had done a real number on it. Swastikas sprayed all over the walls. Children's drawings from a local death camp torn to shreds.'

'Bastards,' Archie muttered. 'And the painting?'

'Sliced out of its frame and taken with them.'

'But what would they want with it?'

'That's what I've been wondering.'

'Unless the painting was what this was all about. Unless they were trying to be clever by disguising a robbery as some sort of anti-Semitic attack.'

'I came to the same conclusion,' said Tom. 'So I made some calls. And it seems that over the last year or so there have been six thefts of Bellak paintings from private collections across Europe. The cases have just stuck with the local police in each area. I only found out because I knew who to ask.'

'Someone's going to a lot of trouble to steal a bunch of supposedly worthless paintings.' A pause. 'Tom? You listening?'

'Don't turn round,' Tom said in a low voice, 'but we're being followed.'

'Followed? You sure?' Archie asked.

'Track suit, bomber jacket and white trainers. Noticed him glancing over at us five minutes ago. He's about thirty yards back.'

'We're nearly at the motor. We could make a run for it.'

Tom followed Archie's gaze to his DB9 about thirty yards down the road.

'Oh shit!' Archie swore. A wheel clamp glowed bright yellow against the gunmetal-grey bodywork. 'They've only gone and bloody clamped me.'

Something felt wrong. Behind them a man who had followed them from the market; ahead, a street sweeper whose shoes looked a little too new; in front of Archie's car, a van with blacked-out windows; and the car itself conveniently immobilised.

'This isn't right,' Tom breathed. 'Get out of here. Now!'

As Tom shouted, the rear doors of the van flew open and three men jumped to the ground. At the same time the street sweeper threw his broom away and swung a semiautomatic out from under his coat. Tom heard the heavy thud of fast-approaching feet from behind.

Archie peeled away to the left, while Tom darted right, down an alleyway that emerged onto a narrow lane bordered by a wire fence. Grabbing the galvanised mesh, he hauled himself up, the metal shuddering noisily. He was on the point of vaulting over when he felt a hand close round his left ankle. Instead of trying to shake him off, Tom lowered himself until his feet were level with the man's head, then kicked out, freeing his foot and striking him across the chin. With a strangled gasp, the man fell to the ground.

Tom swung himself over into a strip of wasteland that had been turned into a temporary car park. Hearing the clang of metal behind him, he turned to see two of the men from the van clambering up the fence.

At least they hadn't shot him, Tom thought as he sprinted out of the car park and headed back to the market. If they'd wanted him dead, they could have taken him through the fence. Clearly they had other plans.

He plunged back into the market, where he slowed to a walk, snaking between the shoppers. Stopping next to a wine stall, he glanced over his shoulder. His pursuers had reached the market entrance and were scanning the crowd, their right hands tucked inside their coats. He cautiously made his way towards the north exit, attaching himself to a group of chattering tourists. As they left the market, he broke away, heading for the main road.

With a screech of brakes, a large black Range Rover pulled up alongside him. Tom turned on his heel but slipped on some the wet cardboard boxes. Before he could scramble back to his feet, the rear passenger door flew open and he caught a glimpse of Archie sitting in the back seat.

The front passenger window retracted a few inches and a pale hand appeared in the crack clutching a government identity badge.

'Enough fun and games, Kirk. Get in.'

2

Black Pine Mountains, nr Malta, Idaho: January 5, 5.34 a.m.

'What's the latest from inside the compound?' Special Agent Paul Viggiano spoke over the noise of technicians and ringing telephones.

Bailey, sitting at the table of the cabin they had commandeered as their operational HQ, answered, 'No movement, nothing. Not a single phone call.'

'What about their dogs? Have you seen them?' Silvio Vasquez this time, the leader of the FBI Hostage Rescue Team assigned to the investigation.

'No.' Bailey shook his head. 'Nothing.'

'So that's weird, right?' Vasquez concluded. 'A dog's gotta take a leak.'

'When did it last snow?' Viggiano asked.

'Two days ago,' Vasquez answered.

'And there are no footprints? You're seriously saying no one has stepped outside that farmhouse for two days?'

'Not unless they can fly,' Bailey confirmed. 'And that includes the dogs.'

'I still say you boys have screwed up big time.' A tubby man with ginger hair and a closely trimmed moustache, Sheriff Hennessy seemed to be in a permanent sweat. 'I know these people,' he said. 'They're law-abiding, God-fearing folk. Patriots.'

'So you say,' Bailey said, resentment welling inside him. 'But they're on a Federal blacklist for suspected links to the Aryan Nations and the Klan.'

Viggiano gave a slight shake of the head, warning Bailey to back off. 'Now, Sheriff, it's true we don't know for sure that these people have done anything wrong,' he said in a conciliatory tone, 'but we do know that three days ago an exhibit was stolen from the National Cryptologic Museum in Maryland, leaving no physical evidence that we've been able to find.'

'Apart from the security guard they strung up like a hunk of meat in a cold store,' Bailey couldn't help himself from adding.

'We also know,' Viggiano continued, 'that our Salt Lake office got a call yesterday suggesting these law-abiding patriots of yours were involved.'

'I know all that,' Hennessy said. 'But that call don't prove nothing.'

'It proves that the caller knew about the theft. With the press blackout the NSA have imposed, the only people outside of law-enforcement agencies who could know about that are the people who did it. So this is a lead,

Sheriff, and we're going to follow up whether you agree or not.'

Hennessy slumped back into his chair, muttering under his breath.

Bailey smiled. 'So what's the plan?' he asked.

'Well, I'm not sitting on my ass till these jokers run out of water and cream crackers,' Viggiano declared. 'We're going in today. But remember, there are families in there—women, kids. So we knock on the door nice and easy. We ask to come inside. Any sign that this is more than a plain vanilla secure-and-search operation, we pull back. The Bureau can't afford another high-profile hostage situation.'

Vasquez nodded his agreement. 'You got it.'

'OK then.' Viggiano slapped the table. 'Let's move out. I want to hit this place after lunch.'

Borough Market, Southwark: January 5, 12.56 p.m.

The driver flicked his eyes up to the mirror and then back to the road, a smile playing around the corner of his mouth as the car accelerated away.

The man in the passenger seat peered back over his shoulder and nodded at them both. 'I'm William Turnbull,' he said.

From what he could see of Turnbull, Tom estimated that he must weigh about eighteen stone, little of it muscle. He appeared to be quite young, thirty-five or so, and was dressed in jeans and an open-necked shirt.

'Sorry about that. I thought you wouldn't come if I just asked, so I—'

'Let me guess,' Tom interrupted angrily. 'Somebody's got knocked off and you think we might know something about it? Am I right? How many times have I got to tell you people, we don't know anything.'

'This has nothing to do with any job,' Turnbull replied. 'And I'm not the police. I work for the Foreign Office.' He flashed his identity card again.

'The Foreign Office?' Archie said incredulously. 'Well, that's a new one.'

'Not really,' said Tom quietly. 'He's a spook.'

Turnbull smiled. 'We prefer "intelligence services". In my case, Six.'

MI6 wasn't the sort of organisation Tom wanted to get caught up in. Not again. He'd done five years in the CIA, and had only just lived to regret it.

'So what do you want?'

'Your help,' came the toneless reply.

'What sort of help?' Tom asked quietly.

Turnbull smiled. 'As much as you want to give. No threats. No phoney deals. If you help us it will be because you're going to want to.'

'Come on, Tom. Let's get out of here,' Archie pleaded.

'I want to hear him out,' Tom said, his curiosity piqued.

'Good.' Turnbull released his seat belt and turned to face them. 'Have you ever heard of a group called Kristall Blade?'

'No,' said Tom.

'They're a small band of extremists with loose ties to the National-demokratische Partei Deutschlands or NPD, the most active Neo-Nazi political group in Germany. They're supposedly run by a former German army captain called Dmitri Müller. They're a sophisticated paramilitary organisation who are still fighting a war the rest of us think ended in 1945.'

'Hence the name?' Tom guessed that Kristall Blade had drawn their inspiration from Kristallnacht—the night in late 1938 when attacks on Jewish businesses left the streets of Germany's cities littered with broken glass.

'Exactly,' Turnbull said. 'They fund their activities through small-scale drug and protection rackets. They're suspected of involvement in a range of terrorist atrocities aimed at Jewish communities in Germany and Austria. There are just ten or twenty active members, with perhaps a hundred supporters. So they slip under the radar of most law-enforcement agencies.'

'Like I said, I've never heard of them.'

Turnbull continued, undeterred. 'Nine days ago, two men broke into St Thomas's Hospital and murdered three people. Two of them were medical staff—witnesses, most likely. The third was an eighty-one-year-old patient by the name of Andreas Weissman. He was an Auschwitz survivor who moved here after the war. They amputated Weissman's left arm at the elbow while he was still alive. He died of a heart attack.'

'What the hell for?' Tom asked.

'That's where we want your help,' said Turnbull. 'The killers stole the surveillance tapes from the ward, but one of them was caught on CCTV as they left the building.' He produced another photo and passed it back.

Tom and Archie took it in turn to examine the image.

'No idea,' said Archie.

'Never seen him before,' Tom agreed.

'But *we* have,' Turnbull continued. 'Which is how we made the link to Kristall Blade. He's Dmitri's number two, Colonel Johann Hecht.' He handed Tom a third photograph. 'He's about six foot seven and has a scar down his right cheek and across his lip, so you can't exactly miss him.'

'I'm still waiting for the punch line here.' Tom passed the photo to Archie without even glancing at it. 'What's this man got to do with me?'

'Christ!' Archie grabbed Tom's arm. 'Look at who he's sitting opposite.'

The colour drained from Tom's face as he recognised the man Archie was pointing at. 'It's Renwick,' he stammered. 'What's he got to do with this?'

'That's what we'd like to find out,' Turnbull replied.

'What do you know?'

'Not as much as you. Given that you and Uncle Harry were almost family.'

'You'd be surprised,' Tom said bitterly. 'The Harry Renwick I knew was funny, kind and caring.' He couldn't stop his voice from softening at the memory of Renwick in his tatty old white linen suit. 'I don't want to talk about Harry Renwick.'

'Tell me what you knew about Cassius then,' Turnbull asked.

Tom took a deep breath. 'Everyone in the business knew Cassius. Knew *of* him, that is. Nobody had ever seen him. Or rather, seen him and lived.'

'He was a ruthless, murdering bastard,' said Archie. 'His crew had a crooked finger in every crooked art scam going. Thefts, forgeries, grave-robbing, smuggling—you name it. And if you didn't play along, well . . .'

'And no one dreamt that all along Cassius was Uncle Harry,' Tom said.

'Have you spoken to him since?'

Tom gave a short laugh. 'Last time I saw him, he tried to shoot me—until I severed his hand in a vault door. We're not exactly on speaking terms.'

'Yeah, I've read the FBI case file on what happened in Paris.'

Tom met his eye, surprised. 'And what did it say?'

'That, although a known thief, you cooperated with the US Government to recover five priceless gold coins stolen from Fort Knox. And that you helped unmask Renwick as Cassius and apprehend a rogue FBI agent.'

'And Renwick? What did it say about him?'

'Not much more than what you've just told us. That's the problem. We've picked up rumours, but that's it. That his syndicate has disintegrated. That he's lost everything. That he's on the run. And we've intercepted messages from others who seem to be trying to hunt Renwick down.'

'The coded personals ads in the *Tribune*?'

'You know about those?' Turnbull's surprise was evident.

'Only since yesterday. Any ideas on who's running them?'

'They're sent by post. Typed. Standard laser printer. Different country of origin each time. Could be anyone.'

'Well, I don't care either way,' Tom shrugged. 'Whoever gets him first will be doing us all a favour. Good luck to them.'

'Except that this isn't just about Renwick. Kristall Blade is a violent, fanatical sect bent on restoring the Third Reich. Our sources tell us that they are looking to fund a massive expansion of their activities. We'd like your help. You know Renwick better than anyone. We need to find out what he's working on with Hecht before it's too late. I suggest you start by looking at these hospital murders.'

Tom shook his head. 'Look, I'm sorry. No one wants to see Renwick stopped more than I do, but I'm not getting involved.'

'And how long before Renwick decides to come looking for you? How long before he decides it's time to settle old scores?'

'That's my problem, not yours,' Tom said with finality.

Turnbull stared at him stonily, then sighed and turned to face the front. 'Take this, then.' Bending his arm back over his shoulder, he held out a piece of paper with a number scrawled on it. 'In case you change your mind.'

The car slowed to a halt and the door flashed open. Tom and Archie stepped blinking onto the street. It took them a few seconds to realise that they were back at Archie's car. The clamp had been removed.

'So, what do you want to do?' asked Archie as he beeped the car open and slipped behind the wheel.

'Nothing, until we've checked him out,' Tom said, settling into his seat as the engine snarled into life. 'I want to know what he's really after.'

Tivoli Gardens, Copenhagen: January 5, 2.03 p.m.

Harry Renwick paid his admission money and walked inside. It was still quiet at this hour, most people, he knew, preferring to visit after dusk, when the Tivoli turned into an oasis of light in the dark winter city. He was certainly dressed for the cold weather, a blue velvet trilby pulled down low over his ears, a yellow silk scarf round his neck, and his chin buried in the upturned collar of his dark blue overcoat. Only his nose and eyes could be seen, intelligent, alert, and as cold as the snow around him.

He paused in front of a souvenir stall and shifted his right arm in his pocket, wincing slightly. No matter how well he wrapped it up, the cold penetrated the stump where his right hand had once been and made it ache. Eventually he found what he was looking for and pointed it out to the sales assistant, handing over a hundred-kroner note. She slipped his purchase into a red bag, counted out his change and smiled as he tipped his hat in thanks.

He walked on to the Chinese pagoda, where he stepped into the warmth of the Det Kinesiske Tårn restaurant housed within. A cloakroom attendant relieved him of his hat and coat, revealing a charcoal-grey double-breasted suit. In his mid-fifties, Renwick was tall and still obviously strong. He had a full head of white hair, and under a pair of craggy eyebrows his large green eyes looked younger than his face, which was etched with wrinkles.

'Table for two. In the back,' he demanded.

'Of course, sir. This way please.'

The maître d' steered him to a table. Renwick ordered some wine and checked his watch, a rare gold 1922 Patek Philippe chronograph.

Hecht arrived five minutes later, towering over the waiter who ushered him over. He was wearing lace-up boots, jeans and a brown leather jacket. Hecht folded his long legs awkwardly under the table. He had a cruel face, the scar down his right cheek pulling his mouth into a permanent grin. His dyed black hair had been oiled to his scalp.

Renwick indicated for the waiter to fill Hecht's glass. 'So? Did you get it?' he asked, his tone casual.

'You wouldn't be here if you didn't think I had.' Hecht unzipped his jacket and withdrew a short cardboard tube.

Renwick snatched it from him, popped the plastic cover off one end and emptied the canvas into his lap. He unscrolled the painting and inspected its battered surface. Seeing nothing there, he flipped it over to examine the reverse. His face fell. Nothing.

'Damn.'

'I don't know where else to look.' Hecht's voice was laced with disappointment. 'That's six we have taken, and none of them the right one. Perhaps if we knew what you were looking for, it would help us find it.'

'That is not our arrangement,' Renwick snapped. 'I am paying you to steal the paintings, nothing more.'

'Then perhaps it's time the deal changed.' Hecht's eyes sparkled.

'What do you mean?' Renwick asked sharply.

'That Jew you asked us to keep an eye on . . .'

'What about him?'

'He's dead. We killed him.'

Renwick's eyes widened. 'You killed . . . You idiot,' he spluttered. 'You have no idea what you are meddling in. How dare you—'

'Don't worry,' Hecht interrupted him with a wink. 'We got the arm.'

Renwick nodded slowly, as if trying to calm himself, although in truth he had known for several days about the thoughtless attack on Weissman.

'And now I suppose you think that entitles you to a seat at the top table?'

'We want a share in whatever it is you are after.'

'And what do I get in return?'

'You get the arm and whatever it can tell you.'

Renwick pretended to consider Hecht's offer. 'Where is the arm now?'

'Still in London. One phone call from me and it will be flown out here—or destroyed. You choose.'

Renwick shrugged. 'Very well. Eighty–twenty split.' He had no intention of splitting anything, but it would arouse suspicion if he didn't negotiate.

'Fifty–fifty.'

'Do not push your luck, Johann. Seventy–thirty. That's my final offer.'

'Done.' Hecht took out his phone. 'Where do you want it delivered?'

'I will go to London,' Renwick said with a wry smile. 'Things are already in motion there. Maybe we can use this to our advantage.'

'You still haven't told me what this is all about.'

Renwick shook his head. 'The full story will have to wait for Dmitri.' He reached into the red bag by his chair. His hand emerged clutching a small model steam train. He placed it on the table and pushed it over to Hecht.

'What is this? Some sort of joke?' Hecht's tone was suspicious.

'No joke.'

'But it's a train,' he said dismissively.

'Not just any train. A gold train.'

Location unknown: January 5, 4.32 p.m.

Large damp patches had formed around his armpits and across his back as he leant forward on the long table and stared at the black conference phone that lay in the middle of it, a red light on one side flashing steadily.

'What is it?' The voice that floated up from the phone was calm and cold.

'We've found him. In London. The last one. He's dead.'

'How do you know?'

'I've seen the police report. And I've seen the photos taken at the autopsy and a copy of the dental records. They match.'

A long silence. 'It is over,' the voice eventually sighed. 'He was the last.'

'No, it's just the beginning.' As he spoke, he spun the gold signet ring on his little finger. The ring's flat upper surface was engraved with a small grid of twelve squares, one of which had been set with a lone diamond.

'The beginning?' the voice laughed. 'What are you talking about? Everything is safe now. He was the only one left who knew.'

'He was murdered. Killed in his hospital bed.'

'He deserved a far worse death for what he had done.'

'His arm was cut off.'

'Cut off?' The question was spat into the room. 'Who by?'

'Someone who knows. Why else would they have taken it?'

Silence. Then, 'I will have to call the others together.'

'British Intelligence is involved, too. They're working with someone.'

'Who? Cassius? We'll have caught up with him before he gets any further. He knows nothing. The same goes for all the others who've tried.'

'No, not Cassius. Tom Kirk.'

'Charles Kirk's son? The art thief?'

'Yes. What do you want me to do?'

'Watch him. See where he goes, who he talks to.'

'Do you think he could—?'

'Never!' the voice cut him off. 'The trail is too cold. Even for him.'

Clerkenwell, London: January 5, 8.35 p.m.

Tom had never really been one for possessions. There had been no point in owning anything: until recently he had rarely spent more than two weeks in the same place. The few pieces he'd recently bought at auction were a tangible sign, therefore, that he had changed. That he was no longer a wandering mercenary. He had a home now. Roots. Responsibilities.

The huge open-plan sitting room had been simply furnished with sleek modern furniture. The polished concrete floor was covered in nineteenth-century Turkish kilims, while the walls were hung with late Renaissance paintings, most of them Italian.

'Sorry I'm late,' Dominique panted as she came through the door. 'Went for a run and sort of forgot the time.'

'Well, at least you're here,' Tom said, turning from the stove to face her.

'Oh no, Tom, he hasn't cancelled again, has he?' she said. 'Let me guess. He had a card game, or greyhound racing, or he got tickets to a fight?'

'Right first time,' Tom said with a sigh. 'At least he's consistent.'

'I can't believe that you used to place your life in the hands of someone so unreliable,' she said as she sat down at the breakfast bar that separated the kitchen area from the main sitting room.

'Yeah, well, that's the thing. Archie never got the job wrong, not once. He might forget his own birthday, but he'd still be able to tell you the make and location of every alarm system in every museum from here to Hong Kong.'

'You don't think it's all getting a bit out of control?'

Tom rinsed his hands under the tap. 'He's always been a gambler. It's in his nature. At least now he's just playing for money. The stakes were much higher when we were still in the game.'

'If you ask me, the gambling's all an excuse anyway,' she said, her eyes twinkling. 'I think he just doesn't like your cooking.'

Tom grinned and flicked water at her.

'Stop it,' she laughed. 'You'll ruin my mascara.'

'You never wear make-up.'

'I thought I might go to a club after dinner. Lucas and some of his friends said they would be going out. Do you want to come?'

'No, thanks,' he shrugged. 'Not really in the mood.'

'Are you OK?' she asked.

'Me? Fine. Why do you ask?'

'You just seem a bit down, that's all. I just wondered whether it was because . . . well, you know, because it's today?'

Tom gave her a blank look. 'What's today?'

'You know, your father's birthday.'

It took a few seconds for the words to register in Tom's brain.

'I'd forgotten.' He could barely believe it himself, although part of him wondered whether, subconsciously, he'd deliberately blocked it out, like all those other things he'd blocked out from his childhood.

'You know, it might help if you sometimes spoke about him.'

'And say what?'

'I don't know. What you felt about him. What you liked. What annoyed you. Anything other than the big hole you're always trying to step around.'

'You know what he did to me.' Tom could feel the resentment building in his voice. 'He blamed me for my mother's death. As if it was my fault she let me drive the car. I was thirteen, for God's sake. Everyone else accepted the crash was an accident, but not him. I got sent to America because he couldn't bear to see me around. He abandoned me when I needed him the most.'

'And you hated him for it.'

'That's not the point. The important thing is that I was prepared to try and start over. And it was working. We were beginning to get to know each other again, build something new. Then he died.'

'You know he never forgave himself for what he did to you, Tom. He talked about it a lot. It never left him. I think that's partly why he took me in. To try to make things right.'

Tom frowned. 'Took you in? Dom, what are you talking about?'

She took a deep breath. 'I never knew my parents,' she began. 'All I remember is being passed from foster home to foster home as quickly as it took me to set fire to something or get into a fight. When I was seventeen I ran away. Spent a year living on the streets in Geneva. I was close to the edge.'

Tom had always known that Dominique had a darker side. That she was a little wild. This, however, was totally unexpected.

'But those stories about your family, about studying fine art, about going to finishing school in Lausanne—you made that stuff up?'

'We all have our secrets,' she said softly, her eyes locking with his.

'Did my father know?'

'I first saw him at a taxi stand one night. He'd just been to the cinema. I never expected him to see me. Normally people would be halfway home before they'd notice their wallet was gone. But your father was so quick.'

'You stole his wallet?' Tom was not so much shocked as impressed.

'Tried to. But he caught me with my hand in his jacket. And the amazing thing was that, rather than call the police, he just told me to keep it.'

'He did what?' Tom couldn't help smiling as he pictured the scene.

'He told me I could keep it. But if I wanted a fresh start in life, I should bring it to him at his shop and he'd help me. I stared at that damned wallet for four days. Then on the fifth day I went to see him. Just as he'd promised, he took me in. Gave me a job in his shop, taught me everything I know, never asked for anything in return. I wouldn't be here today without him.'

For a few seconds Tom was silent. Dominique's confession explained some of the contradictions in her character. Less clear was his father's motivation in helping her, or indeed his reasons for keeping it a secret.

'He should have told me,' Tom said. 'You both should.'

'You're right,' she said. 'And I'm telling you now because I think that today, of all days, you should know that, all the time he was with me, he was trying to make up for not being with you. He knew that he would never be able to forgive himself for what he had done. But he always hoped that, one day, you'd understand and not hate him so much.'

There was a long silence, broken only by the hum of the refrigerator.

Abruptly, Tom said, 'I think we should have a drink. A toast. To him. There's a bottle of Grey Goose in the freezer.'

'Good idea.' She smiled and stood up, then crossed to the refrigerator and opened the door. She gave a short, sharp scream.

Tom crossed the room in an instant. She pointed into the freezer, the cold air inside swirling like fog. Tom could just make out what she was pointing at.

An arm. A human arm. And it was holding a rolled-up canvas.

3

The large H-shaped farmhouse and its assortment of outbuildings nestled in a wide clearing in the middle of the forest. Bailey lay in the snow, hidden among the trees. Viggiano was lying to one side of him, a pair of binoculars glued to his face, with Sheriff Hennessy on the other.

'How many people did you say were in there?' asked Viggiano.

'Twenty to twenty-five,' Bailey replied.

Viggiano picked up his radio. 'OK, Vasquez—move in.'

Two teams of seven men rose from their hiding places and vaulted over the low fence. They moved in rapidly on the front and rear entrances to the main building, crouching along the side walls to the left of each door.

Bailey ran his binoculars along the two SWAT teams in their helmets, gas masks and bulletproof vests. In addition to submachine guns and pistols, one man in each unit was equipped with a large metal battering ram.

'OK,' came Vasquez's voice over the radio. 'Still no sign of activity inside. Alpha team, stand by.'

A voice amplified through a bullhorn rang out. 'This is the FBI. You are surrounded. Come out with your hands up.'

'I said to keep it low-key, Vasquez, you macho idiot,' Viggiano muttered.

Silence from the farmstead. Again the amplified voice blared out. 'I repeat, this is the FBI. You have ten seconds to show yourselves.'

Viggiano's radio crackled. 'Nothing doing, sir. It's your call.'

'Make the breach,' Viggiano ordered. 'Now.'

At each entrance the man with the battering ram stepped forward and slammed it into the lock. Both doors splintered and flew open. A second man lobbed a tear-gas canister through each doorway. A few seconds later, the canisters exploded, sending choking clouds of gas billowing out.

'GO, GO, GO!' yelled Vasquez as the men disappeared into the house.

Bailey could hear muffled shouting and the pop and fizz of further tear-gas grenades being let off, but nothing else. No screams. No crying children. Certainly not a gunshot. Then the radio crackled into life.

'Sir, this is Vasquez . . . There's nobody here. The place is empty. We searched every room, including the attic. It's deserted and it looks like they left in a hurry. There's half-eaten food on the table. The whole place stinks.'

Bailey swapped a confused look with Viggiano and then with Hennessy, who looked genuinely concerned.

'I'm coming down,' Viggiano said. 'I want to see this for myself.'

Viggiano and Bailey were met by one of Vasquez's men, who led them into the large kitchen where Vasquez was waiting for them. He nodded towards a door. 'We haven't checked the basement yet.'

'The basement?' Viggiano looked at the plan of the compound. 'There is no basement,' he said.

'Then what do you call that?' Vasquez threw open the door to reveal a narrow staircase leading down into darkness.

The warm air that rushed up to meet them was thick with flies and a heady smell that Bailey recognised only too well. The smell of rotting flesh.

Guided by Vasquez's flashlight, they descended the stairs. At the bottom was a narrow, unlit corridor. Vasquez signalled for them to wait as he entered a doorway. He re-emerged, grim-faced, a few seconds later. 'I hope you guys skipped lunch.'

Viggiano and Bailey stepped inside. In the centre of the room was a German Shepherd, its tongue lolling out of its mouth. Next to it were two blood-soaked pit bulls and a scraggy mongrel. The stench was unbearable.

'Guess now we know why no one had seen the dogs,' said Vasquez drily.

'Sir?' Another of Vasquez's men appeared in the doorway behind them. 'We got something else.'

They followed him back along the corridor into a smaller room, empty apart from a desk against one wall. The floor was littered with paper. Bailey picked up a print-out—a list of flight times to Washington DC.

On the far side of the room, a large architectural drawing had been pinned to the wall, with various parts of the building circled in red. In the bottom left-hand corner was an inscription: *National Cryptographic Museum—Plans; Structural Drawings; Heating/Ventilation System—1993*.

Bailey pointed it out to the others. 'Looks like these were our guys.'

'What's through there?' Viggiano pointed to a rusty metal door set in the facing wall.

Vasquez approached and shone his flashlight through a small glass inspection panel set into the door. 'We got 'em!' he exclaimed. 'They're in here. This opens onto a door to another room. Jesus, they're squashed in tight.'

'Let me see.' Viggiano peered in.

'Are they still alive?' Bailey asked.

'Yeah. One of them has just seen me.' He stepped back.

Bailey took his turn at the window. 'She's waving her arms,' he said with a frown. 'Like she wants us to leave.'

'Let's get these doors open,' Viggiano urged.

'Are you sure?' Bailey asked. 'She doesn't look like she wants it opened.'

'Screw what she wants,' Viggiano fired back.

'Sir, I really think we should check it out first,' Bailey insisted. 'There must be a reason they're signalling.'

'It's pretty damned obvious, Bailey. Someone locked them in. And the sooner we get them out, the sooner we all get a hot shower. Vasquez?'

With a shrug, Vasquez unbolted the first door and pulled it open. But as he reached the door on the other side, a shout stopped him in his tracks.

'Look!' Bailey pointed his flashlight at the inspection window of the second door. It was filled by a scrap of white material on which a message had been scrawled in what appeared to be black eyeliner: *You'll kill us all*.

'What the hell—?' Viggiano began, but he was interrupted as Vasquez began to cough loudly, his body doubling over with the effort.

'Gas,' he gasped. 'Get out . . . gas.'

Bailey grabbed him by the shoulders and dragged him towards the exit, his last sight the woman's face pressed to the inspection panel, her eyes large and round and red. As he watched, she collapsed out of sight.

'Get everyone out of here,' Bailey shouted.

He shoved a convulsing Viggiano back up the stairs, into the kitchen, out through the hall and back outside. The rest of the SWAT team spilled out onto the snow ahead of them, sucking down lungfuls of mountain air.

'What happened?' Sheriff Hennessy came running up as they emerged.

Bailey released Vasquez into the care of a paramedic team, then bent to rest his hands on his knees. 'The place has been booby-trapped,' he panted.

'Booby-trapped?' Hennessy looked bewildered. 'How?'

'Some sort of gas. It must have been rigged to the door. They're all still inside. They're dying.'

'They can't be,' Hennessy cried out in anguish. 'That was never the deal.'

Bailey looked up. 'That was never *what* deal, Sheriff?'

Bloomsbury, London: January 5, 9.29 p.m.

Tom took a mouthful of cognac, swilling it round his mouth before swallowing it, then sat down heavily in an armchair and glanced about him. This was only the second time Tom had been to Archie's place.

'Sorry about your game,' Tom said.

'Don't worry. I was losing anyway. Is she all right?' Archie tilted his head in the direction of the closed bathroom door in the hallway.

'She'll be fine,' Tom said.

'What the hell happened?'

Tom handed him the rolled-up canvas. 'Take a look.'

Archie unscrolled the painting on the coffee table. He looked up in surprise. 'It's the Bellak from Prague.' He ran his fingers over a series of small holes that punctured the surface of the painting. 'Where did you find it?'

'Somebody kindly left it in my freezer. And it wasn't the only thing they left. There was a human arm in there, too. It's still in there.'

Archie's eyes bulged in disbelief. 'It's that two-faced bastard Turnbull.'

Tom laughed. 'Come on, Archie. You said he checked out.'

'He did, according to my contact. MI6, originally on the Russian desk at GCHQ. But that doesn't mean he didn't do it. Think about it. He shows up wanting our help. We refuse, and a few hours later the missing forearm miraculously shows up among your frozen peas. It's a bloody set-up.'

'You're assuming the arm belongs to Turnbull's Auschwitz survivor.'

'How many severed arms do you think there are floating around London?'

'We shouldn't jump to conclusions. Besides, there is another option . . .'

'Here we go,' Archie muttered.

'Whoever is behind the murder of that old man is also behind the theft of the painting.'

'You think it's Renwick, don't you?'

'We know he's working with Kristall Blade, and we know they killed that man. Since he only has one hand, thanks to me, he probably appreciated the irony of dropping off someone else's limb as his calling card.'

'And the Bellak paintings?'

'Stolen by them at his request,' Tom said with a shrug.

'Bellak?' Unnoticed by either of them, Dominique had slipped into the room, her earlier shock replaced by a calm resolve. 'The painter?'

'You've heard of him?' Tom glanced at Archie. 'How come?'

'Because your father spent the last three years of his life looking for Bellak paintings. It became quite a big thing for him. He had me scanning data bases and newspaper files and auction listings to see if I could find anything. I never did. By the end, I think he had almost given up.'

Tom clicked his fingers. 'That's where I'd heard the name before. Now you mention it, I think he even asked me if I could come up with anything.'

'But why on earth would he want to collect them?' Archie asked.

'He wasn't collecting them.' Dominique sat down cross-legged on the hearth rug. 'He was looking for one in particular—a portrait of a girl. He said it was probably in a private collection. He said that it was the key.'

'The key to what?' Archie asked.

'I don't know,' Dominique sighed.

'Well, Renwick clearly does,' Tom said bitterly. 'That's why he's put this here—to show me how close he is to finding it.'

'Which is why you shouldn't let him get to you,' Archie said firmly. 'Look, I know Cassius. This is just one of his sick games . . . Tom? What are you doing?'

'Calling Turnbull,' answered Tom, picking up the phone and extracting Turnbull's number from his wallet. 'We can't just ignore this.'

'He's playing with you. Let it go,' pleaded Archie.

'I can't let it go, Archie,' Tom snapped. 'If Renwick's after something my father spent years looking for, then I'm not just going to stand by and watch him get it first. I'm not having him make a fool of me. Not again.'

Forensic Science Service, Lambeth, London: January 6, 3.04 a.m.

'Well, the wounds are consistent with the manner in which the victim's arm was removed . . .' Dr Derrick O'Neal rotated the limb, examining it under a high-powered magnifying lens. 'But the DNA tests will confirm whether it's his. We should have the results in a few hours.'

He yawned, clearly still missing the warmth of the bed from which Turnbull had summoned him.

'It's remarkably well preserved. Where did you find it?' O'Neal asked.

'In someone's freezer.'

'That makes sense. Strange thing to hang on to, though.'

'What can you tell me about this?' Turnbull pointed at a livid red rectangle on the inner arm where a patch of skin had been cut out.

O'Neal bent for a closer look. 'What was there?'

'A tattoo. The sort you get in a concentration camp.'

'Oh!' This piece of information finally jolted O'Neal awake.

'I need to know what it said.'

O'Neal sucked air through his teeth. 'Oh, that could be tricky. It depends on the depth of the incision. Given the crude tattooing methods employed by the Nazis, it may be deeper than usual. But if the people who did this cut right down into the hypodermis, it's unlikely we'll find anything.'

'And have they?'

O'Neal examined the wound closely. 'We might be lucky. The ink will have penetrated the deep dermis, maybe even the lymph cells, which could assist us with recovery. But it's going to take time.'

'Time is one thing you haven't got, Doctor. I was told you were the best forensic dermatologist in the country. I need you to work some magic on this one. Here's my number—call me as soon as you get something.'

Greenwich, London: January 6, 3 p.m.

Turnbull was waiting for them outside number 52, a handsome Victorian red-brick house identical to all the others on the terrace. He was dressed in a cavernous dark blue overcoat, whose heavy folds hung round his stomach.

'Thanks for meeting me here,' Turnbull said. 'And for helping.'

'We're not helping yet,' said Tom firmly.

'Well, for handing in the arm, at least. You could have just got rid of it. Others would.' He glanced at Archie as he said this.

'What are we doing here?' Archie demanded impatiently.

'Meeting Elena Weissman. The victim's daughter.'

Turnbull opened the gate and they made their way up the path to the front door. There was no bell, just a brass knocker in the shape of a lion's head. Turnbull gave it a loud rap, and they waited patiently until they heard footsteps and saw a shadow through the rippled glass panels.

The door opened to reveal a striking woman, with jet-black hair secured in a chignon by two lacquered red chopsticks that matched her lipstick. Tom put her age at forty, or thereabouts. The foundation she was wearing couldn't fully disguise the dark circles under her sad green eyes.

'Yes?' She had an immediately arresting presence, her voice strong.

'Miss Weissman? My name is Detective Inspector Turnbull. I'm with the Metropolitan Police.' Turnbull flashed a badge that, Tom noticed, was different from the one he had shown them yesterday. No doubt he had a drawer full of badges to choose from. 'It's about your father . . .'

'Oh?' She looked surprised. 'But I've already spoken to—'

'These are two colleagues of mine, Mr Kirk and Mr Connolly,' Turnbull continued, speaking over her. 'Can we come in?'

She hesitated for a moment, then stepped aside. 'Yes, of course.'

She showed them into what Tom assumed had once been the sitting room. A sofa and two armchairs were covered in white dustsheets and several cardboard boxes stood in a corner, their lids taped down.

'I apologise for the mess,' she said, flicking the dustsheets onto the floor and indicating that they should sit. 'But I've got to get back to Bath. I run a property business there. I'm told it could be weeks before you release the body.' She flashed an accusing stare at Turnbull.

'These matters are always difficult,' he said gently. 'I understand how painful this must be, but we must balance the needs of the family with the need to find those responsible.'

'Yes, of course.' She swallowed hard. 'What did you want to ask me?'

Turnbull took a deep breath. 'Did your father ever talk about his time in Poland? In Auschwitz?'

She shook her head. 'No. I tried to talk to him about it many times. But he said that he had locked everything away in a dark corner of his mind that he couldn't look into again. In a way, that told me all I needed to know.'

'And the tattoo on his arm—did he ever show you that?'

Again she shook her head. 'I saw it, of course, now and again. But he usually wore a long-sleeved shirt. My father was a very private man.'

'I see,' said Turnbull. There was a pause before he spoke again. 'Miss Weissman, what I'm about to tell you may be difficult for you to hear.'

'Oh?'

Turnbull hesitated. 'We have recovered your father's arm.' He snatched a glance at Tom.

'Oh.' Her reaction was one of relief, as if she'd been dreading a more traumatic revelation. 'But that's a good thing, isn't it?'

'Yes . . . Except that his tattoo had been . . . sliced off.'

Her hand flew to her mouth in horror. 'Oh my God.'

'However, by analysing the scar tissue and pigmentation in the deeper skin layers,' Turnbull continued, 'our forensic experts were able to reconstitute his prisoner number. Are you familiar with the Auschwitz system?'

She shook her head silently.

He gave a weak smile. 'Neither was I, until this morning. It seems Auschwitz was the only camp to tattoo its prisoners systematically. The numbering system used either simple consecutive numbers or a combination of letters and numbers. The numbers on Jewish prisoners mostly followed the unlettered series, although in many cases this was preceded by a triangle, until the A and B series took over from May 1944.'

'Why are you telling me this?' There was a hysterical edge to her voice.

'Because the number on your father's arm didn't follow any of the known Auschwitz number series.'

'What?' Even her make-up couldn't disguise how white she had gone.

'It was a ten-digit number with no alphabetical or geometric prefix. Auschwitz numbers never rose to ten digits . . .' He paused. 'Miss Weissman, it is possible that your father was never actually in a concentration camp.'

They sat there in embarrassed silence as she rocked gently in her seat, hands covering her face, shoulders shaking.

Tom gently laid his hand on her arm. 'Miss Weissman, I'm sorry.'

'It's OK,' she said. 'I've almost been expecting something like this.'

'What do you mean?' Turnbull's brow creased in curiosity.

She lowered her hands. Her face shone, not with tears but with anger.

'There's something I have to show you.' She got up and led them out into the hall, pausing outside the next door down. 'I haven't touched anything since I found it. I think part of me was hoping that one day I'd come in and it would all just be gone, as if it had never been here.'

She opened the door and led them inside. The room was dark and smelt of pipe smoke and dust. In front of the window stood a desk, its empty drawers half open. She walked to the window and pulled open the curtain.

'I found it by accident,' she said as she approached the bookcase. It was empty apart from one book. She pushed against the book's spine. With a click, the middle section of the bookcase edged forward slightly.

Tom sensed Archie stiffen next to him.

She tugged on the bookcase and it swung open to reveal a green door set into the wall. She stepped forward, then paused, her hand on the door handle, flashing them a weak smile over her shoulder. 'It's funny, isn't it? You love someone all your life. You think you know them. Then you find out it's all been a lie.' Her voice was flat. 'You never knew them at all.'

The door swung open and Tom gave a start as a mannequin in full SS dress uniform loomed out of the darkness. Behind it, on the far wall of a small chamber, a vast swastika flag had been pinned, while the right-hand wall was lined with shelves holding a vast collection of guns, daggers, swords, identity cards, books, badges, photographs, leaflets and armbands.

'You never knew about this?' Tom asked.

She shook her head. 'He would lock himself in his office for hours. I thought he was reading. But he must have been in here.' Her voice was expressionless. 'I hoped it was a sort of post-traumatic reaction—a morbid fascination brought about by what happened to him. Until I saw this.'

She reached up and removed a photograph from the top shelf, then took it across to the window. Tom and Turnbull followed her. As she angled it to the light, the photo revealed three young men in SS uniform.

'I've no idea who the other two are, but the man in the middle is . . . is my father.'

'When was this taken?' Tom asked quietly.

'In 1944, I think. There's something else on the back, written in Cyrillic.'

'December—that's Russian for December,' said Turnbull, peering over Tom's shoulder.

'Tom, we should take this.' Archie's voice came from inside the chamber. He appeared a moment later, carrying the mannequin's jacket and cap.

'Why?' Turnbull asked.

'You ever seen anything like this before?' He pointed at the circular cap badge, which appeared to show a swastika with twelve arms rather than the usual four, each shaped like an SS lightning flash. 'I know I haven't.'

'You think Lasche can help?' Tom asked.

'If he'll see us,' said Archie, sounding unhopeful.

'Who?' Turnbull butted in.

'Wolfgang Lasche,' Tom explained. 'He used to be one of the biggest dealers in military memorabilia.'

'Used to be?'

'He's been a semi-recluse for years. Lives on the top floor of the Hotel Drei Könige in Zürich. He trained as a lawyer originally. Made a name for himself pursuing companies for alleged involvement in war crimes. He won hundreds of millions of dollars in compensation for Holocaust survivors. Then, rumour has it, he hit the jackpot. He uncovered a scam by one of the big Swiss banks to appropriate billions of dollars of unclaimed funds deposited by Holocaust victims. It went all the way to the top. So they bought him off.'

'So his antiques dealership . . . ?'

'Part of the deal was that he got out of the Nazi blame game. He's a major collector now. Nobody knows that market better than him.'

'And he never goes out?'

'He's sick. Confined to a wheelchair with twenty-four-seven nursing care.'

While they were talking, Elena Weissman had disappeared into the chamber. She was sobbing as she re-emerged. 'I could have forgiven him, if he'd told me . . . I loved him so much. I could have forgiven him anything . . .'

Tom saw that she was clutching a Luger pistol in her right hand.

'Even this.' Her voice rose as she lifted the gun to her mouth.

'No!' Tom leapt towards her, hoping to knock the gun out of her hand before she could pull the trigger. But he was too late.

FBI Headquarters, Salt Lake City: January 6, 8.17 a.m.

Paul Viggiano poured himself another cup of coffee from the machine, then turned to face Sheriff Hennessy and his attorney, Jeremiah Walton. A wiry, aggressive man with a thin face and sunken cheeks, Walton seemed unable to sit still on the plastic seats. Bailey was sitting on the opposite side of the table. A tape recorder was humming to his right.

'Face it, Hennessy, it's over,' Viggiano said, struggling to contain the excitement in his voice. 'Whatever little scam you've been running up there is finished now. So tell us what you know and make this easier on yourself.'

Hennessy stared at Viggiano stonily.

'My client wants to talk about immunity,' Walton said.

'Your client can go to hell,' Viggiano snapped. 'I got twenty-six corpses out there. Women. Kids. Whole families. That's twenty-six people—dead. Immunity isn't even in the dictionary as far as your *client* is concerned.'

'You got nothing. Just one man's word against another.' Walton glanced at Bailey. 'A throwaway comment made in the heat of the moment that has been taken completely out of context.'

'Hell, maybe you're right,' said Viggiano. 'Maybe we don't have much.' He leaned across the table towards Hennessy. 'But we'll turn your life upside-down and shake it hard and have a good look at everything that drops out. Whatever we need, we'll find it.'

Walton flashed a questioning glance at Hennessy, who raised his eyebrows in response, then gave a brief shrug.

'Very well, then,' Walton conceded. 'We want a deal.'

'Accessory to multiple homicides. Criminal conspiracy. Armed robbery. The best deal he'll get is avoiding the Row,' Viggiano said.

'And if he cooperates?' Walton asked, licking the corners of his mouth.

'If he cooperates, we won't push for the death sentence. And there may be the chance of parole down the line.'

'A minimum-security facility?'

'We can do that,' said Viggiano. 'But we want everything—names, dates, locations. You tell me what you got, then I'll tell you if it's enough.'

Hennessy glanced at Walton, who whispered a few words in his ear. The sheriff straightened and nodded slowly. 'OK, I'll talk.'

'Good,' Viggiano said. 'Let's start with some names.'

'I don't know his name,' Hennessy began. 'Not his real one, at least. Everyone just called him Blondi.'

'This is the guy who you think did this?'

'Uh-huh. He approached us.'

'Who's us?'

'The Sons of American Liberty.'

'Now, Bill,' Walton cautioned him, 'let's not get into details.'

'Why? I'm not ashamed,' Hennessy said defiantly, before turning back to face Viggiano. 'Yeah, I was one of them. Why the hell not? It's like I said before, they're patriots.' He locked eyes with Bailey. 'True Americans. Not a bunch of lazy, drug-dealing immigrants.'

Bailey stared back at Hennessy with a hostile intensity.

'Where was this Blondi from?' Viggiano continued.

'Europe.'

'That's two hundred and fifty million people,' Bailey observed drily.

'I'm telling you what I know,' Hennessy hissed.

'What did he want?' Viggiano again.

'He said that he wanted an Enigma machine. That he would pay us fifty thousand to get him one. Half up front, half on delivery.'

'And you agreed?'

'Who wouldn't? That was big money. He had all the plans and blueprints. Three guys volunteered and they hit the museum. From what I hear, the whole thing went pretty smooth.'

'Then what happened?' Viggiano asked. 'After they got the machine?'

'I don't know. I wasn't there.'

'Yeah, let's talk about that. How come he managed to get everyone else into that room apart from you? Did you know what he was planning?'

'No.' Hennessy's vehement denial interrupted him. 'I was meant to be there, but there was a snowstorm that night and I couldn't get through. All I knew was that it was meant to be a straight swap. The cash for the machine. The first I heard of a problem was when you guys showed up.'

'So you're saying it's just dumb luck you're the only person who's met him who's still alive?' Bailey's tone was disbelieving.

'Hey, I never said I met him. I only ever saw him twice and each time I was on the other side of the compound. The boys were careful to keep me away from outsiders in case word got out that I was part of the group.'

'You're lying,' Bailey snapped.

'I'm not. These people were my friends. Some of them were just kids. If I knew the son-of-a-bitch who did this, I'd tell you. I want you to find him.'

'And how do we do that exactly, if everyone who has met him is dead?'

4

The Captain Kidd, Wapping High Street: January 6, 4.42 p.m.

Tom pushed away his Guinness, untouched. 'That poor woman,' he said.

'I know.' Archie shook his head. 'At least Turnbull dealt with the cops. What do you make of him?' he went on.

Tom shrugged. 'Well, given that he's in MI6's antiterrorist unit, it's clearly these Kristall Blade people he's really after. Renwick . . . that was just the bait to get us on board.'

'Do you buy his story?' Archie reached for his cigarettes and lit one.

'About Weissman?' Tom pushed the ashtray across the table. 'I guess so. A lot of people had secrets to hide at the end of the war. About things they'd done. About things they'd seen or heard. Posing as a concentration camp survivor would have been one way to escape and start a new life.'

'And the tattoo?'

'Maybe it's just a botched attempt to fake a concentration camp serial code. Maybe there's more to it than that. Somebody obviously thinks it was worth having. Hopefully Lasche will be able to explain some of this.'

'That reminds me,' Archie said. 'Hand me the uniform, will you?'

'What for?' asked Tom, reaching down and opening the bag at his side.

'I found something else in that room. Something I thought you'd want to keep Turnbull away from.' Archie took the jacket from Tom and reached into the inside pocket. His hand emerged clutching a faded brown envelope, from which he removed a dog-eared photograph. 'Recognise this?'

As Tom took the photograph, his eyes widened with surprise. 'It's the Bellak from Prague—the synagogue. How—?'

'There are two more,' Archie continued. He flicked the faded black and white photographs onto the table. 'A castle somewhere, and . . .'

'It's the portrait,' Tom breathed, picking it up. 'The one my father was looking for. It must be.' He turned over the photograph. 'Is anything written on the back of the other two?' he asked.

'No, I already looked. But there is this.'

On the reverse side of the envelope someone had written a return name and address in cramped italic script. The address was in Kitzbühel, Austria.

'Until we know exactly what Renwick wants with these paintings, let's keep this to ourselves,' said Tom. 'It's got nothing to do with Turnbull.'

Hotel Kempinski Vier Jahreszeiten, Munich: January 7, 3.07 p.m.

Harry Renwick walked into the hotel and up to the main reception desk.

The concierge looked up with tired eyes. *'Guten Abend, mein Herr.'*

'Guten Abend. I am here for Herr Hecht.'

'Ah, yes. I believe he is expecting you, Herr . . . ?'

'Smith.'

'Smith, yes.' He gave a distracted smile as he searched through the entries on the screen in front of him. 'He is in the Bellevue Suite on the seventh floor. I'll ring ahead and let Herr Hecht know you are here.'

'Thank you.'

The concierge, his hand shaking a little from what Renwick guessed was tiredness, reached for the phone as Renwick turned on his heel and walked across the lobby to the lifts.

A sign on the seventh floor pointed him towards the Bellevue Suite. Renwick knocked, and a few moments later Hecht opened the door.

He led Renwick through to the sitting room and waved him to a beige sofa, then sat on the one opposite.

'Drink?'

Renwick shook his head. 'Where is Dmitri?'

'He is here.'

Renwick looked around the room. 'We agreed—no games, Johann.'

'Calm yourself, Cassius.' The voice came from a speakerphone on the table between the sofas. The accent was a mixture of American vowels and clipped German consonants.

'Dmitri?' Renwick asked uncertainly.

'I apologise for the rather melodramatic circumstances, but unfortunately it is very difficult for me to travel unobserved.'

'What is this? How do I even know it is you?' Renwick asked.

'We are partners now. You must trust me.'

'Trusting people do not live long in my business.'

'You have my word of honour, then.'

'The difference being . . . ?'

'The difference being nothing to a businessman like yourself, but everything to soldiers like Johann and me. To a soldier, honour and loyalty count above all else.'

'A soldier?' Renwick gave a half-smile. 'In whose army?'

'An army fighting a war that has never ended. A war to protect our Fatherland from the Jews and immigrants who defile our soil.' As Dmitri's voice grew in intensity, Hecht nodded fervently. 'A war to remove the shackles of Zionist propaganda, which for too long has choked the German nation with guilt, when it is *we*, the true Germans, who suffered for our country.'

'Your war is no concern of mine,' said Renwick. 'But what I have to tell you will give you the means to win it.'

'I have here in front of me the little toy that you gave to Colonel Hecht in Copenhagen. Most amusing. A gold train?'

'There is more to this than gold,' said Renwick. 'Much more.'

Hotel Drei Könige, Zürich: January 7, 3.07 p.m.

Gripping a large brown leather holdall, Tom walked across the hotel's grey marble floor to the semicircular walnut reception desk. The fresh-faced girl behind it smiled a welcome.

'I'd like to see Herr Lasche, please.'

Her smile vanished. 'We have no guest here by that name.'

'I have something for him.' He deposited the bag on the desk. 'He'll want to see this. And give him my card.' He slipped a card across the desk.

The receptionist reached under the counter and pressed a button.

Almost immediately a burly man wearing a black polo neck and jeans appeared from the room behind her. '*Ja?*'

Tom repeated what he had just said to the girl.

The man's face remained impassive as he opened the bag and unzipped it, feeling gingerly around inside. Satisfied that it contained nothing dangerous, he jerked his head towards an opening in the wall. 'Wait in there.'

Tom stepped in to what turned out to be the bar. No sooner had he sat down than the receptionist beckoned him back through to the lobby.

'Herr Lasche will see you now, Mr Kirk. If you don't mind, Karl will search you before you go up.'

The guard approached Tom with a black handheld scanner, which he passed over his body. Satisfied, he escorted Tom to the lift. Tom stepped inside but, rather than follow him, the guard simply leant in, waved a card across a white panel and stepped back.

The lift opened into a large room. Three windows ran along the left-hand wall but their shutters were closed, light seeping through the slats. In between, ornate arrangements of antique swords, pistols and rifles radiated like steel flowers. Looking up, Tom saw that the ceiling had been removed, leaving the joists exposed. From each joist a battle-worn regimental flag had been suspended. But Tom's attention was grabbed by a massive bronze cannon that sat parallel to the desk on two thick oak plinths. He found himself unable to resist stroking its smooth flanks.

'Beautiful, isn't she?'

The sound of Lasche's voice made Tom jump. A door had opened to the right of the desk to admit a man in a wheelchair, closely followed by a male nurse, his white coat worn open over a grey suit, his blond hair clipped short. He was eyeing Tom sourly, gripping the brown holdall in one hand.

Lasche himself was almost bald and the skin of his face seemed thin and papery with an unhealthy yellow sheen. His grey, misty eyes peered at Tom through thick steel-framed glasses. An oxygen mask hung round his neck. Strapped to the undercarriage and back of the chair were gas bottles and small black boxes from which ran wires and tubes that disappeared into the front and sleeves of his brown silk dressing gown.

'It's a sister to the cannons the British melted down to provide the metal for the Victoria Cross,' Lasche continued in a thick German accent.

'So it's Chinese?' Tom asked.

Lasche smiled, impressed. 'Most people think the metal for the Victoria Cross came from Russian cannons captured at the battle of Sevastopol. But, yes, it came from Chinese weapons.' He spoke haltingly, drawing breath with a rasping rattle between sentences. 'I don't normally receive visitors. But, given your reputation, I thought I would make an exception.'

'My reputation?'

'I know who you are. But I'd heard you'd retired.' Lasche began to cough. The nurse leapt forward and slipped the oxygen mask over his face. Slowly, the coughing subsided and he signalled to Tom to continue.

'I *have* retired. But I'm looking into something I wanted your help with.'

Lasche shook his head. When he spoke, his voice was muffled by the mask. 'I haven't opened the bag you sent up. Like you, I'm also retired.'

'Please, just take a look,' Tom appealed. 'It will interest you.'

Lasche's grey eyes considered Tom for a moment, then he summoned the nurse, his arm shaking with the effort. The nurse handed the bag to Tom with an accusing stare. Tom drew back the zip and removed the Nazi jacket.

Lasche navigated his way to his desk, then indicated that Tom should hand the jacket to him. Lasche's hands shook as he held it.

'It's obviously an SS uniform,' he said between strained breaths, pointing at the distinctive silver double lightning bolts on the right-hand collar badge. 'The uniform is based on the M1943 design, but from the fabric and quality I'd say it was tailor-made, which is strange. Tailoring was common for senior officers, but not for an *Unterscharführer.*'

Tom tilted his head at the unfamiliar word. 'A what?'

Lasche pointed at the left-hand collar badge, a single silver pip on a black background. 'It's the owner's rank. I suppose it would translate as corporal. So either this particular officer was very rich or . . .'

Lasche had just caught sight of the cuff title, a thin strip of black material embroidered with gold that had been sewn to the left-hand sleeve.

'Where did you get this?' he croaked.

'London. Why?'

'Why? Why? Because, Mr Kirk, this jacket belonged to a member of *Der Totenkopfsorden.* The Order of the Death's Head.'

Hotel Vier Jahreszeiten Kempinski, Munich: January 7, 3.31 p.m.

'The Order of the Death's Head?' The voice from the speakerphone sounded sceptical. 'Never heard of it.'

'Not many people have,' Renwick said. 'It has taken me years to piece together the little I know. As you will know, Heinrich Himmler turned the SS into the most powerful force in the Reich. Everything about the SS, from the black uniforms to the runic symbols and badges, was designed to enhance their mystique and elite status. Inspired by the story of King Arthur and how he gathered his twelve noblest knights at a round table, Himmler chose twelve men, of *Obergruppenführer* rank, to be his knights. These twelve were to stand for everything that was best about the Aryan nation and the SS.'

'How is it I have never heard of this?' The voice from the speakerphone was laced with scepticism.

'The existence of the Order was unknown even to the Führer himself. They wore no outward badge or sign that they belonged to the SS's most exclusive club—except when they were together. For their secret meetings, they swapped their normal uniforms for ones that declared their status.'

'In what way?'

'Standard SS uniforms display the regimental title on their cuff— *Liebstandarte* Adolf Hitler, *Das Reich*, Theodor Eicke. The Order was no different, except they used gold rather than silver thread.'

'Why has this never come out before?' Hecht asked, his impatience clear.

'Because every single member of the Order vanished in early 1945, and with them their secret. Some say that they escaped abroad. Others that they died defending Berlin. But I believe that they lived . . . Or, at least, they lived long enough to carry out one last order. To protect a train.'

'Finally, we get to the train,' Hecht sighed sarcastically.

'And that is where the story gets interesting,' said Renwick. 'You see—'

Before he could continue, the door burst open and three uniformed men sprang into the room, machine guns slung round their necks.

'What is it, Konrad?' Hecht asked the first man, a square-set blond.

'*Fünf Männer*,' Konrad panted. '*Mehr draußen. Stellen unten fragen.*'

'We've got company,' Hecht said.

'Police?'

Hecht looked at Konrad, who responded, '*Ja. Ut Bundesnachrichtendienst.*'

'The secret service?' It was Dmitri's turn to speak. 'How the hell did they get on to us so fast?'

'The concierge,' said Renwick slowly, recalling the man's shaking hands. 'I thought he was just tired, but he knew something. He was expecting me.'

'We'll deal with him later,' Dmitri snarled. 'Have you a way out, Colonel?'

'Of course.'

'*Gut*. Use it. We'll continue this later.' He rang off.

Hotel Drei Könige, Zürich: January 7, 3.31 p.m.

'So there were twelve members of the Order?' Tom asked.

'Yes. Like the Knights of the Round Table. Himmler himself selected them, not only for their Aryan looks and racially pure bloodlines, but also for their total loyalty to him. They were his own Praetorian Guard.'

'But you said that the twelve knights were all *Obergruppenführer* rank and above. Yet that uniform belonged to a corporal. How can that be?'

'I'm not sure.' Lasche shook his head. 'It's possible that if they were knights, they had retainers.'

'It would certainly explain why someone so young got to wear such a coveted uniform,' Tom said.

'Who?'

'The man this uniform belonged to. He died ten days ago. He was in his eighties. There was a photo, taken in 1944, of him wearing the uniform. That would have made him about twenty at the time.'

'What was his name?'

'Weissman. Andreas Weissman.' Tom saw the surprised look on Lasche's face. 'It's a Jewish name, I know. He adopted an alias in order to escape after the war. Passed himself off as an Auschwitz survivor—even tattooed a fake prisoner number on his arm. We don't know his real name.'

'You know, many members of the SS had their blood type tattooed on their left underarm, in case they were wounded. After the war, Allied investigators used the blood group tattoo to identify potential war criminals. Many SS members burnt or disfigured their underarm to avoid capture.'

'Or perhaps tattooed another number over the top to disguise it?'

'Possibly,' Lasche said.

'Did the Order have any specific symbols, apart from regular SS ones?'

'Just one. A black circle, or disc, within two further circles, twelve spokes radiating from its centre in the form of SS lightning bolts. One for each member of the Order. They called it the *Schwarze Sonne*—the Black Sun.'

'Like this?' Tom asked, handing Lasche the cap recovered from Weissman's house and pointing at its badge.

'Yes, yes. It is as I thought!' Lasche looked up at Tom excitedly. 'This is the symbol of the Order, a corruption of an Alemannic sun wheel from the third century AD. It was intended as a reference to a time when the SS would shine down on the world as their racial masters.'

'What happened to the Order in the end?' Tom asked.

'In December 1944, with the spectre of defeat looming, Himmler summoned the Order for one last meeting. It's not known what instructions he gave them, but not long afterwards they disappeared and were never seen again.'

Kitzbühel, Austria: January 7, 3.31 p.m.

Archie picked his way through the traffic, one eye on his map and the other making sure he didn't knock anyone over—Kitzbühel's snow-laden streets were buzzing with people. Luckily, the house he was searching for was only a short way from the town centre, and he pulled into the drive with relief.

The house had been painted a bright yellow, and the wooden cladding on the upper storey looked to have been recently replaced. Archie climbed the steps to the porch, and rang the front doorbell.

The door opened almost immediately, taking him by surprise.

'*Ja?*' It was a woman, about thirty years old, her hair tied up in a blue polka-dot scarf, her hands sheathed in yellow rubber gloves.

'*Guten Tag*, I'm looking for Herr Lammers—Manfred Lammers,' Archie said, reading from the envelope he had found at Weissman's house.

She looked at him with a sad expression on her face. 'I'm sorry,' she replied with a thick accent, 'but Herr Lammers is dead. Three years ago.'

'Oh.' His face fell. Back to square one.

'Can I help? I am his niece, Maria Lammers.'

'I don't think so,' Archie said with a resigned shrug. 'Not unless you recognise these.' He handed her the three photographs. 'Your uncle sent them to someone in England. I was hoping to find the original paintings.'

She took the photos and leafed through them. '*Nein* . . . no, sorry. I have never . . .' As she came to the last picture, she paused. 'This one'—she held up the photograph showing a painting of a castle—'I have seen before.'

'Where?' Archie stepped forward eagerly. 'Can you show it to me?'

She weighed her answer. 'You have come from England to see this?'

'Yes, yes, from England.'

'Come.' She peeled off her gloves and pulled the scarf from her head. Her hair, dyed a vivid henna, fell round her face in a scruffy bob. She grabbed a coat, then tugged it on and led him back onto the street. Turning left, she cut through a small park then down a hill. Eventually they came to the church, its snow-covered Gothic steeple towering above the surrounding roofs. The interior was surprisingly ornate and bright.

'*Kommen.*' She led him down the nave to the marble-floored chancel and then turned right into the side chapel. 'You see?'

Archie peered up at the stained-glass window overhead. It was identical to the painting of the castle in Weissman's photograph.

'How long has this been here?' was Archie's slightly bemused question.

'It was a gift from my uncle. In memory of my aunt. She died before I was born. In fifty-five, fifty-six. Cancer.'

'Do you mind if I take a picture?'

She looked over her shoulder, saw that the church was empty, and shrugged her consent.

Archie slipped the digital camera Tom had lent him out of his pocket and took several shots of the window and the plaque underneath it. Then he turned to Maria again. 'What did he do, your uncle? You know, for a job.'

'He was professor of physics at Universität Wien,' she said proudly.

'And before that? In the war?'

'Uncle Manfred didn't fight. He was too young.'

'One last thing. Would you take a look at this? Tell me if you recognise anyone.' He handed over a copy of the photograph of three men in SS uniform that they had found at Weissman's house.

She took it from him and studied it. When she looked up her eyes were angry and her voice hard. 'You have made this as a joke, yes?'

'No, of course not.'

'I not believe you. This picture is a lie.' She was almost shouting now, her voice resonating off the stone walls. 'Why you come here? To trick me?'

'Is one of those men your uncle?' Archie guessed.

'You know this. Why else are you here?'

'We found this picture yesterday in London,' Archie explained. 'I swear, until just now I had no idea your uncle was in it. Which one is he?'

She looked down at the photo again. 'The man on the left.'

'I'm sorry.' Archie sighed.

'Sorry? Why?' Her tone switched from anger to indifference. 'This is mistake. Uncle Manfred was too young to fight. He told me.'

'I'd love to believe you,' said Archie. 'But you see the man in the middle? His daughter didn't think he had fought either. She was wrong. He'd lied to her. She was the one who discovered this photo, not me.'

'And she thinks . . . she thinks this is real?' Maria seemed to have shrunk visibly, her voice fading to a whisper, her eyes brimming with tears.

'Oh yeah,' Archie said, trying to erase the image of Elena Weissman's bloody corpse from his mind. 'She discovered a secret room where her father had hidden his wartime mementoes. Uniforms, flags, medals . . .'

'Medals?' She looked up. 'War medals?'

'Yes.' Archie frowned. 'Why?'

'*Kommen*.' She drew herself up straight once again. 'I must show you.'

She walked out of the church and hurried through the churchyard. They retraced their steps in silence. Maria's shock seemed to have been replaced by an unsmiling resolve. Once inside the house, she directed him to the sitting room and disappeared into one of the rooms at the back.

Archie had just sat down on the sofa when Maria returned, carrying a wooden box of polished walnut. It was about eight inches across and five inches wide with a small brass key protruding from the lock. But it was the symbol inlaid into the lid that grabbed Archie's attention. Concentric circles with a black disc at their centre and runic lightning bolts radiating out from the middle, twelve of them in all. It was identical to the symbol he had seen on the cap badge of Weissman's uniform.

'He died in a fire.' She placed the box on the coffee table in front of him. 'The house had to be almost completely rebuilt. This was the only thing that survived. I found it in his car. I thought he had bought it at a fair somewhere, that it wasn't his. Now . . .' Her voice faded. 'Please take it with you. I don't want it in the house any more.'

Archie turned the key and gingerly opened the lid. Inside, on a red velvet lining, lay a medal, its black, red and white ribbon folded underneath it.

A Nazi Iron Cross.

5

As he approached Viggiano's office, Bailey heard raised voices. Before he had a chance to knock, the door flew open and Viggiano marched out, his face red with rage. He shouldered roughly past Bailey towards the exit.

Regional Director Carter was sitting at Viggiano's desk when Bailey entered the office. In front of him were a service revolver and an FBI badge.

'Bailey.' Carter's voice was businesslike. 'Shut the door and sit down.'

Bailey closed the door behind him and sat down nervously.

'As you can see, Agent Viggiano and I were just clearing up a few . . . administrative details. After what went down in Idaho, it's best for him and for us that he sits out the next few months until we get a clear picture of exactly what happened up there. Anyway, it's out of my hands now.'

Bailey's heart sank. He could see where this was heading.

'Vasquez tells me you cautioned against opening that door. Is this true?'

'Eh . . .' The question caught Bailey off-guard. 'Yes, sir. I thought I saw someone signalling at us not to come in.'

'But Viggiano overruled you?'

'Well . . .' Bailey wavered. He didn't want a reputation as a snitch.

'Don't worry, Vasquez gave me the full run-down.' Carter smiled. 'Said you saved his life. Way I see it, you did a great job up there. If Viggiano had listened to you instead of . . . Well, let's just say you did a great job.'

'It would have been a great job if we'd saved those people, sir.'

'You did the best you could. I can't ask anyone to do any more than that.'

'No, sir.'

'So, what leads have you got?'

'We've got a Photofit of our suspect, based on Hennessy's description. He's a European male. Five ten. Cropped blond hair.'

'That's it?'

''Fraid so. And now Hennessy's attorney is arguing that until he sees a written offer, that's all we'll get.'

'A written offer for what in return?' Carter demanded. 'I mean, he's not given us much, has he? No ID, no distinguishing marks, just some bullshit story and a name, Blondi, that's probably an alias.'

'You know that was the name of Hitler's favourite dog?'

Carter looked nonplussed. 'You think that might be relevant?'

'Well, so far we've got someone using the name of Hitler's dog, the theft of a Nazi Enigma machine, and the involvement of a Neo-Nazi group. It sure doesn't sound like a coincidence.'

'You could be right,' Carter said. 'Let's get everything we can on the Sons of American Liberty and any other extremist groups they might have links to. See if this Blondi surfaces anywhere else. Let's check out the Enigma machine too—see if we can come up with a list of likely buyers.'

'Actually, sir, I've already done some work on that. An Enigma machine is a pretty unusual item to steal. I figured that Blondi might be working for a collector or dealer. So I ran down all the major military memorabilia auctions over the last five years and cross-referenced the lists of buyers.'

'And?' Carter asked expectantly.

'About twenty dealers account for about eighty per cent of the volume. But I narrowed the list down to European dealers, since Hennessy said Blondi was from Europe. That cuts it down to seven. And I asked Salt Lake City International to supply security footage for all flights to the cities where those seven dealers are based. I figured Blondi would want to be out within forty-eight hours of picking up the Enigma machine, so it was worth taking a look at the tapes in case any passengers matched our Photofit.'

'And?'

'One man. Boarded the American flight to Zürich under the name Arno Volker.' Bailey laid the file he'd ben clutching on the desk and opened it. He pointed at a fuzzy still from a surveillance tape, then laid the Photofit next to it. There was a resemblance.

'That could be him,' said Carter. 'Good work. What's your next move?'

'Track down the dealer in Zürich and put him under surveillance,' Bailey said confidently. 'If Blondi is working for him, the chances are he'll surface there, given that he doesn't know we're on to him yet.'

Carter sat back in his chair, as if weighing the merits of Bailey's plan. 'OK,' he said eventually. 'I want you to run with this. I'm going to hook you up with an Agency buddy of mine in Zürich. His name's Ben Cody.'

'You want *me* to fly to Zürich?' Bailey couldn't believe it. A few minutes ago he'd thought Carter was going to ask for his badge.

'Let's be clear—I'm not cutting you loose out there. I just want you to observe and report back to me on anything you learn or see, you got that?

Nothing happens without the green light from me.'

'Yessir. Thank you, sir.'

Carter leaned across the desk and shook his hand. 'By the way,' he said as he turned to leave, 'what did you say this dealer's name was?'

Bailey consulted his notes. 'Lasche. Wolfgang Lasche.'

Hauptbahnhof, Zürich: January 7, 7.12 p.m.

It was a Friday night and the station was busy. Tom chose a café with a good view of the platforms and bought a strong black coffee. He had just settled into a chair under a heat lamp when his phone rang. It was Turnbull.

'Any news?' said Turnbull, clearly in no mood for small talk.

That suited Tom just fine. 'Yeah. But none of it makes any sense.'

Tom summarised Lasche's account of the Order of the Death's Head.

'Didn't Lasche come up with anything else?'

'Not much. Just that the badge we found on Weissman's cap was the symbol of the Order. What about your end? Any further intel on Weissman?'

'Well, the first sighting is in Northern Germany. Weissman was picked up, half-starved, near the Polish border by a patrol looking for Nazi officials. He claimed he'd been liberated from Auschwitz. He didn't match the description of anyone they were looking for, and the tattoo sort of clinched it for him. Eventually he was offered the choice of asylum in the US, Israel or Britain. He chose us. He'd trained as a chemist before the war and got a job working for a pharmaceutical company. Paid his taxes. Lived a quiet life. The model citizen.'

'Did he ever travel abroad?'

'He renewed his passport three years ago and flew to Geneva. Apart from that, he stayed put.'

'Clearly he had, or knew, something. Something Renwick and your Kristall Blade people wanted enough to kill him for.'

ARCHIE DROPPED his bag and sat down at the table with a sigh. They were in a restaurant a short walk from the station.

'Good trip?' Tom asked.

'Delayed, and the stewardess had a moustache. Apart from that, perfect.'

Tom laughed. 'And what did Lammers have to say?'

'Not much. I think the six feet of earth and the gravestone may have been muffling the sound of his voice.'

'He's dead?' Tom exclaimed.

'Three years ago. House fire.'

Tom shook his head ruefully. 'So we're back where we started.'

'Not quite.' Archie smiled. 'It turns out that his niece now lives in his old house. I showed her the photos of the paintings and she took me to see this.' He took Tom's digital camera from his pocket and handed it over.

'It's the castle in the painting,' said Tom, scrolling through the images.

'I think you'll find it's an exact copy of the painting. Lammers donated the window in the fifties after his wife died of cancer.'

'Meaning that he must have had access to the original,' Tom said.

'Exactly. Question is, where is it now? Assuming it survived the fire.'

'What I'd like to know is what was so important about the painting that he had the window made in the first place? Did the niece know anything?'

'This was all news to her. I showed her the photo of Weissman and the two other men in uniform. Guess who she recognised?'

'Uncle Manfred?'

Archie nodded. 'She didn't take it very well. But she did give me this.' He reached into his bag and pulled out the walnut veneer box. 'Said she didn't want it in the house any more. Open it.'

Tom turned the small key in the lock and eased back the lid.

'It's an Iron Cross,' said Archie.

'Not quite . . .' Tom had taken the medal out of the box and was studying it. 'It's a Knight's Cross,' he said. 'I've come across them before. Looks the same, but there's a different finish. The edge is ribbed, not smooth, and the frame is silver rather than just lacquered to look like silver. Only about seven thousand were awarded by the Third Reich, compared to millions of Iron Crosses. They're very rare.'

'Meaning that either Lammers was a collector, or . . .'

'Or it was his and he'd done something that merited special recognition.' Tom turned it over and then looked up with a frown. 'That's weird. These normally have an embossed date on the back—1813, from when they were first issued in the Napoleonic wars.'

'What's that one got? I didn't really look.'

'You tell me.' Tom held it out, reverse side up. It was engraved with a series of seemingly random lines, curves and circles.

'You know, there was a medal like this round the neck of that mannequin at Weissman's house. I had to unclip it before I could get the jacket off.'

'Worth checking out,' Tom said. He opened the box again and put his index finger into the main compartment to measure its depth. It only came up to his second knuckle. 'That's strange,' he muttered. He pressed his finger against the side of the box. It was an inch deeper. 'There's a false bottom,' Tom exclaimed.

'I thought so,' said Archie. 'Christ knows how to open it, though.'

Tom tried each side of the box in turn, pressing his thumb against the wood, just above the bottom edge, and pushing it away from him. Nothing. He repeated the exercise in reverse, tugging each side towards him.

The last one he tried moved easily, exposing a small drawer with an ivory handle. His eyes wide with anticipation, Tom slid the drawer out. Like the main compartment, it was lined in red velvet. Under the restaurant's dim lighting, the object inside glinted like tarnished silver.

Tom looked up, his eyes shining. 'It's a key, I think.'

Archie reached in and grasped it. 'Funny sort of key.'

About two inches long, the key was square rather than flat, and it had no teeth. Instead, each of its gleaming surfaces was engraved with a series of small hexagonal marks.

'I think it's for a digital lock. Like in that private bank in Monte Carlo.'

'And what do you make of this?'

The key's sleek steel shaft was housed in an ugly triangular handle made of moulded rubber. On one side of the handle was a small button. The other side had been stamped with a series of interlocking calligraphic letters. Tom thought he could make out a V and a C, but it was hard to tell.

'Owner's initials? Maker's logo? Could be anything.'

'How are we going to find out?' Archie asked.

Tom smiled. 'We're in Zürich. How do you think I'm going to find out?'

'Raj?' Archie sounded deeply suspicious.

'Who else?'

Wipkingen, Zürich: January 7, 10.40 p.m.

Away from the town centre, the River Limmat flexes its way northwest into Zürich's industrial zone. Tom and Archie made their way across Wipkingen Bridge, along Breitenstein Strasse and left into Ampere Strasse, then negotiated the steep steps leading down to a path that ran parallel to the river.

'Are you sure it's down here?' Archie asked.

An embankment loomed above their heads, its brickwork obscured at ground level by decades of graffiti and fly posting.

'It was, last time I came,' Tom answered.

'You've been here before? When?'

'Three, four years ago. When we did that job in Venice, remember?'

'Oh, yeah,' Archie chuckled. 'If only they were all like that.'

'If it hadn't been for Raj, I'd have had to drill my way into that safe.'

'All right, all right,' Archie conceded. 'So he's a good locksmith.'

'He's the best in the business and you know it.'

'Mmm . . .' Archie shrugged noncommittally.

Raj Dhutta still owed them a couple of thousand dollars for some information they had supplied him with a few years before, hence Archie's misgivings. To Archie, debtors were to be treated with extreme caution.

Tom stopped beside a steel door set into the embankment. He ran his hand over the brickwork to the right of the door at about waist height. Eventually he found a brick that sat slightly proud of those around it. It sank slightly under his touch, then sprang back to its original position.

'Yes, hello?' A high-pitched voice came over the intercom.

'Raj? It's Tom Kirk and Archie Connolly.'

There was a long silence, then: 'Look, I haven't got the money, if that's what this is about. I can get it. I can get it tomorrow, OK?'

'Forget the money, Raj,' Tom said, earning himself an angry look from Archie. 'We need your help. Let's just call it quits on what you owe us.'

There was another, even longer pause, then the door buzzed open.

'Half of that money's mine, don't forget,' Archie reminded Tom as they stepped inside. 'Next time, you might ask me before just giving it away.'

'You drop more than that every time you pick up a hand of cards,' Tom said quietly. 'I don't think you'll miss it.'

They found themselves in a steel cage, half blinded by the lights.

'Raj?' A silhouette appeared in front of the lights.

The lights snapped off and Tom made out a slight figure approaching the cage, fumbling with a bunch of keys. Raj Dhutta was a slender five foot four, with wavy black hair. His eyes furtively skipping between them, he selected a key and inserted it into a lock. Then he repeated the action with a second and then a third lock, pausing before the final turn of the key.

'We have a gentleman's agreement?' Dhutta's tone was still disbelieving.

'Yes, we've got an agreement,' Tom confirmed.

'Excellent!' Dhutta's face broke into a broad smile. 'Excellent.'

The cage door swung open and Tom and Archie stepped into the room.

Dhutta locked the cage behind them. 'Let's shake on it.' He grabbed Tom's hand and pumped it up and down vigorously, then turned his smile on Archie. 'It is a pleasure to meet you finally, Mr Connolly.'

They shook hands awkwardly.

'Is there somewhere we can talk?' Tom asked.

'My apologies.' Dhutta gave a half bow. 'I am a poor host. Come, come.' He scampered across to the far side of the room.

'What is this place?' Archie asked. 'Or rather, what was it?'

'An old electricity substation.' Dhutta led them up a short flight of stairs to another steel door, which he unlocked with a second set of keys.

'You live here?' Archie again.

'No, no, no. This is merely my workshop. I reside on the street overhead. Come, come,' he urged, stepping through the doorway.

On his previous visit, Tom had not been invited into this part of the complex.

'Tea?' asked Dhutta. 'I have Earl Grey, Darjeeling, Assam, Nilgiri . . . Whatever tickles your fancy. I have just boiled the kettle.'

'Earl Grey,' Archie replied, taking in the arched brick ceiling rising twenty feet above their heads.

'Coffee. Black,' said Tom, to Dhutta's obvious disapproval.

'As you wish. Please make yourselves at home.'

Dhutta waved them to two threadbare sofas arranged round an old tea chest on the left-hand side of the room as he darted to the sink and busied himself with mugs and milk. Tom and Archie both dropped their small overnight bags by the door and sat down.

'I must admit, I am surprised to see you, Mr Tom. I had heard that you would no longer have need of my services.'

'It's true. Archie and I have moved on,' Tom replied. 'We're just here for some information.'

Dhutta handed them their drinks and sat down. 'What sort of information?'

'There's something I want to show you,' said Tom. He placed the walnut box on the tea chest's rough surface.

Dhutta picked it up, shook it, examined it carefully. Then, in four quick movements, he slid the drawer out and snatched up the key.

'I see you've not lost your touch,' Tom said with a smile.

But Dhutta didn't seem to be listening. 'Well, well!' he exclaimed.

'What do you think the key fits?' asked Tom.

'Something like a safe-deposit box? Somewhere with tip-top security.' He squinted at the italic script etched into the key's rubber grip. 'These initials looks like a V and a C,' he said. 'But that's impossible. It's the logo for Völz et

Cie, the private bank. They do not offer safe-deposit boxes. Not any more.'

'I've never heard of them,' said Tom.

'You wouldn't, unless you had an account there. They're based here in Zürich. Very prestigious. Very secretive. They don't advertise. If they think you're suitable, they find you.'

'Well, if their logo's on it, the key must have some connection with the bank,' Tom insisted.

'Come, gentlemen.' Dhutta jumped up. 'I want to try something.'

The hall was divided into three main areas. The smallest was the one they had just come from; steel shelving formed a ten-foot-tall metal barricade separating this area from the rest. Dhutta led them through a gap in the shelving to his workshop area. Along the far wall were half a dozen LCD panels, their screens small puddles of light. In the left corner two large racks hummed with computer and telecoms equipment.

Dhutta switched on a desk lamp and examined the key carefully. 'It is as I thought,' he exclaimed after a few seconds. 'A three-dimensional laser-tooled varying matrix.' He sounded impressed.

'Which means what, exactly?' Archie asked.

Dhutta turned to him with a smile. 'When you insert the key into a lock, four electronic eyes examine these laser-burnt markings to ensure that they are correctly sized and positioned. It's almost impossible to duplicate. And, if I'm not mistaken . . .' Dhutta pointed the key at a black box screwed to the wall and pressed the small button in the key's rubber grip. A long series of numbers flashed onto the screen beside him.

'What's that?' Tom asked.

'When the key has been read by the laser, you press this button to trigger an infrared data exchange with the locking mechanism.' He indicated the display on the screen. 'It seems to be an algorithm, probably a 128-bit key. Very hard to break.'

'You ever see anything like this before?'

'Only once, on a system developed for the Israeli military for access to their missile silos. Except that they insisted on one extra level of security: biometric analysis, to ensure that the person inserting the key was indeed meant to have it. In the Israeli case, palm prints.'

'So we've no way of getting in without—'

'Raj,' Archie interrupted, 'how many numbers in a Swiss bank account?'

'Between eight and sixteen.'

'What are you thinking?' Tom took a step towards Archie.

'I'm thinking that maybe now we know why Cassius wanted Weissman's arm. That tattoo must have been an account number, not a camp number.'

'But why would Weissman have had the account number and not the key?' asked Tom.

'Just because we didn't find a key, doesn't mean he didn't have one.'

'And we don't know that Lammers had the key but no account number,' Tom said, picking up on Archie's logic. 'They probably both had access.'

'It would make sense,' Archie agreed. 'Especially if what they were hiding was valuable. Problem is, they're both dead. Even if we're right about the key and the account number, there's no way we can get into that box.'

Tom smiled. 'Isn't there?'

Parc Monceau, Paris: January 8, 7.46 a.m.

The two men approached the chipped green bench from different directions. The older of the two sat down and took out that day's edition of *L'Equipe*; the younger man slid onto the bench next to him.

The two men wore gold rings on the little finger of their left hands. Each was engraved with a twelve-box grid, with a small diamond set in one of the boxes. Where they differed was in the position of the diamond: the older man's was in the bottom left box, the younger man's in the top right.

'Why have you asked me here?' the older man mumbled behind his paper.

'The situation has deteriorated,' the second man said, his lips barely moving as he stared across the ornamental lake. 'Kirk is making progress.'

'Tsss,' the older man snorted dismissively. 'What sort of progress?'

'One of his associates paid a visit to Lammers's niece yesterday.'

'She suspects nothing,' the older man replied. 'Besides, we turned that place upside-down before we set fire to it. There was nothing there.'

'Apart from the stained-glass window in the local church.'

'What window?' The man put down his paper.

'A window that Lammers commissioned. Of a triangular castle.'

'*Merde!* Why didn't we know about this?'

'Because you had him killed before he could tell us. And that's not all. She gave him something. He arrived empty-handed and left with a bag.'

Silence as the first man considered what he had just been told.

'Where is he now, this associate? Where's Kirk, for that matter?'

'In Zürich. He went to see Lasche yesterday.'

'Lasche!' the man exclaimed in disgust. 'That old fool will never—'

'Sir,' the second man interrupted, 'I think the time has come for more . . . radical measures. It is no longer enough to trust to providence.'

'What do you mean?'

'Kirk followed the trail from Weissman to Lammers in only forty-eight hours. It took us three years, albeit working in the opposite direction. Kirk discovered the window. A window we didn't even know existed. How long before he starts to make some connections?'

'And Cassius?' the man asked sullenly. 'Did you get him, at least?'

'No,' replied the other. 'We had him last night in Munich, but he got away. It seems he isn't acting alone any more.'

'You were right to call me here,' the first man said grudgingly. 'If Kirk finds out what's really down there, it will only make him more determined. We must take steps. If we don't act now, it may be too late.'

'What sort of steps?'

'The window must be destroyed.'

'Obviously. And Kirk?'

'They must all be dealt with—Kirk, his colleague and anyone else they have come into contact with. We can't afford to take any more chances.'

Wipkingen, Zürich: January 8, 9.35 a.m.

Tom had slept badly. Although the two sofas that Dhutta had offered them for the night had been comfortable enough, his overactive mind had kept him awake into the small hours and then woken him again shortly after six.

Eventually he had got up, showered, and dressed in his usual jeans and a fresh shirt. He'd waited until nine thirty before waking Archie with a cup of coffee, which Archie accepted grudgingly. He was not a morning person.

'I got through to Turnbull last night. He agreed to send Weissman's arm over by medical courier first thing. It should be here any time now.'

'You got me out of bed for a courier!' Archie remonstrated.

A bell rang and a few moments later Dhutta appeared, his hair still glistening from the shower. 'Good morning, gentlemen,' he called cheerily. 'I hope you both slept well. If you will excuse me, it seems I have a visitor.'

'Actually, I think it's for me,' Tom admitted. 'I needed something delivered and gave them the directions to the back door and the bell. Don't worry,' he added, seeing the look on Dhutta's face. 'You can trust them.' The bell rang again. 'I'm sorry, I should have told you yesterday, but I didn't want to disturb you any more than we already had.'

Dhutta waved his apology away. 'If you say I can trust them, Mr Tom, then that's good enough for me. I will go and let them in.'

Archie got up and yawned. He was wearing crumpled blue boxer shorts and a white T-shirt. Tom thought he looked strangely out of place without his suit on.

The sound of voices filtered through the open doorway, one Dhutta's, the other female. Archie looked up in surprise as the voices drew nearer.

'This way, please,' came Dhutta's muffled instruction.

Moments later, Dominique stepped into the room. Archie snatched up his bedclothes and held them in front of him.

'Dom?' he said in surprise, as Dhutta disappeared into his workshop.

'Morning, boys!' She grinned. 'Here you go, Archie—got you a little present.' She tossed a carton of duty-free cigarettes to him.

He instinctively reached out to catch it, letting go of the bedclothes.

'Gotcha!' she laughed.

'Very funny,' Archie muttered. He grabbed his suit and stumbled to the bathroom.

'I've just made some coffee,' Tom said to Dominique. 'You want some?'

'Sure,' she said, tossing her ski jacket over the back of one of the sofas.

'You weren't followed?'

'No,' Dominique confirmed. 'I doubled back a few times, to be certain.'

'And Turnbull met you at the airport this morning, as agreed?'

'Yeah, although I think he was a bit surprised that I was a woman.'

'That's because he doesn't know what sort of a woman you really are.' Tom grinned. 'No problems with Customs or anything?'

'None.' She smiled her thanks as he handed her a mug. 'I never thought it would be so easy to transport a human body part across Europe.'

'Oh yeah.' Tom sat down next to her. 'It's great cover. Archie and I used to do it all the time. As long as the paperwork checks out, they don't touch a medical courier box. What about the medals?'

'He gave me those, too. Archie was right. Weissman did have a Knight's Cross.' She pulled an envelope from her pocket and handed it to Tom.

He opened it and slid the medal it contained into the palm of his hand, flipping it over so he could see the reverse, before giving her a satisfied nod.

'It has the same markings as the one we got from Lammers's niece,' Tom confirmed. 'Raj,' he called. 'Come and have a look at this.'

Dhutta re-emerged and took the medal from Tom.

'I brought the Bellak painting, as well,' Dominique added. 'Thought it might be useful. By the way, did you notice the holes in it?'

'Yes. What about them?'

'They struck me as odd, that's all. They're very neat. All the same size.'

Archie reappeared from the bathroom, his composure seemingly restored now that he had his suit on.

'I meant to ask—what is this?' Dhutta pointed at the design on the lid of the walnut box that the key had been hidden in.

'A Nazi symbol,' Tom explained. 'A type of swastika with twelve arms instead of four. It's known as the Black Sun. Have you seen it before?'

'No . . .' Dhutta shook his head, his finger stroking the veneer. 'Although the swastika has been a Hindu religious symbol for thousands of years. The word is derived from Sanskrit. The literal translation is "good to be". In holy texts it can mean *Brahma*, which is luck, or *Samsara*, which is rebirth.' He looked up. 'I wonder, which will it be for you, Mr Tom?'

6

Financial district, Zürich: January 8, 12.42 p.m.

A man in a smart blue suit greeted Tom and Archie in the entrance vestibule for Banque Völz et Cie. It was more like a private house than a bank—two side tables, travertine marble resting on ebony legs engraved with gold leaf, flanked a large bronze door.

'*Guten Morgen, meine Herren.*'

'*Guten Morgen,*' Tom answered. 'We're here to see Herr Völz.'

'I'm sorry, but Herr Völz is a very busy man. If you leave your name and number, I will ask someone to call you.'

'We have a safe-deposit box here. We wish to inspect it immediately.'

'There are no boxes here. We are a bank, not a left-luggage office.'

'Tell Herr Völz that we have the key,' Tom insisted, dangling it in front of him. 'And that we're not leaving until he sees us.'

The man stared at the key uncertainly. 'Wait here,' he snapped eventually, walking over to the table on the left. His eyes never left them as he dialled a three-digit number.

'Herr Völz?' He turned away from them, spoke rapidly into the phone and nodded as he listened to the reply. Replacing the handset, he turned back to face them. 'Herr Völz will see you immediately. This way, please.'

He threw open the bronze door and ushered them through the main entrance hall into a small office. Then he knocked gently at a massive wooden door beyond. A brass plaque indicated *Rudolf Völz, Direktor.*

There was no response from within, and Tom followed the man's eyes to a miniature set of traffic lights to the left of the door. It was on red, so they stood there patiently until it flashed to green. The man opened the door, informed them they should go in, then shut it behind them.

The low winter sun streamed in through the window to the left of the elaborate marble fireplace, cutting Völz's office diagonally in two: one half was swathed in shadow while the other was flooded with light.

'What do you want?'

The voice was clipped and hostile. Tom, squinting, made out the shape of a man hunched over the desk on the far side of the room.

'Herr Völz?' Tom walked towards the desk while Archie hung back.

The man stood up and ignored Tom's outstretched hand. 'The boxes are all gone. An ill-advised diversification strategy by my grandfather during the war that my father dismantled in the 1960s.'

As the man leant forward, Tom was able to see the face. Still quite young, perhaps in his early forties, Rudolf Völz's dark brown hair was neatly cut, with just a hint of grey. His glasses were frameless with clear plastic arms.

'The sixties?' Tom asked, throwing the key from the walnut box onto the desk. 'That's your crest on the key. And, unless I'm very much mistaken, the lock that it opens is state of the art.'

Völz stared at the key. 'Do you have an account number?'

Tom recited the numbers Turnbull had given him the previous night.

Squinting, Völz removed his glasses and typed the digits into his computer, then hit return. After a pause, he looked up with a smile.

'Welcome to Banque Völz, gentlemen. My apologies. Please forgive the little misunderstanding earlier.' Völz's frosty welcome gave way to smiles. 'We get so many people trying their luck that we have to be cautious.'

'What are they looking for?' Archie asked.

'Either accounts abandoned by Holocaust victims or something else to sue us for. My father was wise enough to shut down the safe-deposit business, and contribute all unclaimed assets to the Holocaust survivors' fund.'

'But not all the boxes were shut?' Archie again.

'Of course not.' Völz smiled. 'We are a bank, after all. Our first duty is to our customers, not to the Jewish lobby.'

Tom bit his lip. 'And our account . . . ?'

'Is exactly as was initially instructed. Nothing has been touched. Not since it was last accessed, at least.'

'Which was when, exactly?' Archie asked.

Völz removed his glasses and consulted his screen. 'May 1958.'

The same year Lammers had posted the photos of the three Bellak paintings to Weissman, according to the postmark.

'A long time,' said Tom. 'All the more reason—if you don't mind, Herr Völz—not to delay any longer.'

'Of course, of course.' Völz leapt to his feet. 'Follow me, gentlemen.'

He led them through the small office, back into the hall, and then through another doorway into a large stairwell. A door was set into the wall under the staircase, and it was to this that Völz went. Taking a key from his pocket, he unlocked the door, reached in, and flicked a light switch, illuminating a narrow flight of dirty steps.

'The wine cellar,' Völz explained.

The stairs led down into a low room that smelled old and musty. The room was lined with wine racks cradling row upon row of dusty bottles.

Völz went to a rack at the rear of the cellar and pulled it towards him. It swung forward to reveal a large steel door. Reaching into his pocket, he took out another key and unlocked it.

As the door opened, the lights inside blinked on. A stainless-steel table took up the middle of the room, a flat-panel computer monitor was set at chest height on the far wall and, to the right of it, a steel drawer.

Völz walked to the computer panel and tapped it lightly with his finger. Immediately the screen pulsed into life. He turned back to face them. 'The account number again, please.'

Tom typed in the code recovered from Weissman's arm. The screen went blank, then flashed a greeting:

Wilkommen
Konto: 1256093574
Konto Name: Werfen
Bitte Schlüssel einführen

Account name *Werfen*, Tom mused. What or who was that?

Völz interrupted his thoughts. 'Please insert your key,' he translated, pointing at the small square hole beneath the screen.

Tom slipped the key into the hole and seconds later a small graphic of a padlock opening confirmed that it had been successfully read by the lasers.

'Now the infrared,' Völz prompted.

Tom pressed the button on the key's rubber handle until a graphic of a door opening confirmed that the algorithms had matched. So far, so good.

'Well, gentlemen, your key matches your account. Now the palm scan.'

'Herr Völz,' Tom said, turning to face him. 'I wonder whether you could give my colleague and me a little privacy?'

'Of course,' said Völz. 'Just place your hand against this panel.' He indicated a glass plate on the left of the computer screen. 'The system will retrieve your box and place it in here.' He pointed at the drawer front.

'Thank you for your help,' Tom said, shaking his hand.

As soon as the sound of the banker's footsteps had receded up the stairs, Tom slid his briefcase onto the table and opened it. Weissman's arm had been packed with ice and sealed inside a clear plastic bag. Even so, it had begun to smell.

'Christ!' muttered Archie, peering over Tom's shoulder. 'That is rank.'

Tom extracted the arm from under the ice, holding it above the wrist. It felt like a dead fish. He approached the glass panel and placed the lifeless hand against it. A crosshatch of red beams lit up from deep within the glass and scanned the hand's surface. The screen flashed a warning.

'Scan failure,' Tom translated. 'Two more tries and then it locks us out.'

'I hope we've got this right.'

'Turnbull told me that Weissman travelled abroad only once—to some conference in Geneva three years ago. That's when Völz upgraded the security system. I doubt it's a coincidence. Weissman could have got the train here, had his palm scanned, and got back to Geneva in time for dinner.'

'Press the fingers harder against the glass,' Archie suggested.

Tom pressed his own hand to the back of Weissman's, forcing it flat. The red grid flared into life once more, then extinguished itself.

'Scan failure,' Tom said with a rueful shrug. 'I think the reader's picking up the edge of my fingers. You try. Your hands are smaller than mine.'

'OK,' said Archie, taking the arm and pressing his hand against Weissman's so that the fingers were splayed across the glass.

The screen went blank, then flashed up another message.

'Scan successful,' Tom breathed.

Archie dropped the arm back into the plastic bag and shut the briefcase.

There was a whirring noise from behind the wall. Then the drawer front buzzed and jumped forward a few centimetres. Archie pulled it towards him. It contained a battered-looking metal box, which he lifted out and placed on the table. The box was about three feet long, a foot wide and six inches deep. He slowly lifted the lid and they both peered inside.

Wipkingen, Zürich: January 8, 2.32 p.m.

'That's it?'

Tom understood the disappointment in Dominique's voice. They had all been speculating feverishly about what lay inside the safe-deposit box. In the end, all it had contained was the thin brown leather pouch that Tom had just placed on the tea chest in front of them.

'Someone's having a laugh,' was Archie's typically forthright analysis.

'What is inside, please?' Dhutta enquired.

'A map,' Tom answered. 'Is there somewhere where we can we pin it up?'

'I have the very place. This way, please.' Dhutta darted through to the computer area and pointed at an expanse of bare wall.

Tom tacked the four corners to the wall.

'*Deutsche Reichsbahn*—German Railways,' Dominique translated. 'It's a map of the Nazi rail network. June 1943.'

'They must have produced tens of thousands of these maps,' said Archie.

Tom pinched the end of his nose in thought. 'This one must be different in some way . . . Raj? Have you got a projector here?'

'Of course.' Dhutta sprang forward.

'Great. Dom, see if you can find a 1943 map of the German Railway network on the web. We'll blow it up to the same size as this one and overlay the images. That way, if there are any differences, we should see them.'

Dominique busied herself at the computer while Tom readied the projector. A few minutes later, she turned round with a smile.

'The 1943 printing was standard issue. I found a copy on a university website. We may need to play with the sizing a bit, but it should work.'

The image flashed up on the wall and Tom adjusted the projector until he was satisfied that he had got as close a fit as he could. Then all four of them approached the overlaid maps and studied them carefully.

'Well, if they are different, I can't see where,' Archie said.

'Me neither.' Tom rubbed his eyes wearily.

'What about ultraviolet light?' Dhutta suggested brightly. 'It might show something. I have a blacklight here.' Dhutta dived into his workshop, emerging a few moments later with a handheld fluorescent tube trailing a long black flex. Dominique killed the lights. Tom, taking the blacklight from Dhutta, approached the wall and began to move the tube across the map's surface. Black marks began to appear—small circles around place names and, next to them, numbers.

Tom read out the names and numbers, and Dominique compiled a list.

'There's a funny mark here too.' Tom was pointing at a large L-shape in the bottom left-hand quadrant of the map. He marked it with a pencil.

Archie turned the lights back on. 'Read them back,' he suggested.

'I've arranged them alphabetically,' Dominique said. 'Brennberg 30/3, Brixlegg 21/4, Budapest 15/12, Györ 4/2, Hopfgarten 15/4, Linz 9/4, Salzburg 13/4, Vienna 3/4, Werfen 16/5.'

'Maybe those numbers are dates,' Tom suggested. 'Order them that way.'

Dominique read: 'Budapest 15/12, Györ 4/2, Brennberg 30/3, Vienna 3/4, Linz 9/4, Salzburg 13/4, Hopfgarten 15/4, Brixlegg 21/4, Werfen 16/5.'

'Look.' Tom had placed a pin in each place as it was read out. 'The place names move east to west, as if this is some sort of journey, from Budapest, across Europe, to . . . well, look where it was headed until it got to Brixlegg.' Tom pointed to the border just a hundred miles from the village.

'Switzerland.' Archie this time.

'And by the looks of things it almost made it, but then turned back to Werfen.' Tom tapped the map with his neatly clipped right index finger.

'Werfen? Wasn't that the name of the safe-deposit account?'

'That's right,' said Tom. 'We should go and see Lasche again, find out whether he knows anything about this.'

Hotel Drei Könige , Zürich: January 8, 4.04 p.m.

It was, as Tom had remembered, an awe-inspiring sight—battle flags shimmering from the rafters, Napoleonic swords winking from the walls. To Archie it was all new, and he leapt from piece to piece like an eager child.

'Where did he get all this stuff? It must be worth a small fortune.'

'Rather a large fortune, in fact, Mr Connolly.'

Lasche had entered the room unseen and was now advancing rapidly towards them in his wheelchair. Archie spun round, clearly surprised.

'Yes, I know who you are.' Lasche gave a rasping laugh. 'I know all the key players. You, I understand, are one of the best.'

'Was. I've retired now. We both have, haven't we, Tom?'

Tom didn't answer. He had noticed that Lasche's voice was strong compared to their last meeting. And his breathing seemed greatly improved.

'It's good of you to see me again, Herr Lasche. You seem much better.'

'Full blood transfusion.' He smiled. 'I have one every four weeks. For a few days I almost feel human again. Now, why have you returned, Mr Kirk?'

'It is regarding a map. Or, more accurately, a journey. A train journey.'

'A train journey? I suppose I will have to hear you out, one final time.'

He steered his chair across the room and parked himself behind his desk, indicating with a wave that they should sit opposite.

'We came across a map. A railway map. It seemed to indicate a train journey that was made in the war. Perhaps if we read you the names of the places the train passed through . . .'

'By all means, read away,' Lasche shrugged.

Tom began to read from the list Dominique had prepared. 'Budapest, Györ, Brennberg, Vienna, Linz, Salzburg, Hopfgarten, Brixlegg, Werfen.'

Lasche's eyes narrowed. 'Werfen? Did you say Werfen?'

'Yes.' Tom nodded eagerly. 'Does that mean something to you?'

'You are forcing an old man to operate at the limits of his memory.' He turned to his nurse. 'Heinrich, please go and fetch me file number fifteen. Oh, and sixteen too. It's in one of them, I'm sure of it.'

The nurse returned a few moments later clutching two large red files. Lasche opened the first one, leafed through it, then turned his attention to the second. He looked up. 'Well, it seems I may know your train after all. What you have just described is the itinerary of the Hungarian Gold Train.'

'Gold Train?' Archie turned to Tom, excitement in his voice.

'Let me set the scene for you,' Lasche said. 'By December 1944, over-whelming Russian forces had almost encircled Budapest. The Germans were in disarray, their thousand-year Reich collapsing round their ears. So, by express order of Adolf Eichmann, who was at that time in charge of the Office for Jewish Emigration in Vienna, a train was prepared. It was to take vast quantities of treasure plundered from some of the half-million or so Hungarian Jews he had sent to their deaths, and carry it far beyond the reach of the advancing Russian troops.'

'What sort of treasure?' Tom asked.

'Gold, obviously. More than five tons of it. Beyond that . . .' Lasche con-sulted his file and read: 'Nearly seven hundred pounds of diamonds and pearls, one thousand two hundred and fifty paintings, five thousand Persian and Oriental rugs, silverware, porcelain, rare stamps, coin collections, furs, watches, alarm clocks, cameras, typewriters, even silk underwear. The list goes on and on.' He looked up. 'The spoils of war. The fruits of murder.'

'It must have been worth millions.'

'Two hundred and six million dollars in 1945 money, to be exact. And all on one train of fifty-two carriages, of which'—Lasche consulted his file again—'twenty-nine were freight cars.'

'So it got away safely?' Archie asked. 'The Russians didn't capture it?'

'It left Budapest on December the 15th.'

Tom checked his list. The date tallied with the date marked on the map.

'Then it stopped in Győr, where its load was increased by a hundred old masters from the municipal museum. Over the next three months it travelled barely a hundred miles, its journey hampered by the battles raging around it and ten robbery attempts, which the Hungarian soldiers detailed to protect the train's special cargo successfully fought off.'

'Where was it headed?' Archie again.

'Probably Switzerland. But on April the 21st the railway bridge at Brixlegg was bombed and the train's route to Switzerland blocked.'

'So it was captured?'

Lasche smiled. 'I think *found* would be more accurate. The 3rd Infantry Division of the 15th Regiment discovered it in the Tauern tunnel, only a few miles from Brixlegg where the Germans had abandoned it, still crammed with its precious cargo. The Americans moved it to Werfen and then on to Camp Truscott on the outskirts of Salzburg, where all twenty-seven freight cars were unloaded into secure warehouses.'

'And what happened to it then?' Tom asked.

Lasche shook his head ruefully. 'Although it was known that the assets on the Gold Train were Hungarian Jewish in origin, they were designated "enemy property". High-ranking US officials requisitioned the entire load.' Lasche sounded angry.

'Hang on a minute,' Archie said. 'You just said that the Yanks unloaded twenty-seven freight cars? But earlier you said there were twenty-nine.'

Lasche smiled. 'Indeed I did. Because it appears, Mr Connolly, that somewhere between Budapest and Werfen, two carriages disappeared.'

CIA Substation, Zürich: January 8, 4.51 p.m.

'It's him!' Bailey tapped the screen excitedly with his finger. 'It must be.'

'Are you sure?' Cody urged. 'We only get one shot at this.'

'Sure as I can be. Stocky, cropped blond hair, early forties. And, according to your guy on the inside, he's just come down from Lasche's floor.'

'Fine. Get a still off to the lab,' Cody instructed the girl standing next to him. 'See if they come up with a match.'

'What about his buddy?' Bailey asked. 'We should check him out too.'

'Good idea,' said Cody. 'Chances are, he's not acting alone.'

The girl nodded, then disappeared into the adjacent room.

'What do you want to do, sir?' one of the operatives asked.

'Our FBI friend says he's a match'—he winked at Bailey—'so tell Roberts to roll.'

She turned back to her screen. 'Mobile One, this is Central. Subject has been confirmed as our primary mark. Track and hold your distance.'

The image on the monitor jerked as the agent with the concealed camera set off, confirmed by the shifting red dot on the plasma screen above.

'All agents,' the operator continued, 'primary mark is leaving the hotel and heading towards Bahnhofstrasse.'

'Bahnhofstrasse? Shit,' Cody muttered. 'Who have we got down there?'

'Marquez and Henry can be there in sixty seconds. Jones, Wilton and Gregan will take about two minutes to get in position.'

'Get them all down there, ASAP. Stay with him, Roberts,' he muttered. 'Don't lose him.'

The man identified as Roberts stayed close. Two more agents closed in, one from each side, so they now had three camera feeds of the same scene from different angles on the monitors in front of them.

The targets paused in front of one of the innumerable jewellers, shook hands and then headed briskly off in different directions.

'What do you want to do?' Cody spun to face Bailey. 'This is your call.'

'Shit!' Bailey anxiously rubbed the bridge of his nose. 'Blondi. Follow Blondi. That's who we came here for.'

'You got it. Roberts, Marquez, Henry—stay on the primary mark,' the operator intoned. 'Roger,' came the crackled response.

The man known as Blondi moved on, casually surveying the shop windows. And then, without warning, just as a tram came past, he broke into a run.

'He's made us,' Cody exclaimed. 'All units move in. Let's take him down.'

'He's getting on the tram,' the speaker crackled.

'Well, get on it with him. Don't lose him.'

The three agents broke into a run. They closed the gap on the tram and leapt aboard just before the doors shut.

'Where is he?' Bailey breathed.

'Find him and get him off,' Cody ordered.

The images showed the tram's interior and close-ups of other passengers' surprised faces. But there was no sign of the man they had followed.

'There!' Cody exclaimed, thumping his finger against the screen.

On one of the monitors they could see, through the tram window, a man standing on the pavement, waving them goodbye.

'Jesus,' Cody said. 'It's like he knew we'd be waiting for him.'

'Maybe he did, sir.' Returning from the room next door, the young operator handed Cody a piece of paper.

'What's that?' asked Bailey.

'Austrian police have just put out an APB on a man they are looking for in connection with the murder of a woman, Maria Lammers,' Cody replied, reading from the paper, 'and the fire-bombing of a church in Kitzbühel in the Austrian Alps early this morning,'

'What's that got to do with this case?'

'Several witnesses have reported seeing a stranger with the victim the previous day. They were able to give a description.'

Cody held up the Photofit faxed through by the Austrian police and next to it the still photo just taken of Blondi leaving the Hotel Drei Könige.

It was unmistakably the same man.

7

Wipkingen, Zürich, January 8, 5.17 p.m.

'What's wrong?' Dominique's eyes were wide with concern.

'Is Archie back?' Tom was breathing heavily, his voice strained.

'Why, what's happened? Are you OK? You're not hurt, are you?'

'No, I'm fine. It's Archie I'm worried about. A man followed us when we came out of the hotel, so we split up. He was waiting for us.' He turned to Dhutta. 'Have you told anyone we're here?'

'No, Mr Tom, I can assure you that—'

Tom took off his overcoat and threw it onto a sofa. There was a long, uncomfortable silence until the shrill sound of the bell broke the spell.

Dhutta slipped gratefully out of the room, then reappeared moments later with Archie only a few steps behind him.

'Sorry I'm late.' Archie sat down heavily on one of the sofas. 'Spot of bother. I'm sure Tom filled you in.'

'What the hell did he want with us?' Tom asked.

'They, you mean,' Archie observed drily. 'I counted at least three. And in case you hadn't noticed, it was me they were after, not you.'

'You been up to anything I should know about?'

'Course not.' Archie sounded almost offended.

'Your recent American trip? You never did say what that was about.'

'Nothing that's got anything to do with this. That should be enough for you.'

'You're right, I'm sorry,' Tom conceded. 'Guess I'm a bit jumpy. Anyway, I'd say it's about time we moved on. We got what we came for.'

Tom quickly recounted what Lasche had told them about the Hungarian Gold Train.

'The point is, two carriages were taken from that train and we haven't got a bloody clue what was on them or where they are,' Archie said resignedly. 'So I'm not sure we did get what we came for.'

'Oh, I wouldn't say that,' Dominique said, smiling.

Tom looked at her. 'You've found something, haven't you?'

'It occurred to me that the map wasn't the only thing they were protecting in that safe-deposit box,' she said. 'This was kept in there too.' She picked up the frayed leather satchel that the map had been kept in and pointed at the front flap. 'The stitching's a different colour. It's newer than the rest. So I unpicked it. And I found something inside.' She handed a small, flat shard of what initially looked to be orange-brown plastic to Tom. He examined it, then passed it silently to Archie.

'It's lined with gold leaf,' Dominique said.

'No.' Archie turned the shard over in his hands. 'It isn't. It can't be.'

'Why not?' Tom breathed. 'It makes perfect sense. That must have been what was on those missing carriages.'

Archie looked up. 'You realise what this means?'

'No, I'm afraid I don't,' said a confused-looking Dhutta.

'It's amber,' Dominique said slowly. 'Jewellery-grade amber.'

Tom nodded. 'Renwick is after the Amber Room.'

The room was quiet. All eyes were on the small shard of amber that lay cradled on Archie's rough palm. It was Dhutta who broke the silence.

'Please forgive my ignorance, but what is this Amber Room?'

Tom paused. 'Imagine a room so beautiful that it was called the eighth wonder of the world. A room commissioned by Frederick the Great of Prussia, gifted to Peter the Great of Russia and completed by Catherine the Great. A room created from tons of Baltic amber resin. The resin was infused with honey, linseed and cognac, then moulded into thousands of panels backed with gold and silver, accented with diamonds, emeralds, jade, onyx and rubies. Then imagine that it disappeared.'

'Disappeared?' Dhutta asked, his eyebrows raised quizzically.

'When they laid siege to St Petersburg in 1941, the Nazis removed the room from the Catherine Palace and reinstalled it at Königsberg Castle, dismantling it again in 1945 because they feared a British bombing raid.'

'Then it vanished,' Archie continued. 'Not a whisper. Until now, maybe.'

'You really think that's what was on the train?' Dominique said excitedly.

'Why not?' said Tom. 'It was one of the greatest works of art ever made. It must be worth hundreds of millions of dollars. What else would have warranted Himmler assigning his most elite troops to guard duty?'

'Remember how fascinated your father was with the story of the Amber Room?' Dominique reminded Tom.

Tom nodded. 'He'd been looking for it for as long as I can remember.'

'That's what this is all about,' said Dominique. 'The Bellak portrait must contain some clue to where the Amber Room is hidden.'

'But what would Renwick—or Kristall Blade, for that matter—do with the Amber Room? It's not as if they can sell it,' Archie pointed out.

'Not whole, no. But they could break it up. Sell it piecemeal—a panel here, a panel there. There's no shortage of people who'd pay hundreds of thousands for a fragment of the Amber Room, and not ask too many questions about where it came from. They could clear fifty or sixty million easy.'

'Enough for Renwick to get back on his feet and for Kristall Blade to fight their war,' said Archie.

'Which is why we've got to stop them.' Tom's eyes blazed with determination. 'This isn't just about Renwick any more.'

'If he's got the portrait, we'll never catch up with him,' Archie sighed.

'But he doesn't have it,' Tom observed. 'If he did, he wouldn't have left Weissman's arm and the other Bellak painting for me to find. It's in some private collection somewhere and he's trying to use us to join the dots.'

'What did you say?' Dominique's eyes narrowed.

'I said, why else would he have left Weissman's arm and—'

'No. About joining the dots?' without waiting for an answer, Dominique hurried through to the far room and unpinned the railway map from the wall. The others followed.

'Here, lay it out on the floor,' she said, handing it down to Tom. 'I wondered what the holes in the painting were for.' She snapped her fingers impatiently, indicating that Archie should hand her the rolled Bellak painting that lay on the desk. 'They'd been made too carefully to be accidental.' She unscrolled the canvas and laid it flat on the map, aligning the bottom left corner with the L-shape that had revealed itself under the blacklight.

'Give me a pencil.'

Dhutta pulled one from his shirt pocket and handed it to her.

Gripping the pencil tightly, she pushed its end into the first hole and swivelled it round to mark the map underneath. She did the same in each of the nine other holes, then peeled the map away and let it spring shut.

'They show the same route we revealed before,' Dhutta exclaimed.

'It's like you said.' Dominique was beaming proudly. 'Join the dots.'

Tom stared at the map. Dhutta was right, the pencil marks had fallen precisely on the towns revealed by the blacklight earlier and confirmed by Lasche as the route of the Gold Train.

All the dots apart from one. A village in northern Germany. Above it was a symbol, which the key told him denoted a castle. Wewelsburg Castle.

CIA Substation, Zürich: January 8, 6.01 p.m.

'So you lost him?' The several thousand miles between them could not hide the disappointment in Carter's voice.

Bailey winced. 'Yes, sir. And he doesn't show up on any of the systems.'

'I'm sorry, Chris,' Cody sighed, leaning in towards the speakerphone. 'I put my best guys on this. I guess we didn't figure he'd read us so fast.'

'You did what you could,' Carter reassured him. 'And I appreciate it. But he was our one and only lead.'

'Not quite,' said Bailey thoughtfully. 'We've still got Lasche to follow up on. And there's the guy we saw with Blondi. He *did* show up on the system. He's got form. Some sort of high-end art thief. His name is Tom Kirk.'

'A thief!' Carter exclaimed. 'He must be in on this whole thing too.'

'Except it turns out he cooperated with one of our agents on a case last year and got his slate wiped clean by way of a thankyou. Now the general view is that he's gone straight.'

'I'll check into it,' Carter said.

'Meanwhile, we get his name and description out to all airports, railway stations and border police,' Bailey suggested. 'If he tries to leave the country, we'll know about it. With luck, his friend Blondi may not be far behind.'

'Make it happen,' Carter agreed. 'And, next time, let's make sure we bring at least one of them in.'

Wewelsburg, Westphalia, Germany: January 9, 2.23 a.m.

Wewelsburg was the only triangular castle in Europe, Dominique had told them during the seven-hour drive from Zürich, so far as she had been able to establish from the research she had done on her laptop. It consisted of one large round tower in the north corner and two smaller ones south of it, all linked by heavily fortified walls.

In 1934, a hundred-year lease had been taken out on the castle and its grounds. The signatory? A certain Heinrich Himmler. His plan was to establish the castle as the spiritual home of the SS. A concentration camp was established close by to provide slave labour for the work planned. The castle was never fully operational, or indeed finished. On Himmler's orders, it was blown up in March 1945, but the ceremonial hall and the crypt in the north tower survived. The rest was rebuilt after the war.

The castle chose that moment to loom out of the surrounding forest, its mullioned windows glinting in the yellow sweep of their headlights. A small church stood silhouetted against the night sky as they rounded the final corner. Tom killed the lights and put the car into neutral and they coasted the final yards in the moonlight. The car came to rest in front of what Dominique identified as the old SS guardhouse, now a museum.

'Well, we're definitely in the right place,' Archie said.

Tom nodded. The castle was unquestionably the one in the photo of the Bellak painting. He turned to face Dom. 'You're sure it's empty?'

'It's a youth hostel and a museum these days, but it's pretty quiet at this time of year. There won't be anyone around until morning.'

They got out of the car. It was drizzling, a thick, icy rain. Tom opened the boot and took out two large packs, handed one to Archie, and strapped the other to his back. Then he turned to survey the castle. The wide moat had long since been drained, its banks now sheltering a manicured garden.

'This way.' Dominique led them down a flight of steps to the floor of the moat, where two doors had been set into the base of the east wall.

'That one,' she whispered, pointing at the right-hand door.

It was locked, although Tom had it creaking open in seconds. They stepped into a vaulted passage and Dominique indicated with a wave of her torch the narrow staircase that led off to their right. The staircase ended at another iron grille, which Tom had to pick open.

The circular crypt was about twenty or thirty feet across. The walls were built from carved stone blocks, the floor of polished limestone. A vaulted ceiling climbed perhaps fifteen feet above their heads. In the middle of the room was a round stone pit with a shallow depression at its centre.

It was to this smaller circle that Tom went, stopping in the middle, directly beneath the apex of the ceiling.

'Look!' Archie pointed his torch up above Tom's head. The outline of a swastika, made from a different-coloured stone, was clearly visible above.

'What was this place?' Tom asked.

'A sort of SS burial ground, apparently,' said Dominique. 'According to Himmler, the centre of the world lay here, in the hills of Westphalia,' she explained. 'He planned to build a massive SS complex radiating out for miles from where you're standing.'

Tom looked down at his feet and shifted uncomfortably.

'At that precise spot an eternal flame was to be lit,' she continued. 'The theory is that the ashes of senior SS leaders were to be placed on one of these.'

She crossed to the wall and indicated a low stone pedestal that Tom had not noticed before. He looked around him and saw that there were twelve identical pedestals spaced around the chamber's walls.

'Clearly, the Order was to remain united in death as it had been in life.'

'Then this is where we'll start,' said Tom, stamping on the stone floor. 'Where the flame was to have burned. At the centre of their world.'

Crouching in the pit, Tom and Archie set to work, chiselling away at the mortar surrounding the large stone set into the centre of the floor. It was slow, painful work, but after five or ten minutes the sound of metal striking stone gave way to another, unexpected sound.

'There's something under here,' said Archie excitedly.

They levered the first stone out, then set to work on the ones surrounding it, eventually clearing a wide area and revealing the outline of a three-foot-square metal plate, about half an inch thick.

Dominique handed Tom a long metal spike from one of the packs. He used it to prise the heavy metal slab away from the ground. Archie managed to slip his fingers into the gap and he hauled the plate upright until it was standing on edge. He pushed it away, sending it toppling to the floor with a crash. As the cloud of dust cleared, a fetid stench rose from the dark hole.

Dropping to their hands and knees, they crawled to the hole's edge and peered into it. A dark, impenetrable nothingness stared back at them.

'I'll go down first,' Tom volunteered. He grabbed a rope and secured one end to the gate, then threw the other end down the hole. Gripping his torch between his teeth, he lowered himself into the inky void.

The floor appeared to be made of white stone, with a dark disc at its centre, directly beneath where he was coming down. It was only when his feet unexpectedly landed on the disc that he realised it was, in fact, a large table. He let go of the rope and took the torch from his mouth.

The table was made of wood and was surrounded by twelve oak chairs, each adorned with a tarnished silver plaque engraved with a different coat of arms and a family name. But Tom's eye was drawn less to the chairs than their occupants. For assembled around the table, like guests at some apocalyptic dinner party, were twelve gleaming skeletons in full SS dress uniform.

Hardly daring to breathe, he let his torch beam play across chests gleaming with medals and ribbons, down to the lower left arm where he found their embroidered cuff-band.

The gold lettering glowed against the black material, revealing their owners' regimental title: *Totenkopfsorden*. The Order of the Death's Head.

'They're here,' Tom shouted as he jumped down from the table between two of the skeletons, flicking his torch from one to the next. 'They're all here.'

'Who?' Archie shouted from the floor above.

'The Order.' He noticed a hole in the right temple of one of the skulls, saw the same wound in the others, then a gun on the floor next to one of the chairs. 'Looks like they killed themselves in some sort of suicide pact.'

'I'm coming down,' Archie announced. A few seconds later, he slid down the rope and landed in the centre of the table.

'Christ!' he exclaimed as his torch picked out the Nazi skeletons. 'You weren't joking.' He sounded genuinely shocked.

'They must have lowered themselves in here, got someone else to replace the stones upstairs, then pulled the trigger.'

'And assured themselves of a much more pleasant death than they had ever allowed anyone else,' Archie said with feeling as he jumped down to the floor. 'Shall we take a look around?'

'Wait for me.' Dominique had noiselessly lowered herself down the rope onto the table behind them. She held up her lantern so she could get a good look at the corpses. 'It almost seems like they're waiting for us.'

'Or for someone else,' Tom added. 'Come on, let's see what else is here.'

They turned their attention to the chamber itself. It was about thirty feet across and the only way in or out seemed to be the hole above them.

'Well, if there's something down here, I can't see it.' Archie said.

'Agreed,' said Tom. 'But there's one place we haven't looked.'

'The bodies,' Dominique breathed.

Without waiting for an answer, she turned towards the table and walked slowly around it, her forehead creased with concentration. Finally she came to a halt behind one of the chairs. 'Let's try this one first.'

'Why that one?' Tom asked. It looked no different from the others.

'Look at the table.'

Tom directed his torch beam where she was pointing and saw that the table's surface had been divided into twelve equal slices, one opposite each knight. And each slice had been inlaid with a different type of wood.

'Oak, walnut, birch . . .' She pointed each one out in turn, her lantern moving round the table. 'Elm, cherry, teak, mahogany . . .' She paused when she came to the segment facing the chair she had stopped behind. 'Amber.'

Dominique gingerly unbuttoned the skeleton's jacket, two of the silver buttons coming away in her hand where the thread had dissolved. Then, pulling the jacket to one side, she began checking the pockets.

'Nothing,' she said, sounding disappointed. 'I got it wrong.'

'I'm not so sure,' said Archie, peering down at the glittering array of medals pinned to the jacket Dominique had just unbuttoned. 'He's wearing a Knight's Cross.' He drew the medal out from under the uniform's collar. 'Dom, have you got the other two?'

She nodded and removed them from her coat pocket, placing them face down on the table so that the markings were visible. Archie laid the one they'd just found alongside the other two.

'They must mean or do something,' Tom said.

'Maybe it's a picture,' Dominique suggested. 'Maybe the lines meet up to show you something that you can't see when they're apart . . .' She began to slide the medals around to see if any of the lines matched up. After ten minutes she had exhausted every positional combination. Then suddenly she clicked her fingers. 'Of course! It must be three-dimensional. The medals don't go next to each other; they go on top of each other.'

She grabbed one medal and placed it on top of another, sliding it this way and that to see whether a pattern emerged. Then she tried changing one of the medals, then the other, until finally she smiled. 'Here you go.'

By sliding the second medal over to the left and up from the centre of the bottom one, she'd managed to align several of the marks. She placed the final medal on top of the others, sliding it to the right and then up from the second medal. As she moved it, the lines suddenly came together to form an image that could be seen from above. Two elaborate crossed keys.

'The keys of St Peter,' Tom breathed.

'St Peter? As in Rome?' asked Archie. 'Well, it can't be there.'

'It's unlikely, I agree,' Tom said pensively. 'What else could it mean?'

'While you two think that one through,' Archie said, stooping to pick up a lantern he had placed on the ground, 'I'll see if our friends here have got anything else interesting on them. You never know— Hang on,' he interrupted himself as he raised his head level with the table. 'What's that?'

He pointed at the side of the table where a small shape had been cut into the wood. A very distinctive shape.

'I wonder . . . Here, give me one of those.'

Dominique handed him one of the medals and he lined it up with the hole. It was a perfect fit. He slipped the medal inside.

'I'll bet there are two more holes just like this one,' Archie said excitedly.

'Here's one!' Dominique pointed at the table's edge to Archie's right.

'And here,' Tom confirmed, having moved round to the other side of the table so that they were now standing at the three points of a triangle.

Archie slid the remaining two medals across the table. 'Put them in and then let's all press on the medals.'

Tom and Dominique did as he suggested. As they all pressed together, a click echoed round the chamber.

'The table,' said Tom. 'Look at the middle of the table.'

He shone his torch at a roundel in the centre of the table that had popped a few millimetres higher than the surrounding surface. Kneeling on the table, Tom pulled out his knife and levered the roundel free, revealing a deep recess. He reached inside with his fingertips and removed a small dagger with runic symbols on its blade. A piece of paper had been wrapped round its ivory hilt.

Tom hopped to the floor, then unscrolled the paper. 'It's a telegram,' he said. 'Here, Dom, you read it. Your German's better than mine.' He handed the piece of paper to her and shone his torch onto it so she could read.

'*All is lost. Stop. Prinz-Albrecht-Strasse overrun. Stop. Gudrun kidnapped. Stop.*' She looked up questioningly. 'Gudrun? Wasn't that Himmler's daughter's name? The one in the portrait?'

'Yes,' Tom confirmed with a nod. 'And Prinz-Albrecht-Strasse was Himmler's HQ. What else does it say?'

'*Hermitage most likely destination. Stop. Heil Hitler.*' She looked up. 'It's dated April 1945. It's addressed to Himmler.'

'The Hermitage,' Tom said, shaking his head in frustration. 'That's what the keys of St Peter meant. We're meant to be looking in St Petersburg.' He looked up excitedly. 'The missing Bellak is in the Hermitage.'

Hotel Drei Könige, Zürich: January 9, 2.51 a.m.

'There you go—' Lasche pointed to the wooden box on his desk. 'I've only sold one Enigma before. A few years ago now. He was a Russian collector.'

'And the other components?' The voice was soft and lilting, hinting at lazy evenings on a porch somewhere in South Carolina or Louisiana.

'Already in the machine. Of course, the final settings are up to you, Mr Foster.' Lasche was tired but it was unavoidable, given the hour. He'd had little warning, merely a phone call informing him that someone would be coming to make the exchange and to ensure that he was alone.

Foster was a large, rugged-looking man, his thick beard melting into unkempt brown hair, his steel-grey eyes still and watchful. A dangerous man, thought Lasche. 'Any problems getting hold of this?'

'Not really. I have my contacts. People I trust for this sort of job. Besides, they're the last people on earth anyone would imagine I was involved with.'

'You mean the Sons of American Liberty?' Foster asked with a smile.

'How do you know that?' Lasche was at once amazed and angry. Amazed they knew, angry because it meant that they'd been watching him.

'Cassius does not take chances. As soon as he was certain that your man Blondi had taken delivery of this'—Foster patted the wooden box—'and was on his way home, he asked me to go and . . . meet with your people.'

'*Meet* with them? What do you mean?'

'I mean that I locked them all in a booby-trapped room and tipped off the Feds so that they'd be the ones to set it off.'

'All of them?' Lasche gasped, feeling his chest tightening. 'Why?'

'Loose ends.' Foster reached into his pocket, pulled out a silenced 9mm pistol and pointed it at Lasche's chest. 'Cassius won't stand for loose ends.'

8

Nevsky Prospekt, St Petersburg: January 9, 3.21 p.m.

Tom and Dominique made their way down the Nevsky Prospekt towards the honeyed bulk of the Admiralty.

'So when do you think Archie will get here?' Dominique asked.

'You missing him already?' Tom laughed, his voice muffled by a thick scarf. 'Don't worry, he should be here by this evening.'

'Was it worth him travelling separately? I mean, if someone *is* looking for him, they're as likely to spot him on his own as with us, aren't they?'

'True,' said Tom. 'But he seemed to think he'd have a better chance with only himself to worry about.'

'And Turnbull?'

'I updated him on everything we've found. Well, everything he needed to know. He's due here tomorrow.'

At the end of the Nevsky Prospekt, they turned right into Palace Square. Dominique slipped her arm through Tom's, feeling strangely warm and content, despite the icy wind. 'You've been here before, right?' she asked.

'No.'

'No? Why not?'

'I guess I just never got round to it.'

Something in his tone told her not to probe further. Instead, she changed the subject. 'That must be it—the Hermitage.'

'That's it,' Tom confirmed.

'It's huge. You really think the missing Bellak painting is in there?'

They had reached the river bank and were standing on Palace Bridge, looking out towards the Peter and Paul Fortress.

'It makes sense,' Tom said. 'Himmler's headquarters would have been one of the Russians' key strategic targets. If Himmler didn't destroy Bellak's painting of his daughter, I think there's every chance the Russians found it there and brought here as a trophy. The problem is going to be finding it.'

'Why's that?'

'There are three million items in there, but only one hundred and fifty thousand are actually on display. The rest are housed in vast attic store-rooms and underground depositories, most of it poorly catalogued.'

There was a long silence. Dominique caught a distant look in Tom's eye.

'Tom, what's really kept you from coming here before?'

He didn't answer right away, his eyes firmly fixed on the far shore. 'When I was eight, my father bought me a book about St Petersburg. He told me he'd bring me here one day. That he'd show me its secrets. I guess I was waiting for him to ask me. I never thought I'd come here without him.'

Dominique was silent. Then, surprising herself more than anyone, she reached up and gave him a kiss on the cheek.

Decembrist's Square, St Petersburg: January 9, 4.03 p.m.

Boris Kristenko felt guilty. With only three weeks to go till the grand open-ing of the new Rembrandt exhibition, his colleagues were working flat out. He should have been back at the museum, coordinating the hanging. But he'd made a promise to his mother. So he had slipped out of the office and was now hurrying along the Leytenanta Schmidta embankment. His mother wanted three Russian dolls as gifts for her nephews and nieces in America.

It was a small shop, catering mainly for tourists, with a fine selection of Russian souvenirs. He purchased the dolls and emerged back onto the street, checking his watch.

The first punch, to the side of the head, caught him unawares. The second, he saw coming, although it still winded him as it slammed into his stomach. He dropped to the ground, gasping for air, his head ringing.

'Get him over there.' He registered a voice, then felt himself being dragged by his arms into an alleyway. He didn't have the strength or the will to fight them. He knew who they were and he knew he couldn't win.

They threw him to the filthy cobblestones. His head bounced off a wall, and he felt a tooth break as his chin connected with the bricks.

'Where's our money, Boris Ivanovich?' came the voice. He looked up and saw three of them looming over him.

'It's coming,' he mumbled, finding it difficult to move his jaw.

'It had better be. Two weeks. You've got two weeks. And next time, just so you know, it won't be you we come for. It'll be your mother.'

One of the men kicked him hard in the head, the boot catching his nose. He felt the warm trickle of blood down his face as the shadows faded, their cruel laughter rising through the air like steam. Alone, he began to cry.

Catherine Palace, Pushkin: January 9, 4.37 p.m.

As dusk fell with a crimson mantle, and the first streetlights blinked on, Tom stepped through the gilt and black filigree entrance gates to the Catherine Palace. He was glad that Dominique had not come with him. He needed time on his own. He ascended the main staircase, passed through the main door into the entrance hall and turned left. He knew the way, having memorised it long ago from a plan in the book his father had given him. His pace quickened, masterpieces he would normally have lingered over getting no more than a cursory glance. Instead he was drawn to the far doorway, his path lit by the glow from the room beyond. The Amber Room.

It wasn't the original room, of course, but a modern replica, crafted to celebrate the city's 300th anniversary. Even so, the result was stunning. The glittering walls spanned a spectrum of yellow, from smoky topaz to the palest lemon. And while most panels were undecorated, some were adorned with delicately crafted figurines, floral garlands, tulips, roses and seashells.

Only one other visitor was present, examining a panel on the far wall.

And a stern-faced attendant occupied a giltwood chair near the entrance.

'It took twenty-four years . . .' The visitor had crossed the room to join him. 'Twenty-four years to rebuild it. Amazing, is it not? '

Tom turned to look at the man. From the side, he could barely make out the profile of his face, obscured as it was by a black bearskin hat pulled down low. And yet there was something in the man's voice that he recognised.

'Hello, Thomas.' Slowly, the man turned to fix him with a pair of unblinking steely green eyes. Harry Renwick's eyes.

'Harry?' Tom gasped. 'Is that you?'

'My dear boy!'

Tom's surprise evaporated, a cold, biting rage taking its place. He took a step forward, his fist clenched at his side.

'Careful, Thomas,' Renwick said softly, edging away. 'Do not try anything rash. I would not want you to get hurt.'

There was a scrape of wood, and Tom turned to see the frightened attendant being bundled from the room by two shaven-headed thugs. Two more marched in after them, their coats open to display the guns tucked into their waistbands. The taller of the two made his way to Renwick's side. Tom recognised him as the man filmed leaving the hospital after Weissman's murder. The other approached Tom and patted him down, before relieving Renwick of his bearskin hat and retreating across the room.

'I believe you have not yet had the pleasure of meeting Colonel Hecht?' said Renwick. 'He is a . . . colleague of mine.'

'What do you want?' Tom asked sullenly.

'Ah, Thomas,' Renwick sighed heavily. 'It is sad, is it not? After everything that has passed between us, the time we have spent together, that we should not be able to meet and talk as friends.'

'Save it,' Tom spoke through gritted teeth. 'Our friendship was built on your lies. The day you betrayed me, we lost anything we ever had. You mean nothing to me now. So if you've come to kill me, let's just get it over with.'

'Kill you?' Renwick laughed. 'My dear boy, if I had wanted you dead, you would not be here. There have been any number of opportunities over the past few days. No, Thomas, your death, while satisfying the need to avenge the loss of my hand, would not serve my purposes.'

'Your purposes?' Tom gave a hollow laugh. 'You think I'd help you?'

'Oh, but you have done so much already, Thomas. The key you recovered from Lammers, the safe-deposit box, the identification of a possible location for the contents of the missing carriages—'

'How the hell . . . ?' Tom started, before realising what this meant. 'Raj! What have you done to him?'

'Ah, yes,' Renwick sighed. 'Mr Dhutta. A very loyal friend, if I may say. Right until the end.'

'You callous bastard . . .' Tom's voice cracked. He blamed himself for getting Raj involved.

Renwick gave a smile. 'So, now you know what I have known for some time,' he said eventually. 'The Order was sent to protect a train. When they realised it was not going to reach Switzerland, they took it upon themselves to remove the most precious part of its cargo and hide it, committing the secret of its location to a painting that now lies in some private collection.'

Tom said nothing. He was thinking of Raj's corpse lying in some alley.

'Think about it, Thomas—the original Amber Room.' Renwick's eyes flashed. 'Finally recovered after all these years. Think of the money. It must be worth two, three hundred million dollars.'

'You think I care about the money?' Tom seethed.

'Your father spent half his life on its trail. Imagine what he would say if he could be where we are now—so close.'

'Don't bring my father into this,' Tom said icily. 'He wanted to find it so he could protect it. All you want to do is destroy it.'

'Your father is already involved, Thomas.' Renwick was smiling now. 'How do you think I found out about this in the first place? He told me.'

'If he did, it's because he had no idea who you were.'

Renwick gave a cruel laugh. 'Do not play games with me, Thomas. It does not suit you. You cannot deny that you have thought it, at least.'

'Thought what?' Tom's mouth was dry, his voice a whisper.

'How it was that he never knew about me, even though we were colleagues for twenty years, friends for longer. How there must have been a chance, however slight, that he not only knew but helped me. Worked for me.'

'Don't say that. You don't know—'

'You have no idea what I know,' Renwick cut him off. 'And if you did, you would never believe it. Just as I know that you will fail to believe this.'

He pulled out his pocket watch and dangled it in front of Tom, who recognised it instantly. It was a rare gold 1922 Patek Philippe chronometer. He even knew its case number: 409792. It was his father's watch.

'Where did you get that?' Tom asked in a whisper. 'You have no right—'

'Where do you think? He gave it to me. Do you not see, Thomas? We were partners. Right until the end.'

Pulkovoz Airport, St Petersburg: January 9, 6.47 p.m.

A black car glided to a halt outside the airport entrance, larger and cleaner than any of the vehicles around it. Hitching his bag onto his shoulder, Bailey climbed into the back of the car.

'Man, it's colder than a well-digger's ass out there!'

The man extending a welcoming hand through the gap between the front seats was Laurel to the driver's Hardy: tall and thin with neatly combed brown hair, while his colleague was stout with a circle of greying blond hair.

'I'm Bill Strange and this is Cliff Cunningham. Welcome to Russia.'

Bailey shook Strange's hand. 'Special Agent Byron Bailey. You guys Bureau or Agency?'

'Bureau.' Strange smiled. 'Carter figured you'd want to see a friendly face.'

'Carter was right,' Bailey said gratefully. Cody had been helpful, but he was happy to be back with his own people. 'So, any sign of my guy yet?'

'Look familiar?' Strange handed a photo to Bailey.

'That's him, yeah.' Bailey's eyes flashed. 'When did he come through?'

'An hour or so ago. Took the flight from Bonn, like you said. He's just checked in at the Labirint.'

'That's where Kirk's staying, too,' Cunningham added. 'Checked in with a young female. Separate rooms.'

'Looks like you made a smart call,' said Strange.

'I got lucky,' Bailey corrected him with a smile. As soon as they realised that Kirk had booked a flight to St Petersburg, they had circulated a description of Blondi to all major European airports offering flights to Russia. Confirmation of Blondi's booking had come through from an alert official at Bonn Airport, and Carter had immediately dispatched Bailey after him.

He settled back into the soft leather seat as Cunningham pulled out into the traffic and headed for the town centre.

Hotel Labirint, St Petersburg: January 9, 7.22 p.m.

The shower consisted of a yellowing curtain covered in spots of mould suspended over a chipped bath, but the water was hot and Tom soon forgot where he was, his mind flicking back to the Amber Room. To Renwick.

The man was right, of course. Since discovering what Renwick was really like, Tom had indeed questioned the nature of his father's friendship with him, wondered whether he had suspected the truth. But he had never for a moment considered that his father had been directly involved in his murderously criminal activities.

Tom stepped out of the shower, dried himself and got dressed. The phone rang, but he ignored it. Then came a knock at the door.

'Come in.'

Archie's head appeared. 'Anyone home?'

'You made it!' Tom smiled with relief. 'Any problems?'

'Long day,' said Archie, collapsing into an armchair. 'Where's Dom?'

'Getting changed. She'll be down in ten.'

Archie stretched out his legs. 'So, what have you been up to?'

'Oh, nothing much . . .' Tom shrugged. 'Took a stroll down Nevsky Prospekt; went for a look at the new Amber Room; bumped into Renwick.'

'Cassius? He's here?'

'Oh, he's here all right. In fact, he's been with us ever since London. Watching and waiting for us to do his legwork for him and locate the last Bellak painting.'

'So he knows?'

'He knows everything he managed to beat out of Raj.'

'What?' Archie jumped up, concern etched into his face.

Tom held out a reassuring hand. 'I tracked him down. Apparently they fished him out of the river last night. Shot twice but still alive. Just about.'

'Wait 'til I get my hands on that bastard,' Archie said, glowering.

'You'll have to get past his new friends first. He's got Hecht with him. The Kristall Blade guy Turnbull fingered as Weissman's murderer.'

Archie slumped back into his chair. 'So what did dear old Uncle Harry want exactly?'

'He wanted to find out what we know.'

'Meaning he's no closer to finding the room than we are.'

'I'd say he's further. He still thinks the Bellak's in a private collection.'

'Won't take him long to figure out why we're here, though, will it?'

'No,' Tom conceded. 'So I hope you've got a plan.'

'Don't worry. It's sorted. Well, it will be. There's this client, or rather ex-client of mine. Of ours, really.'

'Which ex-client?' Tom asked sceptically.

Archie held out his hands, palms up. 'Viktor, of course. Who else?'

Undisclosed location, Germany: January 9, 9 p.m.

There were twelve men. Each wore a gold ring engraved with a twelve-box grid, with a single diamond in one of the boxes. They had dispensed with names. It was safer that way. Instead, they were known by the names of cities.

'There is no cause for panic,' said Paris, an elderly man sitting at the head of the table. 'This means nothing.'

'Nothing? Nothing?' Vienna, sitting opposite him, spluttered incredulously. 'Did you not hear what I just told you? A crypt's been found at Wewelsburg Castle. A secret crypt with twelve SS generals in it. It's all over the news. The caretaker went in and there the entrance was, right in the middle of the floor. A crypt we never even knew existed. It's Kirk. He's following the trail. If that's not a cause for panic, what is?'

A murmur of agreement bubbled up, the candles along the table flickering slightly in their agitated breath.

'What if he found something?' Berlin said. 'How much closer will he get before you take this seriously? What if he finds the Bellak?'

At this, the room around him exploded into argument.

'Brothers!' Vienna stood up, the noise subsiding grudgingly. 'I say it is time to act. Firstly, I suggest we eliminate Tom Kirk without further delay. We lost him in Zürich, but I've just heard from one of our sources that he took a flight to St Petersburg. If we can get a fix on him there, we must act.'

'I can take care of that,' said Berlin. 'Just let me know where he is.'

'Secondly, we move it. I say we break the link. Relocate the painting where no one will find it. A place only we know.'

'This is preposterous!' Paris pleaded. 'We have a code, a duty to protect it but *never* move it. To do so would risk alerting the world to its existence.'

'That code was for a different time,' Vienna insisted. 'It is no longer appropriate. Just as your being the only person who knows its precise location is no longer appropriate. We need to adapt to survive.'

'This is madness,' said Paris.

'Is it? Or is it madness to ignore what is happening? To entrust ourselves to the whims of an old man? We must change before it is too late.'

'There's only one person here who has consistently warned us against the danger that we are now facing, and that is Vienna,' Krakow urged. 'He is the man to hold the secret and take whatever steps are necessary to protect it.'

'Only one man is ever to be entrusted with that secret,' Paris said firmly.

'Then I demand a ballot.' Berlin slammed his fist on the table. 'Either we vote for Paris and his ineffectual ways, or for Vienna and action.'

'I am honoured that you deem me worthy of consideration,' said Vienna.

Chair legs screeched across flagstones as the table emptied. One by one, they lined up behind Vienna's chair.

'It is a burden to last for life,' Paris said softly. 'It is my burden.'

'No longer,' Vienna replied. 'It is the unanimous decision of this group that it is time for another to carry the flame. Alone.'

Berlin reached into his pocket and drew out a small pad and a white pill. Walking round to Paris, he laid the pad on the table and then set the pill next to it, sliding a glass of water within easy reach. This done, he stepped back.

Fighting back tears, Paris took out his pen and wrote on the pad. He tore out the page, folded it in two, and handed it to Berlin, who walked it round to Vienna. Solemnly Vienna unfolded the note, read the contents, then touched the paper to a candle flame. The paper flared into life, then died.

Shoulders shaking, Paris removed his ring and placed it on the table. He placed the pill on his tongue and washed it down with a mouthful of water.

Two minutes later he was dead.

Tunnel Nightclub, Petrograd Island, St Petersburg: January 10, 1.13 a.m.

Their driver, Igor, confessed to being a schoolteacher by day. At night, however, he moonlighted as a *chastnik,* cruising through the streets offering unlicensed taxi rides to anyone who didn't care about insurance, heating or the windows going up all the way. Licensed or not, he had not required any directions to the nightclub where Archie had arranged to meet Viktor.

The Tunnel was a concrete shed set between two apartment blocks. The entrance was patrolled by three hulking security guards in paramilitary uniforms, with a wolflike German Shepherd in tow. The solid steel door had been wedged open with a decommissioned AK-47.

'It's an old nuclear bunker,' Archie explained to Tom and Dominique. 'Viktor owns it. Don't worry, we'll be looked after.'

The security guards checked their names against the guest list and waved them past a queue of miserable-looking people shivering in the cold.

A blast of stale, warm air hit them as they began to descend the rough stairs. At the bottom was another thick steel door, and as it swung open a wall of bass slapped them in the chest.

Two more guards in paramilitary gear and sunglasses waved them to an opening in the wall. A beautiful dark-haired woman wearing little more than her underwear took their money and their coats, then tapped the sign behind her with a varnished nail. It was in printed in Russian, but underneath was a translation: *No guns or blades. Please to leave at entrance.*

Pistols and knives of all shapes and sizes filled the metal basket below the sign, each weapon labelled with a bright pink coatroom number.

'How well do you know this Viktor?' Tom asked Archie.

'We've done business for years. Big collector. Eclectic, though—Picassos and military memorabilia, mostly.'

'Yeah, well, nice place he's got here,' Tom said sarcastically.

They stepped through a metal detector and entered the club. The bunker extended some fifty feet under a barrelled roof that amplified the music into a deafening roar. At the far end was a cage with a DJ installed at its centre and two women writhing round brass poles at either side.

'I'll get us a drink,' Tom shouted over the noise.

He fought his way through the crowd, brushing up against a beautiful woman in a red dress, a ruby nestling in her bronzed cleavage. She smiled and seemed about to say something, but was ushered away by her escort.

The bar consisted of two trestle tables staffed by three girls wearing boob-tubes and mini skirts made out of camouflage material. One table was stacked with shot glasses and bottles of Stolichnaya, the other with champagne flutes and bottles of Cristal. Payment was strictly in US dollars only.

Tom bought champagne then fought his way back to the others.

'Didn't they have a beer or something?' Archie complained.

'It was this or vodka. I've just paid three hundred bucks, so enjoy it.'

'Table, sir?' A waiter had appeared at his elbow and was pointing to a small table in the corner of the room.

'How much is it?' Archie eyed the man with suspicion.

The waiter frowned. 'How much? Nothing. You are Viktor's guests.'

Archie turned to Tom with a smile. 'See, I told you we'd be looked after.'

'What about that one?' Tom pointed to a table further from the stage.

'Oh no.' The waiter looked panicked. 'Viktor says that table. Please sit.'

Tom shrugged. With a look of relief, the waiter showed them over and refreshed their ice bucket as they sat down.

Dominique took a sip from her glass. 'So what now?' she asked.

'I guess we wait,' said Archie.

Thirty minutes later, there was still no sign of Viktor. Tom was about to ask one of the waiters where Viktor had got to when a man, flanked by a blonde woman, approached their table and shouted something in Russian.

'What?' said Tom.

'He says this is his table,' the blonde translated in a thick accent.

'Well, that's going to be difficult because, as you can see, we're sitting here. But he's welcome to try the floor,' Archie countered.

The girl translated and the man's face broke into an unsmiling grin. He said something and the girl translated again.

'He says he's happy to sit on floor, if he can rest his feet on your head.'

Archie leapt to his feet and the man stepped back. In a flash another man jumped between them, his right hand already reaching inside his jacket.

'Hey . . .' Tom stood up with a conciliatory smile, his palms raised in defeat. 'Our mistake. Here—it's all yours. Leave it, Archie.'

Muttering angrily, Archie followed Tom and Dominique to the other side of the room. 'It's the Wild West out here,' he complained.

'Stay out of trouble,' Tom said. 'It's not worth getting shot over a table.'

'OK, OK,' Archie conceded.

Tom scanned the room, wishing this Viktor would show up, when two men near the entrance caught his eye. Despite the heat, they were both still wearing their thick outdoor coats. The crowd seemed to part in front of them as they strode to the table where the man and the blonde, closely monitored by their bodyguard, were clinking glasses. Then they opened their coats and each swung an Uzi from under his arm. Before any of the table's occupants could react, they started firing in precise, controlled bursts at point-blank range.

People dived to the floor screaming. Those nearest the door scrambled towards it. The music stopped, the palpitation of the bass replaced by the mechanical thud of gunfire. Then, his clip empty, one of the men drew a handgun and calmly fired a bullet into each of his victims' temples. Satisfied, the men retreated nonchalantly across the room, and disappeared up the staircase.

As soon as they had gone, real panic set in. Women screamed, men began shouting. There was a stampede for the exit.

'Let's get out of here,' Tom shouted, hauling Archie and Dominique to their feet, 'before they realise they got the wrong people and come back.'

'You think—?' Disbelief and shock spread across Dominique's face.

'Yeah,' said Tom. 'I think the waiter was a bit too insistent that we sat at that particular table.'

People were surging towards the stairs, only to be swept back into the club as flashing blue lights heralded the arrival of the police.

'That way,' yelled Tom, pointing at a group of people who were heading through a door by the cage. 'There must be another exit.'

They found themselves in a narrow corridor with a small box room at the end. Set into the far wall was a ladder of narrow iron hoops that led up to ground level. A chaotic stream of bodies was scrambling up the rungs.

'Come on,' Tom shouted. He fought his way through to the base of the ladder and held people off so that Dominique and Archie could climb up ahead of him before clambering up himself. After about twenty feet, the ladder emerged through a submarine-type hatch onto a strip of wasteland.

'Let's go,' he called, the growing cacophony of sirens telling him that it would be only a matter of minutes before the police located the rear exit.

'I thought Viktor was a friend of yours,' Tom observed as they ran. 'You must have done something to piss him off.'

'I didn't do anything,' Archie wheezed. 'It's a mistake. It must be.'

They reached a junction and Tom slowed down, trying to get his bearings. Before he could orientate himself three black Cadillac Escalades roared up the street behind them, screeched to a halt, and surrounded them in a crude semicircle. The rear passenger door of the middle car flew open and the waiter who had shown them to their table leaned out, his face pale.

There was a loud crack and the waiter's body crumpled back into his seat. Dominique gasped. A red stiletto tipped the waiter's body out onto the street with a shove into the small of his back. Then a bronzed leg emerged, followed by a hand clutching the still-smoking gun. Finally, an oval face with wild blue eyes framed by long dark hair appeared, and a tanned, full bosom adorned by a flaming red ruby.

'*Zdrástvuti*, Archie,' she said with a smile.

Tom flashed Archie a questioning look, but he was climbing into the car. '*Zdrástvuti*, Viktor.'

As soon as they were all inside, the car accelerated away. Tom was in the front, Archie and Dominique on the back seat with Viktor, while an unsmiling bearded brute who responded to the name Max was driving, a Kalashnikov propped against the dash in front of him.

'Stop the car,' Tom demanded, as soon as he judged they were far enough from the club. 'Enough fucking around—what's going on?'

'Tom!' Archie remonstrated, for once the pacifist. 'Easy.'

Tom was in no mood for diplomacy. 'We nearly got killed tonight, Archie. I don't know about you, but I've had enough surprises. First she invites us to her club'—he tilted his head in Viktor's direction—'then she makes sure we sit at a particular table so that two gunmen can use us for target practice.' He nailed Viktor with a stare. 'By the way, who was the poor sod you just redecorated the sidewalk with?'

'An employee of mine. A traitor.' She spoke with a gently lilting Russian accent, her face impassive. 'I apologise for his betrayal.'

Tom snorted. 'You're telling us you had nothing to do with all that?'

'*Niet*.' She shook her head. 'I told him to get you a table, that's all. He must have told them which one it was.'

'But the assassins didn't realise that the people sitting there were not the ones they'd been sent to kill,' Dominique said bitterly.

'Who were they?' Tom asked.

'I have never seen them before,' said Viktor. 'Chechens, most likely. They do one job then disappear. The money buys weapons for their war.'

'But who were they working for?' Archie this time.

'Whoever could afford them. But not me. I have my own people.'

'Well, that's comforting,' Dominique muttered darkly.

'How did they know where to find us?' Tom demanded. 'You were the only person who knew we'd be at the club.'

'It was not me,' said Viktor. 'I put your names on the list, but they were three among a hundred.'

'The phone!' Archie clicked his fingers. 'The phone must have been tapped.' He turned to Viktor. 'We discussed all the arrangements then.'

'Well, you can't go back to your hotel,' said Viktor. 'You will stay with me instead. I'll send some people round to collect your luggage.'

'No,' Tom insisted. 'I think we'll be better on our own.'

'That wasn't an offer,' Viktor replied unsmilingly. 'I've got three dead customers, and half of the St Petersburg police are crawling over my club. Until I find out what's going on, you're staying with me.'

The car began to lose speed as the lead vehicle in their three-car convoy pulled up at a red light. Suddenly there was a blinding flash, followed by a massive bang. The car in front of them lifted seven feet off the ground and smashed down onto its side. The explosion rocked them all in their seats.

Through the smoke a figure materialised at the driver's window, slapped something against the glass, then disappeared. Tom recognised the shape at once, despite the distorting effect of the tape that secured it to the glass.

'Grenade!' he shouted, sliding into the footwell for shelter.

The grenade detonated with an ugly bang, shards of glass flying across the car's interior despite the windows clearly being armoured. The figure appeared again, opening fire with an automatic weapon. The driver didn't stand a chance as the bullets smashed through the now weakened glass.

Grabbing the wheel, Tom leant across and pressed the driver's lifeless foot to the accelerator. The car sprang forward, careering violently as they clipped the burning wreck of the vehicle in front of them, bullets thumping into the rear windows as they accelerated away. When he judged them to be clear, Tom sat up and opened the driver's door, heaving the man's body out onto the street before slipping behind the wheel.

As he accelerated, Tom made eye contact in the rearview mirror with a grim-faced Archie, then Dominique, who gave him a nervous smile.

'Take this.' He passed the Kalashnikov back over his shoulder.

Viktor climbed into the passenger seat next to Tom. She was still holding her handgun.

'What about the other car?' she asked.

Tom checked his mirror and saw the second escort car lying in a twisted tangle of burning steel and rubber. 'I don't think they made it.'

'When I find out who's done this I will make them pay.' Viktor's eyes flashed. 'Now, head south for the river, Tom' she ordered, pointing at the road ahead. 'Get to the bridge.' She checked her Rolex. 'There's still time.'

Tom gunned the car in the direction she had indicated and a minute later they could see the Trotsky Bridge and a long line of traffic leading to it.

'Take the left lane,' Viktor instructed.

Tom swung the car into the oncoming traffic, horns blaring as cars swerved up onto the pavement to avoid them. Ahead, two large barriers had just come down across the road, preventing any more traffic from passing.

'What's happening?' Tom asked.

'They're raising the bridge to let the ships through. They do it every night. Once the bridge is up, it won't go down again until three a.m. If we get across now, the people following us will be stuck here.'

Tom slammed the brakes on as they reached the barrier, the car slewing to a sideways halt. 'We'll have to run for it from here.'

He hit the ground running and vaulted over the barrier, the others only seconds behind him.

'This way,' urged Viktor.

They ran past a gesticulating guard onto the main bridge. Tom felt it slowly begin to rise under them as they ran.

'We're not going to make it,' he panted.

'We have to. Look!' Viktor was pointing at something behind them.

Tom glanced back to see a car accelerating towards them. Two gunmen with semiautomatics were firing at them from the windows.

Hauling Archie with him, Tom ran as fast as he could up the steepening gradient as the bridge rose. With one final effort they surged towards the edge and jumped the small gap that had opened up between the two halves of the bridge. Only Viktor paused at the top, gripping her gun with both hands and emptying it into the windscreen of the pursuing car until it swerved and crashed through the handrail into the river.

In those few seconds' delay, the gap had become a chasm. Arms outstretched, she launched herself across it, her fingertips somehow making contact with the rim. She hung there, helpless, above the freezing waters of the Neva, until Tom's hand closed round her wrist, his other hand reaching down to haul her to safety. Once over the lip, they tumbled headlong down the raised bridge section, landing in a confused heap at the bottom.

'*Spasibo*,' she said, pulling herself to her feet, her legs and arms raw and bruised where she had fallen.

'Don't mention it,' said Tom, a sudden stab of pain in his left shoulder making him wince.

'You've been hit,' she exclaimed, kneeling down next to him.

'It's nothing,' Tom panted, looking down at his fingers, now scarlet where the blood had run down his arm. He realised that he couldn't feel them.

9

Reki Fontanki Embankment, St Petersburg: January 10, 2.53 a.m.

It was more bordello than bedroom. A huge chandelier hung from the mirrored ceiling, the walls were pink and gold, the giltwood chairs covered in leopardskin, and in front of the black marble fireplace was a polar bear rug.

Tom stared up at his reflection in the mirror over the bed, trying to keep his mind off the searing pain in his shoulder.

Viktor, perched on the bed next to him, stopped what she was doing and looked intently into his eyes. 'You don't like it?'

Tom shrugged. 'It's not my style.'

'Nor mine. I inherited it. I would have changed it, but in Russia rooms like this make people respect you.' She gave a tight smile. 'This will hurt.'

According to Viktor, who had a surprising familiarity with gunshot wounds, the bullet had lodged itself in the muscle round the shoulder blade. Although she had access to discreet doctors, she had advised against involving outsiders. The incident with the waiter at the club had proved that even those she trusted could betray her. Tom had agreed, though it meant allowing Viktor to extract the bullet, without anaesthetic.

'Ready?' she asked, stainless-steel tongs poised over the wound.

'As I'll ever be,' said Tom, bracing himself.

The room seemed to go dark as the burning in Tom's arm burst into a blazing fire. His ragged breathing came through clenched teeth.

'You've done this before?' he gasped, hoping that conversation would help take his mind off the pain.

'Many times.'

'You were a nurse?'

'No.' A smile flickered across her face. 'I used to work.' She shrugged. 'You know . . .'

Even in his present state, Tom could see that she was a striking woman, with the slim, firm body of a dancer. The events at the bridge had left her red dress torn and dirty, her bronzed skin grazed and bruised, and her sleek ebony hair in disarray. And yet this seemed to complement the wild, exotic beauty of her face. But he saw a hardness there too, and an unspoken hurt.

'You were a prostitute?' Tom asked uncertainly. Archie had whispered something about this when they arrived at Viktor's house.

'Yes.'

'So how . . . ?' Tom winced as she twisted the tongs.

'Did I end up here?' She gave a mirthless laugh. 'It's a long story.'

'I'm not going anywhere.'

There was a long silence as she probed the wound. Then she spoke. 'When I was sixteen my parents sold me to a man called Viktor Chernovsky. He was one of the Mafia bosses here in St Petersburg. At first I was lucky. He wouldn't let anyone else touch me, just raped me himself.'

Tom mumbled something about being sorry, but she didn't seem to hear.

'When he got bored, he gave me to his friends to use. They were bad men. And when they came back injured from some robbery or shoot-out, I was the one who had to patch them up. That's how I learned how to do this.'

'Where did you learn to speak English so well?'

'One of Viktor's men was American. He taught me. He was the only one who ever really cared. I think I almost loved him.'

'Why didn't you just leave?'

'You don't leave this life—either you're in, or you're dead. Besides,' she continued tonelessly, 'I got pregnant. Viktor found out and made me have an abortion. There.' She held the tongs out so Tom could see the pea-sized lump of metal. 'It doesn't look as though the bullet hit anything vital.'

'Good. Ah . . .' Tom grimaced as Viktor swabbed the wound with iodine solution. 'Then what?'

'Then? Then he punished me.' Viktor hesitated, then lifted her hair away from the left-hand side of her head. Tom saw with horror that, where her ear should have been, there was a hole surrounded by angry pink scar tissue.

'So I killed him.' She spoke matter-of-factly. 'One night I stabbed him in the back of his neck. Then I dumped him in the river.'

'And all this . . . ?' Tom indicated the room with a sweep of his hand.

'Was his. Like I said: I inherited it.'

'Just like that?' Tom's tone was disbelieving.

'There were some who thought a woman shouldn't be head of the family. But people respect strength. They soon learned to take me seriously. I took on Viktor's name to ease the blow. A lot of people think he's still around.' She signalled for Tom to sit up so she could bandage his shoulder.

'What's your real name?' he asked.

She paused. 'You're the first person to ask me that in almost ten years.'

'And?'

Before she could answer, there was a knock at the door. Viktor hurriedly swept her hair back across her ear as Archie and Dominique walked in.

'How are you doing?' said Dominique, concern etched on her face.

'He'll be fine,' said Viktor. 'In the morning I'll get antibiotics.'

'Close one.' Archie pulled up a chair and sat down. 'Good thing Viktor's used to patching people up.'

'So I've been hearing.' Tom looked at Viktor, his eyes meeting hers.

'Don't worry, we'll be out of your way in the morning,' Archie told her.

'Make yourself comfortable, Archie,' she replied. 'No one's going anywhere until you tell me what's going on.'

Archie shook his head. 'It doesn't involve you. There's nothing to say.'

'Doesn't involve me? I lost six of my men. Because of you, my club will be shut for weeks. That's money. My money. You understand what that means?'

'It means I owe you,' said Archie sullenly.

'No. It means I *own* you. I own you until I say otherwise. So, whatever you're planning, I want a piece of the action. What's going on?'

Archie looked questioningly at Tom, who gave a reluctant nod.

'We're looking for a painting.'

'A painting? I thought you were out of that business.'

'I am. We both are.'

'Both?' Viktor looked momentarily confused.

'Tom was my partner. That Matisse out in the hall? He got it for you.'

She stared at Tom, clearly reappraising him. 'I like that painting.'

'So did the Fine Arts Museum in Buenos Aires,' he replied with a smile.

'So this is just another job?'

'No,' said Archie. 'Not a normal sort of job, anyway. We think the painting may tell us where something was hidden.'

'What is this "something"?'

'We're not sure, yet,' Tom intervened, unwilling to share the secret. 'But it's valuable.'

'And we want to stop anyone else getting to it first,' Dominique added.

'"Anyone else" being the people responsible for tonight?'

'Could be,' said Archie. 'We don't know.'

'What *do* you know?' Viktor sounded exasperated.

'We know that someone went to a lot of trouble to hide a series of clues that lead to a painting we think is hidden in the Hermitage storerooms.'

'The Hermitage?' She rolled her eyes. 'You'll never get in there.'

'First things first,' said Archie, brushing aside her reservations. 'We need to find it. Then we can worry about getting it out. Can you help?'

'Maybe.' Viktor shrugged. 'It depends.'

'On what?'

'On what's in it for me.'

US Consulate, St Petersburg: January 10, 3.12 a.m.

'It's a war zone down there.' Special Agent Strange entered the small, windowless meeting room, sank into a chair and put his feet up.

'How many dead?' Bailey asked.

'Three. Two men and a woman. They weren't your suspects, though.'

'What happened?' Bailey asked.

Strange sniffed. 'Two guys walked up to their table, took 'em out, then walked straight out again. Pretty goddamned cold.'

'Local cops let half the people who were in the club get away,' Cunningham growled. 'Apparently there was some sort of escape tunnel.'

'What about Blondi and the other two?'

'We saw him and the others go in, but the cops didn't bring them out.'

'Then, of course, there's the car bomb,' Strange added.

'The car bomb?' Bailey exclaimed. This was going from bad to worse.

'Convoy of three Cadillac Escalades got ambushed two miles from the club,' Strange replied. 'The main vehicle shot its way out. It was found near the Trotsky Bridge. The occupants got over the bridge just as it went up.'

'Any witnesses?'

'From what we've picked up off the police scanner, there were four people at the scene. Two men, two women. Three of the descriptions match

Kirk, Blondi and the girl who's with them.'

'And the cars belonged to Viktor,' Cunningham added. 'So it's short odds that's who the fourth person was.'

'I thought you said the fourth person was a woman?' Bailey said.

'Her real name is Katya Nikolaevna Mostov. A hooker from Minsk who made the big time by killing her mafioso boyfriend and taking over his operation and his name. The Tunnel nightclub belongs to her.'

'If these guys have hooked up with her, then they're mixed up in some serious shit,' said Cunningham. 'And she could help them disappear.'

'Maybe we should just go in and get them now,' Bailey said, 'before they have a chance to disappear. Haven't you guys got some sort of arrangement with the local cops?'

'Sure, but they don't apply to her,' Strange said. 'Viktor pretty much runs this town. The police, judges, politicians—she's got them all covered.'

'Our best hope is to sidestep the authorities here, wait till Blondi's out in the open and send in a snatch team,' Cunningham said slowly. 'We can worry about getting him home later. It's not ideal, but we've done it before.'

'What about Kirk?' asked Bailey. 'We should pick him up, too.'

'We haven't got the manpower for both of them,' said Cunningham.

'I'll talk to Carter, see what he says,' Bailey said. 'I guess this is really about Blondi, anyway.' He shrugged. 'That's who they sent me here for.'

'We've got eyeballs on Viktor's place,' Strange reassured him. 'If any of them leave, we'll know about it.'

'That's right,' Cunningham said eagerly. 'First chance we get, we'll move in. Believe me, Blondi won't see us coming.'

Reki Fontanki Embankment, St Petersburg: January 10, 6.18 p.m.

The throbbing in Tom's shoulder had woken him. Checking his watch, he realised that he'd slept through the day, the painkillers and exhaustion finally catching up with him. He pulled the satin bedsheets aside and sat up, noticing an untouched tray of food at the foot of the bed.

Giving up on typing his shoelaces, he found his way past several armed guards who were patrolling the wide, parquet-floored corridors as if it was a government facility, and entered the dining room where Archie and Dominique were sitting at a massive ebony table.

'Tom!' Dominique exclaimed as she saw him. 'How are you feeling?'

'I'm fine. How are things here?'

'Great, except that Viktor won't let us leave the house,' Archie said with a resigned shrug. 'We can't even use the phone.'

Viktor chose that moment to stride into the room wearing beige combat trousers and a tight-fitting black top.

'You're better.' It was a statement rather than a question.

'Much.'

'Good. Because we found someone . . .'

Two of her men marched a hooded and handcuffed figure into the room. 'He showed up at your hotel, asking questions. Said he knew you.'

She reached up and snatched the hood off the man's head. Turnbull stood blinking at them, disorientated, a piece of tape plastered over his mouth.

Archie got up and walked over to him. 'No, never seen him before,' he sniffed, sitting back down. 'He must be one of them.'

'Take him down to the cellar,' Viktor ordered.

At this, Turnbull's eyes widened and he began to struggle frantically.

'It's OK,' Tom said. 'That's Archie's idea of a joke. He's with us.'

'Oh.' Viktor indicated with a wave that her men should remove the gag.

'Very funny,' Turnbull said angrily as soon as he could speak. He said something in Russian to one of Viktor's men. Viktor nodded her consent, and the handcuffs were whipped off.

'Serves you right for snooping around,' Archie shot back.

'I wasn't snooping.' Turnbull rubbed his wrists. 'Kirk told me you were staying there. He knew I was coming. We're meant to be working together, remember?'

'Together?' Archie laughed. 'You weren't the one getting shot at last night.'

'That was you?' Turnbull gasped. 'It's all over the news. What happened?'

'We're not sure,' said Tom.

'You think it's Renwick?'

'No . . .' Tom quickly briefed Turnbull on the events of the previous afternoon, including his encounter with Renwick in the Catherine Palace. 'If Renwick wanted me dead, he could have done it there and then.'

'So Renwick knows about the Amber Room?'

'The Amber Room?' Viktor stepped forward, her voice eager. 'Is that what this is all about?'

'Maybe,' Tom said slowly, silently cursing Turnbull's indiscretion.

'What do you know about it?' Archie challenged her.

'Viktor told me all about it. He was obsessed with the war. I've got a room full of his old maps and uniforms and flags. He even had an old

Enigma machine restored so that he could use it to send messages to one of his American contacts for fun. But the Amber Room—it's just a myth.'

'So what do you call this?' Archie handed her the fragment of amber they had recovered from the satchel in Völz's vault.

Viktor gazed at it suspiciously. 'It can't be . . . it's impossible.'

'You're probably right. But, to be sure, we need to find that painting.'

'Then maybe I can help, after all,' Viktor conceded. 'The deputy curator at the Hermitage, Boris Kristenko. He's into me for a bit of money. A gambling debt he can't shake. He'll play along. We just need to squeeze him.'

'Nobody gets hurt,' Tom warned.

'I'm just talking about applying a little pressure. The sort that is most effective in getting people to cooperate. Fear and greed.'

Griboyedova Canal, St Petersburg: January 10, 7.05 p.m.

It was a short drive to *Greshniki*, or Sinners, a four-storey gay club on the Griboyedova Canal. According to Viktor's informants, Kristenko was in the habit of stopping by for a drink here on his way home.

The club opened at six but the place was still quiet when Tom and Viktor made their way up to the first-floor bar to wait for Kristenko. She ordered a bottle of vodka and two shot glasses, then filled them both to the brim.

'*Na zdorovje*,' she said, clinking glasses with him. No sooner had she downed the shot than she poured herself another. Tom did the same.

'Who's Harry?' Viktor suddenly asked.

'What?' Tom's voice registered his surprise at this unexpected question.

'Harry. When I looked in on you last night, you were talking in your sleep. Something about Harry. You seemed angry.'

'He's someone I used to know,' Tom said dismissively. 'He's no one.'

'You know, I think maybe we're alike, you and me.'

'Why do you say that?' he asked.

'You're angry, like me. I can see it in your eyes. I heard it in your voice.'

'Am I?' Another pause. 'Angry about what?'

She shrugged. 'I'd say you've been hurt. A betrayal, perhaps. Someone you thought you could trust. Now you've lost the ability to care about most things, most people—but yourself, especially. You're bitter.'

'Once maybe,' Tom said slowly. 'But less so now.'

'You can't suddenly change who you are.'

'Are you talking about me or you?'

She seemed not to have heard him. 'I've become like Viktor. Become the very thing I once despised. The irony is that I'm trapped. I'm even more of a prisoner now than I was when he was alive. At the first sign of weakness, someone will make a move against me and I'll be the one they fish out of the Neva. And nobody will care.'

'The choices we make have consequences,' Tom ventured. 'I should know—I've made some bad decisions, and suffered for them. But you can always get out. I used to think you couldn't, but you can. It's never too late.'

She shook her head. 'It's not that easy. They'd never let me go.'

'Then don't tell them.'

'I've saved enough money to live several lives. I could leave tomorrow.' A pause. 'I'm only telling you this because you saved my life yesterday.'

'I was saving myself and my friends, too.'

'In the car, maybe. But up there on the bridge? You could have let me fall. No one would have known.'

'I would have known,' Tom said. 'That's not who I am.'

A pause, then she said. 'By the way, it's Katya.'

'What is?'

'My name. Katya Nikolaevna. That's who I am.'

She held out her hand. Taking it in his, Tom kissed it theatrically. She laughed, and snatched it away from his mouth.

'You should do that more often,' he said.

'What?'

'Laugh.'

Her face dropped immediately and Tom sensed that she was wishing she hadn't let her guard down quite so far.

Kristenko walked in a few moments later, a slight, wiry man with steel glasses that magnified his large brown eyes, giving them a look of perpetual surprise. He looked to be in his late thirties, and had clearly tried to disguise the thinning of his fine blond hair by brushing it across his head.

The curator didn't look the violent type, yet his left eye was yellow and puffy, his top lip split on one side. Tom flashed Viktor a reproachful glance, but she responded with a shrug as if to say she had no idea how he'd received his bruises. Somehow, Tom doubted that.

Kristenko ordered a beer and a vodka, downing the shot immediately and chasing it down with a mouthful of Russian lager. He sighed, sat on a bar stool and looked along the bar in their direction.

'*Zdrástvuti*,' he greeted Tom.

Viktor stepped between the two men. '*Zdrástvuti*, Boris Ivanovich.'

Kristenko's eyes narrowed with confusion as he tried to place her face.

'You don't know who I am, do you?' she asked.

He shook his head dumbly.

'They call me Viktor.'

Kristenko, all colour drained from his face, looked as if he was going to be sick. 'Two weeks,' he whispered. 'You said I had two more weeks.'

'And you still do,' she said. 'Although you and I both know it will make no difference.'

'It will,' he insisted. 'I'll win it back. I will, I will.' He began to sob.

Viktor nodded at Tom and then stepped aside.

'We're looking for this.' Tom slid the photo of the Bellak portrait across the bar to Kristenko. 'It was last seen in 1945, in Berlin. We think that it was seized by the Russian Trophy Squad, and that they stored it in the Hermitage. It's by an artist called Karel Bellak.'

Kristenko wiped his eyes on his sleeve. 'It could be anywhere.'

'I'll pay you,' Tom offered. 'Twenty thousand dollars if you find it. Fifty thousand if you bring it to me.'

'Fifty thousand?' Kristenko picked up the photo and gazed at it.

'Can you find it?' Viktor demanded.

'I'll try,' said Kristenko.

'You'll do better than that,' Viktor said menacingly.

'Here.' Tom handed him five thousand dollars in cash. 'I'm serious.'

Kristenko's hand curled round the thick wad of notes as he stared at them in disbelief, then his head jerked up and he looked questioningly at Viktor.

'Keep it,' she said. 'Pay me out of the fifty thousand when you get it.'

He slipped the money gratefully into his jacket. 'How can I find you?'

'You don't. From now on, you deal with him.' She nodded at Tom.

'Take these,' said Tom, handing Kristenko his digital camera and a mobile phone loaned to him by Viktor. 'I'll need proof—photos of the painting—before we line up the cash. When you have it, call me. There's only one number in the memory.'

The Hermitage, St Petersburg, January 10, 8.01 p.m.

On the Hermitage's top floor, lost in the dark labyrinth of attic storerooms, a dimly lit corridor ends in a rusty door. Very few people are allowed into this hidden corner of the museum. Even fewer know it exists. Those that do have learned not to ask what lies inside.

Even Kristenko had needed to forge a note from the museum director to gain access. Fortunately, the armed escort detailed to accompany him had been happy enough to wait outside, lighting up with typical Russian disregard for the 'no smoking' signs.

The door was stiff from lack of use, and as soon as he was inside he tugged it shut behind him, metal striking metal with a dull crash.

Six doors led off a corridor, each one opening onto a different *spetskhran*, or special storage area. According to the rough plan he held in his trembling hand, it was *spetskhran 3* of this, the so-called Trophy Squad Annexe, that held the bulk of the paintings seized from Berlin at the end of the war.

Opening the door, his throat dry with anticipation, Kristenko felt for the switch just inside the room. As the low-level lighting flickered on, he saw that the paintings had been loaded onto three wooden racks, each two tiers high and twenty feet long. Kristenko pulled on a pair of white cotton gloves and started with the rack nearest to him. The canvases were heavy and it wasn't long before he had broken into a sweat, the dust adding a grey tint to his skin. But his tiredness evaporated when, among the second column of paintings, he discovered a large, badly damaged work.

Kristenko recognised it immediately as a Rubens—*Tarquin and Lucretia*. Reluctantly, he returned the masterpiece to the pile and continued his search. But no sooner had his heartbeat returned to its normal rhythm than he found a Raphael. The label identified it as *Portrait of a Young Man*. Then, ten minutes later he stumbled upon a Van Gogh.

For the next hour, as Kristenko continued his search, he fumed over the cavalier treatment of these great treasures. Given his mood, it was hardly surprising that the Bellak portrait almost passed him by. Not the most prepossessing of subjects, he thought: a plain-looking girl in a green dress, sitting next to an open window with sky and fields beyond.

Kristenko lifted the portrait clear of the rack. Then, holding it carefully in front of him, he flipped off the light, closed the door behind him, and retraced his steps to where he'd left the guards.

'Found what you were looking for, Boris Ivanovich?' one of them asked good-naturedly, stubbing out his cigarette on the heel of his boot.

'Yes, thank you,' said Kristenko. 'You can lock up now.'

He navigated his way cautiously down the stairs to the Restoration Department on the second floor. The main atelier was dark and empty, as he had known it would be.

His palms sweating, Kristenko pulled the mobile phone from his pocket and dialled the number stored in the memory.

Decembrist's Square, St Petersburg: January 10, 9.56 p.m.

Even on a cold January evening, the area around the base of the Bronze Horseman was thronged with tourists and locals taking pictures. Peter the Great and his rearing horse seemed frozen in the glare of the sodium lights, a gleaming shadow thrown up into the clear night sky.

Tom was talking to Archie on the two-way radio, the microphone clipped to his collar.

'You feeling any better?' Archie asked.

'Yeah,' Tom lied. Although the painkillers and the vodka were helping, just buttoning up his coat had made his shoulder throb. 'Where is everyone?'

'I'm on the north side of the square. Turnbull and the others are over on the south side. Viktor's men are standing by, in case we need them.'

Tom glanced round and located Archie, then looked away. 'I see you.'

'And I've just spotted Kristenko.'

'OK, let's switch to the main frequency.' Tom pressed one of the pre-set buttons on the radio in his pocket. 'Viktor, Dom—Kristenko's on his way.'

On cue, Kristenko turned the corner of the Admiralty and began to cross the square. Tom gave him a barely noticeable nod.

Under the rearing horse's flashing hoofs, the two men shook hands.

'Do you have my money?' Kristenko's eyes were wide and scared.

'Show me the painting first,' Tom insisted.

Kristenko fumbled in his pocket and brought out the digital camera Tom had lent him. Tom scrolled through the images, then looked up with a nod. He held out a frayed bag he'd borrowed from Viktor. 'It's all there,' he said.

Kristenko unzipped the top and peered inside, then his face relaxed. 'OK, OK. So now we make the exchange?'

'Where's the painting?'

'Still inside. I'll go back in and get it, then meet you back—'

With a shout, four men suddenly ran towards Kristenko, guns materialising in their hands. Terrified, he raised his hands in surrender, the bag tumbling to the floor. But the men ran straight past him. Instead, they piled into Archie, knocking him to the floor. A white van swerved onto the square and screeched to a halt alongside them, its side door sliding open.

'What the hell's going on?' Tom screamed into the radio.

The four men bundled Archie into the vehicle, then jumped in after him. Before Tom could react, the van accelerated away, the door slamming shut. The whole operation had lasted less than ten seconds.

Tom turned to Kristenko. The curator stood transfixed, his eyes locked on the retreating van. Finally, with a despairing glance at Tom, he snatched the camera, turned on his heel and walked briskly away, never once looking back, not even at the bag of money lying on the ground.

'THEY LOOKED well trained,' Dominique said, still breathless from having run the width of the square to reach him.

'I agree,' said Tom. 'Military, or a police hostage-rescue team.'

'Maybe I can help find out what's going on,' Viktor said. 'If it is the police, we've got people on the inside. You concentrate on Kristenko.'

'You're right,' Tom conceded. 'We need someone to follow him.'

'Already done,' said Viktor. 'One of my men will call us as soon as he gets to wherever he's headed.'

There was a crackle of static from Viktor's radio. She turned it up and a disembodied Russian voice rose into the cold night air.

'He's arrived back at the museum and gone straight up to the Restoration Department,' Viktor translated.

Tom's phone rang. He checked the caller ID and looked up in surprise.

'It's him—Kristenko.' He answered the call with a confused look. 'Yes?'

'What just happened?' Kristenko's voice was a strangled whisper.

'I've no idea,' Tom said soothingly.

'I thought . . . I thought for a moment they had come for me,' Kristenko muttered. 'This was a very bad idea. I don't know what I was thinking.'

'You were thinking about fifty thousand dollars,' Tom reminded him gently. 'You were thinking about paying Viktor off.'

'What's the point, if I'm in prison?'

'Fine. I'll tell Viktor that you don't want—'

'No, no. But I'm not taking it outside. I'll . . . leave it for you. Yes, I'll leave it for you here in the museum. You can come in and get it yourself.'

'That wasn't the deal,' said Tom.

'You said fifty thousand if I brought it to you, twenty thousand if I found it. Well, I've found it. Twenty thousand will clear my debts. The rest, well, it's not worth the risk. I'd rather take my chances. I won't survive prison—'

'OK, Boris, calm down. I'll come and get it.'

'Good.' Kristenko sighed with relief. 'I'll leave it in the Restoration Department. There's a vault.'

'What's the combination?'

'I'll give you that when you give me the money.'

Tom smiled. 'Fine. I'll call you when I'm in.' He punched the off button and turned to Viktor. 'Kristenko's too scared to bring it out, so I'll have to go in. Can you get me some tools and a floor plan?'

'Done,' said Viktor.

Tom turned to Turnbull. 'How's your Russian?'

'Good enough.'

'It'll need to be. Because you're coming in with me.'

US Consulate, St Petersburg: January 10, 11.02 p.m.

'Fuck off,' Archie snapped.

The short, fat American who'd introduced himself as Cliff Cunningham smiled. 'You'll have to do better than that, Blondi.'

'I've nothing to say. Not to you, or any other copper.'

Cunningham shook his head. 'We're FBI.'

'Am I meant to be impressed?' Archie's voice was confident, but he had to admit he was confused.

'We've got the big picture,' drawled the other Fed—Bailey, he'd said his name was. 'We just need the details.'

'Details of what?' snapped Archie.

'Why kill all those people?' asked Bailey, suddenly angry. 'What did they know that was so dangerous?'

'What the hell are you on about?'

'We have proof that you were in the States, airport security footage—'

'So I went to Vegas—big deal. There was a poker thing on. Ask around. There'll be plenty of witnesses.'

'And Lasche? Why kill him? Covering your tracks again?'

'Lasche is dead?'

Cunningham nodded, eyeing Archie coldly. 'He was lucky compared to the Lammers woman. The Austrian police sent us the crime-scene photos.'

'Lammers? Maria Lammers? She's dead too?' Now Archie was totally lost. How could all these people be dead? 'This is a joke, right?'

'Why did you steal the Enigma machine?' Bailey spoke again, his voice calm and measured.

'*What?*' said Archie, deciding that he'd heard enough, 'OK. If you're going to charge me with something, do it. It doesn't matter, anyway. My lawyer will have me out of here quicker than you can say extradition treaty.'

'Lawyer?' Cunningham gave a hollow laugh. 'You think a lawyer's going to stop us flying you back to the States in the diplomatic bag? You're going nowhere, Blondi. Not till you tell us exactly what we want to know.'

10

The Hermitage, St Petersburg: January 10, 11.27 p.m.

The queue snaked in front of them, the air thick with cigarette smoke. A few consulted their watches; others swapped jokes or chatted on their mobiles, half an eye on the gate as they waited for their shift to start.

At 11.30 p.m., the guards opened the doors and ushered everyone inside. Tom shuffled forward with the rest, ready to follow Turnbull's cue if anyone spoke to them in Russian. For her part, Viktor had conjured up blue overalls and freshly laminated badges that identified them as working for the company contracted to clean the Hermitage each night.

The first guard gave Tom's badge a cursory glance and waved him in. Turnbull followed. Tom walked through the metal detector. It remained silent. Turnbull stepped through after him, the alarm triggering noisily.

'Must be all the iron I've been pumping,' Turnbull joked in Russian to the guard who beckoned him over.

'Raise your arms,' ordered the guard, a handheld metal detector at his side, the green LED display flickering.

Turnbull complied, and as the guard moved in with the detector, Tom noticed his thumb slide almost imperceptibly over the On/Off switch. The green LED faded.

'You're clear,' said the guard.

'Well, that wasn't too bad,' Turnbull whispered as they followed the other cleaners along a corridor and down a flight of stairs into the basement.

The staircase gave on to a large room filled with mismatched chairs. Tom and Turnbull took off their coats and hung them on hooks.

A man entered and began calling out names—the shift manager, Tom guessed. People came up to him in twos, took a piece of paper, disappeared into a side room and re-emerged wheeling a small trolley bristling with brooms, mops, buckets, bin liners and bottles of detergent and polish.

'You guys new?' the shift manager asked, as Turnbull and Tom stepped up. His name badge identified him as Grigory Mironov.

'That's right,' Turnbull replied in perfect Russian, a by-product, he had revealed to Tom, of five years on the Moscow listening post at GCHQ.

'No one told me,' complained Mironov.

'No one told us until a few hours ago.'

Mironov sighed. 'Don't you talk?' he asked Tom.

'Never shuts up,' Turnbull answered for him.

Mironov looked suspiciously at Tom, who returned his stare unblinkingly. Mironov's face broke into a grin. 'I can see that,' he chuckled, handing Turnbull a piece of paper. 'You'll find the gear in there. Head for the second floor. You get lost, just ask one of the guards.'

They collected their equipment and rolled the trolley to the lift.

'We drew the second floor of the Western Wing,' Turnbull said, as the door shut. Tom pulled out the floor plan he had brought with him. 'That puts us on the right floor but the wrong side of the building. We need to get to the northeast corner, where the restoration rooms are.'

The door rolled open and a guard greeted them with an upturned hand.

'What?' Turnbull asked in Russian.

'The work schedule. What room are you in?'

'Oh,' Turnbull lowered his voice to a whisper. 'No schedule tonight. The director's expecting an important guest tomorrow, but his office isn't due for a clean until the day after. So he's paid us cash to do it for him tonight. I gave a third to Mironov and here's a third for you. We don't want any schedules screwing things up for us, do we?'

The guard closed his hand round the notes Turnbull had slipped him. 'Understood.' He stepped back from the lift. 'Do you know your way?'

'Just down there, isn't it?'

'That's it. Last door on the right.'

They headed off in the direction of the administrative offices.

Suddenly Tom felt a tug on his sleeve. Turnbull indicated the door beside them and translated the inscription: '"Department of the History and Restoration of Architectural Objects"—looks like this is the one.'

It was locked. Turnbull glanced over his shoulder to check that there were no guards in sight, then unzipped the front of his overalls and detached the small pouch that had been strapped to his belt. The same pouch that had set off the metal detectors on the way in.

Tom pulled on his gloves and took his pick and tension wrench from the pouch. He had the door open in seconds.

BORIS KRISTENKO was sitting in the dark in his office, gnawing anxiously on a ball-point pen. A pipe gurgled somewhere, and he jumped, convinced that it heralded the arrival of a horde of angry police officers. He fixed the door with a fearful stare, his heart hammering in his chest, but it remained shut.

The phone rang. 'Hello.'

'We're here. In the Restoration Department.'

He struggled to his feet. 'I'm on my way.'

MOONLIGHT FILTERED through the overhead skylights in the main atelier of the Restoration Department, turning the shrouded statues and sculptures into ghostly apparitions. In the far corner, black and forbidding, was the vault door. Tom examined it curiously as they waited for Kristenko.

'Could you get us in?' Turnbull asked.

'If I had to,' said Tom. 'It's not exactly state of the art.'

Turnbull's head snapped towards the door. 'Someone's coming—quick.'

They ran to the far side of the room and crouched behind one of the workbenches. The door opened.

Tom peeked round the edge of the bench. 'It's Kristenko,' he breathed.

Kristenko jumped in fright as they both stood up.

'Right,' said Tom, 'let's get this over with.'

'My money?'

'Here.' Tom tossed the shoulder bag over impatiently. 'Open the safe.'

'I'll stand outside,' Turnbull said. 'I'll whistle if I hear someone coming.'

'Good idea,' said Tom.

Grabbing a mop and bucket, Turnbull let himself out of the room.

Kristenko approached the safe and fiddled with the combination until, with a clunk, the door eased open. The vault consisted of a steel-lined room, about six feet square.

Kristenko stepped inside and emerged a few seconds later holding a painting. 'Here it is,' he said. 'Although God knows what you—'

A low whistle came from outside. Tom's eyes snapped towards the door as Turnbull stepped back into the room.

'Who is it?' Tom whispered urgently.

But Turnbull didn't answer. His eyes locked pleadingly with Tom's as he reached towards him, but as his mouth opened to speak he collapsed to the floor. A knife handle jutted awkwardly from the base of his skull.

Kristenko let out a low, terrified moan.

'Good evening, Thomas,' Renwick intoned as he swept into the room, Hecht and his two heavies lining up behind him.

'Renwick,' Tom said through clenched teeth.

'My thanks for your efforts in locating the missing Bellak.' Renwick snapped his fingers at Kristenko, who, with a confused glance at Tom, handed him the painting. Renwick studied it, then he smiled.

'Well done. You have what you wanted.' Tom's voice was glacial.

'Not quite,' Renwick sighed. 'Stories like ours rarely have happy endings. It is unfortunately the nature of things.'

Hecht stepped forward, a silenced gun in his hand, and levelled it at Tom's head. Tom's jaw tightened, his mind going blank as Hecht fired.

The bullet caught Kristenko in the throat and he staggered back. A second shot caught him square in the chest and he collapsed to the floor.

'What was the point of that?' Tom shouted.

'Loose ends, Thomas. You know how I hate loose ends.'

The two other men stepped forward, picked Kristenko up under the arms and dragged him into the safe. They dropped him to the floor then stepped outside and repeated the procedure with Turnbull.

'You too, Thomas,' Renwick ordered. 'Keep them company. That way the authorities will not have to look too far to find someone to blame.'

Tom walked into the vault. 'This isn't over, Harry.'

'It is for you.' Renwick smiled. 'Believe me, by the time the Russian police have finished their interrogation, you will wish I had just shot you.'

The door edged shut, a final sliver of light framing Renwick's face before it vanished, accompanied by a dull clang as the bolts slammed home.

Silence, broken only by the pounding of his heartbeat. Total darkness.

Squatting next to the corpses, Tom pressed a button on his digital watch. A cold blue glow lit up their faces. Disgusted by Renwick's handiwork, he released the button. He was used to working in the dark.

He turned his attention to Kristenko first, patting him down and finding the mobile phone—useless inside the vault—and the digital camera he had given him. He pocketed them both. Next, he felt his way over to Turnbull, searching the body until he came across his toolkit. He then edged his way to the door and ran his hands over its surface until he located the square inspection hatch located at about waist height.

GRIGORY MIRONOV cleared the final flight of stairs and headed for the Western Art gallery. It was his responsibility to check that all the cleaners had followed their instructions and were doing a good job.

He entered the Rodin Room and ran a finger along the nearest frame. It came away dusty. Then he made his way to the Gauguin Room, only to discover that it too had yet to be cleaned. He felt the anger building inside him.

The three guards who were supposed to be on patrol were in the Renoir

Room, taking a cigarette break. 'You seen the two cleaners for this section?' Mironov demanded. 'A big fat guy and his mute friend?'

One guard broke away from the others and hustled Mironov from the room. 'Don't worry. They explained everything. I let them through.' He winked.

'What?'

'A third for you, a third for me. The director gets his office cleaned and everyone's happy.' He laughed and went to rejoin his colleagues.

Mironov stood seething with rage. So, those two jokers were freelancing, were they? Muttering angrily to himself, he set off for the staff offices.

THE DOOR OF THE VAULT swung open and Tom stepped gratefully back into the main atelier of the Restoration Department. But his elation was short-lived. Someone was approaching. He could hear footsteps. His eyes shot to the door handle. Would Renwick have bothered to lock it?

Unwilling to take the risk, Tom gently pushed the vault door shut behind him and slipped under the sheet covering a tall statue of Mercury near the door. As the footsteps grew louder, he huddled close to the statue.

He heard the door creak open. A squeak of shoe leather on the marble floor, and then nothing. Tom guessed that whoever it was had stopped for a good look round. There was a slight gap between the sheet and the floor, and Tom could just make out a pair of well-polished shoes. He heard someone muttering and the shoes turned back towards the door.

They were almost out of the room when they stopped again. The man crouched down, Tom was able to make out an outstretched index finger being run across the floor's surface. As the finger was lifted, Tom could see the dark stain left by Turnbull's blood. Then the man sprang up, the shoes swivelling and following the trail of blood to the vault. Tom leapt from his cover as the man ran past, the sheet coming with him as he charged him. The impact sent the guard crashing into one of the workbenches.

Tom scrambled to his feet, desperately trying to wrestle his way out of the sheet that was still wrapped round his head and arms in case the guard went for his gun. But in that moment a large bottle on the workbench, unbalanced by the impact of the collision, teetered off the edge and dropped onto the Russian's skull.

GRIGORY MIRONOV turned the corner just in time to hear the sound of breaking glass, followed almost immediately by the sound of the door to the Restoration Department being locked.

'Who's there?' he shouted, beating on the door with his fist. 'Open up.'

There was no answer, just the sound of more glass being broken.

He rattled through the massive bunch of keys attached to his leather belt, identified the one he was looking for and tried it. The door opened.

He leapt into the room, his torch raised as a makeshift club. But the room was empty. A bite of cold air on the back of his neck made him look up. A skylight had been smashed. The intruder had escaped onto the roof.

Glass crunched beneath his feet and he looked down. The floor was wet. He followed the stream of dark liquid to the guard's body, slumped against a workbench. Mironov ran to his side and felt for a pulse. Seeing that he was still alive, he laid him down on the floor and radioed for assistance. Within forty-five seconds, men were pouring through the door, guns drawn.

'What happened?' demanded the senior officer.

'We had two new men start tonight. I sent them up to clean a few of the Western Art galleries, but they never showed up. I think they bribed one of the guards to allow them down here. I came looking for them. All I heard was a shout and then the sound of breaking glass. I think they must have gone up there.' He pointed up at the shattered skylight.

'I want people up on the roof and all exits sealed,' the senior officer said. 'Then I want a room-by-room search. Alexei?'

'Yes, sir.' A young guard stepped forward.

'Stay here with Ivan. I'll get a medical team up here as soon as I can.'

'Yes, sir.'

Mironov and the guards trooped out of the room, their voices excited and determined. Alexei squatted down next to Ivan and loosened his collar.

CROUCHING BEHIND the worktop, Tom's mind was racing. Smashing the skylight had convinced the guards that he had escaped through it. But the trick would only last as long as it took them to get up there and find the roof deserted. He had to find a way past the guard and out of this room. Fast.

He peered out from behind the worktop and caught a glimpse of the guard they'd left—Alexei, the others had called him. Tom's heart leapt. It was the same guard who'd deactivated the metal detector when scanning Turnbull. Clearly, he owed Viktor a favour. Tom hoped the debt would extend to helping him.

He stood up and the guard's hand shot instinctively to his hip.

'Wait,' Tom said urgently.

'You go.' The guard looked terrified. His eyes flicked to the door.

'How?' Tom pulled out his map and pointed at it questioningly.

The guard grabbed it and traced a route with a shaking finger. It led down an adjacent stairwell, all the way along the first floor into the Small Hermitage, then into the Great Hermitage until . . .

Tom squinted, uncertain that he was seeing it right. 'The canal?' he asked uncertainly.

'*Da*,' said the guard, then made some hand and leg movements that seemed to imply that Tom should climb down into the canal and swim away.

Now wasn't the time to explain that, with his shoulder in its current state, he wouldn't be able to climb or swim anywhere. Muttering '*spasibo*' he grabbed the key that the guard held out to him.

'Call Viktor. Let her know what's happening,' said Tom, acting out making a phone call while thrusting the scrap of paper Viktor had given him with her number written on it into the guard's hand.

The guard nodded dumbly in response, but Tom was already sprinting out of the room. The key the guard had given him unlocked the door at the top of the staircase. Tom flew down it, emerging onto the first floor. The corridor was deserted and he broke into a run across the parquet floor. Following the map, he crossed the small bridge into the northern pavilion of the Small Hermitage, then used the key to enter the passage gallery that led into the Great Hermitage.

Finding himself in the museum's Italian collection, he slowed to a cautious walk. In the distance he could make out a man's silhouette. The rooms here were all interconnected and Tom estimated that the person he had seen was no more than two rooms away. Tom crouched by the door, his back flat to the wood-panelled wall, hidden in the shadows. A few moments later, the guard entered the room and walked straight past him.

As soon as the man had moved on, Tom slipped into the adjacent room, then the one after that. He was almost at the northeastern corner of the building. Ahead he could see the glazed bridge that led over the Winter Canal to the Hermitage Theatre.

As soon as Tom was certain it was safe, he padded over to the far wall and looked out of the window. His heart sank. Not only was the canal's surface frozen, but even if he'd been able to negotiate the thirty-foot drop, his escape route to the river beyond was barred by a thick iron grille.

He turned, desperately seeking inspiration before another guard appeared, and found himself locking eyes with a large white marble bust of Catherine the Great. She gave him an idea. He examined the windows that gave on to the narrow canal. They were alarmed but, thankfully, not screwed shut. Whatever the risks, it beat getting shot in the back by a panicked guard.

He went over to the bust and, grimacing with pain, lifted it off its plinth and staggered over to the window, sliding it with relief onto the deep wooden windowsill. He climbed up onto the sill, took a deep breath, then lifted the latch and opened the window. Immediately a deafening alarm filled the room and he heard the sound of shouts and running feet.

With a firm kick, he toppled the statue over the edge. Its white bulk sailed gracefully through the air and crashed into the ice, splitting a wide hole in its surface then sinking out of sight.

Tom stood up and looked over his shoulder. Five guards were bearing down on him, guns raised. The first shot rang out, the bullet fizzing past his ear and slamming into the plasterwork. Without hesitating, Tom jumped.

The cold water bit savagely into him as he arrowed feet first through the hole in the ice. The shock made him inhale sharply, his lungs only half filling with air before the water closed over his head. His momentum carried him down to the canal floor. Immediately Tom kicked off in what he believed to be the direction of the iron grille and the river, his hands scooping the water ahead of him.

A sharp knock on the back of his head told him that he'd hit the ice, a series of high-pitched plinks echoing above him confirming it—bullets drilling into the thick ice as the guards fired on him from the rooms above. For a moment he was grateful that the ice was as thick as it was, until he remembered that he was trapped beneath it.

His damaged shoulder had seized up completely. With his other hand he reached out and felt a wall to his left—the side of the Hermitage. Using it as a guide, he half dragged himself, half swam towards the river, each kick of his legs tightening the metal fist that was closing round his lungs. Every muscle, every organ in his body was crying out for air. With a last, desperate thrust, he propelled himself forward and felt the grille in front of him. He pulled himself down its face until finally he found a gap between the canal bed and the bottom of the grille. As he squeezed through it, flashes of light strobed across the inside of his eyelids.

He tried one last kick, but his legs barely moved, the river bed soft and inviting beneath him. Everything was quiet and still.

Two hands suddenly surged out of the darkness and grabbed him. He had the sensation of flying, of soaring towards the stars, his body screaming, his brain roaring. And then he was free, coughing and gasping, his lungs hungrily sucking in air, the knot of his heart slackening off.

'Get him in the boat.' He heard Viktor's voice behind him and realised that she was dragging him backwards through the water. Two pairs of arms reached down and hauled him out, immediately wrapping towels round him. He caught a glimpse of Viktor climbing up the ladder behind him.

'Let's go,' he heard her say.

The engine roared into life, the speedboat lifting its nose out of the water as it accelerated. The Fibreglass hull skipped and slapped across the river's surface as the Hermitage receded into the distance.

Reki Fontanki Embankment, St Petersburg: January 11, 1.36 a.m.

Dominique heard voices and edged her head round the corner. Viktor, her hair still wet, was talking earnestly in a low voice to three of her men. They were listening intently, nodding every so often. Then Viktor handed them several large bags. One of the men glanced through the open door into the room beyond it and asked something.

Viktor's eyes followed his, then looked round with a smile. '*Da.*'

A board creaked under Dominique's bare feet and she snatched her head back. The voices stopped, then she heard footsteps fading away.

'You can come out now.' Viktor's voice echoed down the corridor.

Dominique stepped sheepishly out of the shadows. 'Is he all right?'

'He's fine,' Viktor replied. 'We got him just in time. He just needs sleep.'

'And Turnbull?'

Viktor shook her head. 'He didn't make it. Tom didn't say why. But I told him about Archie. Later on he's going to find out why they're holding him.'

'Can I see him?'

'He's asleep,' said Viktor, shutting the door gently. 'Leave him now.'

'OK.'

There was a long, awkward pause as both women stood in silence.

'You and Tom,' Viktor said eventually, 'you never . . . ?' She let the question hang there suggestively.

'Tom and me?' Dominique laughed. 'Is that what you think?'

'I just wondered. I mean, you're very beautiful and he . . . he's very . . .' Viktor shrugged. 'I just wondered.' She said, not sounding as casual as she probably intended. Then she turned and walked away.

As she returned to her room, Dominique smiled to herself at the effect that Tom had on some women, even women like Viktor who appeared to have no soft edges left.

US Consulate, St Petersburg: January 11, 8.30 a.m.

'I want to see the consul general,' Tom said to the man at the front desk.

The man looked up with a lazy smile. 'Do you have an appointment, sir?'

'No.'

His smile faded. 'Then I'm afraid I can't help you.'

'It's about a man you're holding in custody here,' Tom insisted, fixing him with a firm stare. 'You've arrested a friend of mine. A British citizen. I demand to be told what he's been charged with and to see him.'

'Get him out of here,' the functionary instructed two marines who were standing near the back wall. They grabbed Tom, each one holding an arm, and marched him to the door.

'Get your hands off me,' Tom shouted, struggling vainly and wincing from the pain in his shoulder.

'Hold it,' a voice called out over Tom's shouts.

The marines stopped and turned Tom to face the direction of the voice.

'Are you here about Archie Connolly?' a stout, balding man asked.

'Yeah,' Tom said with relief. 'You know about him?'

'Sure.' The man smiled and waved the marines away. 'I'm Special Agent Cliff Cunningham. Mr Connolly is helping us with our enquiries.'

'Look, whatever he's done or you think he's done, it's just a mistake.'

'Why don't we talk this over inside,' said Cunningham. He turned to the functionary who had just tried to have Tom thrown out. 'It's OK, Roland, he's with me. Sign him in, will you?'

Tom followed Cunningham through a reinforced door and down a flight of stairs to a narrow corridor that seemed to have six cells along it.

'He's in here.' Cunningham reached the far left-hand cell and swiped a card through a magnetic reader. The door buzzed open.

'Archie?' Tom stepped inside the cell.

'Tom,' Archie's face broke into a smile. 'You took your time.' He was lying on a narrow bed, thumbing through a two-year-old edition of *GQ*.

'You two must have a lot of catching up to do,' Cunningham said coldly before slamming the cell door shut.

Tom stared at the closed door then turned to Archie and gave a shrug.

'Nice escape plan, mate,' Archie grunted, turning back to the magazine. 'What did you do? Smuggle a spoon in so we can dig our way out?'

'He's pleasant, isn't he?' Tom sat down heavily on the bed next to him.

'Tell me about it. I've had to put up with his shit all night long.'

'What does he think you've done now?'

'Oh, nothing much,' said Archie. 'Just the odd murder or thirty. Including Lasche it seems.'

'Lasche? But we saw him only a few days ago.'

'Exactly. That's when they think I did it.'

'But why?'

'For the same reason they think I killed Lammers's niece.'

'She's dead too?' Tom gasped.

'Apparently, poor thing,' Archie sighed. 'This whole business is getting out of control. As far as they're concerned, I'm not only involved in a theft that Lasche got me to carry out from some museum in the States, but I then gassed a roomful of Neo-Nazis I'd recruited to do the job. Their kids too.'

'This is ridiculous!' Tom stood up angrily. 'What theft?'

'An Enigma machine.'

'An Enigma machine?' Tom's tone switched from outrage to excitement.

'Yeah.' Archie looked up, his face brightening with sudden understanding. 'Why, you don't think . . .'

'Why not?' Tom nodded. 'A Neo-Nazi group. A wartime decoder. Lasche supposedly involved, then turning up dead. They must be connected.'

'Well, the Enigma's a collectable piece, I guess. But I don't see what use it would be to anyone.'

'Unless you needed to decode something.'

'The final Bellak painting!' Archie breathed. 'There must be a coded message on it. We need to get in touch with Kristenko again and get it out.'

'Unfortunately, it's a bit late for that,' Tom said bitterly, and briefly recounted the previous night's events.

'So Renwick's got the painting and the Enigma,' Archie sighed. 'By now, he's probably halfway to wherever it is he's meant to be. We've got nothing.'

'Maybe we do have something,' said Tom.

'What?'

'My camera. The one I loaned to Kristenko. I grabbed it off him when I was in the vault. It'll be ruined, but the memory card should still work. He took photos of the painting. If we've got that, we might not need the painting.'

'Then we just need to get out of here,' said Archie.

He motioned towards the steel door just as it flew open, and Bailey marched into the room.

He fixed Tom with an excited stare. 'Tell me about this painting.'

'You've been listening?' Tom shot back. 'Who are you anyway?'

'Special Agent Byron Bailey. I was on the first shift in case you two got careless.' He indicated a small black hole over the bed. 'Don't worry, it's turned off now.'

'Like hell it is.' Tom eyed him with distrust.

'Why don't you tell me what's really going on. You want to have a chance of getting out of here, you gotta share. Then maybe I can help.'

'Why should you help us?'

'If my boss knew I was in here, he'd kill me,' Bailey said. 'But I go with my gut. And my gut tells me you guys weren't bullshitting just now.'

'You first, then,' Tom said. 'What is it you think we're involved in?'

'A fortnight ago a guard was murdered and an Enigma machine was stolen from the NSA Museum in Maryland. We got a tip-off that a Neo-Nazi group in Idaho called the Sons of American Liberty were involved. When we went to check out their HQ, someone had locked them all in a booby-trapped room. Every single person inside died. Gassed.'

'But how did that lead you to me?' Archie asked.

'We had an eyewitness. His description matched a man filmed boarding a flight to Zürich. When we checked out the names of Zürich-based major players in the military memorabilia game, Lasche's name came up, so we staked out his hotel. Then you showed up, matching the description.'

'That's impossible,' Archie said dismissively. 'I don't even know where Idaho is. Like I told you, I was in Vegas when this happened.'

'Vegas?' said Tom in surprise. 'Is that what you were up to?'

'Do we have to go into this now?' Archie said, rolling his eyes, before turning back to Bailey. 'Show me the picture.'

Bailey reached into his jacket and drew out a sheet of paper.

Archie unfolded it, studied the CCTV image and looked up sceptically. 'That's not me,' he said with a mixture of relief and indignation.

'That's Lasche's nurse,' Tom said, snatching the paper from his hands.

'Lasche's nurse?' Bailey stammered. 'Are you sure?'

'I never forget a face. Heinrich, I think he said his name was.'

'You're right, now you mention it.' Archie nodded his agreement.

'What's Lasche's involvement in all this?' Tom asked.

'Well,' Bailey began uncertainly, 'we guessed that Lasche was the middle man for the Enigma machine. That you'd stolen it, then sold it on to him.'

'That sounds right,' Tom said. 'Except it wasn't Archie he sent to steal it but Heinrich. Lasche must have been betrayed by whoever he sold the machine to. That same person murdered the Sons of American Liberty, and Lasche as well, to ensure no one could make the link back to him.'

'"Him" being?' Bailey quizzed.

'In my opinion, Harry Renwick, aka Cassius—or someone acting on his behalf. Check your records. Last time I looked, he was on your top ten most wanted list. He's behind this whole thing, I'm sure of it.'

'But what about this painting? And how did you get mixed up in it?'

Tom paused for a second. There was something about Bailey that inspired a sense of grudging confidence. He took a snap decision to trust him.

'We were approached by a guy called William Turnbull from MI6's counterterrorist team,' Tom began. 'They were worried about a terrorist group in Germany who had linked up with Renwick. They wanted our help to find out what they were up to.'

'Why you? Did you know him or something?'

'Old friend of the family,' Tom said with a hollow laugh. 'Anyway, it turns out they were looking for something that was hidden at the end of the war. We think the painting is the final clue to its location. I'm guessing he needed the Enigma machine to unlock a coded message on the painting.'

'And how did that lead you to Lasche?'

'The painting was hidden by a secret order of high-ranking SS officers. Lasche is the expert on that period, so we wanted his opinion.'

'And the girl—Maria Lammers—what was her involvement?'

'Her uncle was a member of the Order,' Archie explained. 'But why Renwick should want to kill her, I don't know. She knew nothing.'

'You're right.' Tom frowned. 'It's like what happened in the nightclub. There's something else going on here that we're missing.'

Bailey blew out his cheeks and leaned back against the wall. 'OK. You two stay here. I'm going to check some of this out.'

Tom jerked his head towards the door. 'Somehow I don't think we'll be going anywhere.'

WHEN BAILEY RETURNED to the cell twenty-five minutes later, it was with a pensive expression and Cunningham by his side.

'Renwick showed up on our system,' Bailey began. 'He fits the profile.'

'No kidding,' Tom said drily.

'Lasche's nurse, too. Heinrich Henschell. The photo we have on file matches the description. Rough customer. Did time in Spain for murder about ten years ago before escaping. The Swiss police think they may have just found him in a ditch twenty miles outside of Zürich.' Bailey paused.

'Why do I think there's a *but* coming up?' Archie asked coldly.

'Because there's no William Turnbull.'

Tom shrugged. 'He's a spook. I'm not surprised he doesn't show up.'

'Since 9/11 we have reciprocal information-sharing agreements with the British on all counterterrorist personnel. Turnbull's not one of them.'

'Well, maybe he's part—'

'He *was* one of them. Until he was shot dead in Moscow. Whoever approached you wasn't MI6, and certainly wasn't William Turnbull.'

'He was a ringer?' Archie's tone was a mixture of surprise and anger. 'He can't be. I checked him out.'

'You checked that there was an MI6 agent by that name,' Tom corrected him, nodding slowly. 'And there was. Only he was dead.'

'But the cars, all those men . . . ?'

'Hired for the day. Oh, he played it beautifully. He knew if he mentioned Renwick's name, I'd listen. That if he pointed us in the right direction, we'd do all the running.' Tom shook his head, furious with himself.

'You think he was working for Renwick?'

'Well, it would certainly explain how Renwick was able to stick so close to us. How he knew exactly where we'd be last night,' said Tom.

'And he topped Turnbull once he'd served his purpose,' Archie added.

'So what now?' Bailey interrupted them.

'We're stuck in here, that's what now,' Archie snapped. 'How can we do anything, unless we get out?'

'I can't let you go,' said Bailey. 'It's a good story but I need hard evidence to make it stick. Besides, I have no jurisdiction here. I'm sorry.' He walked slowly out of the room, nodding at Cunningham on his way out.

'This is crazy,' said Tom. 'We've done nothing wrong.'

Cunningham approached them slowly. 'Bailey's right. He doesn't have any jurisdiction here,' he said. 'But I do. Bailey thinks you're telling the truth, that you're not the people we're looking for. Who knows, he may even be right. But that doesn't mean I can just let you go.'

'So what are you saying?' Tom asked uncertainly.

'I'm saying that I came in here with Bailey. That after he left the room you overpowered me and handcuffed me to the bed.' Cunningham produced a pair of steel handcuffs and dangled them in front of Archie. 'That you took my keys . . .' He dangled his key ring with his other hand. 'And found your way up the back stairs to the fire exit on the south side of the building.'

Archie cautiously accepted the handcuffs and key ring. 'And then what?'

'Then you have about twelve minutes before Bailey comes back and finds me. In fact, make that ten,' he said, consulting his watch. 'After that, we'll be looking for you. The Russkies too. I'd advise you to get out of town.'

'What do you want in return?' Tom asked, snapping the cuffs open.

'A phone call when you catch up with these guys.' Cunningham pulled a worn business card from his top pocket. 'We'll take it from there.'

Reki Fontanki Embankment, St Petersburg, January 11, 11.43 a.m.

It had taken fifteen minutes of fielding questions before Tom was finally able to hold up the memory card retrieved from Kristenko's camera and turn to Viktor. 'You got something that can read this?'

'Sure.'

Viktor led them down a long dark corridor to her office. She switched on the computer and slipped into the chair behind the desk.

She slid the card into a slot on the side of the machine and called up the pictures of the painting. There were six in all: front and rear of the canvas, and one of each of the edges, normally hidden by the frame, but typically included in the photographic record of any major work of art because of the difficulty for the forger of replicating something that could not be seen. It was on these edges that a series of meticulously inked black capital letters could be seen. A code.

He pointed at the screen. 'This must have been what Renwick was after.'

Dominique grabbed a pen and began to scribble the letters on a pad.

'Letters are no use without the decoding machine,' Archie pointed out.

'A decoding machine?' Viktor frowned.

'The Enigma,' Tom explained. 'Renwick had one stolen, remember? It's a German wartime encoding machine, about the size—'

'Of a small briefcase,' Viktor finished his sentence for him. 'I know. I told you, Viktor had one restored so he could use it. It's in the library.'

She left the room and returned a few moments later with two wooden boxes, one much smaller than the other. She placed them both on the desk, unclipped the battered and stained case, and folded it back to reveal a machine that looked like an old-fashioned metal typewriter. Its raised black keys were large and round, with the letters of the alphabet in white. The flat case above the keys was punctured by twenty-six round glass windows with the faint shadow of a letter in each one. And above these were three narrow slots. The front of the box folded down to reveal twenty-six holes, each labelled with a letter of the alphabet, different pairs of which were joined by black cables.

'Have you ever used one of these?' Tom asked Dominique.

'No,' she said. 'But I've read some books on it. All Viktor needs to operate it are the settings. After that it's easy.'

'What settings?' Tom looked at her blankly.

'This machine uses substitution encryption,' said Viktor.

'When one letter is substituted for another?' Archie guessed. 'So A becomes F, B becomes G and so on.'

'Exactly. Enigma is just a very complex substitution system.'

'Complex in what way?' asked Tom.

'The key to breaking any code is spotting a pattern,' Dominique replied, taking over from Viktor. 'The beauty of the Enigma was that it changed the pattern after each letter.'

'Through these?' Tom asked, taking a metal disc with teeth and electrical circuits from the smaller wooden box.

'The rotors,' Dominique confirmed. 'Every time a letter was encoded, the rotors would change position and so would the pattern. And each original letter was mapped to a different starting letter through the wires on the plug board before it even went through the rotors, then the entire process was repeated in reverse before the encoded letter would light up.' She tapped one of the glass windows with her fingernail. 'They say there are one hundred and fifty-nine million million million possible combinations.'

'So, to decode a message, you'd need to know exactly how the original machine had been set up,' Tom surmised.

'Exactly,' Viktor stepped forward. 'They used to issue code books so that, on any particular day, everyone would know what setting to use. If we don't have the settings, we're going to have to involve some expert help.'

'Which will take time. Something we don't have,' Tom said.

'Well, Renwick must know, or he wouldn't have gone to all this bother, would he?' Archie observed. 'There must be some way to work it out.'

'You're right,' said Tom. 'Maybe we missed something. Let's have another look at those photos.' They turned to the screen once again.

'How many wires did you say there were?' Archie asked eventually.

'It varied,' Viktor replied. 'Between ten and thirteen. Why?'

'It's just that there are twenty-six letters along the top edge of the painting,' said Archie. 'And they look like they've been written in pairs.'

Viktor nodded. 'Thirteen pairs of letters. That could easily be the setting for the plug board—U to A. P to F . . .' She quickly reconfigured the wires to match the pairs of letters along the top of the frame. 'There.'

'Which leaves us with what?' Tom enquired, his voice animated.

'The choice of rotors and their settings,' Viktor replied. 'We need to know which three to select and what ring settings to give them.' She took the remaining four rotors out of their greaseproof paper and pointed at a small ring at the side of each rotor. 'These rotate and are then locked into a starting position. Without these, we've got nothing.'

THEY TOOK IT IN TURNS in front of the computer, each trying to make sense of the mass of letters that decorated the painting's edges. But after six hours of fruitless enquiry, the letters had begun to cobweb across their vision.

Archie had long since left the room, complaining of a headache, while Viktor had gone to arrange some food for them. For Dominique, however, solving this puzzle had developed into a personal battle. She stayed at the desk, her eyes glued to the screen. Tom was sitting behind her, eyes closed.

Dominique tried scrolling through the images on the disk from Tom's camera. First the shots of the synagogue in Prague and the painting's empty frame. Then shots of the stained-glass window from the church in Kitzbühel. A castle, a circle of trees, some birds taking wing through an azure sky. Finally the shots of the Bellak portrait.

She paused, frowning, then scrolled back to the pictures of the stained-glass window. She picked up the faded black-and-white photo of the same scene that Archie had found in Weissman's secret room. She looked up at the window, then down at the photo.

'Tom?' she said. 'I think I've found something. The painting and the window. The photos of each one. They're not the same. Look.'

As he sprang to her side, she pointed at the photo of the window on the screen. Then she placed the photo of the painting into his eager hands.

'Let me see.' Tom held the photo up to the screen. 'You're right!' he breathed excitedly. 'The window's different. He must have changed it.'

'It's quite subtle. Here the castle has two turrets, but in the window it has three. Here there are seven trees in the foreground, in the window five.'

'And look, four birds in the painting, two in the window. That means we've got two sets of three numbers.'

'But which ones should we use?'

'The ones in the window,' Tom said confidently. 'Don't forget, Bellak finished that painting years before the Gold Train set out on its journey. But Lammer installed the window after the war and it could easily have been designed to include the Enigma settings. The painting is only useful for its discrepancies with the window. Reading left to right there are three turrets, five trees and two birds in the window. That's three, five, two.'

'It could be the rotors!' Dominique exclaimed. 'There are only five of those. This could be telling us which rotors to use.'

'Which means that the rotor settings might be on here too,' Tom added.

They analysed the photos again, looking for further discrepancies that might provide some sort of clue. But, disappointingly, there were none.

'I don't get it.' Tom shook his head in frustration. 'They must have left some way to break the code, otherwise why go to all this trouble to hide it?'

'Maybe one of the other stolen Bellak paintings had the last piece of the code?' Dominique suggested.

'Maybe,' said Tom. 'Hang on, what's that?' He pointed at a small section of wall below the stained-glass window that Archie had caught on the edge of one photo. 'Can you enlarge it?'

She clicked a few buttons and zoomed in on the area Tom was pointing at. 'It's the dedication plaque. "In loving memory of Eva Maria Lammers",' she translated. '"Taken from us on 13th November 1926".'

'Nineteen twenty-six?' Tom frowned. 'That can't be right. I'm sure Archie told me that Lammers's wife died in the 1950s.'

'What if it's a deliberate mistake? The date could be the ring settings—thirteen, eleven, twenty-six.'

'Let's try it,' Tom agreed.

She selected rotors three, five and two from the tin and then set the first one to thirteen, the second to eleven and the third to twenty-six. Then she lifted the machine's lid, inserted them, and closed it again so that only the top part of the rotors poked through the narrow slit. At that moment Archie and Viktor walked in carrying food and drinks.

'We're just about to try something,' said Tom, and explained what they had discovered.

'Well done,' Viktor said, squeezing Dominique's shoulder. 'So now all we need is the starting position of the rotors.'

'What?' Dominique asked in dismay. 'I thought we had everything.'

'You see those little windows on the top of the machine?' Viktor indicated three small holes next to the rotors. 'The rotors have to be moved until you can see the relevant starting letter through the window.'

'How about EML?' Tom suggested.

'EML? Why those?' Archie asked with a frown.

'They were her initials.' Tom pointed at the plaque that was still on screen. 'Eva Maria Lammers. Or at least, that's the name he put on there. He could have made it up to suit the code.'

'Worth a go,' Dominique agreed, moving the rotors so that the letters could be seen through the openings. She pressed the first letter—A. Z flashed up on the light board. Then L. W appeared. Then X. O was illuminated.

'ZWOLF.' Archie's voice cracked with disappointment once they had deciphered the whole word. That's not a word.

'It's not a word in English,' Tom said. 'But it's German for twelve.'

Soon a second word emerged. *Funf*—five. Then *sieben*—seven.

'Twelve, five, seven,' Archie murmured, as if saying them again would help reveal the hidden meaning.

Dominique continued, Tom translating each number as it emerged. It ended with two familiar words.

Archie read Tom's scribbled translation back out loud. 'Twelve, five, seven, three, six, nine, Heil Hitler.' He paused. 'What does it mean?'

'Aren't map references given with six numbers?' Dominique asked.

'It would be the logical way to pinpoint a location,' Tom agreed.

'And we already have a map,' Archie reminded them, pulling the railway map out of the leather pouch and unfolding it on the floor.

Tom followed the grid reference with his finger until it came to rest at a point on the outskirts of a small Austrian village. The final place the Gold Train had passed through before turning back. A village called Brixlegg.

11

Near Brixlegg, Austria: January 12, 3.32 p.m.

Tom knew this part of Austria well, although his previous visits to the Tyrol had been in the spring, and the snow and ice that now blanketed the pastures and weighed down the tree branches made it almost unrecognisable.

The spot indicated by the coded grid reference lay a short distance off a distinctive kink in the railway line that snaked along the valley floor, roughly following the path of the River Inn. It was reached by turning into a narrow road before the village of Brixlegg itself.

The track ended in a gate, the top of which was hidden under a thick layer of snow. Tom stopped the car and killed the engine. In the rearview mirror he saw Viktor do the same behind him and turn off her headlights.

For a few seconds they sat there in muffled silence.

'Are you worried about her?' Dominique asked.

'Should I be?' said Tom.

'The other night I saw her giving instructions to those three men. It looked like they were planning something. Maybe it was a mistake bringing her along.'

'It's not like we had much choice, is it?' Archie reminded them. 'How else were we going to get out here without being seen?'

Tom nodded. Archie was right. Viktor's offer to smuggle them onto her private jet to Salzburg and to provide two cars at the other end had been their only option. The price had been bringing her and her three men with them to, as she put it, protect her investment.

'I think I trust her,' said Tom. 'But we should keep our eyes open. Maybe try to split them up.'

'Well, we're going to struggle to find anything under that lot anyway.' Archie nodded at the snow-covered mountains that towered above them.

'That's if Renwick hasn't already beaten us to it,' said Tom.

He stepped out of the car and walked towards Viktor, who was at the back of her car, leaning over the open boot with her three men—Grigory, Piotr and Yuri—clustered around her.

'Viktor?' Tom called.

She turned, a snub-nosed Beretta pointing straight at him. Tom froze.

'Here!' She threw it towards him. Tom snatched it out of the air.

'You might need that,' she explained.

'I don't like guns. Never have.'

'I don't like them either,' she said. 'But I'd prefer to have one and not need to use it than not have one and need it.'

'*Argento!*' An unfamiliar voice echoed through the air.

Tom stuffed the Beretta into his pocket before turning to see who was there. An old man, a dog leash looped in one hand, had appeared at the doorway of one of the chalets and was calling to a large German Shepherd.

'*Argento!*' the man called again, before shutting the door behind him and trying to grab the dog's collar as it pranced around his feet.

The dog, however, caught sight of Tom and the others and broke free, sprinting out onto the track. Tom knelt, grasped the dog's leather collar as he came up to him, and held on as the dog licked his face furiously.

'*Danke*,' the old man said as he walked towards Tom. He clipped the leash to the collar. 'Argento gets very excited when we go for a walk.'

'You're welcome,' replied Tom in German. 'He seems quite a handful.'

'Oh, he is. Keeps me young.' The man looked down and patted the dog's head lovingly, then peered at Tom quizzically. 'Are you with the men who came a couple of days ago? They said some others might come . . .'

'Oh, right, yes.' Tom nodded. 'We're with them. I wonder, can you show us where they've gone? My phone doesn't seem to work out here and I can't get in touch.' He took the map from his pocket and opened it for the man.

The old man pointed to a spot on the map. 'That's it.'

Tom frowned. It wasn't the spot indicated by the coordinates decoded from the painting. 'What's there?'

'The old copper mine, of course. I told your colleague that he was wasting his time, but he had the right paperwork so I had to let him through.'

'Paperwork?'

'To open the mine up. Diggers too. Big yellow things. He's been at it non-stop. In this weather—can you believe it? But there's nothing there.'

'How can you be so sure?'

'Because I used to play in it,' the man said simply. 'Of course that was a long time ago now, before the war, but it had long since dried up, even then.'

'And it got blocked up?'

'There was an explosion one night towards the end of the war. A stray bomb or something. The whole thing just collapsed.'

'So what's here?' Tom pointed at the spot indicated by the painting.

The man squinted closely at the map. 'It must be the other entrance.'

'There are two entrances?'

'Oh yes. You see, there used to be two mines until they were joined up. That one was the smaller of the two. It's right next to a ruined cottage. But that entrance has been filled in too.'

'OK, thanks.' Tom shook his hand. 'By the way,' he asked as he turned away, 'when did the others get here exactly?'

'Hmmm. Let me see. About three days ago.'

'OK.' Tom smiled gratefully. 'Thanks for your help. Enjoy your walk.'

'We will. Come on, Argento.' The man clicked his tongue and they both set off, the leash snapping taut as the dog strained to run ahead.

Tom turned to face the expectant eyes of Archie, Dominique and Viktor and translated what the old man had said.

'Three days ago?' Dominique frowned. 'That's not possible. Renwick only got hold of the painting two days ago. He couldn't have known about this place until then.'

'Exactly,' said Tom. 'Put that together with the hit men in St Petersburg that we know Renwick didn't send, and the murder of Maria Lammers, and it tells us that Renwick isn't the only one who's been trying to stop us finding this. Whoever these people are, they didn't need the painting to find it.'

'Who?' asked Viktor.

'If I had to guess,' said Tom, 'the people who hid it here in the first place.'

THE ROUTE UP to the mine was easily identifiable even in the fading light, a narrow path that hugged the side of the mountain on a shallow rise. It was hard going, the snow icy in some places where it had melted and refrozen. Eventually it began to level out and they heard voices, then the sound of a powerful engine.

'Quick!' Tom shepherded them off the path and they half fell, half slid into the trees that lined the steep incline beneath it.

'According to the old man, that's the main entrance up ahead,' Tom whispered. 'From the sound of it, that's where they're trying to get in.'

'How are we going to get past them?' Viktor asked.

'You're not,' Tom said, sensing that his chance to split Viktor and her men had come. 'Archie and I will go round to the other entrance to see what we can find there. You and Dom stay out of sight but keep your eyes on these guys.'

'*Niet.*' Viktor flashed him an indignant look. 'If you're going, so am I.'

'Someone needs to watch our backs,' Tom insisted. 'I'd rather it was you two, who I know I can trust.'

Viktor and Dominique exchanged a glance. 'OK,' Dominique conceded.

'Fine,' Viktor gave a grudging shrug. 'But you'll take Grigory and the others with you. That's the deal.'

Squatting on their haunches, their eyes alert, AKs at the ready, Viktor's men exuded a menacing but reassuring presence.

'Done,' said Tom, grateful, in a way, to have them along. 'We stay in contact.' He patted the radio in his pocket. 'And take this.' He handed her a card. 'It's the number for the FBI agent who helped us in St Petersburg. If anything happens, call him.'

After a final weapons check, Tom and Archie, with Viktor's three men, headed off, the sharp wind slithering through the trees alongside them.

About half a mile on, Archie pointed ahead to where the ruins of a cottage lay in a small clearing. Next to the remains, and disappearing into the side of the mountain, was an opening just large enough to stand up in. Judging from the large pile of earth and rubble below it, staining the snow like a pool of black ink, the opening had only recently been excavated.

'Someone's already here,' Archie whispered, scanning the trees.

Tom edged warily across the clearing and knelt to examine the footprints leading to the entrance. 'I'd say there's six or seven of them. No more.'

'We should radio the others,' said Archie. 'Tell them what we've found.'

'I suppose so.' Tom didn't sound convinced.

'Or, we could have a quick look inside. See if he's still down there. If it is Renwick down there, I'd rather we had the bastard to ourselves.'

'WHERE ARE YOU going?' Dominique asked Viktor. 'Tom said to wait here.'

'Do you always do what Tom tells you?' asked Viktor with a smile.

'It depends.'

'You don't trust me, do you?' Viktor reached into the holster strapped under her arm. 'Know how to use one of these?' She held out a .38.

'Yeah.' A boyfriend had taught her how to handle a gun.

'It's loaded,' Viktor said. 'Maybe that'll help you trust me a bit more.'

Dominique snapped the gun open, checked the chambers, then flipped it shut again. 'It takes more than a loaded gun to make me trust someone.'

'Not in Russia,' Viktor smiled. 'Now, if we stay out of sight and follow the side of the path, we might find a place where we can look over the edge.'

'OK.' Dominique slipped the gun into her jacket. 'Let's go.'

They set off, the sounds of machinery growing ever louder, accompanied now by the roar of at least one engine, maybe two, and the occasional shout or burst of laughter from the crew excavating the mine entrance. They continued round the side of the mountain until, the noise fading slightly, they felt that they had moved a safe distance beyond the main centre of activity.

'I'll go first,' Viktor volunteered. Digging the points of her boots into the snow and using the trees to pull herself up, she scrambled her way to a position from which she was able to get her head just above the edge of the path.

'What can you see?' Dominique called in a low voice.

Viktor reached for her binoculars. 'I count . . . twenty people. About half are armed. The others must be operating machinery.'

'I'm coming up,' Dominique replied. She pulled herself into position at Viktor's side and held out her hand. Viktor passed her the binoculars.

A large digger and a bulldozer had exposed a wide tunnel, the mound of spoil having been dumped on either side of the entrance. Two generators powered lights that washed the whole scene in a yellowish sodium hue.

Suddenly a shout went up. A machine operator raced towards the entrance and then signalled to the armed men. Viktor and Dominique had no difficulty in interpreting the signal.

'Get on the radio to Tom,' Viktor whispered. 'We must let him know they're nearly through.'

'OK,' said Dominique, reaching into her pocket. She depressed the call button and whispered softly, 'Tom, are you there? Come in, Tom.'

There was nothing but the muffled hiss of static.

'Come in, Tom,' she called again.

Still nothing. 'He's not answering,' she said.

'They must be out of range.'

'Not likely,' Dominique said bitterly. 'These things go for miles and we're still all on the same side of the mountain. No, if I know Tom and Archie, they've probably found a way inside and used it.'

'In that case, we've got to get down there and warn them.'

'Agreed,' said Dominique. 'Hold up. Who's that?'

'Which one?'

'The man on the left. Fur hat. Next to the light. Seems to be in charge.'

Viktor took the binoculars from her. 'I don't recognise him.'

'What's he doing?' Dominique squinted.

'I'm not sure,' said Viktor. The man had removed his coat and was now unfolding a white boiler suit that he had taken from a bag at his feet. 'It looks like he's getting changed.'

The man pulled the boiler suit on over his clothes, boots included, then fixed a mask and respirator over his face.

'They're all putting them on. Look!'

'It looks like some sort of NBC suit.'

'NBC?' Viktor frowned.

'Nuclear, Biological, Chemical—standard military issue to avoid contamination in the field.'

'Contamination!' Viktor locked eyes with Dominique. 'Contamination from what? I thought we were here for the Amber Room.'

FROM THE SYMMETRICAL tool-marks that inscribed the walls, the mine looked as though it had been dug out the old-fashioned way, with picks and shovels. Large wooden frames had been positioned every fifteen feet or so to buttress the roof, age having greyed and buckled them.

Tom and Archie lead the way into the mine, Piotr and Grigory bringing up the rear; Yuri had been posted at the tunnel entrance as a precaution. Their torches sliced the air jaggedly as they walked. Their breathing, even the rustle of their clothes, was amplified and bounced back at them off the tunnel walls. Then, unexpectedly, a strip of light appeared in front of them.

'That must be it,' Tom whispered excitedly, flicking his torch off.

They edged silently towards the light until they could see that the tunnel emerged into a large, naturally formed chamber. The space had been lit with four battery-powered spotlights. A massive Nazi flag hung from the roof. A Nazi flag with one crucial difference: the swastika had been replaced with the now familiar symbol of the Black Sun.

'Christ,' Archie breathed as his eyes settled on the two objects positioned directly beneath the flag. 'They're here. They're still bloody here.'

Tom shook his head, hardly believing what he was seeing. It was an incredible sight. Two missing freight carriages from a mysterious train, hauled up an Austrian mountain and hidden deep inside it.

'They don't look like they've been opened yet,' whispered Tom, pointing at the thick iron bars rammed through the hasp of each carriage door.

'Renwick must be down here somewhere,' Archie warned. 'Let's deal with him first.'

They made their way round the two carriages, pausing on the other side, where another, much bigger tunnel disappeared into the darkness.

'That must lead to the main entrance,' Tom said. 'We should check it out. See how long we've got before they break through.'

They set off down the tunnel, treading warily. As the glow of the chamber receded behind them, the noise of the digging at the main entrance grew. When they reached the sheer wall of stone and earth at the end of the tunnel, they could feel the earth shaking beneath their feet.

'They'll be through any time now,' Tom called over the noise.

'Maybe that's what scared Renwick off,' said Archie.

'Possibly,' Tom said sceptically. 'Doesn't seem like him, though—to come so close and then give up. Maybe he's gone to get reinforcements.'

'Well, he's not here now. And I don't know about you, but I'd like to take a look inside those carriages.'

Tom smiled. 'We both would. But we don't want to get caught in here when they break through.'

'Why don't we leave Piotr at this end? As soon as they look like coming in, he can run back and tell us. We can send Grigory up the other end to keep Yuri company and make sure Renwick doesn't sneak in behind us.'

'That should work,' Tom agreed. 'But we'd better be quick.'

After some rapid instructions, mainly communicated through hand signals, Piotr and Grigory left to take up their sentry positions. As soon as both men were out of sight, Tom and Archie turned to the two carriages.

They were of standard construction, wooden panels slatted horizontally into a square frame, with angled crosspieces at regular intervals. Both carriages were remarkably intact, although the left-hand one seemed to be on the losing end of a long fight against rot and woodworm.

They both stepped forward to the door of the first carriage, a large panel almost a third of the length of the car that slid back on metal runners. But just as he was about to pull back on the door, Tom noticed that the holes in the woodwork were too symmetrical to be the product of any natural process. They were bullet holes.

With a sudden chill in the pit of his stomach, Tom grasped the top of the iron bar that had been jammed into the hasp. He tugged it from side to side, until it slid free. He threw the bar to the ground with a clang, then folded the hasp back, the hinge stiff and cold. With Tom pulling and Archie pushing on the iron handle, the door finally scraped back a couple of feet.

Archie clasped his hands together to form a cradle, and Tom stepped onto it and pulled himself through the gap. He switched his torch on, running it over the ceiling and the walls. Nothing. He stood up and took a couple of steps, then stepped on something hard that snapped under his feet. He flicked the torch down to the ground to see what he had trodden on. Recoiling, he saw that it was a bone. A human leg bone.

'Archie, you'd better get up here,' Tom called out.

'Why, what's up?' Archie jumped up to the open door, his legs dangling free and his shoulders only just inside the car.

Tom hauled him inside. 'Look!'

He let his torch play across the floor. There were about thirty bodies, he estimated, all lying across each other, awkward and sunken. Only their skeletons were left, the bones, where they emerged from frayed sleeves and trouser legs or peered out from under rotting caps, glowing white.

'Who were they?' Archie breathed. 'POWs? Civilians?'

'I don't think so . . .' Tom stepped forward, picking his way carefully through the twisted remains and picked up a cap that had rolled free. He pointed at its badge, a swastika, each of its arms ending in an arrow point.

'The Arrow Cross—it was worn by Nazi troops from Hungary.'

'Which is where Lasche said the Gold Train originally set out from.'

'Yeah,' said Tom. 'He said it was guarded by Hungarian troops.'

'How do you suppose this played out?' Archie asked.

Tom shrugged. 'When the bridge at Brixlegg was bombed, the train must have turned back and been hidden in a tunnel—that's where the Americans found it. Clearly, somewhere between Brixlegg and the tunnel, a decision was taken to uncouple these carriages and haul them up here with the help of some of the Hungarian guards. Once they'd got it in here, the guards were disarmed, locked inside the carriage and executed. Finally the tracks leading up here were lifted and the mine roof collapsed to ensure that the secret was safe.'

A quick search of the carriage revealed nothing apart from the bodies.

'So whatever they were protecting must be in the other carriage?'

'There's only one way to find out,' Tom said with a tight smile.

But as they turned, the carriage door rolled shut and they heard the unmistakable rasp of the metal pin being slid back into the hasp.

'WHAT DO YOU THINK we should do?' Dominique threw a questioning glance at Viktor, who, grim-faced, was studying the armed men as they checked each other to make sure the suits were correctly fitted.

'Get down there and tell them.'

'We'll never make it in time,' Dominique pointed out.

Viktor was silent as she tried to think of a way of warning Tom. Her thoughts were interrupted by a sharp tug on her arm.

'Someone's coming,' Dominique hissed.

One of the machine operators had detached himself from the crew and was hurrying in their direction. Viktor ducked down, but the steady crunch of the snow indicated that the man was heading straight for them.

Pressing herself into the slope, her right leg wedged in the cleft of a low branch, Viktor swung her AK-47 out from behind her and gently cocked it.

The footsteps stopped just above her head. Barely daring to breathe, she looked up. Standing on the edge of the path, the man loomed above them. Looking back nervously over his shoulder, the man reached down.

A pale gold stream of urine sliced through the darkness and arced gracefully over their heads, melting a jagged yellow zigzag in the snow below.

Viktor grinned up at Dominique and saw her stifle a laugh. But then a thought occurred to her. A way of getting word to Tom and Archie.

Tom PRESSED his face against the carriage wall and peered through one of the bullet holes. 'Renwick,' he breathed when he saw the figure standing in the middle of the chamber, a triumphant smile carved across his face. Next to him was Johann Hecht. Five other thuggish-looking men were making their way across the chamber to join them.

'How did they get past Viktor's men?' Archie choked, peering through another bullet hole. 'I thought they were guarding the entrance.'

'They were,' Tom said in a grim voice.

'As soon as I heard that you were coming through the forest, I knew that you would not be able to resist going into the mine, Thomas,' Renwick bellowed. 'It was very kind of you to climb inside one of the carriages, though. It certainly made the job of rounding you up a lot easier.'

'Save it, Harry,' Tom shouted. 'The gloating doesn't suit you.'

'Surely you would not deny me my small moment of triumph?' Renwick went on. 'In any case, I have to applaud you, Thomas, for finding this place so quickly. Johann, however, is rather irked by your persistence.'

Standing next to him, Hecht fingered the trigger of his Heckler & Koch.

'Getting out of the museum was one thing,' Renwick continued. 'But decoding a painting you did not even have? That was impressive. Especially when I had gone to the trouble of making sure that there was no chance of Turnbull giving anything away.'

'When did you get here?' Tom asked, trying to buy time as he tested the strength of the walls and tried to detect any loose floorboards, in the hope of identifying an escape route.

'Late last night. It has taken us quite some time to dig out the entrance. As a matter of fact, we had been inside only a few minutes when you appeared. By the way, Thomas, if you are thinking of trying to get out of there, you are wasting your time,' Renwick boomed. 'Those carriages are quite secure. The Nazis had them reinforced to the highest specifications in order to ensure the security of their most precious cargo.'

'Like a platoon of murdered Hungarian soldiers?' Tom called back.

'Like whatever is in the second carriage. We were about to open it when we got word you were on your way. Now you can have ringside seats for the grand unveiling—the first glimpse of the Amber Room in over fifty years!'

Two men armed with bolt cutters advanced towards the rusting padlock that secured one of the carriage doors. A few moments later, there was the sound of a door being rolled back.

'I can't see anything,' Archie whispered. 'Can you?'

Tom shook his head. 'Careful, you idiots,' He heard Renwick shout.

Soon, five or six crates had been carried out to the centre of the room.

'How do you expect to get them out of here?' Tom called. 'You know who's digging out the main entrance, don't you? They can't be far off now.'

'No more than a few feet, I would say. Would you not agree, Johann?' Renwick turned towards Hecht, who gave a curt nod. 'As to who they are, I can only assume that it is some last remnant of the Order. Who else could have located this site without the aid of the code on the portrait?'

'They've been protecting this place for fifty years,' yelled Tom. 'You think they're just going to let you walk away?'

'I doubt they will have much choice.' Renwick smiled. 'You see, among his many talents, Johann is an explosives expert. He has mined both tunnels. One of his men has replaced the unfortunate chap you left near the entrance, and he will alert us the instant they break through. As soon as they do, we will allow them into the tunnel a little way and then set off the charges.'

'You'll kill them all,' Tom exclaimed.

'That is the general idea, yes.'

A sudden roar echoed up the larger tunnel, then the sound of an engine changing gear. Renwick flicked his head towards the noise.

'They're inside,' Hecht shouted. 'They're inside.'

'How can they be?' Renwick seemed shaken. 'We received no word.' He grabbed his radio. 'This is Renwick, come in,' he barked. 'Are you there? Come in, damn you!' He spun to face Hecht, his eyes wide, agitation turning to alarm. 'Your sentry must be dead. Set off the charges.'

Hecht gave a nod and picked up a black box, about the size of a cigarette packet, with four red buttons set into it. He extended its aerial, then turned to face the tunnel. The noise was getting louder.

'Do it, Johann,' Renwick urged, a hint of desperation in his voice. 'Now.'

Hecht depressed the top button. Nothing happened.

'Do it now,' Renwick spluttered, 'or it will be too late.'

'I'm sorry, Cassius,' Hecht said, exchanging the detonator for a gun, which he levelled squarely at Renwick's chest. 'For you, it already is too late.'

At that moment, the bulldozer juddered to a halt at the entrance to the chamber, its headlights forcing everyone to shield their eyes from the glare. Abruptly, the engine was killed, then the lights.

Ten heavily armed men emerged from behind the bulldozer. To Tom's surprise, they were all wearing white chemical-warfare suits and masks. They looked strangely robotic as they fanned out through the chamber.

Two of them approached Renwick and frisked him. Hecht, meanwhile, jerked his head in the direction of the carriage that Tom and Archie were in. Immediately, two of the men ran to the door and opened it, indicating with a wave of their guns that Tom and Archie should jump down. Once outside, they were frisked at gunpoint, then shoved towards Renwick.

One of the men in white made his way to the middle of the chamber and placed a briefcase flat on the ground. Flicking the catches open, he removed what looked like a large microphone and held it in the air above his head while consulting the screen of a small computer inside the case.

Moments later, he called out in German and, with a relieved sigh, the men pulled off their hoods and discarded their respirators.

One man, however, remained hooded, his face still concealed by a mask. Unarmed, he walked slowly up to Hecht. Suddenly, the two men threw their arms round each other and embraced warmly. Tom could just about make out the hooded man's muffled words and Hecht's reply.

The two men broke off and saluted each other smartly.

'What the hell is going on?' Archie exploded. 'Who are you people?'

The masked man turned to them and pulled back his hood before sliding his mask off his face.

Tom spoke first, his voice strangled and disbelieving. 'Völz?'

'Who?' Renwick spoke for the first time.

'He runs the private bank in Zürich where Weissman and Lammers had hidden the map,' Tom explained.

Völz ignored Tom, however, and approached Renwick. 'It's a pleasure to finally meet you, Herr Renwick—or do you prefer Cassius? Colonel Hecht here has spoken very highly of your efforts over the past few months.'

'Is this some sort of joke?' Renwick hissed through clenched teeth.

'No joke, Cassius,' said Völz.

'Then what is the meaning of this?'

'You don't recognise my voice?' Völz breathed.

There was a pause, then Renwick's eyes narrowed. 'Dmitri?'

'As I said, it's a pleasure to meet you finally.'

'What is this circus?' Renwick snapped. 'We agreed, no tricks.'

'We agreed lots of things,' said Völz. 'But that was when you thought you had something to bargain with. The situation has changed somewhat.'

'Why are you dressed up in that gear?' Tom interrupted their exchange. 'What exactly were you expecting to find down here?'

'At last, an intelligent question,' Völz said with a clap. 'And one that you can help me answer. Would you be so kind as to open that crate?' He pointed at one of the crates that Hecht's men had unloaded earlier.

'What?' Tom's voice was uncertain.

'You heard me. Open the crate,' Völz insisted, grabbing a crowbar from one of his men and tossing it to Tom. 'Open it now.'

Tom approached the crate indicated by Völz. Like the others, it had some sort of identification code and a swastika stamped on one side. He slipped the crowbar under the lid and levered it up. It rose a few inches, the nails shrieking as they were pulled free. Tom repeated the procedure on the other side, and the lid came off and flopped to the floor.

The crate was packed with straw, which Tom removed in big handfuls until he was finally able to make out a dark shape. He reached in. It felt soft and silky. He pulled it out.

'A fur coat?' Archie said disbelievingly as Tom held it up. 'Is that it?' He leapt to Tom's side and leaned into the crate, pulling out first one coat, then another, and another, flinging them over his shoulder. 'This can't be right.'

Renwick was staring at the pile disbelievingly, his eyes bulging.

'Open another,' Völz said gleefully. 'Any one. It makes no difference.'

Archie grabbed the crowbar from Tom and opened another crate. 'Alarm clocks,' he said. He opened another. 'Silk underwear.' He held up a bra and camisole before throwing them at Völz. They fell well short.

'OK, Völz, you made your point,' Tom said slowly.

'Surely Lasche told you that these were some of the items loaded onto the train,' Völz asked with a shrug. 'I don't see why you're so surprised.'

'Don't play dumb. Where is it?'

'Where is what?' Völz spoke in mock confusion.

'You know damn well what,' Renwick snapped. 'The Amber Room. Why else do you think we are all here?'

Völz laughed. 'Ah, yes, the Amber Room. The myth that refuses to die.'

'Myth?' Renwick fired back.

'No need to feel foolish. Thousands have fallen for the same deluded fantasy. And I'm certain thousands more will follow.'

'You're saying it doesn't exist?' Tom asked.

'I'm saying it was destroyed in the war.'

'Rubbish,' said Renwick. 'It was moved to Königsberg Castle. Everyone knows that. Then it vanished. It was hidden.'

'It didn't vanish and no one hid it. If you must know, it was burnt. Burnt by the very Russian troops who'd been sent to recover it. They overran

Königsberg Castle in April 1945 and, in their haste, set fire to the Knights' Hall. They didn't know that the Amber Room was being stored there. By the time they realised what they had done, it was too late.'

'If that were true, it would have come out before now,' Renwick said.

'You think the Soviets would admit that their own troops destroyed one of Russia's most precious treasures? I don't think so. Far easier for them to accuse the Nazis of having hidden it. You may not believe me, but I've seen the Kremlin documents in the Central State Archive that confirm it.'

Tom could see that Völz was telling the truth. 'Then what are you here for?' he asked slowly.

'For that.' Völz pointed at the second carriage, beyond the door that Renwick's men had opened. 'Show them, Colonel.'

Hecht grabbed the crowbar from Archie and approached the side of the carriage. He forced the end in between two of the wide wooden planks and levered it sideways. The wood splintered noisily. Then Hecht snapped off more planks, creating a large jagged hole. But instead of being able to see into the carriage, as Tom had expected, they were confronted by an expanse of dull grey metal. Something had been built into the carriage's walls.

'Is that lead?' Tom asked.

'It is,' said Völz. 'A protective layer, to reduce the contamination risk.'

'Contamination from what?' said Tom, already guessing the answer.

'U235,' replied Völz. 'Four tons of it.'

'U-what?' Archie, looking confused, turned to Tom.

'U235,' Tom explained, his voice disbelieving. 'An isotope of uranium. It's the basic component of a nuclear bomb.'

'A nuclear bomb?' cried Renwick. 'You intend to build a nuclear bomb?' Tom couldn't tell whether he was appalled or impressed.

'U235 has a half-life of seven hundred million years. Even a minute amount, attached to a conventional explosive and detonated in an urban area, will create widespread radioactive fallout, triggering mass panic and economic collapse. Can you imagine the price this material would fetch? For years we have been building our organisation in the shadows. Now we have the means to win our war. Now we are ready to reveal ourselves.'

'But where has this come from?' Tom asked. 'How did it get here?'

'Do you know what those markings denote?' Völz pointed at the series of flaking letters and numbers on the side of the second carriage.

'Some sort of serial number?'

'Exactly. It identifies the contents as having come from Berlin. From the

Kaiser Wilhelm Institute for Physics in Dahlem, to be precise. The head-quarters of the Nazis' effort to produce a nuclear bomb.'

'So how far did they get?' Tom asked.

'Far enough to accumulate a considerable amount of fissile material. When the Red Army reached Berlin in April 1945, they discovered three tons of uranium oxide, two hundred and fifty kilograms of metallic uranium and twenty litres of heavy water. Enough to allow Stalin to start working on Russia's first atomic bomb.'

'So you're saying that they didn't find all the uranium?'

'Himmler had already moved several tons by placing it in lead boxes built into the walls of a specially modified carriage. The Order personally supervised the shipment, meeting up with the Gold Train in Budapest in December 1944 and attaching their carriage to it. But they soon realised that they wouldn't make it to Switzerland. So they unhitched their carriage and another one and brought them up here, to be recovered at a later date.'

'And now the Order of the Death's Head lives on, is that it?' Tom asked.

'The Order has nothing to do with me or my men,' Völz retorted. 'We wouldn't have stood by playing at knights while Germany was bleeding.'

'Then how do you know all this? How did you find this place?'

Völz hesitated, then reached inside his coat and produced a large black wallet. He withdrew a tattered black and white photograph, which he handed to Tom. The same photograph they had found in Weissman's house.

'Weissman and Lammers,' Tom said, looking up.

Renwick held his hand out for the photo and studied it closely.

'And the third man?' Völz asked. 'Do you recognise him?'

Tom glanced at the photo again, then gave Völz a long, searching look. There was a definite resemblance in the high forehead, straight, almost sculpted nose and small round eyes.

'Your father?' Tom ventured.

'Uncle. The other two men were called Becker and Allbrecht. Weissman and Lammers were names they hid behind after the war.'

'So you learned all this from him?' Archie asked.

'Some I know from him; some you have helped me discover. My uncle and his two comrades were plucked from the ranks because of their scientific knowledge and initiated into the Order as retainers.'

Tom nodded, remembering that Weissman was a chemist and Lammers a physics professor. 'Three retainers for twelve knights,' he said slowly. 'In the same way that the Black Sun has three circles and twelve runes.'

'Exactly!' Völz smiled. 'Just as there were three medals and three paint-ings. My uncle accompanied the Order on the Gold Train's ill-fated escape across Europe while Lammers and Weissman prepared the crypt at Wewelsburg Castle. Then, as ordered, all three of them made their way back to Berlin, hiding what they knew even from each other. Just before the end, all three were entrusted with one final instruction.'

'Which was?' Renwick asked, a blood vessel pulsing in his neck.

'To protect an encrypted message. A message that could only be deci-phered with an Enigma machine configured with the right settings. A message that they hastily scrawled on a painting in a place that couldn't be seen once the frame was on. A painting that they found hanging in Himmler's office because he couldn't bring himself to destroy it.'

'A painting that they then lost to the Soviets,' Tom guessed.

'The Russians made it to Berlin far faster than anyone expected. Lammers and Weissman risked everything by returning to the SS building to recover the painting, but soon realised that the Trophy Squad had beaten them to it. The only two Bellaks they could find were the ones of Wewelsburg Castle and the Pinkas Synagogue in Prague.'

'So, Lammers and Weissman knew where the painting was headed, and they had the settings for the Enigma machine to decode the message, but they didn't know the actual location of the Gold Train,' said Tom.

'Only my uncle knew that,' Völz confirmed. 'Realising this, they drew together a series of clues using the two Bellaks they had managed to save, the specially engraved medals and the map of the railway system so that others might follow—those of pure Aryan blood, true believers, who could use the riches of the Gold Train to found a new Reich.'

'But if you knew all this,' asked Archie, 'why have you waited until now to come here and find the train?'

'Because *I* didn't know where the train was either.'

'You said your uncle had helped put it here. Surely he told you?'

Völz gave an exasperated laugh. 'Unlike his two comrades, my uncle ended the war disgusted at what he had seen and what he had done. He realised how potent a weapon had been stored in this mountain and was determined that no one should ever exploit it. So he set up his own council of twelve. Unlike the Order, their mission was to protect life, not destroy it. They did this by guarding the location of the site, whatever the cost. When he died five years ago, I was asked to take his seat on the council.'

'Didn't they tell you the train's location?'

'My uncle had decreed that only one man—the leader of the council—should be entrusted with the location of the Gold Train. Only if the train was in imminent danger of being uncovered was the secret to be disclosed.'

'You used me to make them think their precious secret was in danger,' Renwick said through gritted teeth.

'Johann and I had been fuelling rumours about the Gold Train for years in the hope that it might help bring the portrait to light. When we discovered that you had taken the bait, I suggested that we flush you out by putting a price on your head through adverts in the *Herald Tribune*.'

'So the raid in Munich was not real?'

'Those were my men in the lobby. You were never in any danger. We wanted to make you think you were getting close, and to show the council that their methods were failing. That they needed a change of leader.'

'Is that why you involved me?' Tom asked. 'To make them sweat?'

'I didn't involve you,' Völz said. 'Turnbull was working for Cassius.'

Tom shot Renwick a look, but Renwick's eyes were locked on Völz.

'The irony was that the key to all this had been lying in my vault all the time,' Völz continued. 'Until you showed up, I had no idea who that safe-deposit box belonged to. Had I known, all this might have been avoided.'

'But you knew that Weissman and Lammers had left a map.'

'The council tracked Lammers down a few years ago and made him talk. Unfortunately, his heart gave out before he could disclose the location of the crypt or the final painting. But he did reveal the settings for the Enigma machine, and the fact that Weissman was living in the UK.'

'Why did you excavate the main entrance when you could have come in the back like us in half the time?' asked Archie.

'Apart from the fact that I need to get trucks down here if I am to move everything out? Simple. Three days ago, when we first got here, I didn't know about the smaller entrance. My uncle had only passed on the location of the larger entrance, through which he'd helped bring the carriages. It was the painting that divulged the existence of the smaller entrance. Perhaps the Order felt that route would be easier to access—who knows? When Johann told me how you'd got here and what you'd found, I decided to leave you to it. It was a way of keeping you busy and out of our way.'

'The council will never let you get away with this,' said Tom. 'When they find out what you're up to, they'll do everything in their power to stop you.'

'Which council? This one?' Völz reached into his pocket and pulled out a handful of gold rings that he threw disdainfully to the floor. Identical rings with a single diamond set into an engraved twelve-box grid. 'It's a shame, really. I would have liked to have seen their faces when they realised that, indirectly, they had provided us with the means to shatter everything they have fought to protect all these years.'

HECHT MARCHED them up the smaller tunnel at gunpoint, roughly cuffed them with plastic tags, then pushed them to the ground.

'I will not forget your betrayal, Hecht,' Renwick said through gritted teeth. 'I will make you pay.'

'I doubt it, Cassius,' Hecht sneered. 'The next time I press this button, the explosives *will* work.' He held up the remote detonator and waved it tauntingly in front of Renwick's face.

As Hecht tramped off down the tunnel, leaving two men standing guard, sounds of hammering, drilling and sawing came from the chamber. Tom guessed that Völz's men were even now dismantling the carriage and preparing to transport its lethal cargo to wherever they wanted. Once unleashed, Völz would be unstoppable.

Archie seemed to be reading his thoughts. 'Can he really make an atomic bomb out of that lot?'

'I doubt it,' said Tom. 'At least not without buying a lot of extra equipment and expertise. But he doesn't have to. He could make enough money auctioning the uranium off to finance a small army.'

'So much for the Amber Room,' Archie noted gloomily.

'I can't believe that, for all these years, everyone's been looking for something that didn't even exist.'

'Your father thought it existed,' Renwick said.

'Don't even mention his name,' Tom snapped.

'Do not forget it was to me he turned, not you, when he heard rumours linking the Amber Room to a Nazi Gold Train and Bellak paintings.' Renwick gave a faint smile. 'I thought nothing more of it until a few years ago when I came across an original Bellak in an auction in Vienna. I knew then that if one had survived Himmler's cull perhaps others had too, including the portrait—and with them the chance of finding this place. Unfortunately, your father believed that the painting had ended up in a private collection, which is where I focused my search. I enlisted your help because I thought a fresh pair of eyes might be of use. I was right.'

'Yeah, well, it didn't do you much good, did it?' Archie pointed out tartly. 'In case you hadn't noticed, you're about to get buried under a mountain.'

'There's one thing I want to know.' Tom locked eyes with Renwick. 'Back in St Petersburg, you said that my father had known all along who you were. That he had worked with you. Was that another one of your lies?'

Renwick returned Tom's stare, but just as he seemed about to speak, Hecht returned. At the sight of him, the two guards stood up straight.

'One of you go and tell Dmitri that the charges are armed,' Hecht ordered.

The guard nodded and trotted off obediently towards the chamber, passing a man in a hard hat and reflective jacket who was heading towards them.

'What are you doing up here?' Hecht growled as the man approached. 'You're all meant to be in the chamber helping to unload that train.'

The man shrugged and then, noticing that one of his laces was undone, stooped to tie it. As he did so, he raised his eyes towards Tom's and winked.

It was Viktor. Tom glanced at Archie, who nodded. He had seen her too.

'I asked you a question,' Hecht challenged the still crouching Viktor.

'You bastard,' Tom shouted, rolling onto Archie and kneeing him in the stomach. 'This is your fault. Your greed's going to get us both killed.'

Archie kicked out as he tried to roll out from under him.

'If it's anyone's fault, it's yours,' he shouted back. 'I told you to drop it.'

Hecht stepped forward and placed a firm hand on Tom's shoulder to yank him free. Tom, however, reached round and sank his teeth into the flesh between his forefinger and thumb. Hecht cried out in pain.

Viktor, meanwhile, had stood up behind the remaining guard, whose attention had been drawn to the fight. Taking careful aim, she landed a heavy blow on the back of his head. He fell to the ground.

Hecht spun round, his bleeding hand clasped to his chest, the other reaching for his gun. Lying beneath him, Archie kicked out and caught his arm, sending his gun clattering to the ground. With a furious roar, Hecht launched his huge frame at Viktor, sending her sprawling. She lashed out from where she had fallen, catching Hecht in the groin and bringing him down with a pained cry. The delay was long enough for Viktor to reach the gun and scoop it up. She stepped towards Hecht, then brought the butt of the gun down hard on his temple. His face slammed into the dirt floor.

'Am I glad to see you!' Tom wheezed between pained breaths.

'We told you not to go inside.' She smiled as she pulled a knife from her boot and sliced Tom's hands free.

'Where did you get the outfit?' Archie asked as she cut his cuffs off too.

'One of Völz's men decided to take a leak a little too close for comfort.' She grinned. 'Luckily, his clothes fitted.'

'How did you know we were in here?' asked Tom.

'I didn't, but Dominique guessed you would be. Said you wouldn't be able to help yourselves. Good thing for you she knows you both so well.'

'Where is she?' Tom looked around. 'She's OK, isn't she?'

'She's gone to phone that FBI number you gave her. She remembered seeing a phone line running into that old man's house. Come on, let's go.'

'We can't just leave them to it,' said Tom. 'Once Völz makes it out of here with that uranium, no one will hear from him again until it's too late.'

'You're right,' said Archie. 'But there's only three of us and over twenty of them. What do you have in mind?'

'Four of us if you untie me,' Renwick observed.

Tom ignored him. 'The detonator,' he exclaimed. 'We can use Hecht's charges to collapse the mine and trap them until the police arrive. Search him. He must still have it on him.'

Archie turned Hecht over and patted him down, recovering the detonator from one pocket and a folded piece of paper in the other. He smoothed the piece of paper out on the floor and held his torch over it. 'It's a schematic of where the charges are. They're numbered one to four. There seem to be two sets in each tunnel, one at the entrance and one near the chamber.'

'So if we let off charges two and three, we'll seal the chamber at both ends?'

Archie frowned. 'That's what it seems to be saying.'

'Well, that's good enough for me,' said Tom. 'Let's get clear and then we'll set them off. We just cannot allow Völz to unload that train.'

As they turned to leave, Renwick called out and stopped them in their tracks. 'Thomas, dear boy. Surely you are not just going to leave me here?'

'Aren't I?' said Tom drily. 'Just watch me.'

'They will shoot me, you know that.'

'Good. Then it will save me the trouble,' Archie said.

Renwick ignored him, his eyes boring instead into Tom's. 'You cannot do this, Thomas. Think about the way things used to be between us. Unless you help me now, it will be as if you pulled the trigger.'

'Don't listen to him, Tom,' Archie warned.

'Answer my question.' Tom walked over to where Renwick was still propped against the mine wall. 'Did my father know who you were? Did he work with you?'

'Let me go, then I will tell you.'

Tom shook his head. 'No. I'm fed up with negotiating with your lies.' He reached into Renwick's jacket pocket and pulled out the gold Patek Philippe pocket watch that had once belonged to his father. 'I'll take this,' he said, slipping it into his coat. 'You won't be needing it again.'

THEY SPRINTED DOWN the tunnel until the glow of the snow in the moonlight told them they were near the exit. Seconds later they spilled out into the fresh air, relief making them momentarily dizzy.

'Are you ready?' Tom asked when he had located a suitably broad tree to shelter behind. He was grasping the remote detonator in his right hand. They nodded, the mood suddenly sombre. He flicked the unit on and extended the aerial. Four small lights glowed red next to each button.

'Two and three,' Archie reminded him. 'That'll seal either side of the chamber. Just two and three.'

'OK.' Tom pressed the button marked two. Far below them they heard a deep boom and then felt the ground shake. The snow that had accumulated on the branches of the fir trees above them fell to the ground with a thump.

'Now three,' Viktor prompted him gently.

Tom pressed button number three. This time the sound was much louder and closer, chased out of the mine in a cloud of dust that cloaked everything in a white shroud. As it settled, they stepped towards the mine entrance.

'You still got your radio, Viktor?' Tom asked. 'Let's call Dom and see whether she's managed to get down to that chalet yet.'

Viktor located her radio and swapped it for the detonator. He turned it on and entered the encryption code that would allow him to tune it to the agreed frequency. But before he could speak into it, Viktor's voice rang out.

'Tom, look out.'

She threw herself across him, shoving him to the ground as the crack of a gunshot split the night. He landed heavily on his back, Viktor on top of him, her body suddenly limp and heavy. She'd been hit.

Tom scrambled backwards, dragging Viktor with him, until he reached a large snow-covered boulder. A few moments later, Archie slid next to him as two further shots landed harmlessly in the snow.

'How is she?' Archie asked.

'Not good,' Tom said grimly, cradling her head in his lap. A bullet slammed into the rock above Tom's head, and he pulled his head back just in time to avoid a second shot, a firework of snow exploding overhead.

Archie snatched a look round the other side of the rock. 'It's Hecht.'

'Hecht! Shit.' Tom kicked himself for not having tied him up. He rolled

Viktor over onto her side and saw the snow sticky and red where the bullet had penetrated her lower back. 'Viktor needs help fast. We've got to do something before he works out that we don't have a gun.'

'Any ideas?'

'What about the fourth charge? Didn't you say it was near the entrance? If we set that off, we'll bury him.'

'Where's the detonator?'

'Viktor had it,' Tom said, feeling inside her pockets. 'She took it off me when she gave me the radio. She must have dropped it.'

He peered round the side of the rock and saw the detonator's sleek black shape lying in the snow.

'Can you see it?' asked Archie.

'Yeah,' said Tom. 'About ten feet away.'

'Then I'll draw his fire while you run and get the detonator.'

Archie jumped up and burst over to the right, heading for the nearest tree. A barrage of gunfire erupted from the mine entrance. At the same time, Tom rolled out from the other side of the boulder and sprinted towards the detonator. He grabbed it and turned to make his way back.

Suddenly, the shooting stopped. Tom looked up fearfully and saw Hecht standing in the mine entrance, staring straight at him, the gun poised to fire. Tom froze, momentarily transfixed, but then he noticed a shadow, with a knife glinting in its hand, peel away from the mine wall behind Hecht.

With a frenzied cry, Renwick jumped on Hecht, plunging the knife into the small of his back. Hecht roared in pain, the gun dropping from his grasp. With an angry shout he spun to face Renwick, who lunged at him again, and both men tumbled to the ground and rolled into the mine.

When Tom reached the boulder, Viktor had regained consciousness. She smiled at him weakly.

'Hang in there,' he said, drawing her to him. 'Dom will have some people up here in no time. We'll soon have you back home.'

'I'm not going back home,' she said simply.

'Of course you are,' Tom protested. 'We'll patch you up. You'll be fine.'

'I'm never going back. I've got it all planned. That's why I came here with you. So they couldn't stop me. I'm getting out. While I still can.'

'Good for you,' Tom said, tears filling his eyes.

'Like you said, it's never too late,' she said with a smile.

Tom said nothing, his throat swollen as he felt the life ebb out of her.

With a final burst of energy, Viktor reached up and pulled Tom's lips down to hers. 'Thank you,' she exhaled, her hand slipping down his neck, along his arm, to his hand where he was holding the detonator. Her eyes flickering shut, she pressed the fourth button.

This time the explosion was ferocious and immediate as the mine entrance collapsed. As the echo faded, a thick cloud of dust and smoke remained, hanging in the air like a heavy fog, making Tom cough and his eyes stream. He heard a shout and saw Dominique emerging into the clearing, accompanied by about ten armed Austrian policemen.

Tom looked down at Viktor's pale face. A smile was frozen onto her lips.

EPILOGUE

Alexander Nevsky Cemetery, St Petersburg: January 13, 3.02 p.m.

The freshly turned earth lay in a mound, a narrow black finger against the whiteness of the snow. Tom knelt down and grasped a handful. He rubbed it through his fingers, the cold already freezing the moisture so that it crumbled like grains of ice to the ground.

'What do you think we should put on her gravestone?' asked Archie.

'Her name was Katya,' Tom said firmly. 'Katya Nikolaevna Mostov.'

'To me, she'll always be Viktor,' Archie said with a shrug. 'Katya just doesn't seem to fit, somehow.'

'It fits who she once was and who she hoped to be again, one day,' Tom said. 'She never really wanted her life as Viktor. She just sort of fell into it and found she couldn't escape.'

'I think that's what she liked in you,' Archie said, drawing on a freshly lit cigarette. 'The fact that you'd also ended up in a place you realised you didn't want to be and had somehow walked away.'

Tom shifted his weight to his other foot as he stared silently at the ground. 'Any news on Dmitri?' he asked eventually.

'Bailey called me last night. There's no sign of him yet. Lucky bastard must have been outside when we set off the charges.'

'Any survivors?'

'Sixteen in all. Four dead. They must have been caught in the tunnel.'

'What about the uranium? What's going to happen to that?'

'It's safe, although apparently the Germans and Austrians can't agree who it belongs to.'

'No surprises there,' Tom said. 'What about Bailey? Is he in the clear?'

'As far as I know. He said something about transferring to New York.'

'Tom? Archie?' Dominique's voice rang out. 'Over here. I've found him.'

They picked their way over to where she was standing and found her at the foot of an open grave.

'There.' She pointed.

A brass plaque was screwed into the coffin's lid and Tom could just make out the name engraved on its already dull and faded surface.

HENRY JULIUS RENWICK

'It's over, Tom,' Dominique said gently.

Tom nodded. He knew that he should feel some sense of relief, elation even, that this man who had betrayed him, lied to him and tried to kill him, was finally dead. But instead he felt sad. Sad as the memories of the good times he had spent with Renwick as a boy came flooding back. Sad that yet another link to his father had been severed.

'You all right?' asked Archie.

'Yeah,' said Tom, gently taking out his father's gold pocket watch and twirling it by its chain, the case winking lazily as it caught the sun.

Archie caught sight of the watch. 'You don't really think your father—?'

'No, of course not,' Tom said with a firm shake of his head. He allowed the watch to spin for a few seconds longer. Then he grabbed it and flung it into the grave, smashing it against the coffin lid.

For a few moments the three of them stood there, staring at the watch's white face, hands frozen, the shattered glass scattered around it like small drops of ice, springs and screws strewn like shrapnel.

'Let's go and get a drink,' said Dominique eventually.

'Yeah,' said Tom, a sad smile on his face. 'Let's go and get several.'

Archie threw his cigarette to the ground, where it flared for a few seconds, flickered, then went out.

JAMES TWINING

Born: December 1972, London
Favourite football team: Arsenal
Website: www.jamestwining.com

RD: Where did the inspiration for *The Black Sun* come from?

JT: Amazingly enough, from a dream. I woke up several years ago with this incredibly vivid image of a concentration camp survivor having his arm sawn off so that someone could get hold of the prisoner number tattooed onto it. This now forms the basis of the first chapter of the book. I then combined this beginning with a couple of relatively unknown stories from the war that I had come across—namely the tale of the Hungarian Gold Train and the sinister goings-on at Wewelsburg Castle.

RD: What is the Black Sun?

JT: It's a runic symbol inlaid into the floor of the Hall of the Supreme Leaders in the North Tower of Wewelsburg Castle in Germany. Based on a seventh century AD Alemannic sun-wheel, it combines the symbol of the Swastika with the stylised victory runes made infamous by the SS.

RD: Is the artist Karel Bellak based on anyone real?

JT: No, but the name is taken from the wall of the Pinkas Synagogue in Prague that features in the novel. The walls are painted with the names of all the Bohemian and Moravian victims of the Holocaust—80,000 in total.

RD: Did you visit any of the places described in the book?

JT: I've been to most if not all of them, including Wewelsburg Castle, a sinister and foreboding place. Also visiting the castle when I was there was a group of neo-Nazi skinheads, who seemed to be treating their visit as a sort of pilgrimage. Seeing them reinforced the impression I got when researching the book, that there is a huge and worrying amount of anti-Semitic feeling still out there, both in Europe and the USA.

RD: How did you research behind the scenes at the Hermitage?

JT: No one outside the Hermitage staff has a clear idea of what it's really like but I don't think I'm too far off. I used a combination of my imagination (always a fertile source of descriptions!) and a couple of articles I found written by people who claimed they'd been invited into the Hermitage storerooms. What is certain is that the Red Army confiscated a huge amount of art, only a fraction of which has been owned up to, let alone put on display. It's got to be there somewhere!

RD: Where did your interest in codes and puzzles come from?

JT: My father is a demon at crosswords and so I think this is something I've picked up from him. Clearly, within the context of a novel, it's always exciting to be on the trail of a code or puzzle that needs solving. Writing about the Nazis provided me with the excuse to incorporate aspects of the greatest code-breaking story of them all—Enigma.

RD: Is your hero Tom Kirk based on anyone in particular?

JT: When I was growing up and people asked me what I wanted to do, I would always oblige them by telling them what they wanted to hear—a lawyer, or an accountant. The truth was, though, that from an early age I had harboured a secret ambition to become one of the world's greatest art thieves—dancing around infrared trip wires, abseiling down the sides of buildings, cracking open safes. So in a way Tom Kirk has been living in my thoughts and fantasies ever since I was a child. But I have to confess that, although he shares my love of watches and backgammon, he's very much a fantasy figure.

RD: And how about your arch villain, Harry Renwick?

JT: Renwick draws heavily on my old boss from when I used to work in the City. Worryingly, he was quite flattered by the comparison!

WEWELSBURG CASTLE

Wewelsburg Castle in Germany was intended by Heinrich Himmler to be a spiritual centre for his elite SS troops. The Black Sun (see page 433), which was inlaid into the floor of the North Tower, was placed there to symbolise the centre of the Nazi world. The emblem combines the three most important symbols of Nazi ideology—the sun-wheel, the swastika and the stylised victory rune. Towards the end of the war, Himmler, not wanting Wewelsburg to fall into enemy hands, ordered a task force to destroy the castle. It has since been rebuilt and is used today as a youth hostel and regional museum.

MIRACLE IN THE ANDES © Nando Parrado 2006
Published by Orion

THE LINCOLN LAWYER © Hieronymus, Inc. 2005
Published by Orion

THE WEDDING OFFICER © Anthony Capella 2006
Published by Time Warner

THE BLACK SUN © James Twining 2006
Published by HarperCollins

Illustrations and Photos:
Page 4: Michael Connelly © Mogjam Azimi; Anthony Capella © Anthony Capella; James Twining © Joanna Twining; page 5 © Nando Parrado.
Miracle in the Andes: 6–8: Images: © Group of Survivors/Corbis. Page 130–1: 1 © Group of Survivors/Corbis; 2: © Gamma; 3: © Group of Survivors/Corbis; 4: © Nando Parrado; 5 and 6: © Group of Survivors/Corbis; 7: © Nando Parrado; 8: © Group of Survivors/Corbis; 9: © Rex Features Ltd/Sipa Press (SIPA); 10, 11 and 12: © Nando Parrado.
The Lincoln Lawyer: 132–3: images: © Corbis; illustrator: Curtis Cozier; page 284 © Mogjam Azimi; page 285: images: © Alamy Images/Coston Stock.
The Wedding Officer: 286–7: images: © Colin Thomas Photography Ltd; page 430 © Anthony Capella; page 431: © Jon Arnold images: photographer Demetrio Carrasco.
The Black Sun: 432–3: images: © Corbis; page 574 (and back jacket): © Joanna Twining; page 575 © Kreismuseum Wewelsburg: photographer: R. Rohlf.
Dustjacket spine: © Corbis.

Printed and bound by GGP Media GmbH, Pössneck, Germany

243/06